Trends in Mathematical Optimization

4th French-German Conference on Optimization

Edited by

K.-H. Hoffmann
J.-B. Hiriart-Urruty
C. Lemarechal
J. Zowe

1988

Birkhäuser Verlag
Basel · Boston

ISNM 84:
International Series of Numerical Mathematics
Internationale Schriftenreihe zur Numerischen Mathematik
Série internationale d'Analyse numérique
Vol. 84

Edited by
Ch. Blanc, Lausanne; R. Glowinski, Paris;
H. O. Kreiss, Pasadena; J. Todd, Pasadena

Birkhäuser Verlag
Basel · Boston

Editors

Karl-Heinz Hoffmann
Institut für Mathematik
Universität Augsburg
Memminger Straße 6
D–8900 Augsburg

Jochem Zowe
Mathematisches Institut
Universität Bayreuth
Universitätsstrasse 30
D–8580 Bayreuth

Jean-Baptiste Hiriart-Urruty
U.F.R. Mathématiques, Informatique
Université Paul Sabatier
118, Route de Narbonne
F–31062 Toulouse Cédex

Claude Lemarechal
INRIA
Rocquencourt
F–78153 Le Chesnay

Library of Congress Cataloging in Publication Data

French-German Conference on Optimization (4th : 1986 : Irsee. Germany)
Trends in mathematical optimization : 4th French-German Conference
on Optimization / edited by K.-H. Hoffmann . . . [et. al.].
p. cm. – – (International series of numerical mathematics =
Internationale Schriftenreihe zur numerischen Mathematik = Série
internationale d'analyse numérique : v. 84
   Bibliography: p.
   Includes index.
   ISBN 0-8176-1919-4 (U.S.)
   1. Mathematical optimization – – Congresses.   I. Hoffmann. K.-H.
(Karl-Heinz)   II. Title.   III. Series: International series of
numerical mathematics : v. 84.
QA402.5.F736   1986
510–dc19   87-34215

CIP-Titelaufnahme der Deutschen Bibliothek

Trends in mathematical optimization / 4th French German
Conference on Optimization. Ed. by K.-H. Hoffmann ... –
Basel ; Boston : Birkhäuser, 1988
   (International series of numerical mathematics ; Vol. 84)
   ISBN 3–7643–1919–4 (Basel) Pb.
   ISBN 0–8176–1919–4 (Boston) Pb.
NE: Hoffmann, Karl-Heinz [Hrsg.]; French German Conference on
   Optimization <04, 1986, Irsee>; GT

© 1988 Birkhäuser Verlag Basel
Printed in Germany
ISBN 3-7643-1919-4
ISBN 0-8176-1919-4

Preface

This volume contains a collection of 23 papers presented at the *4th French-German Conference on Optimization*, hold at Irsee, April 21 – 26, 1986.

The conference was attended by ninety scientists: about one third from France, from Germany and from third countries each. They all contributed to a highly interesting and stimulating meeting. The scientifique program consisted of four survey lectures of a more tutorial character and of 61 contributed papers covering almost all areas of optimization. In addition two informal evening sessions and a plenary discussion on further developments of optimization theory were organized.

One of the main aims of the organizers was to indicate and to stress the increasing importance of optimization methods for almost all areas of science and for a fast growing number of industry branches. We hope that the conference approached this goal in a certain degree and managed to continue fruitful discussions between "theory" and "applications".

Equally important to the official contributions and lectures is the "nonmeasurable" part of activities inherent in such a scientific meeting. Here the charming and inspiring atmosphere of a place like Irsee helped to establish numerous new contacts between the participants and to deepen already existing ones.

The conference was sponsored by the Bayerische Kultusministerium, the Deutsche Forschungsgemeinschaft and the Universities of Augsburg and Bayreuth. Their interest in the meeting and their assistance is gratefully acknowledged.

We would like to thank the authors for their contributions and the referees for their helpful comments.

Last but not least our thanks go to Mrs. M. Eberle (Augsburg) for her assistance in the organization and for her excellent typing of the manuscripts.

K.-H. Hoffmann
(Augsburg)

J. Zowe
(Bayreuth)

J.-B. Hiriart-Urruty
(Toulouse)

C. Lemarechal
(Paris)

TABLE OF CONTENTS

International Series of
Numerical Mathematics, Vol. 84

Rate of convergence for the saddle points of convex-concave functions

D. Aze

A.V.A.M.A.C.

University of Perpignan

66025 Perpignan Cedex/France

Abstract. In the lines of H. Attouch and R. Wets, two kinds of variational metrics are introduced between closed proper classes of convex-concave functions. The comparison between these two distances gives rise to a metric stability result for the associated saddle-points.

Key words: Convex-concave functions, stability, saddle points, variational convergence, monotone operators, duality.

1. Introduction.

We are concerned in this work with the metric point of view for the stability of a convex duality scheme (see [16], [30]) when the perturbation function varies. The topological point of view has been intensively studied during this last years (see [11] and the autors cited in reference in this book). The main tool in order to evaluate rate of convergence for the saddle-point derives from the notion of variational distance between convex function introduced by H. ATTOUCH and R. WETS in [6].

In section 2, we define, analogously with [6], two kinds of variational metrics for the closed classes of convex-concave functions in the sense of [28]. One of these is defined in term of inf-sup convolutive approximation of MOREAU-YOSIDA type, the other relies on the resolvents associated to this approximations (see [3], [19], [37], [38]).

It is proved (Proposition 2.2) that the partial LEGENDRE-FENCHEL transform which associates a class of convex-concave functions to a convex function, is an isometry for a suitable choice of metrics. The comparison between the two metrics defined on the convex-concave function allows us to prove (Proposition 2.6) that the saddle-points of the coercified Lagrangians converge at a rate which is the square root of the distance between the perturbation functions.

These results can be used in convex programming (see [9]) in order to compute the rate of convergence of solutions and multipliers, when objective functions and constraints are perturbed.

2. Variational metrics on convex-concave functions.

Let us begin by a short review of the classical convex duality scheme (see [16], [30]). We consider two pairs (X, U) and (Y, V) of topological vector spaces in separate duality, and we denote by $< .,. >$ the bilinear maps which define the pairing between the spaces (X, U) and (Y, V).

Let $K : X \times Y \to \overline{R}$ be a function which is convex (resp. concave) with respect to the first (resp. second) variable.

We define for $x \in X$, $y \in Y$, $u \in U$, $v \in V$

$$(2.1) \qquad F(x, v) = \sup_{y \in Y} \{K(x, y) + < y, v >\}$$

$$(2.2) \qquad G(u, y) = \inf_{x \in X} \{K(x, y) - < u, x >\}.$$

The function F (resp. G) is then convex (resp. concave), F is the convex parent of K and G is the concave one.

Two convex-concave functions are said to be equivalent if they have the same parents. An equivalent class of convex-concave function is said to be closed if $F^* = -G$ and $(-G)^* = F$.

It is proved in [28] that the map

$$K \longrightarrow F$$

is one to one between the set of closed classes of convex-concave functions and the set $\Gamma(X \times V)$ of closed convex functions defined on $X \times V$ with values in $\overline{\mathbb{R}}$. Moreover the class associated to $F \in \Gamma(X \times Y)$ is the set $[\underline{K}, \overline{K}]$ of convex-concave functions lying between $\underline{K}$ and $\overline{K}$ where

$$(2.3) \qquad \underline{K}(x, y) = \sup_{u \in U} \{G(u, y) + < u, x >\} \, (G = -F^*)$$

$$(2.4) \qquad \overline{K}(x, y) = \inf_{v \in V} \{F(x, v) - < y, v >\}.$$

In the sequel, we shall only consider proper classes i.e. classes whose convex parent F belongs to $\Gamma_0(x \times V)$.

Let us define, following [28]

$$(2.5) \qquad \partial K(x, y) = \partial_1(K(x, y)) \times (-\partial_2(-K)(x, y)) \subset U \times V$$

$$(2.6) \qquad A^K(x, y) = \partial_1 K(x, y) \times \partial_2(-K)(x, y).$$

The operator A^K is maximal monotone, and the following equivalences hold (see [28])

$$(2.7) \qquad (u, v) \in \partial K(x, y) \iff (u, y) \in \partial F(x, -v)$$

$$(2.8) \qquad (u, v) \in A^K(x, y) \iff (u, y) \in \partial F(x, v).$$

From now X and Y will be Hilbert spaces whose scalar products are denoted by $< .,. >$, and $U = X$, $V = Y$.

For every closed proper convex-concave function K, let us define

(2.9) $$K^\lambda(x,y) = \inf_{u \in X} \{K(u,y) + \frac{1}{2\lambda}|x - u|^2\} \quad \text{for every} \quad \lambda > 0$$

(2.10) $$K_\mu(x,y) = \sup_{v \in Y} \{K(x,v) - \frac{1}{2\mu}|y - v|^2\} \quad \text{for every} \quad \mu > 0.$$

The convex parent of K_μ is

(2.11) $$F_\mu(x,y) = F(x,y) + \frac{\mu}{2}|y|^2,$$

the concave parent of K^λ is

(2.12) $$G_\lambda(x,y) = -F^*(x,y) - \frac{\lambda}{2}|x|^2.$$

K_μ is the classical augmented Lagrangian ([18], [31]).

It is proved in [3] and [38] that

$$(K^\lambda)_\mu = (K_\mu)^\lambda := K_{\lambda,\mu}$$

the Moreau-Yosida approximation of K of index (λ, μ):

(2.14)
$$K_{\lambda,\mu}(x,y) = \inf_{u \in X} \sup_{v \in Y} (K(u,v) + \frac{1}{2\lambda}|x - u|^2 - \frac{1}{2\mu}|y - v|^2)$$
$$= \sup_{v \in Y} \inf_{u \in X} (K(u,v) + \frac{1}{2\lambda}|x - u|^2 - \frac{1}{2\mu}|y - v|^2).$$

Moreover ([3]) the above problem admits an unique saddle point $(x_{\lambda,\mu}, y_{\lambda,\mu})$ characterized by

(2.15) $$(\frac{x - x_{\lambda,\mu}}{\lambda}, -\frac{y - y_{\lambda,\mu}}{\mu}) \in \partial K(x_{\lambda,\mu}, y_{\lambda,\mu}).$$

Let us define

(2.16) $$J_{\lambda,\mu}^K(x,y) = (x_{\lambda,\mu}, y_{\lambda,\mu})$$

(2.17) $$A_{\lambda,\mu}^K(x,y) = (\frac{x - x_{\lambda,\mu}}{\lambda}, \frac{y - y_{\lambda,\mu}}{\mu}).$$

We observe that, in the case where $\lambda = \mu$, $J_{\lambda,\lambda}$ and $A_{\lambda,\lambda}$ are respectively the resolvent and the Yosida approximate of index λ of the maximal monotone operator A^k defined in (2.8). Moreover the map $K_{\lambda,\mu}$ is C^1 (see [3], [37], [38]) and

(2.18) $$\nabla K_{\lambda,\mu}(x,y) = (\frac{x - x_{\lambda,\mu}}{\lambda}, -\frac{(y - y_{\lambda,\mu})}{\mu}),$$

using (2.6) and (2.17), it follows

(2.19) $$A^{K_{\lambda,\mu}} = A^K_{\lambda,\mu}.$$

Let us prove now the

Proposition 2.1.

    i) $(K_{\lambda,\mu})_{\lambda',\mu'} = K_{\lambda+\lambda',\mu+\mu'}$.

    ii) $(A^K_{\lambda,\mu})_{\lambda',\mu'} = A^K_{\lambda+\lambda',\mu+\mu'}$.

    iii) $A^K_{\lambda,\mu}$ is $\frac{l}{\inf(\lambda,\mu)}$ Lipschitzian.

    iv) $J^K_{\lambda,\mu}$ is $\frac{\sup(\lambda,\mu)}{\inf(\lambda,\mu)}$ Lipschitzian.

    v) $|A^K_{\lambda+\lambda',\mu+\mu'}(x,y)| \le \frac{\sup(\lambda,\mu)}{\inf(\lambda,\mu)}|A^K_{\lambda',\mu'}(x,y)|$.

    vi) $J^K_{\lambda,\mu}(x,y) = (J^{\psi_K}_\lambda(x), J^{\varphi_K}_\mu(y))$.

    vii) $A^K_{\lambda,\mu}(x,y) = (A^{\psi_K}_\lambda(x), A^{\varphi_K}_\mu(y))$.

    viii) $K_{\lambda,\mu}(x,y) = (\psi_K)_\lambda(x) = -(\varphi_K)_\mu(y)$,

where $\psi_K(\xi) = K_\mu(\xi,y)$, $\varphi_K(\eta) = -K^\lambda(x,\eta)$.

Proof.

$$i) \quad (K_{\lambda,\mu})_{\lambda',\mu'} = [(K_{\lambda,\mu})^{\lambda'}]_{\mu'}$$
$$= \{[(K_\mu)^\lambda]^{\lambda'}\}_{\mu'}$$
$$= [(K_\mu)^{\lambda+\lambda'}]_{\mu'}$$
$$= [(K^{\lambda+\lambda'}_\mu)]_{\mu'}$$
$$= (K^{\lambda+\lambda'})_{\mu+\mu'}$$
$$= K_{\lambda+\lambda',\mu+\mu'}.$$

(The relations $K^{\lambda+\lambda'} = (K^\lambda)^{\lambda'}$ and $K_{\mu+\mu'} = (K_\mu)_{\mu'}$ are an easy consequence of (2.11), (2.12)).

    ii) follows from the equivalence

(2.20) $$(u,v) \in A^K_{\lambda,\mu}(x,y) \iff (u,v) \in A^K(x-\lambda u, y-\mu v).$$

    iii) Let us observe that

$\forall(x_1,y_1) \in X \times Y, \forall(x_2,y_2) \in X \times Y,$

$(x_1,y_1) - (x_2,y_2) = \textcircled{H}[A^K_{\lambda,\mu}(x_1,y_1) - A^K_{\lambda,\mu}(x_2,y_2)] + J^K_{\lambda,\mu}(x_1,y_1) - J^K_{\lambda,\mu}(x_2,y_2)$

where $\textcircled{H}(u,v) = (\lambda u, \mu v)$.

    Using the monotonicity of $A^K_{\lambda,\mu}$ and the relation $A^K_{\lambda,\mu}(x,y) \in A^K(J^K_{\lambda,\mu}(x,y))$, we derive

$$< A^K_{\lambda,\mu}(x_1,y_1) - A^K_{\lambda,\mu}(x_2,y_2), (x_1,y_1) - (x_2,y_2) > \ge < A^K_{\lambda,\mu}(x_1,y_1) - A^K_{\lambda,\mu}(x_2,y_2),$$
$$\textcircled{H}(A^K_{\lambda,\mu}(x_1,y_1) - A^K_{\lambda,\mu}(x_2,y_2)) >,$$

hence

$$|A_{\lambda,\mu}^K(x_1,y_1) - A_{\lambda,\mu}^K(x_2,y_2)||(x_1,y_1) - (x_2,y_2)| \geq \inf(\lambda,\mu)|A_{\lambda,\mu}^K(x_1,y_1) - A_{\lambda,\mu}^K(x_2,y_2)|^2$$

and iii) follows.

iv) is a consequence of iii) via the relation

$$J_{\lambda,\mu}^K = I - \textcircled{H}A_{\lambda,\mu}.$$

v) Let $(u,v) \in A^K(x,y)$, from the definition, it follows

$$A_{\lambda,\mu}^K(x,y) \in A^K(J_{\lambda,\mu}^K(x,y))$$

hence

$$< (u,v) - A_{\lambda,\mu}^K(x,y), (x,y) - J_{\lambda,\mu}^K(x,y) >\geq 0$$
$$< (u,v) - A_{\lambda,\mu}^K(x,y), \textcircled{H}(A_{\lambda,\mu}^K(x,y)) >\geq 0$$
$$\inf(\lambda,\mu)|A_{\lambda,\mu}^K(x,y)|^2 \leq \sup(\lambda,\mu)|A_{\lambda,\mu}^K(x,y)||(u,v)|$$
$$|A_{\lambda,\mu}^K(x,y)| \leq \frac{\sup(\lambda,\mu)}{\inf(\lambda,\mu)}|(u,v)|, \quad \forall(u,v) \in A^K(x,y).$$

Let us apply the above results to $K = K_{\lambda',\mu'}$, we obtain

$$|A_{\lambda+\lambda',\mu+\mu'}^K| \leq \frac{\sup(\lambda,\mu)}{\inf(\lambda,\mu)}|A_{\lambda',\mu'}^K|.$$

vi), vii) and viii), define $(\overline{u},\overline{v}) = J_{\lambda,\mu}^K(x,y)$, it follows that $\forall(u,v) \in X \times Y$

$$K(\overline{u},v) + \frac{1}{2\lambda}|x - \overline{u}|^2 - \frac{1}{2\mu}|y - v|^2 \leq K(\overline{u},\overline{v}) + \frac{1}{2\lambda}|x - \overline{u}|^2 - \frac{1}{2\mu}|y - \overline{v}|^2$$

$$\leq K(u,\overline{v}) + \frac{1}{2\lambda}|x - u|^2 - \frac{1}{2\mu}|y - \overline{v}|^2$$

hence, applying the definitions of K_μ and K^λ (see (2.9), (2.10))

$$K_\mu(\overline{u},y) + \frac{1}{2\lambda}|x - \overline{u}|^2 \leq K_{\lambda,\mu}(x,y) \leq K_\mu(u,y) + \frac{1}{2\lambda}|x - u|^2$$

$$K^\lambda(x,v) - \frac{1}{2\mu}|y - v|^2 \leq K_{\lambda,\mu}(x,y) \leq K^\lambda(x,\overline{v}) - \frac{1}{2\mu}|y - \overline{v}|^2$$

which shows that

$$(\psi_K)_\lambda(x) = K_{\lambda,\mu}(x,y)$$
$$(\varphi_K)_\mu(y) = -K_{\lambda,\mu}(x,y)$$
$$\overline{u} = J_\lambda^{\psi_K}(x) \quad \text{(resolvent of index } \lambda \text{ of } \psi_K)$$
$$\overline{v} = J_\mu^{\varphi_K}(y) \quad \text{(resolvent of index } \mu \text{ of } \varphi_K)$$

hence vi), vii) and viii), which ends the proof of proposition 2.1.   □

It is now possible to define, in the lines of [6], some metrics between classes of closed convex-concave functions.

Let us define, for $\lambda > 0$, $\mu > 0$, $\rho \geq 0$, K and L being two closed proper convex-concave functions

$$(2.21) \qquad d_{\lambda,\mu,\rho}(K,L) = \sup_{\left\{\begin{smallmatrix} |x| \leq \rho \\ |y| \leq \rho \end{smallmatrix}\right.} |K_{\lambda,\mu}(x,y) - L_{\lambda,\mu}(x,y)|$$

and

$$(2.22) \qquad d^J_{\lambda,\mu,\rho}(K,L) = \sup_{\left\{\begin{smallmatrix} |x| \leq \rho \\ |y| \leq \rho \end{smallmatrix}\right.} |J^K_{\lambda,\mu}(x,y) - J^L_{\lambda,\mu}(x,y)|_1$$

where $|(x,y)|_1 = |x| + |y|$.

We observe, thanks to (2.9), (2.10), (2.13), that $K_{\lambda,\mu} = L_{\lambda,\mu}$ for one value of (λ,μ) implies that $K = L$. It is easy to show that, if the functions are normalized ($K(0,0) = 0$ and $(0,0) \in K(0,0)$), the equality $J^K_{\lambda,\mu} = J^L_{\lambda,\mu}$ for one value of (λ,μ) implies that $K = L$.

Let us define, using an increasing sequence (ρ_k) of real numbers which goes to $+\infty$

$$(2.23) \qquad d_{\lambda,\mu}(K,L) = \sum_{k=0}^{+\infty} \frac{1}{2^k} \frac{d_{\lambda,\mu,\rho_k}(K,L)}{1 + d_{\lambda,\mu,\rho_k}(K,L)}$$

$$(2.24) \qquad d^J_{\lambda,\mu}(K,L) = \sum_{k=0}^{+\infty} \frac{1}{2^k} \frac{d^J_{\lambda,\mu,\rho_k}(K,L)}{1 + d_{\lambda,\mu,\rho_k}(K,L)}.$$

These two quantities define metrics on the set of closed classes of convex-concave functions (the functions are assumed to be normalized in the case of the metric $d^J_{\lambda,\mu}$).

Proposition 2.2. The mapping

$$K \longrightarrow F$$

defined in (2.1) is an isometry between the set of closed proper classes of convex-concave functions and $\Gamma_0(X \times Y)$.

Proof. Using [3], remark 1 after theorem 5.2, we know that

$$K_{1,1}(x,y) = F_1(x,y) - \frac{|y|^2}{2}.$$

It follows that

$$d_{1,1,\rho}(K,L) = d_{1,\rho}(F,\Phi)$$

where F and Φ are the convex parents of K and L, and

$$d_{\lambda,\rho}^J(F, \Phi) = \sup_{\left\{\begin{array}{l}|x|\leq\rho\\|y|\leq\rho\end{array}\right.} |F_1(x, y) - \Phi_1(x, y)|$$

F_1 and Φ_1 denoting the Moreau-Yosida approximation of index 1 of F and Φ. $\qquad\square$

It is now possible to compare the metrics $d_{\lambda,\mu,\rho}$ and $d_{\lambda,\mu,\rho}^J$.

Theorem 2.3 *For every K, L, $\lambda > 0$, $\mu > 0$, $\rho \geq 0$*

(2.25) $$d_{\lambda,\mu,\rho}^J(K, L) \leq (\lambda + \mu + 2)(2d_{R,\lambda,\mu}(K, L))^{1/2}$$

where

(2.26) $$R \geq (1 + \frac{3}{\inf(\lambda, \mu)})\rho + 2\sup(|A_{\lambda,\mu}^K(0, 0)|, |A_{\lambda,\mu}^L(0, 0)|).$$

Proof. Let $|x| \leq \rho$, $|y| \leq \rho$ and $\xi \in X$, we obtain, using the subdifferential inequalities

$$K_{\lambda,\mu}(\xi, y) - K_{\lambda,\mu}(x, y) \geq <\nabla_1 K_{\lambda,\mu}(x, y), \xi - x>$$
$$L_{\lambda,\mu}(x, y) - L_{\lambda,\mu}(\xi, y) \geq <\nabla_1 L_{\lambda,\mu}(\xi, y), x - \xi>,$$

adding these two inequalities, it follows
(2.27)
$$(K_{\lambda,\mu} - L_{\lambda,\mu})(\xi, y) - (K_{\lambda,\mu} - L_{\lambda,\mu})(x, y) \geq <\nabla_1 K_{\lambda,\mu}(x, y) - \nabla_1 L_{\lambda,\mu}(\xi, y), \xi - x>.$$

Let us define, as in proposition 2.1

$$\psi_K(\xi) = K_\mu(\xi, y)$$
$$\varphi_K(\eta) = -K^\lambda(x, \eta)$$

and

(2.28) $$\xi = (I + \nabla(\psi_L)_\lambda)^{-1}(x + \nabla_1 K_{\lambda,\mu}(x, y))$$

which is equivalent to

$$\xi - x = \nabla_1 K_{\lambda,\mu}(x, y) - \nabla(\psi_L)_\lambda(\xi)$$

and, thanks to proposition 2.1, vii)

(2.29) $$\xi - x = \nabla_1 K_{\lambda,\mu}(x, y) - \nabla_1 L_{\lambda,\mu}(\xi, y).$$

From (2.27) and (2.29), it follows

$$(2.30) \quad |\nabla_1 K_{\lambda,\mu}(x,y) - \nabla_1 L_{\lambda,\mu}(\xi,y)| \leq \{|(K_{\lambda,\mu}-L_{\lambda,\mu})(\xi,y)| + |(K_{\lambda,\mu}-L_{\lambda,\mu})(x,y)|\}^{\frac{1}{2}}.$$

We observe now that

$$
\begin{aligned}
|\nabla_1 K_{\lambda,\mu}(x,y) - \nabla_1 L_{\lambda,\mu}(x,y)| &\leq |\nabla_1 K_{\lambda,\mu}(x,y) - \nabla_1 L_{\lambda,\mu}(\xi,y)| + \\
&\quad |\nabla_1 L_{\lambda,\mu}(\xi,y) - \nabla_1 L_{\lambda,\mu}(x,y)| \\
&\leq |\nabla_1 K_{\lambda,\mu}(x,y) - \nabla_1 L_{\lambda,\mu}(\xi,y)| + \\
&\quad |\nabla(\psi_L)_\lambda(\xi) - \nabla(\psi_L)_\lambda(x)| \\
&\leq |\nabla_1 K_{\lambda,\mu}(x,y) - \nabla_1 L_{\lambda,\mu}(\xi,y)| + \frac{1}{\lambda}|\xi - x| \\
&\leq (1 + \frac{1}{\lambda})|\nabla_1 K_{\lambda,\mu}(x,y) - \nabla_1 L_{\lambda,\mu}(\xi,y)|,
\end{aligned}
$$

returning to (2.30), we derive
(2.31)
$$|\nabla_1 K_{\lambda,\mu}(x,y) - \nabla_1 L_{\lambda,\mu}(x,y)| \leq (1 + \frac{1}{\lambda})\{|(K_{\lambda,\mu}-L_{\lambda,\mu})(\xi,y)| + |(K_{\lambda,\mu}-L_{\lambda,\mu})(x,y)|\}^{\frac{1}{2}}.$$

Let us estimate ξ. Observe that

$$(I + \nabla(\psi_L)_\lambda)^{-1}(z) = \frac{\lambda z + J_{\lambda+1}^{\psi_L}(z)}{\lambda + 1}$$

hence

$$|(I + \nabla(\psi_L)_\lambda)^{-1}(z)| \leq \frac{\lambda|z|}{\lambda+1} + \frac{|z|}{\lambda+1} + \frac{J_{\lambda+1}^{\psi_L}(0)}{\lambda+1}$$
$$|(I + \nabla(\psi_L)_\lambda)^{-1}(z)| \leq |z| + |A_{\lambda+1}^{\psi_L}(0)|$$
$$\leq |z| + |A_\lambda^{\psi_L}(0)|.$$

We deduce

$$|\xi| = (I + \nabla(\psi_L)_\lambda)^{-1}(x + \nabla_1 K_{\lambda,\mu}(x,y))$$
$$|\xi| \leq |x| + \nabla_1 K_{\lambda,\mu}(x,y)| + \frac{1}{\lambda}|J_\lambda^{\psi_L}(0)|$$
$$\leq |x| + |A_\lambda^{\psi_K}(x)| + \frac{1}{\lambda}|J_\lambda^{\psi_L}(0)|$$
$$\leq |x| + \frac{1}{\lambda}|x| + \frac{1}{\lambda}|J_\lambda^{\psi_K}(0)| + \frac{1}{\lambda}|J_\lambda^{\psi_L}(0)|.$$

Let us remark that

$$
\begin{aligned}
|\nabla_1 K_{\lambda,\mu}(x,y) - \nabla_1 L_{\lambda,\mu}(x,y)| &= |A_\lambda^{\psi_K}(x) - A_\lambda^{\psi_L}(x)| \\
&= \frac{1}{\lambda}|J_\lambda^{\psi_K}(x) - J_\lambda^{\psi_L}(x)|.
\end{aligned}
$$

Returning to (2.31), we obtain, for every $|x| \leq \rho$

$$(2.32) \qquad |J_\lambda^{\psi_K}(x) - J_\lambda^{\psi_L}(x)| \leq (\lambda + 1)(2d_{\lambda,\mu,\rho_0}(K,L))^{\frac{1}{2}}.$$

where $\rho_0 = (1 + \frac{1}{\lambda})\rho + \frac{1}{\lambda}(|J_\lambda^{\psi_K}(0)| + |J_\lambda^{\psi_L}(0)|)$. Using an analogous method, we obtain, for every $|y| \leq \rho$

$$(2.33) \qquad |J_\mu^{\varphi_K}(y) - J_\mu^{\varphi_L}(y)| \leq (\mu + 1)(2d_{\lambda,\mu,\sigma_0}(K,L))^{\frac{1}{2}}$$

where $\sigma_0 = (1 + \frac{1}{\mu})\rho + \frac{1}{\mu}(|J_\mu^{\varphi_K}(0)| + |J_\mu^{\varphi_L}(0)|)$.
Observe that

$$J_{\lambda,\mu}^K(x,y) = (J_\lambda^{\psi_K}(x), J_\mu^{\varphi_K}(y))$$
$$\text{and } J_{\lambda,\mu}^L(x,y) = (J_\lambda^{\psi_L}(x), J_\mu^{\varphi_L}(y)).$$

Combining (2.32) and (2.33) provides

$$\sup_{\left\{ \substack{|x| \leq \rho \\ |y| \leq \rho} \right.} |J_{\lambda,\mu}^K(x,y) - J_{\lambda,\mu}^L(x,y)|_1 \leq (\lambda + \mu + 2)(2d_{\lambda,\mu,R}(K,L))^{\frac{1}{2}}$$

where $R \geq (1 + \frac{1}{\inf(\lambda,\mu)})\rho + \sup(|A_\lambda^{\psi_K}(0)|, |A_\mu^{\varphi_K}(0)|) + \sup(|A_\lambda^{\psi_L}(0)|, |A_\mu^{\varphi_L}(0)|)$.
Let us observe now that

$$|A_\lambda^{\psi_K}(0)| \leq |A_{\lambda,\mu}^K(0,y)| \leq |A_{\lambda,\mu}^K(0,0)| + \frac{1}{\inf(\lambda,\mu)}|y|$$
$$|A_\mu^{\varphi_K}(0)| \leq |A_{\lambda,\mu}^K(x,0)| \leq |A_{\lambda,\mu}^K(0,0)| + \frac{1}{\inf(\lambda,\mu)}|x|$$

hence

$$d_{\lambda,\mu,\rho}^J(K,L) \leq (\lambda + \mu + 2)(2d_{\lambda,\mu,R}(K,L))^{\frac{1}{2}}$$

where

$$R \geq (1 + \frac{3}{\inf(\lambda,\mu)})\rho + 2\sup(|A_{\lambda,\mu}^K(0,0)|, |A_{\lambda,\mu}^L(0,0)|)$$

which ends the proof of theorem 2.3.

In order to estimate the rate of convergence of the saddle-points, we need some results allowing us to compare $d_{\lambda',\mu'}$ and $d_{\lambda,\mu}$ when $\lambda' > \lambda$ and $\mu' > \mu$.

Lemma 2.4. For every $\lambda' > 0$

$$(2.34) \qquad d_{\lambda+\lambda',\mu,\rho}(K,L) \leq d_{\lambda,\mu,\rho_0}(K,L) \text{ where}$$

$$(2.35) \qquad \rho_0 \geq \rho(1 + \frac{\lambda'}{\inf(\lambda,\mu)}) + \lambda' \sup(|A_{\lambda,\mu}^K(0,0)|, |A_{\lambda,\mu}^L(0,0)|).$$

For every $\mu' > 0$

(2.36) $$d_{\lambda,\mu+\mu',\rho}(K,L) \leq d_{\lambda,\mu,\sigma_0}(K,L) \quad \text{where}$$

(2.37) $$\sigma_0 \geq \rho(1 + \frac{\mu'}{\inf(\lambda,\mu)}) + \mu' \sup(|A^K_{\lambda,\mu}(0,0)|, |A^L_{\lambda,\mu}(0,0)|).$$

Proof. Let $|x| \leq \rho$ and $|y| \leq \rho$, we obtain

$$K_{\lambda+\lambda',\mu}(x,y) = (\psi_K)_{\lambda+\lambda'}(x)$$

where $\psi_K(\xi) = K_\mu(\xi,y)$.
It follows that

(2.38) $$K_{\lambda+\lambda',\mu}(x,y) - L_{\lambda+\lambda',\mu}(x,y) = [(\psi_K)_\lambda]_{\lambda'}(x) - [(\psi_L)_\lambda]_{\lambda'}(x).$$

Define $u = J_{\lambda'}^{(\psi_L)_\lambda}(x)$, we derive

$$[(\psi_L)_\lambda]_{\lambda'}(x) = (\psi_L)_\lambda(u) + \frac{1}{2\lambda'}|x - u|^2$$

elsewhere

$$[(\psi_K)_\lambda]_{\lambda'}(x) \leq (\psi_K)_\lambda(u) + \frac{1}{2\lambda'}|x - u|^2.$$

It follows that

(2.39) $$K_{\lambda+\lambda',\mu}(x,y) - L_{\lambda+\lambda',\mu}(x,y) \leq (\psi_K)_\lambda(u) - (\psi_L)_\lambda(u)$$

(2.40) $$K_{\lambda+\lambda',\mu}(x,y) - L_{\lambda+\lambda',\mu}(x,y) \leq K_{\lambda,\mu}(u,y) - L_{\lambda,\mu}(u,y)$$

(see proposition 2.1 viii)).
Let us estimate $u = J_{\lambda'}^{(\psi_L)_\lambda}(x)$.
We obtain $u = \frac{\lambda x + \lambda' J^{\psi_L}_{\lambda+\lambda'}(x)}{\lambda+\lambda'}$,
hence

$$|u| \leq \frac{\lambda|x| + \lambda'|J^{\psi_L}_{\lambda+\lambda'}(0)| + \lambda'|x|}{\lambda + \lambda'}$$

$$|u| \leq |x| + \lambda'|A^{\psi_L}_{\lambda+\lambda'}(0)|$$

$$|u| \leq |x| + \lambda'|A^{\psi_L}_{\lambda}(0)|$$

$$|u| \leq |x| + \lambda'|A^L_{\lambda,\mu}(0,y)| \quad \text{(Prop. 2.1, vii)}$$

$$|u| \leq |x| + \lambda'(\frac{|y|}{\inf(\lambda,\mu)} + |A^L_{\lambda,\mu}(0,0)|) \quad \text{(Prop. 2.1, iii)}$$

(2.41)
$$|u| \leq \rho(1 + \frac{\lambda'}{\inf(\lambda,\mu)}) + \lambda'|A^L_{\lambda,\mu}(0,0)|.$$

Exchanging the roles played by K and L, we obtain

(2.42)
$$L_{\lambda+\lambda',\mu}(x,y) - K_{\lambda,\mu}(x,y) \leq L_{\lambda,\mu}(v,y) - K_{\lambda,\mu}(v,y)$$

where

(2.43)
$$|v| \leq \rho(1 + \frac{\lambda'}{\inf(\lambda,\mu)}) + \lambda'|A^K_{\lambda,\mu}(0,0)|.$$

From (2.40), (2.41), (2.42), (2.43), we obtain (2.34) and (2.35). The proof of (2.36) and (2.37) is then similar.

We also need

Lemma 2.5.

(2.44)
$$d_{\lambda,\mu,\rho}(K,L) \leq d_{\lambda+\lambda',\mu,\rho_0}(K,L)$$

where

(2.45)
$$\rho_0 \geq \rho(1 + \frac{\lambda'}{\lambda} + \frac{\lambda'}{\inf(\lambda,\mu)}) + \lambda' \sup\{|A^K_{\lambda,\mu}(0,0)|, |A^L_{\lambda,\mu}(0,0)|\}$$

and

(2.46)
$$d_{\lambda,\mu,\rho}(K,L) \leq d_{\lambda,\mu+\mu',\sigma_0}(K,L)$$

where

(2.47)
$$\sigma_0 \geq \rho(1 + \frac{\mu'}{\mu} + \frac{\mu'}{\inf(\lambda,\mu)}) + \mu' \sup\{|A^K_{\lambda,\mu}(0,0)|, |A^L_{\lambda,\mu}(0,0)|\}.$$

Proof. With the same notations than in Lemma 2.4, we deduce from (2.39)

(2.48)
$$(\psi_L)_\lambda(u) - (\psi_K)_\lambda(u) \leq L_{\lambda+\lambda',\mu}(x,y) - L_{\lambda+\lambda',\mu}(x,y)$$

where $u = J^{(\psi_L)_\lambda}_{\lambda'}(x) = (I + \lambda' \bigtriangledown (\psi_L)_\lambda)^{-1}(x)$
hence $x = (I + \lambda' \bigtriangledown (\psi_L)_\lambda)(u)$.

Let us consider u as an independent variable and let us estimate x when $|u| \leq \rho$. We obtain

$$
\begin{aligned}
|x| &\leq |u| + \lambda'|A^{\psi_L}_\lambda(u)| \\
&\leq |u| + \lambda'(|A^{\psi_L}_\lambda(0)| + \frac{|u|}{\lambda}) \\
&\leq \rho(1 + \frac{\lambda'}{\lambda}) + \lambda'|A^L_{\lambda,\mu}(0,y)| \\
&\leq \rho(1 + \frac{\lambda'}{\lambda}) + \lambda'\{|A^L_{\lambda,\mu}(0,0) + \frac{1}{\inf(\lambda,\mu)}|y|\} \\
&\leq \rho(1 + \frac{\lambda'}{\lambda} + \frac{\lambda'}{\inf(\lambda,\mu)}) + \lambda'|A^L_{\lambda,\mu}(0,0)|.
\end{aligned}
$$

Returning in (2.48), we have for $|u| \leq \rho$ and $|y| \leq \rho$

$$(2.49) \qquad L_{\lambda,\mu}(u,y) - K_{\lambda,\mu}(u,y) \leq d_{\lambda+\lambda',\mu,r_0}(K,L)$$

where $r_0 \geq \rho(1 + \frac{\lambda'}{\lambda} + \frac{\lambda'}{\inf(\lambda,\mu)}) + \lambda'|A_{\lambda,\mu}^L(0,0)|$.

Exchanging the roles played by K and L, we obtain, for $|u| \leq \rho$ and $|y| \leq \rho$

$$K_{\lambda,\mu}(u,y) - L_{\lambda,\mu}(u,y) \leq d_{\lambda+\lambda',\mu,s_0}(K,L)$$

where $s_0 \geq \rho(1 + \frac{\lambda'}{\lambda} + \frac{\lambda'}{\inf(\lambda,\mu)}) + \lambda'|A_{\lambda,\mu}^K(0,0)|$ which proves (2.44) and (2.45). The proof of (2.46) and (2.47) is then similar. $\square$

It is possible now to give a metric result of convergence for the saddle points of a sequence of convex-concave functions.

Let us consider $\{F^n, F; n \in \mathbb{N}\} \subset \Gamma_0(X \times Y)$ such that

$$(2.50) \qquad \text{for every } \rho \geq 0 \text{ sufficiently large,} \quad \lim_{n \to +\infty} d_{1,\rho}(F^n, F) = 0$$

where

$$(2.51) \qquad d_{1,\rho}(F^n, F) = \sup_{\left\{ \substack{|x| \leq \rho \\ |y| \leq \rho} \right.} |F_1^n(x,y) - F_1(x,y)|.$$

Let us denote by $(\bar{x}_n, \bar{y}_n)$ the unique saddle-point of the convex-concave function

$$(2.52) \qquad K^n(x,y) + \frac{\varepsilon}{2}|x|^2 - \frac{\alpha}{2}|y|^2$$

where $0 < \varepsilon < 1$ and $0 < \alpha < 1$ and K^n is a convex-concave function whose convex parent is F^n (see (2.3), (2.4)).

We also denote by $(\bar{x}, \bar{y})$ the unique saddle point of the convex-concave function

$$(2.53) \qquad K(x,y) + \frac{\varepsilon}{2}|x|^2 - \frac{\alpha}{2}|y|^2$$

the function K being associated to F in the same way.

Proposition 2.6. Under the assumption (2.50), there exists $R_0 \geq 0$ such that

$$(2.54) \qquad |\bar{x}_n - \bar{x}| + |\bar{y}_n - \bar{y}| = 0(d_{1,R_0}(F^n, F))^{1/2}.$$

Proof. Define $\lambda = \frac{1}{\varepsilon}$ and $\mu = \frac{1}{\alpha}$, it follows using the definitions, that

$$(2.55) \qquad \begin{aligned} |\bar{x}_n - \bar{x}| + |\bar{y}_n - \bar{y}| &= |J_{\lambda,\mu}^{K^n}(0,0) - J_{\lambda,\mu}^K(0,0)|_1 \\ |\bar{x}_n - \bar{x}| + |\bar{y}_n - \bar{y}| &\leq (\lambda + \mu + 2)(2d_{R,\lambda,\mu}(K^n, K))^{\frac{1}{2}} \end{aligned}$$

where $R = \sup\limits_{n \in \mathbb{N}} 2(|A_{\lambda,\mu}^{K^n}(0,0)|, |A_{\lambda,\mu}^{K}(0,0)|)$

(it suffices to apply theorem 2.3 with $\rho = 0$).
The real number R is finite since, using (2.50) and theorem 6.3 of [3], we have

$$\lim_{n \to +\infty} A_{\lambda,\mu}^{K^n}(0,0) = A_{\lambda,\mu}^{K}(0,0).$$

We can apply lemma 2.4, observing that $\lambda > 1$ and $\mu > 1$, and we obtain the existence of $R_0 > 0$ independent of n, such that

$$d_{\lambda,\mu,R}(K^n, K) \leq d_{1,1,R_0}(K^n, K)$$
$$\leq d_{1,R_0}(F^n, F) \text{ (prop. 2.2)}.$$

Returning in (2.55) and (2.54) follows. $\qquad\qquad\Box$

Remark. The exponent $\frac{1}{2}$ in proposition 2.6 is optimal, (see [6] and [36]).

References.

[1] Attouch, H.: *Variational convergence for functions and operators.* Pitman Applicable Mathematics Series (1984).

[2] Attouch, H.; Aze, D. and Wets, R.: *Convergence of convex-concave saddle functions: continuity properties of the Legendre-Fenchel transform with applications to convex programming and mechanics.* Publication AVAMAC no. 85-08, Perpignan (1985).

[3] Attouch, H.; Aze, D. and Wets, R.: *On continuity of the partial Legendre-Fenchel transform: convergence of sequences of augmented Lagrangian functions, Moreau-Yosida approximates and subdifferential operators.* Technical report I.I.A.S.A, Laxenburg, Austria, to appear in Proceedings of "Journées Fermat", North Holland (1986).

[4] Attouch, H. and Wets, R.: *A convergence theory for saddle functions.* Trans.A.M.S., Vol. 280, No. 1 (1983), 1 – 41.

[5] Attouch, H. and Wets, R.: *A convergence for bivariate functions aimed at the convergence of saddle values.* Math. Theor. of Opt. (Cecconi, J. P.; Zolezzi, T., eds.) Springer Lect. Notes in Math., No. 979 (1981).

[6] Attouch, H. and Wets, R.: *Isometries for the Legendre-Fenchel transform.* To appear in Trans. of the A.M.S. (1986).

[7] Auslender, A.: *Problèmes de Minimax via l'analyse convexe et les inégalités variationnelles: théorie et algorithmes.* Springer Lect. Notes in Economics and Mathematical systems, No. 77 (1972).

[8] Aze, D.: *Epi-convergence et dualité. Applications à la convergence des variables primales et duales pour des suites de problèmes d'optimisation convexe.* Tech. report AVAMAC - No. 84-12, Perpignan (1984).

[9] Aze, D.: *Rapidité de convergence des points-selles des fonctions convexe-concave.* Tech. report AVAMAC, Perpignan (1986).

[10] Aze, D.: *Rapidité de convergence pour une somme de fonctions convexes.* Tech. report AVAMAC, Perpignan (1986).

[11] Bank, B; Guddat, J.; Klatte, D.; Kummer, B. and Tammer, K.: *Non linear parametric optimization.* Birkhäuser Verlag (1983).

[12] Bergstrom, R. C.: *Optimization, convergence and duality.* Ph. D Thesis, University of Illinois (1980).

[13] Brezis, H.: *Operateurs maximaux monotones et semi-groupes de contractions dans les espaces de Hilbert.* North-Holland (1971).

[14] Cavazutti, E.: *Γ-convergenza multipla convergenza di punti di sella e di max-min.* Boll. Uni. Mat. Ital. 6, 1-B (1982), 251 – 276.

[15] De Giorgi, E.: *Convergence problems for functions and operators.* Proc. int. meet. on recent methods in nonlinear analysis, Roma 1978, Pitagora (ed.), Bologna 1979.

[16] Ekeland, I. and Temam, R.: *Analyse convexe et problèmes variationnels.* Dunod (1974).

[17] Fiacco, A. V.: *Introduction to sensitivity and stability analysis in nonlinear programming.* Academic Press, New York (1983).

[18] Fortin, M. and Glowinski, R.: *Methodes de Lagrangien augmenté.* Dunod (1982).

[19] Fougeres, A. and Truffert, A.: *Régularisation s.c.i. et Γ-convergence, approximations inf-convolutives associées à un référentiel.* To appear in Ann. Di Mat. Pura ed Appl. (1986).

[20] Joly, J.-L.: *Une famille de topologies et de convergences sur l'ensemble des fonctions convexes pour lesquelles la polarité est bicontinue.* J. Math. Pures et appl. 52 (1973), 421 – 441.

[21] Laurent, P.-J.: *Approximation et optimisation.* Hermann (1972).

[22] Moreau, J.-J.: *Théorèmes "inf-sup".* C.R.A.S., t. 258 (1964), 2720 – 2722.

[23] Moreau, J.-J.: *Fonctionelles convexes.* Séminaire du Collège de France (1966).

[24] Mosco, U.: *Convergence of convex sets and of solutions of variational inequalities.* Advances in Math. 3 (1969), 510 – 585.

[25] Mosco, U.: *On the continuity of the Legendre-Fenchel transformation.* Jour. Math. anal. appl. 35 (1971), 518 – 535.

[26] McLinden, L.: *Dual operations on saddle functions.* Trans. A.M.S. 179 (1973), 363 – 381.

[27] McLinden, L. and Bergstrom, R. C.: *Preservation of convergence of convex sets and functions in finite dimensions.* Trans. A.M.S. 268 (1981), 127 – 142.

[28] Rockafellar, R. T.: *A general correspondence between dual minimax problems and convex programs.* Pacific Journal of Math. 25, No. 3 (1968), 597 – 611.

[29] Rockafellar, R. T.: *Monotone operators associated with saddle functions and minimax problems.* Proc. Symp. Pure Maths. A.M.S. 18 (1970), 241 – 250.

[30] Rockafellar, R. T.: *Conjugate duality and optimization.* Regional conference series in applied mathematics 16 (1974), SIAM.

[31] Rockafellar, R. T.: *Augmented Lagrangians and applications of the proximal point algorithm in convex programming.* Maths of operations research, Vol. 1, No. 2 (1976), 97 – 116.

[32] Wets, R.: *Convergence of convex functions, variational inequalities and convex optimization problems.* In: Variational inequalities and complementarity problems, Cottle, R.; Gianessi, F.; Lions, J. L.(eds.); J. Wiley, New York 1980.

[33] Wets, R.: *A formula for the level sets of epi-limits and some applications. Mathematical theories of optimization.* Cecconi, J.P. and Zolezzi, T.(eds.). Lect. Notes in maths., Springer, No. 983 (1983).

[34] Zolezzi, T.: *On stability analysis in mathematical programming.* Math. Progr. Study 21 (1984), 227 – 242.

[35] Zolezzi, T.: *Stability analysis in optimization.* To appear in proc. International school of Mathematics, Stampachia, G, Erice (1984); Conti, R., De Giorgi, E., Giannessi, F. (eds.).

[36] Dontchev, A. L.: *Perturbations, approximation and sensitivity analysis of optimal control systems.* Lect. Notes in control and information sciences, Springer, No. 52 (1983).

[37] Tiba, D.: *Regularization of saddle functions.* Boll. U.M.I. 5, 17-A (1980), 420 – 427.

[38] Krauss, E. and Tiba, D.: *Regularization of saddle functions and the Yosida approximation of monotone operators.* An. Sti. Univ. Iasi, T.XXXI, s.Ia (1985).

International Series of
Numerical Mathematics, Vol. 84
(c) 1988 Birkhäuser Verlag Basel

Optimal Control of ODE Systems with Hysteresis Nonlinearities.

Martin Brokate

Institut für Mathematik

Universität Augsburg

8900 Augsburg, West Germany

1. Introduction and problem formulation.

It is well known that many dynamical systems exhibit hysteresis behaviour in one way or another. Usually this is connected to some memory mechanism present within the system. Within a mathematical model, such a mechanism either can be built in explicitly, or it can be an implicit consequence of the model equations. The former approach has been pursued by Krasnoselskii and several collaborators: They define an operator W, which maps a scalar input function $x = x(t)$ to a scalar output function $y = y(t)$

$$y(t) = (Wx)(t),$$

by a three-step procedure which formalizes the intuitive content of figure 1.

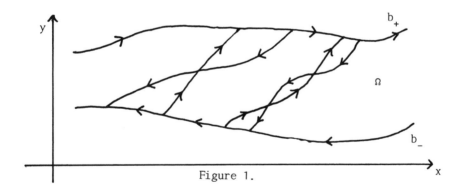

Figure 1.

1.1 Definition

Let $b_+, b_- : \mathbb{R} \to \mathbb{R}$ be C^3 with $b_-(x) < b_+(x)$ for all x, let

$$\Omega = \{(x, y) : x \in \mathbb{R}, b_-(x) \leq y \leq b_+(x)\}$$

Ω is called the hysteresis region with boundary curves b_+ and b_-.

Let $h_+, h_- : \mathbb{R}^2 \to \mathbb{R}$ be C^2 and define $g_+, g_- : \mathbb{R}^3 \to \mathbb{R}$ by

$$g_\pm(x, x_0, y_0) = y_0 + \int_{x_0}^{x} h_\pm(\xi, g_\pm(\xi, x_0, y_0))d\xi.$$

The functions g_+ and g_- describe the interior curves in the positive resp. negative direction. Now define $g : \mathbb{R} \times \Omega \to \mathbb{R}$ by

$$g(x, x_0, y_0) = \begin{cases} g_+(x, x_0, y_0), & x_0 \leq x < r_+(x_0, y_0) \\ b_+(x), & x \geq r_+(x_0, y_0) \\ g_-(x, x_0, y_0), & r_-(x_0, y_0) < x \leq x_0 \\ b_-(x), & x \leq r_-(x_0, y_0) \end{cases}$$

Here

$$r_+(x_0, y_0) = \inf\{x : x \geq x_0, g_+(x, x_0, y_0) = b_+(x)\} \in [x_0, \infty]$$

(and similarly r_-) denotes the point where the interior curve through (x_0, y_0) meets the b_+-boundary. This makes sense, if we assume for all $x \in \mathbb{R}$ and for all 4 combinations $b = b_+$ or b_-, $h = h_+$ or h_-, the sign conditions

$$b'(x) - h(x, b(x)) \leq 0.$$

The pair (Ω, g) is called a hysteron.

It is called a hysteron of first kind if $g_+ = g_-$, otherwise it is called a hysteron of second kind. It is elementary to see that g is Lipschitz-continuous. $\quad\square$

In the first step, the hysteresis operator W is now defined for a monotone continuous function $x : [t_0, t_1] \to \mathbb{R}$ and an initial value $(x_0, y_0) \in \Omega$ with $x(t_0) = x_0$ to be

$$y(t) = (Wx)(t) = g(x(t), x_0, y_0)$$

with g defined in 1.1. This is extended in the second step to piecewise monotone functions $x \in C[0, T]$ by the inductive definition

(1) $$y(t) = (Wx)(t) = g(x(t), x(t_i), y(t_i)), \quad t \in [t_i, t_{i+1}],$$

where $0 = t_0 < t_1 < \cdots < t_N = T$ is a partition such that $x \mid [t_i, t_{i+1}]$ is monotone, and $(x(0), y(0)) = (x_0, y_0) \in \Omega$ is given. The third step, which is crucial for the mathematical analysis, is the extension to a complete space of functions.

1.2 Theorem [1, 2]
Let $\Omega, g)$ be a hysteron, $(x_0, y_0) \in \Omega$.

(i) If (Ω, g) is a hysteron of first kind and

$$X = \{x \in C[0, T] : x(0) = x_0\},$$

then W as defined in (1) can be uniquely extended to an operator

$$W : X \to C[0, T]$$

which is Lipschitz continuous on bounded subsets of X.

(ii) If (Ω, g) is a hysteron of second kind, then the same assertion as in (i) holds with $C[0, T]$ replaced by $W^{1,1}[0, T]$.

Proof: See [3, chapter 1] for (i) and [3, Theorem 29.2] for (ii). A proof for (ii) without the boundary curves b_+ and b_- is also given in [4]. □

We remark that the hysteron considered in [3] has a more general geometry (the boundary curves b_+ und b_- may intersect, or coincide along some interval) and less smoothness concerning b_+, b_-, g_+, g_-. The results presented here are still true; for details see [5].

We want to solve the following problem of optimal control whose dynamics describe a general coupling of an ODE system for the vector function $z : [0, T] \rightarrow \mathbb{R}^n$ and a hysteresis relationship $y = W x$ for the scalar functions $x, y : [0, T] \rightarrow \mathbb{R}$. The control $u : [0, T] \rightarrow \mathbb{R}^m$ enters the right hand side of the ODE system.

1.3 Optimal control problem (K)
Minimize

$$L_T(y(T), z(T), T) + \int_0^T L(y(t), z(t), t, u(t)) dt$$

subject to

$$z(t) = z_0 + \int_0^t f(y(s), s, z(s), u(s)) ds$$

$$y(t) = (W x)(t), \quad x(t) = S^T z(t)$$

$$u(t) \in U \quad \text{a. e.}$$

$$f_T(y(T), z(T), T) = 0$$

Here $T > 0$ can be fixed or free; $S \in \mathbb{R}^n$ is fixed. □

1.4 General assumptions (A)

(i) f, f_T, L, L_T are twice continuously differentiable.

(ii) (Ω, g) is a hysteron; z_0, y_0 and $x_0 = S^T z_0$ are given, $(x_0, y_0) \in \Omega$, W is the hysteresis operator corresponding to (Ω, g) with initial point (x_0, y_0).

(iii) U is a compact subset of $\mathbb{R}^m$.

(iv) f is affine linear w. r. t. u, L is convex w. r. t. u, U is convex. □

The convexity assumption (1.4 iv) is formulated for simplicity; without it our results remain true, if we pass to generalized controls in the sense of Warga [6], see [5].

In the function space formulation below, we take care of the possibly variable end time with the time transformation of [7] and also assume that the problem has been made autonomous in the standard way with an additional z-component if necessary.

1.5 Optimal control problem (P)

Minimize

$$J(y, z, u, v) = L_T(y(1), z(1)) + \int_0^1 v(t)L(y(t), z(t), u(t))dt$$

subject to

(2)
$$z(t) = z_0 + \int_0^t v(s)f(y(s), z(s), u(s))ds$$

$$y(t) = (W\,x)(t), \quad x(t) = S^T z(t)$$

$$u(t) \in U \text{ a. e. }, \quad v(t) \in [T_{min}, T_{\max}] \text{ a. e.}$$

$$f_T(y(1), z(1)) = 0$$

and, if the end time is fixed,

$$\int_0^1 v(t)dt = T$$

in the function spaces

$$x \in W^{1,\infty}(0, 1), \ y \in C[0, 1], \ z \in W^{1,\infty}(0, 1; \mathbb{R}^n),$$

$$u \in L^\infty(0, 1; \mathbb{R}^m), \ v \in L^\infty(0, 1).$$

□

Note that the time transformation makes sense, since the hysteresis operator W commutes with time transformations, as can be easily seen from the definition. The bounds $T_{min} < T_{max}$ are artificial and are made to introduce compactness in the variable end time situation. The function v now plays the role of an additional control variable.

Problem (P) can be viewed as a nonsmooth optimization problem in Banach space, since $W : W^{1,\infty} \to C$ is Lipschitz according to Theorem 1.2, but not Fréchet-differentiable as can be seen by simple examples. Because it appears as an equality constraint

$$y = W\,x$$

with infinite dimension on both sides, none of the results of the abstract approaches to nonsmooth optimization (as far as the author is aware of) can be applied immediately to derive first order necessary optimality conditions (Pontryagin principle).

Instead, we formulate an approximate smooth problem (P_ϵ) and obtain the Pontryagin principle for (P) from the corresponding principle for (P_ϵ) by a passage to the limit. This causes nontrivial technical problems, since one is confronted with jumps in the derivatives (and therefore possibly in the adjoint function) due to changes in sign of the derivative of the input x and due to the transition from interior to boundary curves in the hysteron (Ω, g).

For existence of optimal controls, the hysteresis nonlinearity poses no additional problems as W is nonanticipating (i.e. $(Wx)(t)$ depends only upon $x \mid [0, t]$).

2. The approximating problem.

We discretize and regularize the operator W in order to obtain a smooth operator W_ε^h.

2.1 Definition
Let $\varepsilon, h > 0$ and let $\Delta_h = \{t_i\}$ be an equidistant partition of $[0, 1]$ with stepsize h. We define W^h and W_ε^h by

$$(W^h x)(t) = g(x(t), x(t_i), (W^h x)(t_i)), \quad t \in [t_i, t_{i+1}]$$

$$(W_\varepsilon^h x)(t) = g_\varepsilon(x(t), x(t_i), (W_\varepsilon^h x)(t_i^-)), \quad t \in [t_i, t_{i+1}]$$

Here $g_\varepsilon = \rho_\varepsilon * g$ is the convolution with the standard mollifier $\rho_\varepsilon \in C_0^\infty(\mathbb{R}^3)$ which for $\varepsilon \downarrow 0$ converges to the Dirac distribution δ in the sense of distributions. $\qquad \square$

One observes immediately that, because of the definition of g in 1.1, the operator W^h maps C, $W^{1,1}$ and $W^{1,\infty}$ into itself, whereas W_ε^h introduces discontinuities of order ε at t_i, and therefore

$$W_\varepsilon^h : C[0, 1] \to \prod_i C[t_i, t_{i+1}]$$

as well as for $W^{1,1}$ and $W^{1,\infty}$.

Since the hysteresis effect manifests itself in the discretization parameter h, it comes as no surprise that it should dominate the regularization "error" generated by ε. We achieve this by the somewhat arbitrary choice $\varepsilon = h^2$. We now formulate the approximating problem.

2.2 The approximating problem (P_ε)
Let $0 = t_0 < t_1 < \cdots < t_{N+1} = 1$ be an equidistant partition of $[0, 1]$ with stepsize h, let $\varepsilon = h^2$.
Minimize

$$J_\varepsilon(y, z, u, v) = J(y, z, u, v) + \frac{1}{h}\|f_T(y(1), z(1))\|_2^2 + \|u - u_*\|_\infty^2 + \|v - v_*\|_{1,\infty}^2$$

subject to

(3)

$$z(t) = z_0 + \int_0^t v(s)f(y(s), z(s), u(s))ds$$

$$y(t) = (W_\varepsilon^h x)(t), \quad x(t) = S^T z(t)$$

$$u(t) \in U \ \text{a. e.,} \quad v(t) \in [T_{min}, T_{\max}] \ \text{a. e.}$$

and, if the end time is fixed,

$$\int_0^1 v(t)\,dt = T,$$

in the function spaces

$$x \in W^{1,\infty}(0,1), \ y \in \prod_{i=0}^{N} C[t_i, t_{i+1}], \ z \in W^{1,\infty}(0,1;\mathbb{R}^n),$$

$$u \in L^\infty(0,1;\mathbb{R}^m), \ v \in W^{1,\infty}(0,1).$$

Here $u_* \in L^\infty$, $v_* \in W^{1,\infty}$ are fixed functions (they will be solutions of (P)). □

We have introduced in (P_ϵ) a third kind of approximation, namely penalization of the terminal condition $f_T = 0$ (in order to avoid the controllability problem for (P_ϵ) as far as possible) and of the distance to u_* and v_* (in order to enforce strong convergence of the (P_ϵ)-solutions).

For a-priori estimates we need a growth condition relating f and W. One possibility is the following:

2.3 The growth condition (G)
We assume that there is a continuous function c_1 and a constant c_2 such that

$$z^T f(y, z, u) \leq c_1(u, y)(1 + z^T z)$$

$$|b_+(x)| \leq c_2, \quad |b_-(x)| \leq c_2$$

for all $(x, y, z, u) \in \mathbb{R} \times \mathbb{R} \times \mathbb{R}^n \times \mathbb{R}^m$. □

2.4 Lemma
Let (A) and (G) hold. Then there exists a constant $C > 0$ such that for all (u, v) admissible for (P) resp. (P_ϵ)

(i) the system equations (2) for (P) have a unique global solution $(x, y, z) \in W^{1,\infty}$ with

$$\|x\|_{1,\infty} \leq C, \ \|y\|_{1,\infty} \leq C, \ \|z\|_{1,\infty} \leq C$$

(ii) the system equations (3) for (P_ϵ) have a unique global solution $(x, z) \in W^{1,\infty}$, $y \in BV(0,1)$ with

$$\|x\|_{1,\infty} \leq C, \ \|z\|_{1,\infty} \leq C, \ y = y^a + y^s$$

$$y^a \in W^{1,\infty}, \ \|y^a\|_{1,\infty} \leq C,$$

$$y^s \in BV, \ \text{Var}(y^s) \leq Ch$$

Proof: The key step is to prove an a-priori estimate for $\|z\|_\infty$. Growth condition (G) ensures that the standard proof, which combines the Banach contraction principle and Gronwall's inequality, provides such an estimate. The bounds for (x, z) follow directly from the system equation. Since W can be shown to map bounded subsets of $W^{1,\infty}$ into bounded subsets of $W^{1,\infty}$, (i) is proved. In (ii), the function y^s accumulates the jumps

$$y^s(t) = \sum_{t > t_i}(y(t_i^+) - y(t_i^-))$$

which sum to $O(\frac{\varepsilon}{h}) = O(h)$, and the bound for y^a comes from a uniform estimate of the first partial derivative $D_1 g_\varepsilon$ in 2.1. $\square$

In the case of a hysteron of second kind, a further structure condition is needed, which means that the control u must not appear in the first derivative of the input x.

2.5 The structure condition (H)

If (Ω, g) is a hysteron of second kind, we assume that the state vector z splits as $z = (z^I, z^{II})$, and that

$$x = S^T z = S_I^T z^I \qquad \text{(no dependence on } z^{II})$$

$$f^I = f^I(y, z) \qquad \text{(no dependence on } u)$$

$\square$

(H) is satisfied, for example, if we have

$$\ddot{x} = f(x, y, u), \quad y = W x.$$

By compactness arguments, we now see that problems (P) and (P_ε) have a solution.

2.6 Theorem (Existence)

Let assumptions (A), (G) and (H) hold.

(i) If there exists an admissible (x, y, z, u, v) for (P), then there exists a solution $(x_*, y_*, z_*, u_*, v_*)$ of (P).

(ii) There exists a solution $(x_\varepsilon, y_\varepsilon, z_\varepsilon, u_\varepsilon, v_\varepsilon)$ of (P_ε).

Proof:

(i) Due to the a priori estimates (2.4i) and Arzela-Ascoli's theorem, a minimizing sequence $(x_n, y_n, z_n, u_n, v_n)$ exists where (x_n, y_n, z_n) converge uniformly, u_n converges w^* in L^∞, $v_n \equiv T_n \in \mathbb{R}$ converges in $\mathbb{R}$. (H) guarantees that, if (Ω, g) is a hysteron of second kind, x_n converges strongly in $W^{1,\infty}$. With the aid of Theorem 1.2, we may pass to the limit.

(ii) Because of (2.4 ii), we obtain a minimizing sequence where (x_n, z_n, v_n) converge uniformly (since $\|v_n\|_{1,\infty}$ is bounded), u_n converges w^* in L^∞, and y_n converges pointwise in BV by Helly's theorem. $\square$

To obtain convergence of $(x_\varepsilon, y_\varepsilon, z_\varepsilon, u_\varepsilon, v_\varepsilon)$ to $(x_*, y_*, z_*, u_*, v_*)$ we need a lemma on the approximation properties of the operators W_ε^h.

2.7 Lemma

For x and $\bar{x}$ as described below we have:

(i) If (Ω, g) is a hysteron of first kind, then

$$|W_\varepsilon^h x(t) - W\bar{x}(t)| \leq C_1 (h + \sup_{0 \leq s \leq t} |x(s) - \bar{x}(s)|)$$

(ii) If (Ω, g) is a hysteron of second kind, then

$$|W_\varepsilon^h x(t) - W\bar{x}(t)| \leq C_1 (h + \int_0^t |\dot{x}(s) - \dot{\bar{x}}(s)| ds)$$

The constant $C_1 = C_1(C)$ is uniform for $x, \bar{x} \in W^{1,\infty}(0,1)$ with $x(0) = \bar{x}(0) = x_0$ and $\|x\|_{1,\infty} \leq C$, $\|\bar{x}\|_{1,\infty} \leq C$. In (ii) one must have additionally $\bar{x} \in W^{2,1}(0,1)$, $\|\ddot{\bar{x}}\|_1 \leq C$.

Proof: With $I^h x$ being the piecewise linear interpolant of x,

$$W_\varepsilon^h x - W\bar{x} = (W_\varepsilon^h x - W^h x) + (W^h x - W^h I^h x) +$$

$$+ (W^h I^h x - W I^h x) + (W I^h x - W I^h \bar{x}) + (W I^h \bar{x} - W\bar{x})$$

and one estimates the differences separately. For example, with the discrete form of Gronwall's inequality, one obtains

$$\|W_\varepsilon^h x - W^h x\|_\infty \leq C_2 \frac{\varepsilon}{h} = C_2 h$$

$\square$

Lemma (2.7) allows us to compare solutions of the system equations of (P_ε) and (P), i.e., of

(4)
$$\dot{z}(t) = v(t) f(W_\varepsilon^h S^T z(t), z(t), u(t)), \quad z(0) = z_0$$

$$\dot{\bar{z}}(t) = \bar{v}(t) f(W S^T \bar{z}(t), \bar{z}(t), \bar{u}(t)), \quad \bar{z}(0) = z_0.$$

We obtain the following stability estimate.

2.8 Proposition

Let (A), (G) and (H) hold. Then there is a $C > 0$ such that for all $\varepsilon > 0$, all u, $\bar{u} \in L^\infty(0,1;U)$, all $v, \bar{v} \in W^{1,\infty}(0,1;[T_{min}, T_{max}])$ with $\|\dot{\bar{v}}\|_\infty \leq 1$ we have

$$\|z - \bar{z}\|_{1,\infty} \leq C(h + \|u - \bar{u}\|_\infty + \|v - \bar{v}\|_\infty)$$

$$\|y - \bar{y}\|_\infty \leq C(h + \|u - \bar{u}\|_\infty + \|v - \bar{v}\|_\infty)$$

where z, $\overline{z}$ solve (4) and $y = W_\epsilon^h S^T z$, $\overline{y} = W S^T \overline{z}$.

Proof: Because of (2.4) and (H), the inputs $x = S^T z$, $\overline{x} = S^T \overline{z}$ satisfy the a-priori-bounds required in (2.7). The estimate in (2.7) together with Gronwall's inequality yields the result. □

It now follows that if (u_*, v_*) define a solution of (P) then all solutions of (P_ϵ) converge to this solution.

2.9 Theorem

Let (A), (G) and (H) hold, let $(x_*, y_*, z_*, u_*, v_*)$ with $v_* \equiv T$ be a solution of (P). Then for all solutions $(x_\epsilon, y_\epsilon, z_\epsilon, u_\epsilon, v_\epsilon)$ of (P_ϵ) we have $(x_\epsilon, z_\epsilon, v_\epsilon) \to (x_*, z_*, v_*)$ in $W^{1,\infty}$, $(y_\epsilon, u_\epsilon) \to (y_*, u_*)$ in L^∞, $\dot{y}_\epsilon^a \to \dot{y}_*$ weak star in L^∞, $J_\epsilon(y_\epsilon, z_\epsilon, u_\epsilon, v_\epsilon) \to J(y_*, z_*, u_*, v_*)$, $h^{-1} \| f_T(y_\epsilon(1), z_\epsilon(1)) \|^2 \to 0$.

Proof: Using (2.8), by comparison with the solution of

$$\dot{z} = v_* f(W_\epsilon^h S^T z, z, u_*), \quad z(0) = z_0$$

one finds that $J(y_*, z_*, u_*, v_*) \geq \limsup J_\epsilon(y_\epsilon, z_\epsilon, u_\epsilon, v_\epsilon)$. From this one obtains weak star limits $(x_\epsilon, z_\epsilon, v_\epsilon) \to (\hat{x}, \hat{z}, \hat{v})$ in $W^{1,\infty}$, $(u_\epsilon, \dot{y}_\epsilon^a) \to (\hat{u}, \frac{d}{dt}\hat{y})$ in L^∞. These limits turn out to be admissible for (P), so $\limsup J_\epsilon(y_\epsilon, z_\epsilon, u_\epsilon, v_\epsilon) \geq J(y_*, z_*, u_*, v_*)$, and both inequalities together imply strong convergence $u_\epsilon \to u_*$ in L^∞, $v_\epsilon \to v_*$ in $W^{1,\infty}$. □

3. The maximum principle for problem (P_ϵ).

By construction, problem (P_ϵ) has differentiable structure. The first order necessary optimality conditions for (P_ϵ) can be obtained via an abstract multiplier rule. There are many versions of multiplier rules in the literature; for our purposes, the formulation for so-called "smooth-convex" problems in [8] is most convenient.

3.1 Problem (O)

$$\begin{aligned} \text{Minimize} \quad & I(w, u, v) \\ \text{subject to} \quad & F(w, u, v) = 0. \end{aligned}$$

Here $I : O \times U \times V \to \mathbb{R}$, $F : O \times U \times V \to X$ where O is an open subset of a Banach space X, and U and V are convex subsets of some linear spaces. Moreover, $I(w, \cdot, v)$ and $I(w, u, \cdot)$ are convex, $F(w, \cdot, v)$ and $F(w, u, \cdot)$ are affine linear, $I(\cdot, u, v)$ and $F(\cdot, u, v)$ are continuously Fréchet-differentiable. □

3.2 Theorem (Abstract multiplier rule)

If (w^0, u^0, v^0) solves (O) and if $D_w F(w^0, u^0, v^0) : X \to X$ is surjective, then there is a unique $x^* \in X^*$ such that the adjoint equation

$$(D_w I - x^* \circ D_w F)(w^0, u^0, v^0) = 0$$

and the minimum conditions

$$(I - x^* \circ F)(w^0, u^0, v^0) = \min_{u \in \mathcal{U}}(I - x^* \circ F)(w^0, u^0, v^0) =$$

$$= \min_{v \in \mathcal{V}}(I - x^* \circ F)(w^0, u^0, v^0)$$

hold.

Proof: Apply theorem 3 from [8], p. 71, separately for minimization with respect to u and v. Since $D_w F(w^0, u^0, v^0)$ is surjective, the resulting multipliers are identical. $\qquad\square$

To apply the multiplier rule (3.2) to problem (P_ε), we eliminate $x = S^T z$ and set $w = (y, z)$,

$$X = (\prod_{i=0}^{N} C[t_i, t_{i+1}]) \times W^{1,\infty}(0, 1; \mathbb{R}^n)$$

(5) $$\mathcal{U} = \{u \in L^\infty(0, 1; \mathbb{R}^m) : u(t) \in U \ \text{a. e. }\}$$

$$\mathcal{V} = \{v \in W^{1,\infty}(0, 1) : v(t) \in [T_{min}, T_{max}] \ \text{a. e.}; \int_0^1 v(t)dt = T \ \text{if} \ T \ \text{is fixed .}\}$$

We define $I = J_\varepsilon$ and F by the equations for y_i $(0 \leq i \leq N)$ and z in problem (P_ε). We normalize the multiplier with the aid of the scalar $\gamma_\varepsilon \in \mathbb{R}$, which is defined by

(6)
$$\gamma_\varepsilon = 1, \quad \text{if} \ \frac{2}{h}\|f_T(y_\varepsilon(1), z_\varepsilon(1))\| \ \text{is bounded independently from} \ \varepsilon$$

$$\gamma_\varepsilon = (1 + \frac{2}{h}\|f_T(y_\varepsilon(1), z_\varepsilon(1))\|)^{-1}, \quad \text{otherwise.}$$

We then obtain

3.3 Theorem (Maximum principle for (P_ε))

Let (A) and (G) hold, let $(x_\varepsilon, y_\varepsilon, z_\varepsilon, u_\varepsilon, v_\varepsilon)$ be a solution of (P_ε), let $\gamma_\varepsilon > 0$ be defined by (6). Then there exist $a_i^\varepsilon \in \mathbb{R}^n$, $c_i^\varepsilon \in \mathbb{R}$, $1 \leq i \leq N+1$, and $p_\varepsilon : [0, 1] \to \mathbb{R}^n$ which is absolutely continuous in each interval (t_i, t_{i+1}), such that the adjoint system

$$p_\varepsilon(t) = \left(\sum_{t_i \geq t} a_i^\varepsilon\right) + \int_t^1 v_\varepsilon(s)\left[\gamma_\varepsilon D_z L^\varepsilon(s) + D_z f^\varepsilon(s)^T p_\varepsilon(s) + \right.$$

$$\left. + (\gamma_\varepsilon D_y L^\varepsilon(s) + D_y f^\varepsilon(s)^T p_\varepsilon(s)) D_1 g_\varepsilon(s) S\right] ds$$

$$a_{N+1}^\varepsilon = \gamma_\varepsilon D_z L_T^\varepsilon(1) + \frac{2}{h} D_z f_T^\varepsilon(1)^T f_T^\varepsilon(1) + c_{N+1}^\varepsilon D_1 g_\varepsilon(1) S$$

$$a_i^\varepsilon = c_{i+1}^\varepsilon (D_3 g_\varepsilon(t_{i+1}) D_1 g_\varepsilon(t_i) + D_2 g_\varepsilon(t_{i+1})) S +$$

$$+ \int_{t_i}^{t_{i+1}} (D_3 g_\varepsilon(t) D_1 g_\varepsilon(t_i) + D_2 g_\varepsilon(t)) v_\varepsilon(t) [D_y f^\varepsilon(t)^T p_\varepsilon(t) + \gamma_\varepsilon D_y L^\varepsilon(t)] dt \cdot S$$

$$c_{N+1}^\varepsilon = \gamma_\varepsilon D_y L_T^\varepsilon(1) + \frac{2}{h} D_y f_T^\varepsilon(1)^T f_T^\varepsilon(1)$$

$$c_i^\varepsilon = c_{i+1}^\varepsilon D_3 g_\varepsilon(t_{i+1}) + \int_{t_i}^{t_{i+1}} (v_\varepsilon(t)(\gamma_\varepsilon D_y L^\varepsilon(t) + D_y f^\varepsilon(t)^T p_\varepsilon(t)) D_3 g_\varepsilon(t) dt$$

and for all $u \in \mathcal{U}$, $v \in \mathcal{V}$ the minimum conditions

$$\int_0^1 v_\varepsilon(t)(\gamma_\varepsilon L(y_\varepsilon(t), z_\varepsilon(t), u_\varepsilon(t)) + f(y_\varepsilon(t), z_\varepsilon(t), u_\varepsilon(t))^T p_\varepsilon(t)) dt + \gamma_\varepsilon \|u_\varepsilon - u_*\|_\infty^2 \leq$$

$$\leq \int_0^1 v_\varepsilon(t)(\gamma_\varepsilon L(y_\varepsilon(t), z_\varepsilon(t), u(t)) + f(y_\varepsilon(t), z_\varepsilon(t), u(t))^T p_\varepsilon(t)) dt + \gamma_\varepsilon \|u - u_*\|_\infty^2$$

and

$$\int_0^1 v_\varepsilon(t)(\gamma_\varepsilon L(y_\varepsilon(t), z_\varepsilon(t), u_\varepsilon(t)) + f(y_\varepsilon(t), z_\varepsilon(t), u_\varepsilon(t))^T p_\varepsilon(t)) dt + \gamma_\varepsilon \|v_\varepsilon - v_*\|_{1,\infty}^2 \leq$$

$$\leq \int_0^1 v(t)(\gamma_\varepsilon L(y_\varepsilon(t), z_\varepsilon(t), u_\varepsilon(t)) + f(y_\varepsilon(t), z_\varepsilon(t), u_\varepsilon(t))^T p_\varepsilon(t)) dt + \gamma_\varepsilon \|v - v_*\|_{1,\infty}^2$$

hold. Here we have used the abbreviations

$$D_i g_\varepsilon(t) = D_i g_\varepsilon(x_\varepsilon(t), x_\varepsilon(t_i), y_\varepsilon(t_i^-)) \quad \text{if } t \in (t_i, t_{i+1}]$$

$$D_z L^\varepsilon(t) = D_z L(y_\varepsilon(t), z_\varepsilon(t), u_\varepsilon(t))$$

et cetera.

Proof: The differentiability assumption of (3.1) follows since we work in sup-norm spaces. The surjectivity assumption of (3.2) is implied by the Volterra structure of the equations for y_i and z in (P_ϵ). The derivation of the equations and inequalities in (3.3) from the corresponding ones in (3.2) rests mainly on partial integration. □

4. Controllability.

In this paper, we do not really discuss the question of controllability. In the context of the maximum principle, however, it arises if one wants to prove Kuhn-Tucker type conditions (i.e., a nondegenerate maximum principle) as opposed to Fritz John type conditions. Usually, some controllability condition is sufficient for Kuhn-Tucker type conditions. For example, for linear constant coefficient system (without hysteresis)

$$\dot{z} = Az + Bu$$

the well-known condition for complete controllability is that rank $(B, AB, A^2B, \ldots, A^{n-1}B)$ be maximal. In nonlinear system, this turns into a rank condition for its linearization. Since a linearization is not available for our problem, we formulate a Lipschitz type condition.

4.1 Definition
With $\mathcal{U}$ and $\mathcal{V}$ given by (5), we define by

$$(u, v) \mapsto (y(1), z(1))$$

mappings R, $R_\epsilon : \mathcal{U} \times \mathcal{V} \to \mathbb{R}^{n+1}$, where (y, z) are the solutions of the system equations of (P) resp. (P_ϵ) which belong to (u, v). We set

$$N_\delta(u, v) = \{(\overline{u}, \overline{v}) \in \mathcal{U} \times \mathcal{V} : \|\overline{u} - u\|_\infty + \|\overline{v} - v\|_{1,\infty} \leq \delta\}.$$

□

4.2 Controllability condition (C)
We say that the controllability condition (C) is satisfied for $(u_*, v_*) \in \mathcal{U} \times \mathcal{V}$, if the following holds:
There are α, η, $\delta_0 > 0$ such that for all $\delta \in (0, \delta_0]$ and all $(u, v) \in N_\eta(u_*, v_*)$

$$f_T(R(N_\eta(u, v))) \supset f_T(R(u, v)) + B_{\alpha\delta},$$

where $B_{\alpha\delta}$ denotes the ball in $\mathbb{R}^{n+1}$ with radius $\alpha\delta$. □

The following theorem connects condition (C) to the normalization scalar γ_ϵ in theorem (3.3).

4.3 Theorem
Let (A), (G), (H) and (C) hold, let $(x_*, y_*, z_*, u_*, v_*)$ be a solution of (P) with $v_* \equiv T$. Then there is a $C > 0$ such that for all $\epsilon > 0$

$$\frac{1}{h}\|f_T(y_\epsilon(1), z_\epsilon(1))\| \leq C$$

and therefore $\gamma_\epsilon = 1$ in (3.3).

Proof: The proof uses the Lipschitz stability estimate (2.8) as well as the possibility of decreasing $\|f_T(R(u_\epsilon, v_\epsilon))\|$ by small variations (u, v) of (u_ϵ, v_ϵ), which is implied by (C). See [5], chapter 8, for details. $\quad\square$

5. The maximum principle for the problem (P)

We want to obtain the maximum principle for problem (P) from theorem (3.3), letting ϵ converge to zero. The main problems are estimates for the discontinuities

$$p_\epsilon(t_i^+) - p_\epsilon(t_i^-) = a_i^\epsilon$$

as well as the convergence properties of $D_i g_\epsilon(t)$, whose expected limit $D_i g(t)$ is a discontinuous function due to the hysteresis behaviour. It is quite impossible to present detailed proofs in this paper, but we will formulate several intermediate lemmata. In the general situation, we obtain:

5.1 Lemma
Let (A), (G) and (H) hold, let $(x_*, y_*, z_*, u_*, v_*)$ be a solution of (P).

(i) There is a $C > 0$ such that for all $\epsilon > 0$, the adjoints in (P_ϵ) satisfy

$$\|p_\epsilon\|_\infty \le C, \ |c_i^\epsilon| \le C, \ \|a_i^\epsilon\| \le C$$

(ii) If (Ω, g) is a hysteron of first kind, moreover

$$\mathrm{Var}(p_\epsilon) \le C, \quad \sum_{i=1}^{N+1} \|a_i^\epsilon\| \le C.$$

Proof: Chapters 9 and 10 in [5]. $\quad\square$

By analogy with state constrained control problems, one expects the adjoint for (P) to jump at points where the $(x_*(t), y_*(t))$-trajectory switches from one family of curves to another ($g_+ \to g_-$, $g_- \to g_+$, $b_+ \to g_-$, $b_- \to g_+$) with the exception of the $g_+ \to b_+$ and $g_- \to b_-$ transitions, since in these cases only merging occurs. Therefore, the adjoint p_* for (P) should be piecewise absolutely continuous, if the number of this kind of switching points if finite; if this is not the case, one cannot expect more regularity than that provided by (5.1).

One sees from definition (1.1) that, as long as one stays within one of the four different regions in the domain of definition of g, one has the semigroup property

$$g(x_2, x_1, g(x_1, x_0, y_0)) = g(x_2, x_0, y_0).$$

If one takes the derivative w. r. t. x_1 on both sides, because of the smoothness of g one can conclude that

$$(7) \qquad D_3 g_\varepsilon(t) D_1 g_\varepsilon(t_i) + D_2 g_\varepsilon(t) = O(\varepsilon), \quad t \in (t_i, t_{i+1}],$$

in the interior of each of these four regions.

In the case of a hysteron of first kind, one has only three regions $(b_+, b_-, g_+ = g_-)$, and no convergence problems occur away from $\partial\Omega$, so $b_+ \to g_-$ and $b_- \to g_+$ are the only critical switchings in this case.

The following regularity condition formalizes the notion of "critical switchings".

5.2 Regularity condition (R)

Let $x \in W^{1,\infty}(0,1)$ with $x(0) = x_0$, let $y = Wx$. We say that x is regular between τ_- and τ_+ in $[0,1]$, if the following holds:

(i) If (Ω, g) is a hysteron of second kind: For $I = (\tau_-, \tau_+)$, $\mathrm{sign}(\dot{x}(t))$ is constant a. e. in I, and for all compact $K \subset I$ there exists a $\delta > 0$ such that

$$|\dot{x}(t)| \geq \delta > 0 \text{ a. e. }, t \in K$$

(ii) If (Ω, g) is a hysteron of first kind: The condition in (i) holds for some I_1 and I_2 which have the form
$$I_1 = (\tau_-, \hat{\tau}), \quad I_2 = (\hat{\tau}, \tau_+)$$
and satisfy

$$\{t \in (\tau_-, \tau_+) : (x(t), y(t)) \in \partial\Omega\} \subset I_1 \cup I_2 \subset (\tau_-, \tau_+)$$

We say that x satisfies the regularity condition (R), if there is a finite partition $\{\tau_k\}$ of $[0,1]$, such that x is regular between τ_k and τ_{k+1} for all k. $\qquad\square$

For example, the regularity condition (R) is satisfied if $x \in C^1[0,1]$ and $\dot{x}$ has only finitely many zeros. For a system of the form

$$\ddot{x} = f(x, y, u),$$

(R) holds if and only if $\dot{x}$ has finitely many zeros.

We have introduced condition (R), because we can prove convergence

$$\varphi_\varepsilon(t) = D_3 g_\varepsilon(t) D_1 g_\varepsilon(t_i) + D_2 g_\varepsilon(t) \to 0 \text{ as } \varepsilon \to 0$$

on intervals (τ_k, τ_{k+1}) in a weaker sense than in (7), but sufficiently strong in order to pass to the limit in the equations for p_ε and a_i^ε in theorem (3.3). The result is summarized in the following lemma.

5.3 Lemma

Let (A), (G), (H) be satisfied, let $(x_*, y_*, z_*, u_*, v_*)$ be a solution of (P), let x_* satisfy (R) with the partition $\{\tau_k\}$. Then

(i) For $\varphi_\epsilon(t) := D_3 g_\epsilon(t) D_1 g_\epsilon(t_i) + D_2 g_\epsilon(t)$, $t \in (t_i, t_{i+1}]$, we have $\varphi_\epsilon \to 0$ in $L^1(0,1)$.

(ii) For all $I_k^\sigma = (\tau_k + \sigma, \tau_{k+1} - \sigma)$, $\sigma > 0$, we have

$$\lim_{\epsilon \to 0} \sum_{t_i \in I_k^\sigma} |c_{i+1}^\epsilon (D_3 g_\epsilon(t_{i+1}) D_1 g_\epsilon(t_i) + D_2 g_\epsilon(t_{i+1}))| = 0$$

(iii) We have $D_1 g_\epsilon \to D_1 g$ in $L^1(0,1)$, where

$$D_1 g(t) := D_1 g(x_*(t), x_*(\tau_k), y_*(\tau_k)), \quad t \in [\tau_k, \tau_{k+1}].$$

Proof: See [5], chapter 11. □

We are now ready to formulate the maximum principle for problem (P). We split this task into two parts: In (5.4) we formulate the assertions of the maximum principle, and in (5.5) we state under which conditions which of these assertions hold.

5.4 The assertions of the maximum principle for (P)

For the adjoint variables $p_* : [0, T] \to \mathbb{R}^n$, $\ell_0 \geq 0$, $\ell_1 \in \mathbb{R}^k$, $\ell_2 \in \mathbb{R}$ and the Hamiltonian

$$H(y, z, u, p) = \ell_0 L(y, z, u) + f(y, z, u)^T p$$

we formulate the assertions

(i) The adjoint differential equation

$$\dot{p}_*(t) = -v_*(t)[D_z H(t) + D_y H(t) D_1 g(t) S]$$

(ii) The end condition

$$p_*(1) = \ell_0 D_z L_T(1) + D_z f_T(1)^T \ell_1 + (\ell_0 D_y L_T(1) + D_y f_T(1)^T \ell_1) D_1 g(1) S$$

(iii) The jump conditions

$$p_*(\tau_k^-) - p_*(\tau_k^+) = \alpha_k S, \quad \alpha_k \in \mathbb{R}$$

(iv) The minimum condition

$$H(y_*(t), z_*(t), u_*(t), p_*(t)) = \min_{u \in U} H(y_*(t), z_*(t), u, p_*(t))$$

(v) The constancy condition

$$H(y_*(t), z_*(t), u_*(t), p_*(t)) = \ell_2.$$

□

5.5 Theorem (Maximum principle for problem (P))

Let (A), (G) and (H) hold, let $(x_*, y_*, z_*, u_*, v_*)$ be a solution of (P) with $v_* \equiv T$. Then there are $p_* \in L^\infty(0, 1; \mathbb{R}^n)$, $\ell_0 \geq 0$, $\ell_1 \in \mathbb{R}^k$, $\ell_2 \in \mathbb{R}$ with $(\ell_0, \ell_1) \neq 0$, such that

(i) The minimum condition (5.4 iv) and the constancy condition (5.4 v) hold a. e. in $(0, 1)$.

(ii) If $S = (S_I, 0)$ is a partition according to (H) and if $p_* = (p_*^I, p_*^{II})$ is partitioned accordingly, then p_*^{II} is absolutely continuous in $[0, 1]$, and the adjoint equation (5.4i) and end condition (5.4 ii) hold for p_*^{II}, i.e.

$$\dot{p}_*^{II}(t) = -v_*(t) D_z H(t)^{II}$$

$$p_*^{II}(1) = (\ell_0 D_z L_T(1) + D_z f_T(1)^T \ell_1)^{II}$$

(iii) If (Ω, g) is a hysteron of first kind, then

$$p_* \in BV(0, 1; \mathbb{R}^n)$$

(iv) If x_* satisfies (R) with partition $\{\tau_k\}$, then p_* is absolutely continuous in (τ_k, τ_{k+1}) for all k, and the adjoint equation (5.4i), the end condition (5.4 ii) and the jump conditions (5.4 iii) hold.

(v) If the controllability condition (C) is satisfied, we may choose $\ell_0 = 1$ (i.e. the Kuhn-Tucker conditions hold).

(vi) If the terminal time T in (K) is free, then $\ell_2 = 0$.

Proof: Lemmata (5.1) and (5.3) supply the amount of convergence which is sufficient to pass to the limit in (3.3). See [5], chapter 8 for details. □

To obtain the maximum principle for problem (K), one transforms back in the standard manner. The resulting equations are the same as in (5.4) except that $v^*(t)$ disappears from the adjoint equation (5.4 i), and the constancy condition (5.4 v) is replaced by

$$H(t) = -\ell_0 D_t L_T(T) - D_t f_T(T)^T \ell_1 - \int_t^T D_t H(s)ds + \ell_2.$$

References.

[1] Kozjakin, V. S., Krasnoselskii, M. A., Pokrovskii, A. V.: *Vibrationally stable hysterons.* DAN SSSR 206 (1972), p. 800 – 803; Soviet Math. Dokl. 13 (1972) p. 1305 – 1309.

[2] Pokrovskii, A. V.: *On the theory of hysteresis nonlinearities.* DAN SSSR 210 (1973), p. 896 – 900, Soviet Math. Dokl. 14 (1973) p. 896 – 900.

[3] Krasnoselskii, M. A., Pokrovskii, A. V.: *Systeme mit Hysterese.* (Russian) Nauka, Moscow 1983.

[4] Visintin, A.: *Continuity properties of a class of hysteresis functionals.* Atti Sem. Mat. Fis. Univ. Modena, 32 (1983), p. 232 – 247.

[5] Brokate, M.: *Optimale Steuerung von gewöhnlichen Differentialgleichungen mit Nichtlinearitäten vom Hysteresis-Typ.* Habilitationsschrift, Augsburg 1985. To appear in: Verlag Peter Lang, Frankfurt - Bern - New York, 1987.

[6] Warga, J.: *Optimal control of differential and functional equations.* Academic Press, New York - London 1972.

[7] Dubovitskii, A. Ya., Milyutin, A. A.: *Extremum problems in the presence of restrictions.* USSR Comp. Math. and Math. Phys. 5 (1965), p. 1 – 80.

[8] Ioffe, A. D., Tihomirov, V. M.: *Theory of extremal problems.* North-Holland, Amsterdam – New York – Oxford 1979.

International Series of
Numerical Mathematics, Vol. 84
(c) 1988 Birkhäuser Verlag Basel

Equivalent Perturbations and Approximations in Optimal Control.

A. L. Dontchev

Bulgarian Acad. of Sciences

Institute of Mathematics

1113 Sofia, Acad. G. Bonchev 8

Bulgaria

Abstract. We present a characterization of the continuity of the optimal value (marginal function) of optimal control problems to differential inclusions with respect to the data. Extending our method we study the convergence of finite difference approximations and of the penalty function method for reduction of the state constraints.

1. Introduction

Let X and Y be topological spaces and $f : X \times Y \to R^1$, $M : Y \to 2^X$. The *marginal function* $\hat{f} : Y \to R^1$ is defined as

$$\hat{f}(y) = \inf(f(x, y), x \in M(y)).$$

Classical Berge theorem, see Berge [1], p. 123, says that if X is compact and f and M are continuous in $X \times Y$ and Y respectively, then $\hat{f}$ is continuous in Y. When applied to optimal control problems, however, this theorem usually leads to conditions that are too restrictive.

In this paper we study the continuity properties of the marginal function of optimal control problems developing the following idea: the compactness and continuity requirements can be relaxed if we find a new problem with suitable properties which "approximates" the initial problem in appropriate way. It turns out that the concept of relaxation (in the sense of Bogolyubov and Young) can be applied for that purpose.

Consider the following optimal control problem (P):

(1) $$\varphi(x(T)) \to \inf$$

subject to

(2) $$\dot{x} \in F(x, t), \; x(0) = x^0,$$

(3) $$x(t) \in C(t) \text{ for all } t \in [0, T],$$

where the interval $[0, T]$ is fixed, $x(t) \in R^n$, $\varphi : R^n \to R^1 \cup \{+\infty\}$ and $F : R^n \times [0, T] \to 2^{R^n}$, $C : [0, T] \to 2^{R^n}$. We note that many standard optimal control problems can be reduced to this form.

We recall that every absolutely continuous function that satisfies (2) and (3) is a *viable* trajectory for (2), (3).

The *relaxed* problem (R) associated with (P) consists in minimizing (1) subject to (3) and

$$(4) \qquad \dot{x} \in \overline{co}F(x,t), \; x(0) = x^0.$$

Denoting by $\hat{\varphi}$ and $\hat{\varphi}^R$ the optimal values of (P) and (R) respectively one clearly has $\hat{\varphi} \geq \hat{\varphi}^R$. We say that *relaxation stability* holds if $\hat{\varphi} = \hat{\varphi}^R$. In the further lines we show that the relaxation stability is equivalent to the continuity of the optimal value of (P) with respect to general perturbations of the differential inclusion and the state constraints. Introducing a necessary and sufficient condition for such an equivalence we analyse this condition for linear systems. Next we study a finite-difference approximation to (P) developing parallel results. Finally, the convergence of the penalty function method for reduction of the state constraints is studied. The presented results lead to the conclusion that the perturbations and approximations in optimal control are not only methodologically compatible but in fact equivalent, and can be regarded as different sides of one and the same property: the capability of the problem to preserve its performance under deformations.

2. Perturbations

We consider the following optimal control problem (P_ε) depending on a parameter

$$\varphi(x(T)) \to \inf$$

subject to

$$(5) \qquad \dot{x} \in F(x,t) + G(x,t,\varepsilon), \; x(0) = x^0,$$

$$(6) \qquad x(t) \in C(t,\varepsilon)$$

where ε is a scalar parameter, $\varepsilon \in [0,\varepsilon_0]$. Setting $G(x,t,0) = \{0\}$ and $C(t,0) = C(t)$, for $\varepsilon = 0$ from (P_ε) we get the problem (P). The case $\varepsilon > 0$ is interpreted as presence of perturbations in (P) of the type (P_ε).

Denote by $\hat{\varphi}_\varepsilon$ the marginal function of (P_ε). We say that *perturbation stability* holds if $\lim_{\varepsilon \to 0} \hat{\varphi}_\varepsilon = \hat{\varphi}$. In the sequel we assume the following:

(A1) There exists a bounded set Ω in R^n such that $C(t,\varepsilon) \subset \Omega$ for all $t \in [0,t]$ and $\varepsilon \in [0,\varepsilon_0]$, $C(t,\varepsilon)$ is closed for every $t \in [0,T]$ and $\varepsilon \in [0,\varepsilon_0]$ and $C(t,\cdot)$ is upper semicontinuous at $\varepsilon = 0$ for every $t \in [0,T]$. The function φ is lower semicontinuous in Ω, $F(\cdot,t)$ is upper semicontinuous in Ω for a.e. $t \in [0,T]$ and

$F(x, \cdot)$ is measurable in $[0, T]$ for every $x \in \Omega$. There exist integrable in $[0, T]$ functions $\phi(\cdot)$ and $\psi_e(\cdot)$ such that

$$|F(x, t)| \leq \phi(t), \quad |G(x, t, \varepsilon)| \leq \psi_e(t)$$

for every $x \in \Omega$ and for a.e. $t \in [0, T]$, moreover $\lim_{\varepsilon \to 0} \|\psi_e(\cdot)\|_1 = 0$.

Lemma 1. Let $\varepsilon_k \to 0$ and x_k be a sequence of viable trajectories for (5), (6), corresponding to ε_k. Then this sequence has an accumulation point in $C(R^n, [0, T])$ and every such accumulation point is a viable trajectory of (3), (4).

The proof of this and of the following technical results is omitted.

We introduce the following important condition:

($*$) For every $\delta > 0$ and for every viable trajectory x of (3), (4) there exists $\varepsilon(\delta) \in (0, \varepsilon_0]$ such that for every $\varepsilon \in (0, \varepsilon(\delta))$ there exists a viable trajectory x_e of (5), (6) such that

$$\varphi(x_e(T)) \leq \varphi(x(T)) + \delta.$$

Theorem 1. Every two of the following three conditions imply the third one:
  (i) relaxation stability of (P),
  (ii) perturbation stability of (P_e),
  (iii) condition ($*$).

Proof. First let (R) have not viable trajectories. Then $\hat{\varphi}^R = \hat{\varphi} = +\infty$. It is sufficient to show that $\liminf_{\varepsilon \to 0} \hat{\varphi}_e = \infty$. If (P_e) has not viable trajectories for all sufficiently small $\varepsilon \to 0$, this holds. Let there exist a sequence $\varepsilon_k \to 0$ such that (P_{ε_k}) has viable trajectories and x_k be a sequence of ε_k-approximate solutions of (P_{ε_k}), that is

$$\varphi(x_k(T)) \leq \hat{\varphi}_{\varepsilon_k} + \varepsilon_k.$$

The sequence x_k satisfies the conditions of Lemma 1, hence it has an accumulation point x with respect to the uniform convergence that solves (4). Clearly $x(t) \in C(t)$ for all $t \in [0, T]$. Then x is a viable trajectory of (R) which is a contradiction.

Let (R) have viable trajectories and let the condition ($*$) hold. As before we choose a sequence of ε_k-approximate solutions of (P_{ε_k}) uniformly convergent to x, which is a viable trajectory for (R). Then

$$(7) \qquad \hat{\varphi}^R \leq \varphi(x(T)) \leq \liminf_{k \to +\infty} \varphi(x_k(T)) = \liminf_{k \to +\infty} \hat{\varphi}_{\varepsilon_k}$$

The condition ($*$) implies that for every $\delta > 0$ one can find k_δ such that for $k > k_\delta$ there exists a trajectory x_k viable for (5), (6) and such that $\varphi(x_k(T)) \leq \hat{\varphi}^R + \delta$. Taking into account that $\hat{\varphi}_{\varepsilon_k} \leq \varphi(x_k(T))$, from (7) we get

$$\lim_{k \to +\infty} \hat{\varphi}_{\varepsilon_k} = \hat{\varphi}^R.$$

This means that (i) and (ii) are equivalent.

Now let $(*)$ be not fulfilled. Then there exist $\overline{\delta} > 0$ and a viable trajectory $\overline{x}$ for (3), (4) such that for every $\varepsilon \in (0, \varepsilon_0)$ and for every viable trajectory x_ε of (5), (6) we have $\varphi(x_\varepsilon(T)) > \varphi(\overline{x}(T)) + \overline{\delta}$. This means that

$$\hat{\varphi}_\varepsilon \geq \varphi(\overline{x}(T)) + \overline{\delta},$$

i.e.

$$\hat{\varphi}_\varepsilon \geq \hat{\varphi}^R + \overline{\delta}$$

for every $\varepsilon \in (0, \varepsilon_0]$. Then (i) and (ii) can not be fulfilled simultaneously. The proof is complete. $\qquad\square$

Remark 1. We introduce the perturbation by the parameter ε in order to simplify the notation and to unify the style. By repeating the above argument one can obtain analogous results for more general perturbations, for example

$$(Q) \qquad \begin{aligned} &\dot{x} \in F(x,t) + G(x,t), \\ &x(t) \in D(t). \end{aligned}$$

The problem (P) will be stable with respect to the perturbations (Q) if for every $\varepsilon > 0$ there exists $\delta > 0$ such that if for every $x \in \Omega$ one has $\|G(x,\cdot)\|_1 < \delta$ and $\sup_{x \in D(t)} \inf_{y \in C(t)} |x - y| < \delta$ then $|\hat{\varphi}_Q - \hat{\varphi}| < \varepsilon$, where $\hat{\varphi}_Q$ is the optimal value of φ subject to the constraints (Q).

Theorem 1 has mainly a methodological value outlining the problems connected with the perturbation stability. Since the relaxation stability is broadly investigated in the literature, we focus our attention to the condition $(*)$. In the next two sections we consider linear systems presenting sufficient conditions for perturbation stability.

3. Linear systems

In this section we consider control problems for the following perturbed linear system

$$(8) \qquad \dot{x} = A_\varepsilon(t)x + B_\varepsilon(t)u, \; x(0) = x^0, \; t \in [0, T],$$

where $x(t) \in R^n$, $u(t) \in R^m$, $A_\varepsilon(t)$ and $B_\varepsilon(t)$ are respectively $n \times n$ and $n \times m$ matrices. We suppose that the matrices $A_\varepsilon(t)$ and $B_\varepsilon(t)$ satisfy

$$(9) \qquad \sup_{\varepsilon > 0} \|A_\varepsilon(\cdot)\|_1 < +\infty,$$

$$(10) \qquad \lim_{\varepsilon \to 0} \max_{0 \leq t \leq T} \left| \int_0^t (A_\varepsilon(\tau) - A_0(\tau))d\tau \right| = 0,$$

$$\lim_{\varepsilon \to 0} |B_\varepsilon(\cdot) - B_0(\cdot)\|_\infty = 0,$$

where $A_0(t)$ and $B_0(t)$ correspond to $\varepsilon = 0$.

Lemma 2. Let $\varepsilon_k \to 0$ and the sequence of controls u_k is L_1 weakly convergent to u_0. Let x_k and x_0 correspond to $(A_{\varepsilon_k}, B_{\varepsilon_k}, u_k)$ and (A_0, B_0, u_0) respectively. Then $x_k \to x_0$ uniformly in $[0, T]$.

Remark 2. Let A_ε satisfy (9) and $B_\varepsilon = B_0$, $u_k = u_0$. Then the uniform convergence $x_k \to x_0$ for every initial condition x^0 implies (10).

Let $U \subset L_1(R^m, [0, T])$ be the set of feasible controls. We denote by X_ε the set of the trajectories of (8) for fixed ε. From Lemma 2 we obtain

Corollary 1. The multivalued map $X : \varepsilon \to X_\varepsilon$ is lower semicontinuous at $\varepsilon = 0$ in $C(R^n, [0, T])$. If U is weakly compact then X is continuous with respect to the same convergence.

Denote by $R_\varepsilon(T)$ the reachable set of (8) at $t = T$, i.e.

$$R_\varepsilon(T) = \{y \in R^n, y = x(T), x \in X_\varepsilon\}.$$

Corollary 2. The multivalued map $R_.(T) : \varepsilon \to R_\varepsilon(T)$ is lower semincontinuous at $\varepsilon = 0$. If U is weakly compact then $R_.(T)$ is continuous (with respect to the Hausdorff convergence).

Consider the following optimal control problem (LP_ε):

$$J_\varepsilon(u) = \int_0^T f(x(t), u(t), t) dt \to \inf$$

subject to (8),

(11) $u(t) \in V$ for a.e. $t \in [0, T], u \in L_1(R^m, [0, T]),$

(12) $x(T) \in C,$

where $f : R^n \times R^m \times [0, T] \to R^1 \cup \{+\infty\}$, $V \subset R^m$, $C \subset R^n$. The associated relaxed problem has the form (RL):

$$J^R(u) = \int_0^T f^{**}(x(t), u(t), t) dt \to \inf$$

subject to (8), (11) and (12), where V is replaced by coV and $\varepsilon = 0$. The function $f^{**}(x, u, t)$ is the second conjugate of $f(x, u, t)$ with respect to u. We assume the following:

(A2) The sets V and C are closed, f is continuous with respect to x, u, for every t and measurable with respect to t for every x, u; there exist a nonnegative integrable function $\phi : R_+^1 \rightarrow R_+^1 \cup \{+\infty\}$ such that $\lim_{\rho \rightarrow +\infty} \phi(\rho)/\rho = +\infty$ and an integrable function a_1 such that

$$f(x, u, t) \geq \phi(|u|) + a_1(t)$$

for all x, u and for a.e. $t \in [0, T]$. The optimal value of (RL) is finite. Define the sets of admissible controls:

$$U_e = \{u \in L_1(R^m, [0, T]), u(t) \in V \quad \text{a.e.} \quad [0, T], x_e[u; T] \in C\},$$
$$U_0^R = \{u \in L_1(R^m, [0, T]), u(t) \in coV \quad \text{a.e.} \quad [0, T], x_0[u; T] \in C\}.$$

The respective condition (∗) will have the form:

(∗) for every $\delta > 0$ and for every $u \in U_0^R$ there exists $\varepsilon(\delta)$ such that for every $\varepsilon \in (0, \varepsilon(\delta))$ there exists $u_e \in U_e$ such that $J_e(u_e) \leq J^R(u) + \delta$.

Having the relaxed problem (RL) and the condition (∗) one can prove Theorem 1 under (A2) for (LP_e). The following theorem gives a sufficient condition for (∗):

Theorem 2. Let V and C be convex and

$$(\text{int} C \cap R_0(T)) \cup (C \cap \text{int} R_0(T)) \neq \phi$$

Then the condition (∗) holds for (LP_e) with the relaxation (RL).

The proof we have is long and technical and will be presented elsewhere.

4. Singular perturbations

Now we put the parameter ε in the derivative and show that in this case the problem may be not stable with $\varepsilon \rightarrow 0$.

Consider the singularly perturbed linear system

(13)
$$\dot{x} = A_1(t)x + A_2(t)y + B_1(t)u, \quad x(0) = x^0,$$
$$\varepsilon \dot{y} = A_3(t)x + A_4(t)y + B_2(t)u, \quad y(0) = y^0,$$

where $x(t) \in R^{n_1}$, $y(t) \in R^{n_2}$, $u(t) \in R^m$, the matrices $A_i(t)$ and $B_j(t)$ have respective dimensions and are C^2 in $[0, T]$.

For $\varepsilon = 0$ the second equation reduces to algebraic one. Assuming that $A_4(t)$ is invertible and solving this equation we come to the low-order system

(14)
$$\dot{x} = A_0(t)x + B_0(t)u, \quad x(0) = x^0,$$
$$y(t) = -A_4^{-1}(t)(A_3(t)x(t) + B_2(t)u(t)), \quad t \in [0, T],$$

where $A_0 = A_1 - A_2 A_4^{-1} A_3$, $B_0 = B_1 - A_2 A_4^{-1} B_2$.

Assume that the set of feasible controls is

$$U = \{u \in L_1(R^m, [0, T]), u(t) \in V \quad \text{a.e.} \quad t \in [0, T]\},$$

where V is compact and consider the problem

$$\varphi(x(T), y(T)) \to \inf$$

where $\varphi : R^{n_1} \times R^{n_2} \to R^1$ is a continuous function.

Example 1. The marginal function is not continuous.

$$\varepsilon \dot{y}_1 = -y_1 + u, \ y_1(0) = 0$$
$$\varepsilon \dot{y}_2 = -6y_2 + 3u, \ y_2(0) = 0$$
$$u(t) \in \{-1, +1\}, \ t \in [0, 1]$$
$$\varphi(y) = 0.5((y_1 - 1)^2 + y_2^2)$$

For $\varepsilon = 0$ we have

$$y_1 = u, \ 2y_2 = u$$

and $\hat{\varphi} = .1$. Take the sequence of controls

$$u_\varepsilon(t) = \begin{cases} -1 & 0 \le t \le 1 + \varepsilon ln0.5/6, \\ 1 & 1 + \varepsilon ln0.5/6 \le t \le 1. \end{cases}$$

Calculating the respective solution we get

$$\varphi(y_\varepsilon(1)) = 2^{-11} + 0(\varepsilon),$$

that is $\limsup_{\varepsilon \to 0} \hat{\varphi}_\varepsilon < \hat{\varphi}$.

Denote by $S_\varepsilon(T)$ the reachable set at $t = T$ of (13) and let $P_\varepsilon(T) = \{x \in R^{n_1}, (x, y) \in S_\varepsilon(T)\}$. For $\varepsilon = 0$ the reachable set can be formally defined as

$$S_0(T) = \{(x, y), x \in P_0(T), y \in -A_4^{-1}(T)(A_3(T)x + B_2(T)V)\}$$

where $P_0(T)$ is the reachable set of the reduced system (14).

Assume the following:

(A3) For every $t \in [0, T]$ the matrix $A_4(t)$ is invertible and $\limsup_{\varepsilon \to 0} |Y_\varepsilon(t, s)| < +\infty$ uniformly in $0 \le s \le t \le T$, where $Y_\varepsilon(t, s)$ is the fundamental solution associated with $A_4(t)$ of the second equation in (13). The set

$$M = \{t \in [0, T], \max_i Re\lambda_i(A_4(t)) < 0\}$$

has full measure, where $\lambda_i(A)$ is the i-th eigenvalue of the matrix A.

Let $T \in M$. Introduce the convex and compact set

$$R(T) = \int_0^{+\infty} \exp(A_4(T)s)B_2(T)V \, ds.$$

Let

$$R(x,T) = -A_4^{-1}(T)A_3(T)x + R(T)$$

and

$$S(T) = \{(x,y) \in R^{n_1+n_2}, x \in P_0(T), y \in R(x,T)\}.$$

Theorem 3. Assume that $T \in M$ and (A3) holds. Then

$$S_\varepsilon(T) \to S(T) \quad \text{as} \quad \varepsilon \to 0$$

in the sense of Hausdorff.

Remark 3. Observe that $S_0(T) \subset S(T)$ but $S_0 \neq S(T)$ in general (for example $S_0(T)$ may be not convex, as in Example 1).

Now define the problem

$$\varphi_0(x(T)) \to \inf$$

subject to (14), where

$$\varphi_0(x) = \inf\{\varphi(x,y), \ y \in R(x,T)\}.$$

From Theorem 3 we get

Corollary 3.

$$\lim_{\varepsilon \to 0} \hat{\varphi}_\varepsilon = \hat{\varphi}_0.$$

In other words, we define a new problem, the optimal value of which is the limit of the marginal function $\hat{\varphi}_\varepsilon$ as $\varepsilon \to 0$.

Remark 4. This is not the case if we have an integral functional

$$J(u) = \int_0^T f(x(t), y(t), u(t), t)dt$$

that satisfies, for example (A2). If (A3) holds one can prove that the condition $(*)$ is fulfilled for the low-order system (14).

5. Approximations

Let $\{t_i\}$ be a uniform grid of $[0, T]$, $h = T/N = t_{i+1} - t_i$. We consider the following discrete approximation (D_N) to (P):

$$\varphi(x_N) \to \inf$$

subject to

(15) $$x_{i+1} \in x_i + hF(x_i, t_i), x_0 = x^0,$$

(16) $$x_i \in C(t_i), \ i = 1, \cdots, N.$$

Let $\hat{\varphi}_N$ be the optimal value of (D_N). The discrete approximation is convergent if $\hat{\varphi}_N \to \hat{\varphi}$ as $N \to +\infty$. We suppose that the following conditions are fulfilled:

(A4) There exists a bounded set $\Omega \subset R^n$ such that $C(t) \subset \Omega$ for all $t \in [0, T]$, $C(\cdot)$ is upper semicontinuous in $[0, T]$, $F(\cdot)$ is upper semicontinuous in $\Omega \times [0, T]$ and there exists a constant $k > 0$ such that $|F(x, t)| \le k$ for all $x \in \Omega$, $t \in [0, T]$; φ is lower semicontinuous in Ω.

Every (viable) trajectory x^N of (15), (16) will be considered as a piecewise linear function $x^N(t_i) = x_i^N$, $i = 0, \cdots, N$.

Lemma 3. Let x^N be a sequence of viable trajectories for $N \to +\infty$. This sequence has an accumulation point according to the uniform convergence and every accumulation point is a viable trajectory of the relaxed problem (3), (4).

The condition, analogous to $(*)$, will have the form:

For every $\delta > 0$ and for every viable trajectory x of (3), (4) there exists N_δ such that for every $N > N_\delta$ there exists a viable trajectory x^N of (15), (16) such that $\varphi(x^N(T)) \le \varphi(x(T)) + \delta$.

Clearly, having Lemma 3 and the condition $(*)$ one can prove Theorem 1 for this case. The following lemma shows that if we replace (16) by

$$(17) \qquad\qquad x_i \in C(t_i) + \rho^N B, \ i = 1, \cdots, N$$

where the sequence ρ^N, $\lim_{N \to +\infty} \rho^N = 0$, is suitably chosen and B is the unit ball, then the condition $(*)$ will be automatically satisfied.

Lemma 4. Let Ω be an open set for which (A4) holds, $F(\cdot, t)$ be Lipschitz continuous in Ω uniformly in $t \in [0, T]$. Then for every viable trajectory x of (2), (3) and for every $\delta > 0$ there exists N_δ such that for every $N > N_\delta$ there exists a solution x^N of (15) such that $\|x^N - x\|_C < \delta$.

Corollary 4. Let φ be continuous in Ω, the conditions (A1) and $(*)$ hold and the assumptions of Lemma 4 be fulfilled. Then the following two properties of the problem (P) are equivalent:

(i) the problem (P) is stable in the sense of perturbations (P_ε),

(ii) there exists a sequence ρ^N, $\lim \rho^N = 0$, such that the discrete approximation (15), (17) is convergent.

6. Convergence of the penalty function method

In this section we shall consider "perturbations" which, similarly as the discrete approximation, are introduced artificially, in order to simplify the problem.

Consider the problem (P) under the conditions:

(A5) There exists a bounded set $\Omega \subset R^n$ containing all solutions of (2), the function φ is continuous in Ω, the conditions (A1) for $\varepsilon = 0$ are fulfilled, $F(\cdot, t)$ is Lipschitz continuous in Ω with integrable Lipschitz constant, the relaxed problem (R) has viable trajectories.

Let $\psi : C(R^n, [0, T]) \to R_+^1$ be a continuous function that satisfies the following condition: $\psi(x) = 0$ if and only if $x(t) \in C(t)$ for all $t \in [0, T]$. The penalty function method for reduction of the state constraints consists in replacing the initial problem (P) with the family of problems

$$P_\varepsilon(x) = \varphi(x(T)) + \frac{1}{\varepsilon}\psi(x) \to \inf$$

$$\dot{x} \in F(x, t), \ x(0) = x^0,$$

every one of which is solved for fixed $\varepsilon > 0$. The method is convergent when the optimal value $\hat{P}_\varepsilon$ of (18) tends to $\hat{\varphi}$ when $\varepsilon \to 0$.

We note that Theorem 1 can not be applied in this case since $C(t, \cdot)$ is not upper semicontinuous at $\varepsilon = 0$ ($C(t, \varepsilon) = R^n$ for $\varepsilon > 0$ and $C(t, 0) = C(t)$).

Theorem 4. The following are equivalent:
(i) the problem (P) is stable in the sense of relaxation,
(ii) the penalty function method is convergent.

Proof. Using Filippov-Wazewski theorem and the continuity of φ and ψ we conclude that for every $\varepsilon > 0$ and $\delta > 0$ and for every viable trajectory x of the relaxed problem (R) we can find a solution x_ε^δ of (1) such that

$$|\varphi(x_\varepsilon^\delta(T)) - \varphi(x(T))| < \delta/2, \ |\psi(x_\varepsilon^\delta) - \psi(x)| < \varepsilon\delta/2.$$

This means that

$$P_\varepsilon(x) \le \varphi(x(T)) + \delta$$

i.e. the corresponding condition ($*$) holds. Hence

(19) $$\limsup_{\varepsilon \to 0} \hat{P}_\varepsilon \le \hat{\varphi}^R < +\infty.$$

Now let $\varepsilon_k \to 0$ and x_k be a sequence of solutions of (2) which satisfies

(20) $$P_{\varepsilon_k}(x_k) \le \hat{P}_{\varepsilon_k} + \varepsilon_k, \quad k = 1, \cdots.$$

The sequence x_k can be regarded as convergent to a solution x of the relaxed inclusion (4), see Lemma 1. From the continuity of φ we conclude that $\varphi(x_k(T))$ is bounded, hence, from (19) and (20)

$$\limsup_{k \to +\infty} \frac{1}{\varepsilon_k}\psi(x_k) < +\infty.$$

This means that

$$\lim_{k \to +\infty} \psi(x_k) = \psi(x) = 0,$$

i.e. $x(t) \in C(t)$. Thus, x is a viable trajectory of the relaxed problem, hence

$$\hat{\varphi}^R \leq \varphi(x(T)).$$

From (20) and (21) we get

$$\hat{\varphi}^R \leq \varphi(x(T)) = \lim_{k \to +\infty} \varphi(x_k(T)) \leq \liminf_{k \to +\infty} P_{\varepsilon_k}(x_k)$$
$$= \liminf_{k \to +\infty} \hat{P}_{\varepsilon_k}.$$

Since ε_k is arbitraily chosen,

$$\hat{\varphi}^R \leq \liminf_{\varepsilon \to 0} \hat{P}_\varepsilon.$$

This inequality, together with (20) completes the proof. $\qquad\square$

7. Bibliographical remarks

The relaxation (R) was introduced by Warga [11].

The perturbation stability in optimal control was studied first by Kirillova [7] for a linear time-optimal control problem. Cullum [3] proved lower semicontinuity of the marginal function for a more general problem (in this case the condition (∗) is not needed). Gičev [4] considered a particular problem of the type (LP_ε) and obtained a result, which is generalized by Theorem 2. Tadumadze [9] investigated a nonlinear problem assuming that the state constraints are $x(T) \in x^1 + \rho_\varepsilon B$, where the function ρ_ε satisfy the condition (∗) (in our terminology). Dontchev and Mordukhovič [5] showed that the relaxation stability and the perturbation stability are equivalent, see also Dontchev [6]. Zolezzi [12] generalized this result for differential inclusions, however, under conditions stronger than (∗).

Discrete approximations to differential inclusions were considered by Taubert [10] who got a result analogous to Lemma 3 for multistep schemes but with convexity of $F(x,t)$. Budak et al. [2] showed that the discrete approximation to optimal control problems is convergent if the marginal function is continuous under special "deformations" of the problem. Mordukhovič [13] connected the convergence of the discrete approximations with the relaxation stability. Lemma 4 generalizes his result to differential inclusions.

For a survey on singular perturbations in optimal control, see Dontchev [6] and Kokotovič [8].

References

1. Berge C., *Espaces topologiques. Functions multivoques*. Dunod, Paris 1966.

2. Budak B. M., Vasil'ev F.P., *Some computational aspects of optimal control problems*. Moscow Univ. Press, Moscow 1975.

3. Cullum J., *Perturbations of optimal control problems.* SIAM J. Control 4 (1966), 473 - 487.

4. Gičev T., *Well-posedness of optimal control problems with integral convex performance index.* Serdica 2 (1976), 334 - 342.

5. Dontchev A. L., Mordukhovič B. S., *Relaxation and well-posedness of nonlinear optimal processes.* Systems and Contr. Letters 3 (1983), 177 - 179.

6. Dontchev A. L., *Perturbations, approximations and sensitivity analysis of optimal control systems.* Springer 1983.

7. Kirillova F. M., *On the continuous dependence of the solutions of an optimal control problem with respect to the initial data and parameters.* Uspekhi Math. Nauk 17 (1962) 4(106).

8. Kokotovič P., *Applications of singular perturbation techniques to control problems.* SIAM Review 26 (1984), 501 - 549.

9. Tadumadze T. A., *Some topics of qualitative theory of optimal control.* Tbilissi Univ. Press, Tbilissi 1983.

10. Taubert K., *Converging multistep methods for initial value problems involving multivalued maps.* Computing 27 (1981), 123 - 136.

11. Warga J., *Relaxed variational problems.* J. Math. Anal. Appl. 4 (1962), 111 - 128.

12. Zolezzi T., *Well-posedness and stability analysis in optimization.* Proc. Journées Fermat, Toulouse 1985 (to appear).

13. Mordukhovič B. S., *On the finite-dimensional approximations to optimal control systems.* Prikl. Math. Mech. 42 (1978), 431 - 440.

International Series of
Numerical Mathematics, Vol. 84

On Locally Polyhedral Convex Functions.

Roland Durier
Laboratoire d'Analyse Numérique
Université de Dijon - B.P. 138
21004 Dijon Cedex
France

Abstract: A specific property of convex functions, which is called the diff-max property, plays an important role in some aspects of optimization. This paper shows that in a finite dimensional space a closed proper convex function has this property if and only if it is locally polyhedral. A preliminary study of closed locally polyhedral convex sets is provided and a survey of some applications of the diff-max property in optimization is given.

Key-Words: Convex analysis. Locally polyhedral convex sets and functions. Multiobjective optimization. Finitely convergent algorithms.

1. Introduction

Convex analysis plays a prominent role in optimization; on one hand general properties related to duality correspondences and to differential theory are essential tools; on the other hand considering particular classes of convex functions (e.g. polyhedral) leads to results with weaker assumptions (e.g. a convex program is normal if it is polyhedral and consistent [12]).

This paper presents an analysis in a finite dimensional space of a class of closed convex sets and closed proper convex functions which are more general than the polyhedral ones and which will be called locally polyhedral.

A *locally polyhedral convex set*, as it is introduced in [8], is a convex set whose each point has a relative neighbourhood polyhedral; a *convex* function is said *locally polyhedral* if its epigraph is locally polyhedral.

With a view to optimization theory, a characterization of closed proper locally polyhedral convex functions is provided; the equivalent property is *the diff-max property*, which means that each point of the effective domain is a local maximum for the subdifferential according to the inclusion relation.

The diff-max property is actually used in multiobjective optimization ([4], [5], [6], [7]) and to obtain finite termination properties of algorithm ([9], [10]). As so far as this property is the key of some proofs, it is natural to characterize functions which possess it.

The paper is organized as follows: Section 2. deals with closed locally polyhedral convex sets and gives (Theorem 1.) results complementary to those of [8]. Section 3 is devoted to closed proper locally polyhedral convex functions; it provides (Theorem

2.) the equivalence with the diff-max property and shows off some properties of these functions. Section 4. presents a survey of results already obtained in optimization with the diff-max property - i.e. valid for closed proper locally polyhedral convex functions. Concluding remarks are in Section 5.

Everything will take place in a finite dimensional space, except somewhere in Section 4. The euclidian norm and the usual inner product are denoted by $\|\cdot\|$ and $(.,.)$; B is the corresponding unit ball. For a subset A, int A and ∂A are respectively the interior and the boundary of A; if A is convex, ri A is the relative interior of A.

The fundamental reference for definitions and results in convex analysis is Rockafellar's book ([12]). For instance a convex function g on $\mathbb{R}^k$ is always a convex function with possible infinite values, which is defined throughout the space $\mathbb{R}^k$. The epigraph of $g : \{(x,\mu) \in \mathbb{R}^k \times \mathbb{R}/g(x) \geq \mu\}$ is denoted by epi g; the effective domain of $g : \{x \in \mathbb{R}^k/g(x) < +\infty\}$ is denoted by dom g; $\partial g(x)$ indicates the subdifferential of g at x.

If C is a non-empty convex set, the set of vectors y such that $y + C \subset C$ is the recession cone of C denoted by 0^+C. If C is closed, 0^+C is closed and $y \neq 0$ belongs to 0^+C if and only if, for some $x \in C$, the halfline $\{x + \lambda y/\lambda > 0\}$ is contained in C.

If g is a closed proper convex function, a vector $y \neq 0$ is a direction of recession of g if and only if, for some $x \in$ dom g, $g(x + \lambda y) - g(x) \leq 0$ for every $\lambda > 0$.

2. Locally Polyhedral Convex Sets

A convex set is usually called *polyhedral* or a *polyhedron* provided it is the intersection of a finite number of closed halfspaces. A bounded polyhedron is said a *polytope*.

The following definitions are given in [8] and in [14]:

Definition 1. A convex set is called *boundedly polyhedral* provided its intersection with each polytope is a polytope.

A convex set C is called *locally polyhedral* if, for every $\overline{x} \in C$, some neighbourhood of $\overline{x}$ relative to C is polyhedral.

In fact [8] uses the terms: "polyhedral at all its points" instead of "locally polyhedral".

A bounded convex set which is boundedly polyhedral is a polytope; it is proved in [8] that a boundedly polyhedral set is closed.

On the other hand, without any topological assumption, a locally polyhedral convex set may be far from being polyhedral. Indeed for instance, any open convex set and the set in $\mathbb{R}^2$: $\{(u,v)/u^2 + v^2 < 1 \text{ and } v \geq 0\}$ are locally polyhedral.

To rely these two concepts it is then natural to consider only *closed* sets.

In order to recall a characterization of [8], we give a definition:

Definition 2. Let C be a non-empty convex set and $x \in C$. The *cone of C at x* is:

$$K(x; C) = \{\alpha(y - x)/\alpha > 0, y \in C\}$$

(Note that 0 is in $K(x;C)$ since x is in C).

$$K(x;C) \text{ is called cone } (x,C) \text{ in [8].}$$

Proposition 1. Let C be a non-empty closed convex set. The following are equivalent.
   (i) C is boundedly polyhedral
   (ii) C is locally polyhedral
   (iii) for every $x \in C$, $K(x;C)$ is polyhedral
   (iv) for every $x \in C$, $K(x;C)$ is closed.
See proposition 2.17, Corollary 3.3 and Proposition 5.8 of [8].

   In [1] and [2], $K(x;C)$ is termed the supporting cone (cone d'appui) of x at C and it is proved that a convex cone C is polyhedral if and only if $K(x;C)$ is closed for every x in C.

   The next theorem is a complement to the known Proposition 1; some definitions and auxiliary results are first given.

Definition 3. Let C be a non-empty convex set and $x \in C$. The *tangent cone* to C at x is the closure of $K(x;C)$; it is denoted by $T(x;C)$.
The *normal cone* to C at x is

$$N(x;C) = \{p \in \mathbb{R}^n / \forall z \in C, (p, z - x) \le 0\}$$

Lemma 1. Let C be a non-empty closed convex set and $x \in C$. The set

$$\{z \in C / \forall p \in N(x;C), (p, z - x) = 0\}$$

is the *smallest exposed face* of C containing x. It will be denoted by $F(x;C)$.

Proof. $F(x;C)$ is clearly the intersection of all exposed faces of C containing x; Theorem 5.9 of [3] asserts that it is an exposed face. $\square$

Lemma 2. Let C be a non-empty closed convex set, and let $x \in C$ and $y \in C$. Then the following are equivalent:
   (i) $N(y;C) \subset N(x;C)$
   (ii) $T(x;C) \subset T(y;C)$
   (iii) $F(x;C) \subset F(y;C)$.

Proof. Since $N(x;C)$ and $T(x;C)$ are mutually polar, (i) is obviously equivalent to (ii).

   Let now $N(y;C) \subset N(x;C)$ and $z \in F(x;C)$. We prove that, for every $p \in N(y;C)$, $(p, z - y) = 0$, i.e. $z \in F(y;C)$.
Let $p \in N(y;C)$;

$$.p \in N(y;C) \text{ and } z \in C \text{ imply } (p, z - y) \le 0$$
$$.p \in N(x;C) \text{ and } z \in F(x;C) \text{ imply } (p, z - x) = 0$$

Whence $(p, x-y) \leq 0$. But $p \in N(x; C)$, then $(p, y-x) \leq 0$. Thus we have $(p, x-y) = 0$, and therefore $(p, z - y) = 0$.

Conversely let $p \in N(y; C)$ and $F(x; C) \subset F(y; C)$. Suppose $p \notin N(x; C)$; then there exists $\overline{z} \in C$ such that $(p, \overline{z}-x) > 0$. We have $(p, \overline{z}-y) \leq 0$; whence $(p, y-x) > 0$, which is in contradiction with $x \in F(y; C)$ and $p \in N(y; C)$. $\qquad\square$

We come now on to the theorem of this section.

Theorem 1. Let C be a non-empty closed convex set. Then the following are equivalent:

(i) C is boundedly polyhedral

(ii) for every $x \in C$, there exists a neighbourhood V of x such that, for every $y \in V \cap C$,

$$N(y; C) \subset N(x; C)$$

or equivalently

$$T(x; C) \subset T(y; C)$$
$$F(x; C) \subset F(y; C).$$

Proof. We can suppose that the dimension of C is n by considering only the subspace generated by C, in such a way that the relative interior of C is its interior.

1. Let C be boundedly polyhedral; if $x \in \text{int } C$, $F(x; C) = C$ and, for $y \in \text{int } C$, $F(y; C) = C$.

Let $x \in \partial C$ and let $D = C \cap [I(x)]^n$, where $I(x)$ is the interval: $[-\|x\| - 1, \|x\| + 1]$. Then D is a polytope, $x \in \partial D$ and $N(x; D) = N(x; C)$.

Since each face of D is exposed, $F(x; D)$ is the smallest face of D containing x. The set of faces of D which do not contain $F(x; D)$ is finite; the union of these faces is a non-empty compact set which does not contain x. Then there exists a neighbourhood V of x which does not intersect this compact set and which is included in the interior of $[I(x)]^n$.

Let $y \in V$. If $y \in \text{int } D$, then $y \in \text{int } C$ and $F(y; C)$ is C and therefore $F(x; C) \subset F(y; C)$. If $y \in \partial D$, each face of D containing y contains also $F(x; D)$; then $F(x; D) \subset F(y; D)$ which implies $N(y; D) \subset N(x; D)$.

But, in fact, we have $x \in \partial C$ and $y \in \partial C$, whence

$$N(y; C) \subset N(x; C).$$

2. We suppose that (ii) is satisfied. According to Proposition 1., it is sufficient to prove that C is locally polyhedral. The statement of Proposition 1. is clear if $\overline{x} \in \text{int } C$. Let $\overline{x} \in \partial C$, $J = [I(x)]^n$ and $D = C \cap J$. We claim that D is a polytope.

From the known properties of the normal cones, we have, for every $y \in D$,

$$N(y; D) = N(y; C) + N(y; J).$$

Since J is a polytope - and then boundedly polyhedral - J satisfies (ii). Hence for every $x \in C \cap J$, there exists a neighbourhood $V(x)$ of x such that, for every $y \in V(x) \cap C \cap J$,

$$N(y; C) \subset N(x; C)$$

and

$$N(y; J) \subset N(x; J).$$

Therefore

$$N(y; D) \subset N(x; D).$$

From the covering of the compact D by the family $\{V(x)\}_{x \in D}$, we extract a finite subfamily $\{V(x_\ell)\}_{\ell \in 1, q}$ which is a covering of D. Thus there exists a finite set $\{x_1, \cdots, x_q\}$ in D such that, for every $z \in D$, there exists some $\ell \in [1, q]$ with $F(x_\ell; D) \subset F(z; D)$.

Particularly if z is an exposed point of D, $F(z; D) = \{z\}$ and therefore z is a point x_ℓ. As a consequence, D has a finite number of exposed points and, thanks to Straszewicz's Theorem ([12], Theorem 18.6), D is a polytope. □

3. Locally Polyhedral Convex Functions.

A polyhedral convex function is a convex function whose epigraph is polyhedral (see [12]). The following definition is natural.

Definition 4. A convex function is called *locally polyhedral* provided its epigraph is locally polyhedral.

Examples of locally polyhedral convex functions on $\mathbb{R}$, which are not polyhedral, can be built as follows:

Let f be a real-valued convex function on some interval I of $\mathbb{R}$ and let $(\alpha_n)_{n \in Z}$ be a sequence in I such that $(\alpha_n)_{n \geq 0}$ (resp. $(\alpha_{-n})_{n \geq 0}$) is increasing (resp. decreasing) and its limit is the upper (resp. lower) bound of I.

Let g be the function which is $+\infty$ out of I, continuous on I such that $(g(\alpha_n) = f(\alpha_n)$ for every $n \in Z$ and g is affine on each interval $[\alpha_n, \alpha_{n+1}]$ $(n \in Z)$. Then g is locally polyhedral convex, but not polyhedral.

In the sequel we will consider only *closed proper convex functions*; such a function is locally polyhedral if and only if its epigraph is boundedly polyhedral. In order to prove that this is also equivalent to a specific property of the subdifferential, two preliminary lemmas are now given.

The first one deals with the normal cone to the epigraph; it may have its own interest. The second one discusses the nature of dom g and the continuity of g relative to its effective domain when g is locally polyhedral.

Lemma 3. Let g be a closed proper convex function on $\mathbb{R}^k$ and let $x \in$ dom g.

1. $(p, -\alpha) \in N((x, g(x)); \text{epi } g)$ if and only if

.$\alpha > 0$ and $p/\alpha \in \partial g(x)$

or .$\alpha = 0$ and $p \in N(x; \mathrm{dom}\ g)$

2. $(p, -\alpha) \in N((x, \lambda); \mathrm{epi}\ g)$, where $\lambda > g(x)$, if and only if

.$\alpha = 0$ and $p \in N(x; \mathrm{dom}\ g)$

3. If $\partial g(x) \neq 0$, then $N(x; \mathrm{dom}\ g) = 0^+(\partial g(x))$.

Proof.

a) Let $\lambda \geq g(x)$; $(p, -\alpha) \in \mathbb{R}^k \times \mathbb{R}$ belongs to the normal cone to epi f at (x, λ) if and only if: $\forall y \in \mathrm{dom}\ g$, $\forall \mu \geq g(y)$

$$(p, y - x) - \alpha(\mu - \lambda) \leq 0.$$

As μ can be taken arbitrarily great, α cannot be negative. Therefore the assertion is equivalent to: $\forall y \in \mathrm{dom}\ g$, $(p, y - x) \leq \alpha(g(y) - \lambda)$.

If $\lambda = g(x)$ and $\alpha > 0$, we obtain $p/\alpha \in \partial g(x)$; if $\lambda \geq g(x)$ and $\alpha = 0$, we obtain $p \in N(x; \mathrm{dom}\ g)$.

If $\lambda > g(x)$ and $\alpha > 0$, we obtain, for $y = x$, $0 \leq g(x) - \lambda$ a contradiction. All this proves statements 1. and 2.

b) We now prove statement 3.

Let $p \in \partial g(x)$ and $q \in N(x; \mathrm{dom}\ g)$.

Since $N((x, g(x)); \mathrm{epi}\ f)$ is a convex cone, we have, for $0 < \alpha \leq 1$,

$$(\alpha p + (1 - \alpha)q, -\alpha) \in N((x, g(x)); \mathrm{epi}\ f)$$

and then

$$p + \frac{1 - \alpha}{\alpha} q \in \partial g(x),$$

i.e. $\forall \beta \geq 0 \qquad p + \beta q \in \partial g(x)$.

This means, $\partial g(x)$ being closed, $q \in 0^+(\partial g(x))$.

Conversely let $p \in \partial g(x)$ and $q \neq 0$ be such that

$$\forall \beta \geq 0 \qquad p + \beta q \in \partial g(x);$$

This gives for every $y \in \mathrm{dom}\ g$,

$$\forall \beta \geq 0 \qquad g(y) - g(x) \geq (p, y - x) + \beta(q, y - x).$$

As β may be taken arbitrarily great, $(q, y - x)$ cannot be positive. Therefore, $(q, y - x) \leq 0$ for every $y \in \mathrm{dom}\ g$, i.e. $q \in N(x; \mathrm{dom}\ g)$. $\qquad \square$

Lemma 4. Let g be a closed proper locally polyhedral convex function on $\mathbb{R}^k$. Then dom g is locally polyhedral and g is continuous relative to dom g.

Proof. dom g is the projection of the locally polyhedral set epi g in $\mathbb{R}^k \times \mathbb{R}$ on $\mathbb{R}^k$.

Theorem 6.2 of [8] yields that dom g is locally polyhedral.

Besides, from Theorem 20.5 of [12], a locally convex set is locally simplicial. Whence from Theorem 10.2 of [12], g is continuous relative to dom g. □

A concept already announced in the Introduction is now formally defined:

Definition 5. A closed proper convex function g on $\mathbb{R}^k$ is said to have the *diff-max property* if, for every $x \in$ dom g, there exists a neighbourhood V of x such that, for every $y \in V$, $\partial g(y)$ is included in $\partial g(x)$.

As previously said we consider only closed proper convex functions; such a definition can also work for proper convex functions.

It must be noted that the diff-max property can be viewed as a natural strengthening of the upper semicontinuity of the point-to-set mapping: $x \rightarrow \partial g(x)$.

The next theorem is the central one of the paper. The following notation will be used: If g is a function on $\mathbb{R}^k$ with possible infinite values and if A is a subset of $\mathbb{R}^k$, g_A is defined by $g_A(x) = g(x)$ if $x \in A$ and $g_A(x) = +\infty$ if $x \notin A$.

Theorem 2. Let g be a closed proper convex function on $\mathbb{R}^k$. The following are equivalent:
  (i) g has the diff-max property
  (ii) g is locally polyhedral
  (iii) for every $x \in$ dom g, there exists a neighbourhood V of x such that g_V is polyhedral.

Moreover, for such a function, dom g is locally polyhedral, g is continuous relative to dom g and g is subdifferentiable at each point of its effective domain.

Proof.
  a) We prove first that the diff-max property of g implies that g is subdifferentiable on dom g. If $x \in$ ri (dom g), then $\partial g(x) \neq \emptyset$. If $x \in$ dom g and $x \notin$ ri (dom g), every neighbourhood of V meets ri (dom g) and then there exists y such that

$$\partial g(y) \neq \emptyset \quad \text{and} \quad \partial g(y) \subset \partial g(x).$$

Thus the last properties in Theorem 2. are consequences of the above mentioned fact and of Lemma 4.

  b) Let g have the diff-max property and let $(x, \lambda) \in$ epi g and $\varepsilon > 0$. Since g is lower semi-continuous, there exists a polyhedral neighbourhood V of x such that, for $y \in V$, $\partial g(y) \subset \partial g(x)$ and $g(y) \geq g(x) - \varepsilon$. Let $U = V \times [g(x) - \varepsilon, +\infty]$ and let $(y, \mu) \in U \cap$ epi g. Then $0^+(\partial g(y)) \subset 0^+(\partial g(x))$ and, thanks to Lemma 3.

$$N((y, \mu); \text{epi } g) \subset N((x, \lambda); \text{epi } g).$$

From Theorem 1., epi g is boundedly polyhedral, whence locally polyhedral (Proposition 1.).

Let g be locally polyhedral and let $x \in \text{dom } g$. Then (Theorem 1.) there exists a neighbourhood W of x and $\varepsilon > 0$ such that, if $y \in W \cap \text{dom } g$ and $g(x) - \varepsilon \leq \mu \leq g(x) + \varepsilon$,

$$N((y, \mu); \text{epi } g) \subset N((x, g(x)); \text{epi } g).$$

Thanks to Lemma 4, it is possible to find a neighbourhood V of x, $V \subset W$ such that for $y \in V \cap \text{dom } g$,

$$g(x) - \varepsilon \leq g(y) \leq g(x) + \varepsilon.$$

Therefore, for $y \in V \cap \text{dom } g$,

$$N((y, g(y)); \text{epi } g) \subset N((x, g(x)); \text{epi } g).$$

Let $p \in \partial g(y)$; then $(p, -1) \in N((y, g(y)); \text{epi } g)$, from which we have $(p, -1) \in N((x, g(x)); \text{epi } g)$, whence

$$p \in \partial g(x).$$

Thus we have proved that (i) is equivalent to (ii).

c) Moreover the functions g_V, associated to the abovementioned V is clearly polyhedral. Thus (ii) implies (iii).

Lastly (iii) obviously implies (ii).

The nature of dom g and the continuity of g are in Lemma 4.; since $\partial g(x)$ is non empty for $x \in \text{ri (dom } g)$, $\partial g(y)$ is non empty for $x \in \text{dom } g$.

Corollary. A closed convex set containing 0 in its interior is polyhedral if and only if its gauge has the diff-max property.

Such a result is provided in [5].

Proof. It is sufficient to observe that the level sets of a closed proper locally polyhedral convex function are closed locally polyhedral sets. ☐

Remark. Statement (iii) in Theorem 2 shows that, for local properties, closed locally polyhedral convex functions behave like polyhedral functions. For instance if $g_1, \cdots, g_m$ are closed proper locally polyhedral convex functions such that the sets dom g_i, $i = 1, \cdots, m$, have a point in common, then $g = g_1 + \cdots + g_m$ is a closed proper locally polyhedral convex function and $\partial g(x) = \partial g_1(x) + \cdots + \partial g_m(x)$, for every x.

But this similar behaviour is not true in general for global properties. For instance the conjugate of a locally polyhedral convex function is not necessarily locally polyhedral. Let us give an example in $\mathbb{R}$.

Let f be the function on $\mathbb{R} : f(x) = (x^2 + 1)^{1/2}$; let g be the function such that $g(n) = f(n)$ for every $n \in \mathbb{Z}$, g being affine on each interval $[n, n + 1]$, $n \in \mathbb{Z}$; g is a closed proper locally polyhedral convex function on $\mathbb{R}$.

The conjugate g^* of g is an even function, with dom $g^* =]-1, 1[$, the range of g^* being $[-1, 0[$. More precisely we have for $n > 0$,

$$g^*(x^*) = nx^* - (n^2 + 1)^{1/2} \text{ if}$$

$$(n^2 + 1)^{1/2} - [(n-1)^2 + 1]^{1/2} \leq x^* \leq [(n+1)^2 + 1]^{1/2} - (n^2 + 1)^{1/2}.$$

The intersection of epi g^* with the polytope $[0, 2] \times [-1, 1]$ has an infinite number of exposed points: it is not a polytope. Hence g^* is not locally polyhedral.

4. The Diff-Max Property in Optimization

We present in this section a brief survey of recent results in optimization where the diff-max property is an essential tool: first in multiobjective optimization and then in the study of algorithms which terminate in a finite number of steps.

In multiobjective optimization we consider $m(m > 1)$ closed proper functions $f_1, \cdots, f_m$ on $\mathbb{R}^k$ with the same closed effective domain X. The set E of *efficient solutions* for this problem is classically so defined:

$x \in E$ if and only if no y exists such that
$f_i(y) \leq f_i(x)$ for every i,
with at least a strict inequality.

The set M of *properly efficient solutions* is associated to $f_1, \cdots, f_m$ by a weighting factor technique:

$x \in M$ if and only if there exists $w_i > 0$, $i = 1, \cdots, m$,
such that x is an optimal solution to the problem

$$\text{Min } (w_1 f_1(z) + \cdots + w_m f_m(z)/z \in \mathbb{R}^k).$$

It is obvious that M is included in E. Moreover we have ([4]), using the diff-max property,

Proposition 2. If $f_1, \cdots, f_m$ have no common direction of recession, then M and E are non-empty.

If moreover, each f_i is locally polyhedral, then E and M are closed and equal.

This result is applied to the study of *best approximation relative to a vectorial norm* ([6]).
We suppose that $\mathbb{R}^k$ $(k > 1)$ is direct sum of $m(m > 1)$ non trivial subspaces $X_1, \cdots, X_m$:

$$\mathbb{R}^k = X_1 \oplus \cdots \oplus X_m,$$

and that each X_i is equipped with a norm γ_i.
Let Π_i be the projection on X_i parallel to $\oplus_{j \neq i} X_j$ and let Z be an affine subspace, with $0 \notin Z$.

The set of best approximants of 0 in Z relative to the "vectorial norm (γ_i, X_i)" is the (non-empty) set of efficient solutions relative to the m objective functions on $Z : \gamma_i \circ \Pi_i$ $(i = 1, \cdots, m)$.

When each γ_i is polyhedral, this set is also the set of properly efficient solutions (Proposition 2). As an answer to a question of [11], we prove in [6]:

Proposition 3. If Z is a hyperplane and if each γ_i is polyhedral, the set of best approximants of 0 in Z relative to the vectorial norm (γ_i, X_i) is convex and compact.

In the framework of *location theory* in $\mathbb{R}^k$, a finite set $A = \{a_1, \cdots, a_m\}$ being given, with a norm γ_i associated to each a_i, the objective functions are: $x \to \gamma_i(x - a_i)$, $i = 1, \cdots, m$. If each γ_i is polyhedral, Proposition 2. is applicable. [5] gives a completely different proof of the fact that E and M are equal and uses it to expose a general method to determine E in $\mathbb{R}^2$, the natural framework in location theory, when the norms γ_i are polyhedral.

Efficient points can also be defined in a normed space N, with the norm denoted by $|.|$, for some not necessarily finite subset A. In [7], we consider the set of strictly efficient points $c(A)$ and the set of efficient points $E(A)$:

$x \in c(A)$ if and only if no y exists such that

$$|y - a| \le |x - a| \quad \text{for every } a \in A$$

$x \in E(A)$ if and only if no y exists such that

$$|y - a| \le |x - a| \quad \text{for every } a \in A$$

with at least a strict inequality for some $\bar{a} \in A$.

A geometrical characterization of $c(A)$ and $E(A)$ is provided in [7], by using subsets which play the role of halfspaces in an inner product space: for $\delta \ne 0$,

$$Q_\delta = \{x \in N / \forall \lambda > 0, |x - \lambda\delta| > |x|\}$$

and P_δ is the complementary set of Q_δ.

Proposition 4. If A is compact and if the norm of E has the diff-max property, then $c(A)$ and $E(A)$ are closed and
$x \in c(A)$ if and only if, for every $\delta \ne 0$, $A \cap (x + Q_\delta) \ne \emptyset$
$x \in E(A)$ if and only if, for every $\delta \ne 0$,

$$A \cap (x + Q_\delta) \ne \emptyset \quad \text{or} \quad A \cap (x + \text{int } Q_{-\delta}) = \emptyset.$$

If N is finite dimensional, the second assumption is equivalent for the norm to be polyhedral. Note that Proposition 4. is also valid in a strictly convex normed space and in a two dimensional space, whatever the norm is.

The diff-max property is prevalent to prove that an algorithm terminates in a finite number of steps in [9] and [10].

[9] considers the Fermat-Weber problem associated to a finite set in $\mathbb{R}^k$: $A = \{a_1, \cdots, a_m\}$, with norms γ_i, $i = 1, \cdots, m$. It is the matter of minimizing in $\mathbb{R}^k$, with $w_i > 0$,

$$w_1 \gamma_1(x - a_1) + \cdots + w_m \gamma_m(x - a_m).$$

Using optimality conditions and the partial inverse of Spingarn [13], the Fermat-Weber problem is translated into a fixed point problem; for this problem the algorithm of successive approximations is shown to be finitely convergent if the norms γ_i are polyhedral, when moreover the set of solutions has a non-empty interior.

An analogous technique is used in [10] to study the minimization problem

$$\text{Min } (f(x)/x \in V)$$

where f is a closed proper convex function and V a subspace of $\mathbb{R}^k$. If f and f^* are polyhedral, whence have the diff-max property, an algorithm is described, which is finitely convergent, under qualification assumptions on the set of solutions to the initial problem and the set of solutions to the dual one.

5. Concluding Remarks

As the survey of Section 4 shows it, the diff-max property is a useful tool to obtain results in some domains of optimization. It is then natural to give a characterization of functions which have this property. Geometric results are provided about closed locally polyhedral convex sets and then translated into the language of functions; the hoped characterization is obtained with the concept of closed proper locally polyhedral functions.

There are some directions of research worthy of attention, emanating from the analysis presented here. The first is the extension of Theorem 2. to a vector space without the assumption of finite dimensionality. A first step in this direction should be a characterization of norms with the diff-max property. The second is a complete study of closed proper locally polyhedral convex functions on $\mathbb{R}^k$ in the framework of convex analysis. The third is to continue the work already made to exploit in optimization the diff-max property from a theoretical or from an algorithmitical point of view.

References.

[1] Bastiani, A.: *Polyèdres convexes de dimension quelconque.* Cptes Rendus Ac. Sc. Paris 247 (1958), 1943 – 1946.

[2] Bastiani, A.: *Cones convexes et pyramides convexes.* Ann. Inst. Fourier 9 (1959), 249 – 292.

[3] Brøndsted, A.: *An introduction to convex polyhedra*. Springer-Verlag, Berlin (1983).

[4] Durier, R.: *Weighting factor results in vector optimization*. Working Paper, University of Dijon (1985).

[5] Durier, R.: *On efficient points and Fermat-Weber problem*. Working Paper, University of Dijon (1985).

[6] Durier, R.: *Meilleure approximation en norme vectorielle et théorie de la localisation*. RAIRO Modelisation Mathematique et Analyse Numérique (1986), forthcoming.

[7] Durier, R. and Michelot, C.: *Sets of efficient points in a normed space*. J. of Math. Anal. and Appl. (1986), forthcoming.

[8] Klee, V.: *Some characterizations of convex polyhedra*. Acta Math. 102 (1959), 79 – 107.

[9] Lefebvre, O. and Michelot, C.: *A primal-dual algorithm for the Fermat-Weber problem involving mixed gauges*. Working Paper, University of Dijon (1986).

[10] Lefebvre, O. and Michelot, C.: *Calcul d'un point fixe d'une application prox par la méthode des approximations successives: conditions de convergence finie"*. Working Paper, University of Dijon (1986).

[11] Robert, F.: *Meilleure approximation en norme vectorielle et minima de Pareto*. RAIRO Modelisation Mathematique et Analyse Numérique 19 (1985), 89 – 110.

[12] Rockafellar, R. T.: *Convex Analysis*. Princeton University Press, Princeton (1970).

[13] Spingarn, J. E.: *Partial inverse of a monotone operator*. Appl. Math. and Optimization 10 (1983), 247 – 265.

[14] Valentine, F. A.: *Convex sets*. Mac Graw Hill, New York (1964).

International Series of
Numerical Mathematics, Vol. 84
(c) 1988 Birkhäuser Verlag Basel

Recent results on generalized conjugate functions.

K.-H. Elster and A. Wolf
Technische Hochschule Ilmenau
Am Ehrenberg, Block G
GDR-6300 Ilmenau

We consider several concepts of generalized conjugate functions with the aim of their comparison. To enable this a new concept of P-conjugation is introduced which contains well-known other concepts, e.g. the generalized FENCHEL-conjugation, (with coupling functional) and the Φ-conjugation as special cases. The notion of P-conjugation is based on that of polarity (as a multifunction which was considered) p.e. by Ewers/van Maaren).

Key words: Nonconvex Optimization, Generalized Conjugation, Duality, Polarity

0. Introduction

In the last few years nonconvex optimization problems were treated in the framework of generalized conjugate functions by a remarkable number of papers. Thereby the concepts of conjugation differed strongly from case to case. Caused by the high level of generalization it is difficult to compare these concepts mutually.

Therefore, in the present paper we will discuss such a "comparison of conjugation concepts" and introduce a new concept, denoted as P-conjugation (P stands for polarity), which allows us to describe some conjugation concepts as special cases. In the following, the generalized FENCHEL conjugation (characterized by a coupling functional) ([2], [6], [7], [10], [11], [14]) and the Φ-conjugation introduced by Deumlich and Elster ([1], [3], [4], [5]) will be treated. To introduce the P-conjugation the notion of polarity is used (c.f. Ewers/van Maaren [9]).

Let X, Y be arbitrary nonempty sets and $f \in \overline{R}^Y$ an extended real functional. A conjugation is an operator associating functions at $\overline{R}^X$ to functions at $\overline{R}^Y$ (or vice versa). A well-known conjugation is the generalized FENCHEL conjugation (or c-conjugation) determined by a coupling functional $c : X \times Y \to \overline{R}$. We obtain c-conjugate functions of $f, g \in \overline{R}^X$ according to (for the notation cf. [12])

$$
\begin{aligned}
f^c(y) &= \sup_{x \in D(f)} [c(x, y) \dotplus -f(x)], \\
g_c(y) &= \inf_{x \in D(g)} [c(x, y) \dotplus -g(x)].
\end{aligned}
\tag{0.1}
$$

This concept of conjugation is rather general since we can use quite different coupling functionals for obtaining special cases of the c-conjugation. These c-conjugation can be divided into two classes. In the first case we assume the coupling functional c to be independent of the function f, for instance in [13] (p. 13) we have

$$c(x,y) := \begin{cases} 0 & \text{if } y \notin \Delta\{x\}, \\ -\infty & \text{if } y \in \Delta\{x\}, \end{cases}$$

where $\Delta : 2^X \to 2^Y$ is any polarity (cf. Def. 1.1).

In the second case we assume c to be dependent on f, for instance with respect to the Φ-conjugation (cf. [5], Part I, p. 127) we have

$$c(x,y) := k(x, f(x), y) + f(x)$$

where $X = Y =: L$ is a linear space and $k : L \times R \times L \to R$ is an appropriate special functional.

Consequently, in the second case it is necessary for comparison to find a convenient fixed functional for a given function f.

The following proposition characterizes the level of generality of the c-conjugation.

Theorem 0.1. Let X, Y be nonempty sets, $f \in \overline{R}^X$ a functional and $M : \overline{R}^X \to \overline{R}^Y$ an operator. Then M can be represented, depending on f, by a family of c-conjugations.

Proof. If we set $c(x,y) := f(x) \dotplus (Mf)(y)$, where $f \in \overline{R}^X$ and $(Mf) \in \overline{R}^Y$, then

$$
\begin{aligned}
f^c(y) &= \sup_{x \in D(f)} (c(x,y) \dotplus -f(x)) \\
&= \sup_{x \in D(f)} (f(x) \dotplus (Mf)(y) \dotplus -f(x)) \\
&= \sup_{x \in D(f)} (Mf)(y) = (Mf)(y).
\end{aligned}
$$

In the present paper we will show that, in general, the Φ-conjugation cannot be considered as a special case of c-conjugation independent of f, and vice versa. Hence for a comprehensive comparison of these (and other) conjugation concepts it is useful to introduce a sufficiently general concept assuring the independence of the conjugation of the given function f. In [8] several other generalized conjugate functions will be involved in the P-conjugation concept.

1. Polarities

Definition 1.1. ([9]) A polarity between the sets X, Y is a mapping $\Delta : 2^X \to 2^Y$ which satisfies the condition

$$\Delta(\cup_{i \in I} A_i) = \cap_{i \in I} \Delta(A_i) \tag{1.1}$$

for each family $(A_i)_{i \in I}$, $A_i \subseteq X$, where I is an arbitrary index set.

Example 1. If Δ is the complement operator of sets, then (1.1) is the de Morgan's rule.

Example 2. Let $X = Y = R^n$ and $< x, y >:= \sum_{i=1}^{n} x_i y_i$. Then the mapping $\Delta : 2^X \to 2^Y$, where

$$\Delta(A) := \cap_{x \in A}\{y \in Y| < x, y >\geq 0\}, \ A \subseteq X,$$

is a polarity and $\Delta(A)$ is the polar cone of A.

For the following it is extremely useful to characterize a polarity by a functional.

Theorem 1.1. $\Delta: 2^X \to 2^Y$ is a polarity if and only if there is a functional $p : X \times Y \to \overline{R}$ such that

$$\Delta(A) = \cap_{x \in A}\{y \in Y|p(x, y) \geq 0\}, \ A \subseteq X. \tag{1.2}$$

Proof. Obviously (1.2) is a polarity for a given functional p. Conversely, suppose $\Delta : 2^X \to 2^Y$ is a polarity. Then

$$p(x, y) := \begin{cases} 0 & \text{if } y \in \Delta\{x\}, \\ -1 & \text{if } y \notin \Delta\{x\} \end{cases}$$

generates $\Delta(A)$ in (1.2).

Definition 1.2. The functional p occuring in Theorem 1.1 is called generating functional of the polarity Δ.

By the generating functional of a polarity Δ we introduce the dual polarity of Δ.

Definition 1.3. Let $\Delta : 2^X \to 2^Y$ be a polarity and p a generating functional of Δ. Then the mapping $\Delta^*: 2^Y \to 2^X$ where

$$\Delta^*(B) = \cap_{y \in B}\{x \in X|p(x, y) \geq 0\}, \ B \subseteq Y$$

is said to be the dual polarity of Δ.

Some elementary properties of a polarity are included in

Theorem 1.2. Let $\Delta: 2^X \to 2^Y$ be a polarity and $A, A_1, A_2 \subseteq X, B \subseteq Y$. Then
  (i) $A_1 \subseteq A_2 \Rightarrow \Delta(A_1) \supseteq \Delta(A_2)$,
 (ii) $\Delta(A) = \cap_{x \in A} \Delta\{x\}$,
(iii) $\Delta^* \Delta$ is a closure operator on 2^X,
 (iv) $\Delta \Delta^*$ is a closure operator on 2^Y,
  (v) $B \subseteq \Delta(A) \Rightarrow A \subseteq \Delta^*(B)$,
 (vi) Δ^* according to Def. 1.3 is a polarity;
      $\Delta^{**} = \Delta$,
vii) $\Delta(\emptyset) = Y, \ \Delta^*(\emptyset) = X$.

The correspondence between a generating functional and a given polarity Δ is, in general, not one-to-one. More than one generating functional can exist for a given polarity Δ. If p. e. $p(x,y)$ is a generating functional of $\Delta : 2^X \to 2^Y$ and $f : X \times Y \to R$ is an arbitrary functional with $f(x,y) > 0$ for all $(x,y) \in X \times Y$, then $f(x,y) \cdot p(x,y)$ is a generating functional of Δ, too. Hence the definition of an equivalence relation is suggested.

Definition 1.4. Two functionals $p_1 : X \times Y \to \overline{R}$, $p_2 : X \times Y \to \overline{R}$ are said to be P-equivalent, if

$$\forall (x,y) \in X \times Y : p_1(x,y) \geq 0 \leftrightarrow p_2(x,y) \geq 0.$$

Obviously two polarities Δ_1, Δ_2 are identically if and only if each generating functional of Δ_1 is P-equivalent to any generating functional of Δ_2.

In the following we use polarities on sets $X \times \overline{R}$, resp. $Y \times \overline{R}$. For the generating functional of a polarity $\Delta : 2^{X \times \overline{R}} \to 2^{Y \times \overline{R}}$ the notation

$$p(x,k,y,l) : X \times \overline{R} \times Y \times \overline{R} \to \overline{R}$$

is used.

Definition 1.5. A functional $p(x,k,y,l) : X \times \overline{R} \times Y \times \overline{R} \to \overline{R}$ is called epigraphical if

(i) $\forall (x_0,k_0,y_0) \in X \times \overline{R} \times Y \; \exists l_* \in R$:
$l_* = \min\{l \in R | p(x_0,k_0,y_0,l) \geq 0\}$,

(ii) $\forall (x_0,k_0,y_0,l_0) \in X \times \overline{R} \times Y \times \overline{R} \; \forall l_1 \geq l_0$:
$p(x_0,k_0,y_0,l_0) \geq 0 \Rightarrow p(x_0,k_0,y_0,l_1) \geq 0$.

A functional $p(x,k,y,l) : X \times \overline{R} \times Y \times \overline{R} \to \overline{R}$ is called hypographical if

(iii) $\forall (x_0,k_0,y_0) \in X \times \overline{R} \times Y \; \exists l^* \in R$:
$l^* = \max\{l \in R | p(x_0,k_0,y_0,l) \geq 0\}$,

(iv) $\forall (x_0,k_0,y_0,l_0) \in X \times \overline{R} \times Y \times \overline{R} \; \forall l_2 \geq l_0$:
$p(x_0,k_0,y_0,l_0) \geq 0 \Rightarrow p(x_0,k_0,y_0,l_2) \geq 0$.

For an epigraphical functional $p(x,k,y,l)$ the set

$$\{(x,k,y,l) \in X \times \overline{R} \times Y \times \overline{R} \mid p(x,k,y,l) \geq 0\}$$

can be considered as an epigraph of a functional $e : X \times \overline{R} \times Y \to R$ where

$$e(x,k,y) = \min\{l \in R \mid p(x,k,y,l) \geq 0\}.$$

For hypographical functionals a corresponding proposition holds.

Concluding from generating functionals to polarities we give

Definition 1.6. A polarity $\Delta : 2^{X \times \overline{R}} \to 2^{Y \times \overline{R}}$ is called epigraphical (resp. hypographical), if there exists an epigraphical (resp. hypographical) generating functional of Δ.

The following characterization of such polarities can be given.

Theorem 1.3. (i) A polarity $\Delta : 2^{X \times \overline{R}} \to 2^{Y \times \overline{R}}$ is epigraphical resp. hypographical if and only if Δ has a generating functional p such that

$$\forall (x, k, y, l) \in X \times \overline{R} \times Y \times R : p(x, k, y, l) = -e(x, k, y) + l$$

resp.

$$\forall (x, k, y, l) \in X \times \overline{R} \times Y \times R : p(x, k, y, l) = h(x, k, y) - l$$

where $e : X \times \overline{R} \times Y \to R$, $h : X \times \overline{R} \times Y \to R$ are functionals.

(ii) The functionals e, h are determined uniquely.

Proof (i): The functionals $-e(x, k, y) + l$ and $h(x, k, y) - l$ are obviously epigraphical resp. hypographical according to Definition 1.5. Let conversely $\Delta : 2^{X \times \overline{R}} \to 2^{Y \times \overline{R}}$ be an epigraphical polarity with the generating functional $p(x, k, y, l)$ and let

$$e(x, k, y) = \min\{l \in R \mid p(x, k, y, l) \geq 0\}.$$

The minimum exists on $X \times \overline{R} \times Y$ because of Definition 1.5(i). Now we have to show $\forall (x, k, y, l) \in X \times \overline{R} \times Y \times R$:

$$p(x, k, y, l) \geq 0 \Leftrightarrow -e(x, k, y) + l \geq 0,$$

i.e. the P-equivalence on $X \times \overline{R} \times Y \times R$.

We have for each $(x, k, y, l) \in X \times \overline{R} \times Y \times R$

$$-e(x, k, y) + l \geq 0 \Leftrightarrow -\min\{\overline{l} \in R | p(x, k, y, \overline{l}) \geq 0\} + l \geq 0$$
$$\Leftrightarrow l \geq \min\{\overline{l} \in R | p(x, k, y, \overline{l}) \geq 0\}$$
$$\Leftrightarrow p(x, k, y, l) \geq 0,$$

where the last equivalence holds because of Definition 1.5(i).

(ii): Let us assume that there exist two functionals $e_1, e_2 : X \times \overline{R} \times Y \to R$ such that $-e_1(x, k, y) + l$ and $-e_2(x, k, y) + l$ are P-equivalent and that there exists at least one $(x_0, k_0, y_0) \in X \times \overline{R} \times Y$ such that

$$e_1(x_0, k_0, y_0) = e_2(x_0, k_0, y_0) + d, \quad \text{where } d \in R, d \neq 0.$$

Then by the P-equivalence we obtain for $x = x_0$, $y = y_0$, $k = k_0$, $l_0 = e_1(x_0, k_0, y_0) - \frac{d}{2}$:

$$-e_1(x_0, k_0, y_0) + e_1(x_0, k_0, y_0) - \frac{d}{2} \geq 0 \Leftrightarrow e_1(x_0, k_0, y_0) - e_2(x_0, k_0, y_0) - \frac{d}{2} \geq 0$$

and hence

$$-\frac{d}{2} \geq 0 \Leftrightarrow +\frac{d}{2} \geq 0$$

which contradicts $d \neq 0$.

There is an analogous proof for hypographical polarities.

To define P-conjugate functions we introduce the notion of symmetrical polarities.

Definition 1.7. Let Δ_1, Δ_2 be two polarities on $X \times \overline{R}$. Δ_1 is called symmetrical to Δ_2 if there exist two generating functionals p_1 of Δ_1 and p_2 of Δ_2 such that

$$\forall (x, k, y, l) \in X \times \overline{R} \times Y \times \overline{R} : p_1(x, k, y, l) = -p_2(x, k, y, l).$$

Corollary 1.4. (i) Let $\Delta : 2^{X \times \overline{R}} \to 2^{Y \times \overline{R}}$ be a polarity. Then there exists one and only one polarity $\tilde{\Delta}$ symmetrical to Δ.
(ii) If $\Delta_1 : 2^{X \times \overline{R}} \to 2^{Y \times \overline{R}}$, $\Delta_2 : 2^{X \times \overline{R}} \to 2^{Y \times \overline{R}}$ are polarities, then hold Δ_1 symmetrical to $\Delta_2 \Leftrightarrow \Delta_2$ symmetrical to Δ_1.

Proof. (i) Since the existence of a symmetrical polarity $\tilde{\Delta}$ is trivial we assume that there exist two different polarities $\tilde{\Delta}_1$, $\tilde{\Delta}_2$ symmetrical to Δ. Let p_1, p_2 be the corresponding generating functionals. Because of Definition 1.4, p_1 and p_2 are not P-equivalent. Hence it is impossible to fulfil Definition 1.7.
(ii) is obvious.

2. P-Conjugation

Definition 2.1. Let $\Delta : 2^{X \times \overline{R}} \to 2^{Y \times \overline{R}}$ be a polarity, $\tilde{\Delta} : 2^{X \times \overline{R}} \to 2^{Y \times \overline{R}}$ the polarity symmetrical to Δ and $f \in \overline{R}^X$.
Then the functionals f^Δ, $f_{\tilde{\Delta}} \in \overline{R}^Y$ with

$$f^\Delta(y) := \inf\{l \in R \mid (y, l) \in \Delta(\text{graph } f)\},$$
$$f_{\tilde{\Delta}}(y) := \sup\{l \in R \mid (y, l) \in \tilde{\Delta}(\text{graph } f)\}$$

are called upper resp. lower P-conjugates (or: P-conjugate functions) of f with regard to Δ resp. $\tilde{\Delta}$.

It is possible to introduce upper and lower P-conjugates with regard to arbitrary (i.e. independent) polarities. The above given approach takes into consideration well-known examples such as FENCHEL conjugation and Φ-conjugation (cf. Example 3.1 and Example 3.2).

In general we can not conclude from the identity of two (upper or lower) P-conjugates the identity of the used polarities.

Example 2.1. Let Δ_1, Δ_2 be polarities on $X \times \overline{R}$ and let

$$p_1(x, k, y, l) := \begin{cases} 0 & \text{if } l \in [0, 1], \\ -1 & \text{otherwise,} \end{cases}$$

$$p_2(x, k, y, l) := \begin{cases} 0 & \text{if } l = 0, \\ -1 & \text{otherwise,} \end{cases}$$

be the generating functionals of Δ_1 resp. Δ_2.

Then for any given $f \in \overline{R}^X$ and for each $y \in Y$ holds

$$f^{\Delta_1}(y) = \inf\{l \in R \mid (y, l) \in \Delta_1(\text{graph } f)\}$$
$$= \inf\{l \in R \mid (y, l) \in \cap_{(x,k) \in \text{graph } f}\{(\overline{y}, \overline{l}) \mid p_1(x, k, \overline{y}, \overline{l}) \geq 0\}$$
$$= \inf\{l \in R \mid \forall (x, k) \in \text{graph } f : p_1(x, k, y, l) \geq 0\}$$
$$\equiv 0$$

Analogously we obtain $F^{\Delta_2}(y) \equiv 0$.

In contrast to this we have the assertion of

Corollary 2.1. Let $\Delta_1 : 2^{X \times R} \to 2^{Y \times R}$, $\Delta_2 : 2^{X \times R} \to 2^{Y \times R}$ be epigraphical polarities and $f \in \overline{R}^X$. Then $\forall y \in \overline{R}: f^{\Delta_1}(y) = f^{\Delta_2}(y)$ implies $\Delta_1 = \Delta_2$.

Proof: If p_1, p_2 are the generating functionals of Δ_1 resp. Δ_2, then by the definition of the upper P-conjugates holds for each $(x, k, y, l) \in (\text{graph} f) \times Y \times \overline{R}$:

$$p_1(x, k, y, l) \geq 0 \Rightarrow l \geq f^{\Delta_1}(y),$$
$$p_2(x, k, y, l) \geq 0 \Rightarrow l \geq f^{\Delta_2}(y).$$

Since p_1, p_2 are epigraphical functionals we have for each $(x, k, y, l) \in (\text{graph} f) \times Y \times \overline{R}$

$$l \geq f^{\Delta_1}(y) \Rightarrow p_1(x, k, y, l) \geq 0$$
$$l \geq f^{\Delta_2}(y) \Rightarrow p_2(x, k, y, l) \geq 0.$$

Hence by the assumption $f^{\Delta_1}(y) = f^{\Delta_2}(y) \; \forall y \in \overline{R}$ follows

$$\forall (x, k, y, l) \in (\text{graph} f) \times Y \times \overline{R} : p_1(x, k, y, l) \geq 0 \leftrightarrow p_2(x, k, y, l) \geq 0.$$

Since $f \in \overline{R}^X$ is arbitrary, this equivalence holds on $X \times \overline{R} \times Y \times \overline{R}$, i.e. p_1 and p_2 are P-equivalent. By Definition 1.4 we obtain $\Delta_1 = \Delta_2$.

A similar assertion can be made in the case of hypographic polarities and lower P-conjugates.

By Corollary 2.1 we have the possibility for convenient representations of P-conjugate functions in the case of epigraphic resp. hypographic polarities.

Corollary 2.2. Let Δ_1 be an epigraphical polarity and Δ_2 a hypographical polarity on $X \times \overline{R}$. Then there exist uniquely determined functionals $e : X \times \overline{R} \times Y \to R$ and $h : X \times \overline{R} \times Y \to R$ such that

$$f^{\Delta_1}(y) = \sup_{x \in D(f)} e(x, f(x), y),$$
$$f_{\Delta_2}(y) = \inf_{x \in D(f)} h(x, f(x), y).$$

Proof: By Theorem 1.3 there exist uniquely determined functionals e, h such that $-e(x, k, y) + l$ is a generating functional of Δ_1 and $h(x, k, y) - l$ is a generating functional of Δ_2 for each $(x, k, y, l) \in X \times \overline{R} \times Y \times R$. Hence

$$
\begin{aligned}
f^{\Delta_1}(y) &= \inf\{l \in R | (y, l) \in \Delta_1(\text{graph } f)\} \\
&= \inf\{l \in R | \forall (x, k) \in \text{graph } f : -e(x, k, y) + l \geq 0\} \\
&= \inf\{l \in R | \forall (x, k) \in \text{graph } f : l \geq e(x, k, y)\} \\
&= \sup_{(x,k) \in \text{graph} f} e(x, k, y) \\
&= \sup_{x \in D(f)} e(x, f(x), y).
\end{aligned}
$$

The second relation of the corollary can be proved analogously.

As a consequence from Corollary 2.2 we conclude that for an arbitrary function $f \in \overline{R}^X$ the upper P-conjugate with regard to a hypographical polarity is identically $-\infty$ and the lower P-conjugate with regard to an epigraphical polarity is identically $+\infty$.

The concept of conjugation introduced above can be explained as on operator $P : \overline{R}^X \to \overline{R}^Y$ (cf. [11]). This means especially that a P-conjugation depends only on the polarity $\Delta : 2^{X \times \overline{R}} \to 2^{Y \times \overline{R}}$ but not on the function f.

3. Special Cases

3.1. Generalized FENCHEL Conjugation

Let X, Y be nonempty sets, $\varphi : X \times Y \to \overline{R}$ a coupling functional, $\Delta^\varphi : 2^{X \times R} \to 2^{Y \times \overline{R}}$ a polarity with the generating functional $p^\varphi(x, k, y, l) := -\varphi(x, y) \dotplus k + l$, $(x, k, y, l) \in X \times \overline{R} \times Y \times R$.

By Theorem 1.3 Δ^φ is an epigraphical polarity. The polarity $\tilde{\Delta}^\varphi$ symmetrical to Δ^φ has the generating functional $p_\varphi(x, k, y, l) := \varphi(x, y) \dotplus -k - l$; $\tilde{\Delta}^\varphi$ is hypographical by Theorem 1.3. For the sake of simplicity we write Δ_φ instead of $\tilde{\Delta}^\varphi$.

Now for the P-conjugate function generated by Δ^φ we obtain

$$
\begin{aligned}
f^{\Delta^\varphi}(y) &= \inf\{l \in R | (y, l) \in \Delta^\varphi(\text{graph } f) \\
&= \inf\{l \in R | \forall (x, k) \in \text{graph } f : -\varphi(x, y) \dotplus k + l \geq 0\} \\
&= \inf\{l \in R | \forall (x, k) \in \text{graph } f : l \geq (x, y) \dotplus -k\} \\
&= \sup_{x \in D(f)} ((x, y) \dotplus -f(x)).
\end{aligned}
$$

Analogously we have

$$
f_{\Delta_\varphi}(y) = \inf_{x \in D(f)} ((x, y) \dotplus -f(x))
$$

These relations can also be derived using Corollary 2.2.

By this result the generalized FENCHEL conjugation turns out to be a special case of P-conjugation.

3.2. Φ-Conjugation

Let $X = Y =: V$ be a linear space, $\dim V = 1$, $E := R \times V \times R$, V^* the algebraical dual space of V, $E^* = R \times V^* \times R$, $A : E \to E^*$ a linear mapping with

$$t' = a_0 + <a, x> + cz$$

$$x' = at + Bx + cz$$

$$Z' = ct + <e, x> + bz$$

where a_0, b, $c \in R$, $a, e \in V^*$, $B : V \to V^*$ a symmetrical linear mapping and $(b, e, c) \neq (0, 0, 0)$.

Furthermore, let

$$V^0 := \{(x, z) \in V \times R | c + <e, x> + bz > 0\}$$

Then the function

$$p^{\Phi}(x, z, x^*, z^*) := < A(1, x, z), (1, x^*, z^*) >$$

is the generating functional of a polarity $\Delta^{\Phi} : 2^{V \times \overline{R}} \to 2^{V \times \overline{R}}$, the symmetrical polarity $\tilde{\Delta}^{\Phi}$ has the generating functional

$$p_{\Phi}(x, z, x^*, z^*) := - < A(1, x, z), (1, x^*, z^*) >$$

We set $\Delta_{\Phi} := \tilde{\Delta}^{\Phi}$.

The polarities are in general not epigraphical resp. hypographical. But assuming for each $f \in R^V$ the condition

(3.1) $$c + <e, x> + bf(x) > 0 \quad \forall x \in D(f)$$

we obtain epigraphical resp. hypographical functionals by division with $c + <e, x> + bf(x)$. Exactly for such functions the Φ-conjugation was introduced by Deumlich/Elster.

If (3.1) is valid then we obtain (cf. [3], [5])

$$f^{\Delta^{\Phi}}(x^*) = \inf\{z^* \in R | (x^*, z^*) \in \Delta^{\Phi}(\text{graph } f)\}$$

$$= \inf\{z^* \in R | \forall (x, z) \in \text{graph } f : p^{\Phi}(x, z, x^*, z^*) \geq 0\}$$

$$= \inf\{z^* \in R | \forall (x, z) \in \text{graph } f : a_0 + <x^*, a> +$$

$$+ <x^*B, x> + <a, x> + <x^*, e> + cz + cz^* + <e, x> z^* + bzz^* \geq 0\}$$

$$= \inf\{z^* \in R | \forall (x, z) \in \text{graph } f :$$

$$z^* \geq - \frac{a_0 + <x^*, a> + <x^*B, x> + <a, x> + <x^*, e> + cz}{c + <e, x> + bz}$$

$$= \sup_{x \in D(f)} - \frac{a_0 + <x^*, a> + <x^*B, x> + <a, x> + <x^*, e> + cf(x)}{c + <e, x> + bf(x)}$$

$$= f^{\Phi}(x^*).$$

Analogously, we can show

$$f_{\Delta_\Phi}(x^*) = f_\Phi(x^*).$$

This means that the Φ-conjugation as well as the generalized FENCHEL conjugation can be considered as a special case of the P-conjugation.

4. Comparison

Using the notion of P-conjugation introduced above we can compare generalized FENCHEL conjugation and Φ-conjugation according to

Theorem 4.1. Let L be a linear space, L^* the algebraic dual space of L, $A : R \times L \times R \to R \times L^* \times R$ a linear mapping as in 3.2. and Δ^Φ the corresponding polarity. Then there exists a coupling functional $\varphi_\Phi(x, x^*)$ such that $-\varphi_\Phi(x, x^*) + z + z^*$ is the generating functional of Δ^Φ if and only if A satisfies the conditions

$$e = 0, b = 0, c > 0.$$

Then we obtain

(3.2) $\qquad \varphi_\Phi(x, x^*) := \frac{1}{c}(a_0 + <a, x> + <x^*, a> + <x^*B, x>).$

Conversely, we obtain only for symmetrically bi-affine functions φ linear mappings A such that the conjugations in 3.1. and 3.2. are identically.

Proof: As it was mentioned in 3.2. upper Φ-conjugation is only defined for such functionals $f \in R^L$, where an epigraphical generating functional p^Φ exists to introduce P-conjugation. Hence we obtain

$$p^\Phi(x, z, x^*, z^*) := e^\Phi(x, z, x^*) + z^*, (x, z, x^*, z^*) \in V^0 \times L^* \times R,$$

where e^Φ is uniquely determined because of Theorem 1.3(ii). According to 3.1. for the upper generalized FENCHEL-conjugation with respect to the coupling functional $\varphi : X \times X^* \to \overline{R}$ there exists an epigraphical generating functional, too:

$$p^\varphi(x, z, x^*, z^*) = -\varphi(x, x^*) \dotplus z + z^*, (x, z, x^*, z^*) \in L \times R \times L^* \times R.$$

Hence by Theorem 1.3 we obtain $p^\Phi = p^\varphi$ and, moreover,

$$-\varphi(x, x^*) \dotplus z = e^\Phi(x, z, x^*).$$

According to 3.2 we have

$$e^\Phi(x, z, x^*) = -\frac{a_0 + <x^*, a> + <x^*B, x> + <a, x> + <x^*, e> + cz}{c + <e, x> + bz}$$

and consequently (3.2). The condition $c > 0$ follows by $(x, z) \in V_0$ for e^{Φ}.

Summarizing we can establish the sets of all generalized FENCHEL conjugate functions and the set of Φ-conjugate functions are neither identical nor subsets of each other. There exists a nonempty intersection of that two classes characterized by Theorem 4.1.

References.

[1] Deumlich, R.: *Ein geometrischer Zugang zur Optimierungstheorie auf der Grundlage der Φ-konjugierten Funktionen.* Diss. B, Pädag. Hochschule "N. K. Krupskaja", Halle 1980.

[2] Deumlich, R.; Elster, K.-H.: *On the theory of conjugate function.* Studies on Mathematical Programming, Akademiai Kiadó, Budapest 1980, 19 – 43.

[3] Deumlich, R.; Elster, K.-H.: *Duality theorems and optimality, conditions for nonconvex optimization problems.* Math. Operationsforsch. Statist., Ser. Optimization 11 (1980) 2, 181 – 219.

[4] Deumlich, R.; Elster, K.-H.: *Recent results on Φ-conjugation and nonconvex optimization.* Feichtinger, G. and Kall, P. (eds.): Operations Research in Progress, D. Reichel Publ. Comp. 1982, 27 – 40.

[5] Deumlich, R.; Elster, K.-H.: *Φ-conjugation and nonconvex optimization. A survey.* Part I: Math. Operationsforsch. Statist., Ser. Optimization 14 (1983), 125 – 149. Part II: Math. Operationsforsch. Statist., Ser. Optimization 15 (1984), 499 – 515. Part III: Math. Operationsforsch. Statist., Ser. Optimization 16 (1985), 789 – 805.

[6] Deumlich, R.; Elster, K.-H.; Nehse, R.: *Generalizations of conjugate functions.* Survey of Math. Progr. (Proc. of the 9th Intern. Math. Progr. Symp., Budapest 1976) Akademiai Kiadó, Budapest 1979, Vol. 1, 193 – 204.

[7] Elster, K.-H.; Nehse, R.: *Zur Theorie der Polarfunktionale.* Math. Operationsforsch. Statist., Ser. Optimization 5 (1974) 1, 3 – 21.

[8] Elster, K.-H.; Wolf, A.: *Comparison between several conjugation concepts.* (to appear).

[9] Ewers, J. J. M.; van Maaren, H.: *Duality principles in mathematics and their relations to conjugate functions.* Mathematical Communications, Vol. 16, No. 2 (1981), Dept. of Applied Mathematics, Toronto Univ. of Technology, Enschede, The Netherlands.

[10] Moreau, J. J.: *Fonctions convexes en dualite.* Sem. Math. Fac. Sci., Montpellier 1962.

[11] Moreau, J. J.: *Fonctionelles convexes.* Seminaire sur les Equations aux Derivées Partielles II, Collège de France, Paris 1966 – 67.

[12] Singer, I.: *Conjugate operators.* Hammer, G. and Pallaschke, D. (eds.): Selected Topics in Operational Research and Mathematical Economics. Proc. 8th Symp. on OR, Karlsruhe, Aug. 22 - 25, 1983, Lecture Notes in Economics and Mathematical Systems. Springer Verlag, Berlin - Heidelberg - New York - Tokyo (1984), 80 – 97.

[13] Volle, M.: *Conjugaison par tranches.* Annali di Mathematica pura et applicata, 1985 (IV), Vol. CXXXIX, 279 – 312.

[14] Weiss, E. A.: *Konjugierte Funktionen.* Arch. Math. 20 (1969), 538 – 545.

International Series of
Numerical Mathematics, Vol. 84

Affine and projective transformations in nondifferentiable optimization.

J. L. Goffin

Faculty of Management
1001 Sherbrooke Street West
Samuel Bronfman Building
McGill University
Montreal, Quebec, H3A 1G5
Canada

This research was supported in part by the FCAR of Quebec (CE-130 and EQ-3078),
and the NSERC of Canada (A4152).
Working paper 86-18

Abstract.

The rate of convergence of first order methods, such as subgradient optimization,
applied to the problem of minimizing a convex function depends on the central asphericity of the level surfaces with respect to the optimal point; the optimal behaviour
under affine transformations in the n-space of the independent variable of the central
asphericity depends on a measure of central symmetry which need not be polynomial
in n. This seems to indicate a weakness of many ellipsoid methods, which operate with
n-dimensional ellipsoids.

At a conceptual level, there are two ways to deal with non-symmetry: use projective transformations, as suggested by Davidon, and Karmarkar (for the dual problem),
or use affine transformations in $n + 1$ dimensional space, i.e. the space of the epigraph,
as suggested by Sonnevend. A third possiblity, closely related to the Todd-Burrell
projective method for linear programming, is to look at how the largest ellipsoid in a
level set varies with the function value; this is somewhat equivalent to approximating
a n-dimensional projective transformation or a $n + 1$-dimensional affine transformation
by a n-dimensional affine transformation, parametrized by the $n + 1$st variable, the
objective.

A characterization of the largest volume ellipsoid in the level sets is given using
the classical first order optimality conditions in the space of ellipsoids; this shows that
the shape of the ellipsoid depends on the Lagrange multipliers of that optimization
problem; it also indicates how this optimal shape or affine transformation varies as
the function value changes. An implementable algorithm follows if this shape or these
Lagrange multipliers can be approximated.

It is shown that a deepest cut variant of the classical ellipsoid method applied
to the system of inequalities defining the level set can be used as a subroutine to

approximate the Lagrange multipliers λ for decreasing values of the function value. It is also clear that the deepest cut ellipsoid method is a rather slow way of doing so, as it changes only one λ_i at each iteration (the i corresponds to the subgradient a_i used); the original ellipsoid method of Yudin and Nemirovski does not even seem to approximate the optimal values of λ (on the other hand it does operate under an oracle which for each x returns only the value $f(x)$ and a subgradient).

It is therefore quite interesting to notice that the variants of Karmarkar projective method proposed by Todd and Burrell and by Adler, Resende and Veiga may be viewed as (effective) attempts to approximate the Lagrange multipliers λ. The first method estimates the multipliers λ by the dual variables y, the dual variables y being updated by a step of Karmarkar's original method, using the current best value of f as an estimate for the dual objective. The latter method estimates the Lagrange multipliers by the inverse of the slacks at the current point.

The problem under study is that of minimizing a convex function $f(x)$, $x \in R^n$, where f is polyhedral, and thus has a representation $f(x) = \max_i e_i^t(Ax - b)$ (e_i a n-vector with a 1 in position i, A a $m \times n$ matrix, b a m-vector).
An equivalent formulation of

$$\min_x \{f(x) = \max_{i=1,\cdots,n} (e_i^t(Ax - b)\} \qquad (NDO)$$

is

$$\min_{x,f} f \quad \text{s. t} \quad fe \geq Ax - b, \qquad (P)$$

a linear program whose dual is

$$\max_y - b^t y$$
$$\text{s. t} \quad A^t y = 0$$
$$e^t y = 1 \qquad (D)$$
$$y \geq 0$$

where e is a m-vector of ones.

The conditions for f^*, x^*, y^* to be optimal are f^*, x^* primal feasible, and y^* dual feasible and $f^* Y^* e = Y^* Ax^* - Y^* b$ (complementarity) where $Y^* = \text{Diag} y^* = \begin{pmatrix} y_1^* & 0 \\ 0 & y_m^* \end{pmatrix}$; if one multiplies the complementarity conditions by $A^t Y^*$, one gets $(A^t Y^{*2} A)x^* = A^t Y^{*2}(b + f^* e)$, which may be used to solve for x^* given y^* and f^*.

We wish to contrast the behaviour under affine transformations of the space of the variable x, of two related methods applied to two related problems:
1) the problem of solving linear inequalities $(LI(\overline{f}))$
(here: find $x \in X(\overline{f}) = \{x' : Ax' \leq b + \overline{f}e\}$ where $\overline{f} \geq f^*$)
using the maximal euclidean distance relaxation method of Agmon, Motzkin and Schoenberg [2, 14].

2) the L.P. (optimization, NDO) (find x^*, $f^* = \min f(x)$) using subgradient optimization (Shor [17]).

The two problems can be reduced to one another by noting that $LP \equiv LI(f^*)$, and thus LP can be solved by using $LI(\overline{f})$ with a sliding objective, while $LI(\overline{f})$ may be written as:

[Find $\overline{x}$ which minimizes $\overline{f}(x) = \max\{f(x), \overline{f}\}$].

The key difference between the two methods is that, when using the *maximal* distance relaxation method on $LI(\overline{f})$, one assumes the ability to compute the maximum distance between an arbitrary point and the halfspaces $\{x : e_i^t(Ax - b - \overline{f}e) \le 0\}$, which implies the ability to scale or normalize the inequalities by dividing them by the L_2 norm of the rows of A.

The convergence analysis of both methods is based on two apparently similar concepts:

for LI, the asphericity

$$\overline{p} = \min_{x,r}\{p' : B(x,r) < X(\overline{f}) < B(x, p'r)\}$$

and for LP, the *central* asphericity (with respect to the optimum point x^*)

$$p = \inf_{f > f^*} \inf_{r_f}\{p' : B(x^*, r_f) < X(f) < B(x^*, pr_f)\}$$

where $B(x, r)$ is the sphere centered at x with radius r; this assumes that the level sets are bounded. The convergence theory can be strengthened a bit by using angles rather than asphericity, but not by much, if one assumes, as will be done later, primal and dual unicity.

Neither method guarantees a monotonic decrease of $f(x)$; the relaxation method (applied to $LI(\overline{f})$) guarantees a monotonic decrease at a linear rate $\sqrt{(1 - 1/\overline{p}^2)}$ of the distance to $X(\overline{f})$, while subgradient optimization (applied to LP) guarantees a decrease (not necessarily monotonic) of the distance to $X(f^*)$ at a rate $\sqrt{(1 - 1/p^2)}$ assuming $p \ge \sqrt{2}$). The number of iterations required to reach an ϵ-solution is thus proportional to $\overline{p}^2 ln1/\epsilon$ or $p^2 ln1/\epsilon$; if ϵ is small enough (but still $ln1/\epsilon$ is polynomial in the length of the input data) an exact solution can be reached in at most n steps of a projection method, or of the simplex method.

The question that we wish to answer is:

does there exist an affine transformation $x = T(\xi - \xi_0)$, $T \in R^{n,n}$, such that in ξ-space p or $\overline{p}$ is polynomial in n, and can such a T be computed? In the case of LI, a positive answer was given in [6], but for the LP problem, it appears that conditions like symmetry, or approximate symmetry must be set on the level sets of $f(x)$ [8].

Case 1: Linear inequalities ($LI(\overline{f})$ with $f^* < \overline{f}$)

a) existence: let $E = x + H^{\frac{1}{2}}B$ (where $B = B(0,1)$, $H = TT^t$) be the largest ellipsoid in $X(\overline{f})$; then $E < X(\overline{f}) < n * E$ (where $*$ indicates an homothety with respect to the center of the set E), and thus $T^{-1}E = T^{-1}x + B < T^{-1}X(\overline{f}) < T^{-1}x + nB$ and $p(T^{-1}X(\overline{f})) \leq n$

b) approximate computation: the deepest, or least shallow, cut ellipsoid method generates a bounded sequence of ellipsoids $\{E_q\}$ with limit points E^* satisfying $n^{-1} * E^* < X(\overline{f}) < E^*$. If $X(\overline{f})$ is a simplex, the limit point E^* is unique and $n^{-1} * E^*$ is the largest ellipsoid inscribed in $X(\overline{f})$. Even in that latter case no rate of convergence of the sequence $\{E_q\}$ to E^* has been proved. This method guarantees the computation in polynomial time and space of an ellipsoid E that satisfies $(n+1)^{-1} * E < X(\overline{f}) < E$.

Case 2: Linear programming (LP, NDO)

We assume that the optimal solution is unique, i.e. $X(f^*) = \{x^*\}$, and that the level sets $X(\overline{f})$ are homothetic with respect to x^*, as $\overline{f}$ varies.

A measure of central symmetry of $X(\overline{f})$, p_0, with respect to x^*, for some or any $\overline{f}$, can be defined by drawing a hyperplane h through x^*, and the two supporting hyperplanes h_1 and h_2 to $X(\overline{f})$ parallel to h; then p_0 is the smallest number satsifying $1/p_0 \leq \|h\,h_2\|/\|h\,h_1\| \leq p_0$ for all hyperplanes h. The same measure p_0 can be defined by using lines through x^* (Grunbaum [9]).

It is clear that $p_0 = 1$ if x^* is the center of symmetry of $X(\overline{f})$, and it has been shown that if x^* is the center of gravity of $X(\overline{f})$, then $p_0 \leq n$ (Pogorelov [16]).

Theorem 1: Let $X(\overline{f})$ be an arbitray bounded convex body, x^* a point in the interior of $X(\overline{f})$ and p_0 the associated measure of symmetry; it follows that the largest ellipsoid E inscribed in $X(\overline{f})$ and centered at x^* satisfies $E < X(\overline{f}) < p_1 * E$ with $p_0 \leq p_1 \leq p_0\sqrt{n}$, and also that the smallest ellipsoid E' circumscribed around $X(\overline{f})$ and centered at x^* satisfies $p_2^{-1} * E' < X(\overline{f}) < E'$ with $p_0 \leq p_2 \leq p_0\sqrt{n}$.

Proof: The two statements are equivalent by duality (polarity) with respect to x^*, so we shall sketch a proof of the latter.

Let E' be the smallest ellipsoid centered at x^* containing $X = X(\overline{f})$; assume, without loss of generality, that $E' = B(0,1)$ and $x^* = 0$. Choose a coordinate system $(x_1, \cdots, x_n)$ so that $x = (a,0,\cdots,0)^t$, $a > 0$, is the closest point of the boundary of X from the origin; $x_1 \leq a$ is a supporting hyperplane to X. Let $x_1 = -b$, $b > 0$, be the parallel supporting hyperplane. The theorem is not true if and only if $a < 1/p_0\sqrt{n}$; this implies that $b < 1/\sqrt{n}$. The smallest volume ellipsoid E'' containing $B(0,1)..\{x : |x_1| \leq b\}$, is given by

$$\frac{x_1^2}{\alpha^2} + \frac{\sum_{k=2}^n x_k^2}{\beta^2} \leq 1$$

where $\alpha = b\sqrt{n}$ and $\beta = ((1-b^2)n/(n-1))^{\frac{1}{2}}$, and

$$V[E'']/V[B(0,1)] = \alpha\beta^{n-1} = [b^2 n(\frac{n}{n-1})^{n-1}(1-b^2)^{n-1}]^{\frac{1}{2}}$$

is less than 1 (for $b < 1/\sqrt{n}$) (see Todd [19]). The contradiction with the fact that $E' = B(0,1)$ is the smallest ellipsoid centered at 0, and containing X follows, as E'' is centered at the origin, contains X and has smaller volume than E'.   QED

A known corollary of this theorem is that the affine excentricity of symmetric convex bodies is at most $\sqrt{n}$; the bound $\sqrt{n}$ is reached by cubes and octahedra (the L_∞ and L_1 norm bodies) and their affine transforms.

The proof of this theorem is constructive, and thus can be used to design an algorithm which shall construct a sequence of ellipsoids $\{E_q\}$, centered at x^*, containing $X(\overline{f})$ and such that all the limit points E^* satisfy $P_0 \leq (p_0\sqrt{n})^{-1} * E^* < X(\overline{f}) < E^*$, with x^* being the center of E^*; it does assume the knowledge of p_0, or the ability to construct the parallel supporting halfspace.

Let E_q be an ellipsoid centered at x^* and containing $X(\overline{f})$; locate the halfspace defining $X(\overline{f})$ which is the closest to x^* in the metric implied by E_q. Like in the proof of the previous theorem, transform E_q into $B(0,1)$ and that halfspace into $x_1 \leq a$, and let $b = p_0 a$ (or $x_1 \geq -b$ be the supporting hyperplane to $X(\overline{f})$ parallel to $x_1 \leq a$, where $b > 0$). Construct E'' and retransform to the original space to get the new ellipsoid E_{q+1}, which satisfies

$$V[E_{q+1}]/V[E_q] = \alpha\beta^{n-1} = [b^2 n(\frac{n}{n-1})(1-b^2)] < 1$$

provided that $b < 1/\sqrt{n}$. The fact that $\{E_q\}$ has limit points follows from the fact that $\liminf b_q \geq 1/\sqrt{n}$, by a proof entirely analogous to that given in [7] for the case LI. This variant of the ellipsoid method may be called the deepest cut, symmetric range, ellipsoid method.

Theorem 2: The deepest cut, symmetric range, ellipsoid method generates a sequence of ellipsoids $\{E_q\}$ all centered at x^* and containing $X(\overline{f})$ with limit points E^* which satisfy $(p_0\sqrt{n})^{-1} * E^* < X(\overline{f}) < E^*$, and at least one limit point exists. If $X(\overline{f})$ is an affine transform of a cube, or an octahedron ($p_0 = 1$), then the limit point is unique.

It is clear that p_0, p_1 and p_2 are affine invariants, and that this last theorem shows how to compute, in the limit, a linear transformation T which satisfies $p(T^{-1}(X(\overline{f})) \leq p_0\sqrt{n}$; it is also clear that if p_0 is not polynomial in n, then the same is true for p_1 and p_2.

At a conceptual level, there are two ways to deal with non-symmetry:

1. use projective transformations, as suggested by Davidon [5], and Karmarkar [11] (it is worth noting that the original version of Karmarkar's method is applied to a canonical LP which is the dual (D) of the NDO or primal formulation).

2. use affine transformations in $n+1$ dimensional space, i.e. the space of the epigraph; an implementable ellipsoid algorithm called GEM (graph ellipsoid method) has been suggested and studied by Sonnevend [18], and uses $n+1$ dimensional ellipsoids.

Define the level set, in the space of the epigraph by

$Y(\overline{f}) = \{(x, f) : Ax \leq b + fe, \ f \leq \overline{f}\}$.

A conceptual method implementing affine transformations in $n + 1$ dimensional space could be (**Algorithm 1**):

1.1 Compute the largest $n + 1$ dimensional ellipsoid in $Y(\overline{f})$

1.2 Linesearch from the center of the ellipsoid in the direction of $-f$ in the metric given by the current ellipsoid, down to the graph of $f(x)$, to get the new iterate $\overline{x}_+$, $\overline{f}_+$. Update and loop to 1.1 if needed.

This simple method does have the properties that:

1.a) $(\overline{f}_+ - f^*) \leq \frac{n}{n+2}(\overline{f} - f^*)$, so it would take a polynomial number of iterations

1.b) the best case should be better than its worst case

1.c) finite convergence occurs if $Y(\overline{f})$ is a simplex for $\overline{f}$ close enough to f^*, which is the case if one has primal and dual nondegeneracy

(Proof: after the affine transformation implied by the largest ellipsoid, $Y(\overline{f})$ is a regular simplex, and the linesearch direction points from the center of gravity to the lowest vertex of the simplex, i.e. the optimum point).

This method is implementable if in step 1.1 one relaxes the condition on the inner ellipsoid E to $E < Y(\overline{f}) < (n + 2) * E$; this can be computed in polynomial time by using the deepest cut ellipsoid method applied to the system of linear inequalities $Y(\overline{f}) = \{(x, f) : Ax \leq b + fe, f \leq \overline{f}\}$, thus leading to an implementable polynomial method (probably a rather poor one).

An analogous method using n dimensional affine transformations may be defined (**Algorithm 2**):

2.1 Compute the largest n dimensional ellipsoid in $X(\overline{f}) = \{x : Ax \leq b + \overline{f}e\}$

2.2 Linesearch in the direction of $-f$, from the center of ellipsoid, through the epigraph of $f(x)$ down to the graph of $f(x)$, to get the new iterate $\overline{x}_+$, $\overline{f}_+$. Update and loop to 2.1, if needed.

This method does have the properties that:

2.a) $(\overline{f}_+ - f^*) \leq \frac{n}{n+1}(\overline{f} - f^*)$, so it would take a polynomial number of iterations

(Proof: Assume that E is the unit n-dimensional ball $B(0, 1)$, with center at the origin, so that $B(0, 1) < X(\overline{f}) < nB(0, 1)$.

Clearly $x^* \in X(\overline{f})$, so that $\|x^*\| \leq n$.

The ($n + 1$ dimensional) pyramid with base $(B(0, 1), \overline{f})$ and vertex (x^*, f^*) is included in $Y(\overline{f})$. The vertical linesearch from $(0, \overline{f})$ down to the graph of $f(x)$ (i.e. to the boundary of $Y(\overline{f})$) will thus decrease the vertical coordinate by at least $\frac{1}{n+1}(\overline{f} - f^*)$.)

2.b) the best case should not, in general, be better than its worst case

2.c) finite convergence occurs if, for $\overline{f}$ close enough to f^*, one has :

    (i) $X(\overline{f})$ is symmetric with respect to x^*

    (ii) $X(\overline{f})$ is a simplex, with center of gravity at x^*

    (iii) or in fact all instances where the largest ellipsoid contained in $X(\overline{f})$, and the largest ellipsoid contained in $X(\overline{f})$ and centered at x^* are identical.

This method is implementable if in step 2.1 one relaxes the condition on the inner ellipsoid E to $E < X(\overline{f}) < (n+1) * E$; this can be computed in polynomial time by using the deepest cut ellipsoid method applied to the system of linear inequalities $X(\overline{f}) = \{x : Ax \leq b + \overline{f}e\}$, thus leading to an implementable polynomial method (probably a rather poor one).

It is apparent (ignoring any practical issues related to the actual computation of the maximum inellipsoids, in particular, how to get their shape to converge) that the latter method appears to be poorer than the former, as it does require some condition like symmetry to be finitely convergent; the reason for this difference is that the latter method does not have a *horizontal* component to its linesearch. A way to introduce a horizontal component is proposed in Todd and Burrell [21]:

that is to look at $\overline{x}$ as a function of $\overline{f}$, and to estimate $d = d\overline{x}/d\overline{f}$, somehow, and then to linesearch down to the graph of $f(x)$ in the direction $(-d, -1)$; this would replace the finite convergence of 2.c) by that of 1.c), and thus deal with the absence of central symmetry of the level surfaces.

Characterisation of the maximum volume ellipsoid.

It is useful to characterize the largest inscribed ellipsoid in a convex polyhedron (see [6], or for the smallest ellipsoid circumscribed to a polyhedron the seminal work of Fritz-John [10]), in particular the level set $X(\overline{f}) = \{x : Ax \leq b + \overline{f}e\}$. Let $E = \{x : (x - \overline{x})^t H^{-1}(x - \overline{x}) \leq 1\}$ be the maximum volume ellipsoid enclosed in $X(\overline{f})$; it is the solution of the problem:

max $\ln \det H$

s.t: $(a_i^t H a_i =)$ $Tr(a_i a_i^t H) \leq (b_i - a_i^t \overline{x} + \overline{f})^2$

where a_i^t are the rows of A.

Let the Lagrange multipliers be λ_i^2, then the Karush-Kuhn-Tucker-Fritz-John conditions of optimality (KKT-FZ) may be stated as:

$$\frac{d \ln \det H}{dH} = H^{-1} = \Sigma \lambda_i^2 a_i a_i^t = A^t \Lambda^2 A$$

where

$$\Lambda = \begin{bmatrix} \lambda_1 & 0 \\ 0 & \lambda_m \end{bmatrix}$$

$$= \text{Diag}(\lambda)$$

$$\overline{x} = (A^t \Lambda^2 A)^{-1} A^t \Lambda^2 (b + \overline{f}e), \text{ and}$$

$$\lambda_i^2 [a_i^t \overline{x} - b_i - \overline{f} + \sqrt{a_i^t H a_i}] = 0 \text{ complementarity});$$

if the center of the ellipsoid were fixed (say, to be x^*) then the first and third optimality conditions remain (with different Lagrange multipliers) and the second one drops out.

If we define $s_i = b_i + \overline{f} - a_i^t \overline{x}$ to be the slacks ($s_i > 0$), then $\Sigma \lambda_i^2 s_i a_i = 0$; thus if $\overline{f}$ is close enough to f^*, one has $(\lambda_i^2 s_i)_i // y^*$ (a vector of optimal dual variables).

The particular case where $X(\overline{f}) = \{x : Ax \leq b + \overline{f}e\}$ is a simplex (that is $A \in R^{n+1,n}$, primal and dual nondegeneracy), and there exists π such that $A^t\pi = 0$, $(b + \overline{f}e)^t\pi = 1$, $\pi > 0$. Then it is not particularly trivial to show that $s_i = \sqrt{a_i^t H a_i} = 1/\pi_i$, and that
$$\lambda = y^*(n(n+1))^{\frac{1}{2}}/(\overline{f} - f^*) = \pi(n(n+1))^{\frac{1}{2}}.$$

This means that the optimal shape of the ellipsoid, which is given by the Lagrange multipliers λ_i, is also given by the geometric mean of the inverse of the slacks $1/s_i$ at the center of the ellipsoid and an optimal dual variable y_i^* (i.e. $\lambda_i^2//y_i^*/s_i$). In the particular case of a simplex, the Lagrange multipliers λ_i, the optimal dual variables y_i^* and the inverse of the slacks at the center of the largest ellipsoid in $X(\overline{f})$, $1/s_i$, are all proportional and thus lead to the same shape.

This indicates that, at least in the case of a simplex, the optimal shape (i.e. the shape of the largest ellipsoid) contains information about the dual variables.

Theorem 3: Let $X(\overline{f}) = \{x : Ax \leq b + \overline{f}e\}$ be a simplex, with A a $n + 1 * n$ matrix; apply the deepest cut ellipsoid method to generate a sequence of ellipsoids $\{E_q\}$, where $X(\overline{f}) < E_0$ and $E_0 = \{x : (x - x_0)^t H_0^{-1}(x - x_0) \leq 1\}$ with $H_0^{-1} = A^t Z_0 A$ ($Z_0 = \text{Diag}(z_0)$, $z_0 > 0$) then $H_q^{-1} = A^t Z_q A$, with $Z_q = \text{Diag}(z_q)$, $z_q > 0$.

It then follows that $\lim_{q\to\infty} \sqrt{z_{iq}} = ((n+1)/n)^{\frac{1}{2}} y_i^*/(\overline{f} - f^*)$, and that $\lim_{q\to\infty} x_q = \overline{x}$, the center of gravity of $X(\overline{f})$.

Proof: It was shown in [7] that the limit of the sequence $\{E_q\}$ is the smallest ellipsoid E' containing $X(\overline{f})$, and clearly $E' = n * E$, where E is the largest ellipsoid in $X(\overline{f})$; it follows from the characterization of E, given above, that $E' = \{x : (x - \overline{x})^t H'^{-1}(x - \overline{x})\}$, where $H'^{-1} = A^t Z' A$, $Z' = \text{Diag}(z')$, $z' > 0$, and $z_i' = ((n+1)/n)^{\frac{1}{2}} y_i^*/(\overline{f} - f^*)$. The fact that $H_q^{-1} = A^t Z_q A$ follows immediately from the fact that in the ellipsoid method H_{q+1}^{-1} is obtained by essentially adding to H_q a rank one matrix $a_i a_i^t$ for some i.

So it remains to show that $\lim_{q\to\infty} H_q^{-1} = H'^{-1}$ implies that $\lim_{q\to\infty} z_q = z'$.

One has $0 = \lim_{q\to\infty}(H_q^{-1} - H'^{-1}) = \lim_{q\to\infty} A^t(Z_q - Z')A$, let B be the $n * n$ matrix composed of the first n rows of A, and let $\psi = -B^{-t}a_{n+1}$, where $\psi > 0$ as $(\psi^t 1)A^t = 0$. Then, also

$$0 = \lim_{q\to\infty} B^{-t}A^t(Z_q - Z')AB^{-1} = \lim_{q\to\infty}\left(\sum_{i=1}^{n}(z_{iq} - z_i')e_i e_i^t + (z_{n+1,q} - z_{n+1}')\psi\psi^t\right);$$

the affine independence of the columns of A imply that ψ is not a unit vector e_i, and thus that $\psi\psi^t$ is not a diagonal matrix, and also that $e_i e_i^t$, $i = 1, \cdots, n$ and $\psi\psi^t$ are linearly independent (in the space of symmetric matrices). Hence $\lim_{q\to\infty}(z_{iq} - z_i') = 0$. QED

One should emphasize that no rates of convergence for the sequence $\{z_q\}$ or for the sequence $\{E_q\}$ have been shown.

In the case of the original ellipsoid method (Nemirovsky and Yudin [15]) applied to the problem of minimizing the convex function $f(x)$, it is clear that under similar assumptions the scaled sequence $\{V^{-1/n}[E_q] * E_q\}$, with $A^t Z_q A = H_q^{-1} \det H_q$, has a chaotic behaviour and hence does not converge; one could conjecture that the Cesaro mean $\lim_{q\to\infty}(1/q)\sum_{k=1}^{q} z_q$ converges to a vector proportional to the square of the optimal dual variables y_i^*.

It is apparent from this discussion that the two classical ellipsoid methods mentioned above are extremely poor and slow at computing the optimal shape.

The formula for the center of the largest ellipsoid shows that if one assumes that Λ is constant, or scaled by a positive constant, (and thus the shape is constant as $\overline{f}$ varies), then $d = \partial \overline{x}/\partial \overline{f} = (A^t \Lambda^2 A)^{-1} A^t \Lambda^2 e$. It thus follows that a method (3), which replaces the vertical linesearch of 2.2 by a linesearch in the direction $(-d, -1)$, shares with the method (1) the properties 1.b) and 1.c) (**Algorithm 3**):

3.1   Compute the largest n dimensional ellipsoid in $X(\overline{f}) = \{x : Ax \leq b + \overline{f}e\}$; and let λ be the Lagrange multipliers

3.2   Linesearch in the direction $(-d, -1)$ where $d = (A^t \Lambda^2 A)^{-1} A^t \Lambda^2 e$, from the center of the ellipsoid, through the epigraph of $f(x)$ down to the graph of $f(x)$, to get the new iterate x_+, f_+. Update and loop to 3.1, if needed.

This method does have the property that:

3.c)   finite convergence occurs if $Y(\overline{f})$ is a pyramid for $\overline{f}$ close enough to f^* (i.e. if the problem has a unique primal solution)
(Proof: the largest ellipsoids $(E(f'), f')$ in $(X(f'), f')$, are given by Lagrange multipliers λ' proportional to $f' - f^*$ and therefore $d = dx'/df' = (A^t \Lambda^2 A)^{-1} A^t \Lambda^2 e$; thus $(\overline{x} - \alpha d, -\alpha)$ as α varies $(\alpha > 0)$ coincides with the line (x', f') tracing the centers of $(E(f'), f')$, and thus goes through the point (x^*, f^*).)

The three methods (1), (2) and (3) are, as mentioned, fully implementable if one uses a deepest cut variant as a subroutine to approximate the Lagrange multipliers λ for decreasing values of $\overline{f}$. It is also clear that the deepest cut ellipsoid method is a rather slow way of doing so, as it changes only one λ_i at each iteration (the i corresponds to the subgradient a_i used), but for a scaling of the other $\lambda_j' s$; while the original ellipsoid method of Yudin and Nemirovski does not even seem to approximate the optimal values of λ (on the other hand it does operate under an oracle which for each x returns only the value $f(x)$ and a subgradient).

It is therefore quite interesting to notice that the variants of Karmarkar projective method proposed by Todd and Burrell [21] and by Adler, Resende and Veiga [1] may be viewed as (effective) attempts to approximate the Lagrange multipliers λ. The first method estimates the multipliers λ by the dual variables y, the dual variables y being updated by a step of Karmarkar's original method, using the current best value of f as an estimate for the dual objective; the results on convergence for this method are quite remarquable and include polynomial convergence of both the primal and dual objectives [21]. The latter method estimates the Lagrange multipliers by the inverse of the slacks at the current point, which must be in the interior of the epigraph; no proof of polynomial convergence is known to this author, but very satisfactory computational experiments have been reported in [1].

We shall describe the two methods formally.

Algorithm 4 (Todd-Burrell [21]):

Use the dual variables y for λ.

4.1   the current iterate x, f, y satisfies $f = f(x)$, and dual feasibility with $y > 0$. For an initial dual feasible solution it may be necessary to add in the dual one artificial variable y_{m+1} with column $(-M - e^t A1)$, and, in the primal, the corresponding artificial cutting plane $f \geq -e^t Ax - M$, where M is a large positive number; the vector $e/(m+1)$ is an interior dual feasible solution.

Let $Y = \text{Diag}(y)$

4.2   Compute
$$\bar{x} = (A^t Y^2 A)^{-1} A^t Y^2 (b + fe)$$
CASE A: $f \leq f(\bar{x})$ NEW$(x, f) = $ OLD(x, f)
CASE B: $f > f(\bar{x})$ LINESEARCH TO GRAPH:

$$x'(\alpha) = (A^t Y^2 A)^{-1} A^t Y^2 (b + (f - \alpha)e)$$
$$= \bar{x} - \alpha (A^t Y^2 A)^{-1} A^t Y^2 e$$
$$f'(\alpha) = f - \alpha \qquad \text{where } \alpha > 0,$$

i.e. compute
$$\alpha' : f(x'(\alpha')) = f - \alpha', \text{ and}$$
$$\text{NEW}(x, f) = (x'(\alpha'), f - \alpha').$$

4.3   Send f to dual, and do one classical Karmarkar's (Todd and Burrell) iteration, from the current y, on the problem
Max $(-b - fe)^t y'$ $A^t y' = 0, e^t y' = 1, y' > 0$, to get
NEW$(y) = y'$
Loop to 4.1 if needed.

The convergence analysis of this method is given by the following elegant result:

Theorem 4 (Todd-Burrell [21]): The algorithm given above generates a primal sequence $\{x^q, f^q = f(x_q)\}$ and a sequence of feasible dual variables $\{y^q\}$, which satisfy

$$(f^* - b^t y^q) \leq (f^* - b^t y^0) e^{-q/5n}$$
$$(f(x^q) - f^*) \leq (f(x^0) - f^*) e^{-q/5n}.$$

A consequence of this is that, under the assumption of unique primal and dual solutions, $A^t (Y^q)^2 A$ converges at a linear rate to the shape of the largest ellipsoid included in the level surfaces $X(f^q)$.

Theorem 5: Under the additional assumptions of unicity of the primal and dual solutions $A^t(Y^q)^2A$ converges at a linear rate to the shape of the largest ellipsoid included in the level surfaces $X(f^q)$.

Proof: The unicity of the dual optimum and the previous theorem imply that $\|(y^q - y^*)\| \leq Ke^{-q/5n}$, for some K (such that $\ln K$ is polynomial in the length of the input data).

For q such that $X(f^q) = \{x : Ax \leq b + f^q e\}$ is the 'final' level set, and thus a simplex defined by $n+1$ inequalities, which correspond to the nonzero dual variables y^*, the largest inellipsoid $\{E^q\}$ is:

$$E^q = \{x : (x - \varepsilon^q)^t(A^tY^{*2}A)(x - \varepsilon^q) \leq (f^q - f^*)^2/(n(n+1))\}$$

with $\xi^q = (A^tY^{*2}A)^{-1}A^tY^{*2}(f^q - f^*)e$;

and thus $\|A^tY^{q2}A - A^tY^{*2}A\| = \|A^t(Y^{q2} - Y^{*2})A\| \leq K_1 e^{-q/5n}$

for some K_1 (where $\ln K_1$ is polynomial). QED

This result about fast convergence to the optimal shape, plus the fact that the method uses a linesearch with a horizontal component, designed to deal with the absence of symmetry of the level surfaces, indicates the superiority of the Todd-Burrell method over the classical, original ellipsoid method of Yudin and Nemirovski which has, however, the significant advantage of operating under an oracle which for each x returns only the value $f(x)$ and a subgradient.

Algorithm 5 (Adler-Resende-Veiga [1]):
This method uses the inverse slacks to estimate λ:

5.1 the current iterate x, f, satisfying $f > f(x)$, and the slacks $s = fe - Ax + b > 0$; let $S = \text{Diag}(s)$

5.2 compute the direction $d = (A^tS^{-2}A)^{-1}A^tS^{-2}e$
   LINESEARCH TOWARDS GRAPH:
   $x(\alpha) = x - \alpha d$
   $f(\alpha) = f - \alpha$
   $s(\alpha) = s - \alpha Ad$ $(\alpha > 0)$
   Choose α' to be the largest α so that $s(\alpha) \geq s(1 - \gamma)$, where $\gamma \in (0, 1)$;
   and $\text{NEW}(x, f, s) = (x(\alpha'), f(\alpha'), s(\alpha'))$.
   LOOP to 5.1 if needed.

Here, the convergence of the underlying ellipsoid matrix $A^t(S^q)^{-2}A$ to the shape of the largest ellipsoid included in the level surfaces (under the usual assumption of primal and dual unicity) follows if the discrete path traced by (x^q, f^q) is tangent to the path traced by $(\bar{x}, \bar{f})$, where $\bar{x}$ is the center of the largest ellipsoid contained in $X(\bar{f})$.

It is also apparent, as has been noticed by Adler et al, that this method is implementable (but for the stepsize) under an oracle which for each x returns only the value $f(x)$ and a subgradient. It would thus appear that this variant of Karmarkar's method would be usable for the minimization of a general convex function.

References.

[1] Adler, I., Resende, M. G. C., Veiga, G.: *An implementation of Karmarkar's algorithm for linear programming.* Dept. of Industrial Engineering and Operations Research, University of California, Berkeley, ORC 86-8 (1986).

[2] Agmon, S.: *The relaxation method for linear inequalities.* Canadian Journal of Mathematics 6 (1954), 382 – 392.

[3] Burrell, B. P., Todd, M. J.: *The ellipsoid method generates dual variables.* Mathematics of Operations Research 10 (1985), 688 – 700.

[4] Danzer, L., Laugwitz, D., Lenz, H.: *Über das Lownersche Ellipsoid und sein Analogon unter den einem Eikörper einbeschriebenen Ellipsoiden.* Arch. Math. 8 (1957), 214 – 219.

[5] Davidon, W. C.: *Conic approximations and collinear scalings for optimizers.* SIAM J. Numer. Anal. 17 (1980), 268 – 281.

[6] Goffin, J. L.: *Variable metric relaxation methods, part I: a conceptual algorithm.* SOL Technical Report 81-16, Department of Operations Research, Stanford University, Stanford, California, USA; 101 pp. (Aug. 1981).

[7] Goffin, J. L.: *Variable metric relaxation methods, part II: an implementable algorithm, or the ellipsoid method.* Mathematical Programming 30 (1984), 147 – 162.

[8] Goffin, J. L.: *The ellipsoid method and its predecessors.* Proceedings of the IFIP Working Conference on System Modelling and Optimization held in Santiago, Chile, August 27 - 31, 1984, Lecture Notes in Control and Information Sciences, Springer-Verlag (1986).

[9] Grunbaum, B.: *Measures of symmetry for convex sets.* In V. L. Klee (ed.), "Convexity", Proceedings of Symposia in Pure Mathematics, VII (1963), 233 - 270 (American Mathematical Society, Providence, Rhode Island).

[10] John, F.: *Extremum problems with inequalities as subsidiary conditions.* In Courant Anniversary Volume, Studies and Essays presented to R. Courant on his 60th birthday, January 8, 1948 (Interscience Publishers, New York, NY, 1948), 187 – 204.

[11] Karmarkar, N.: *A new polynomial time algorithm for linear programming.* Combinatorica 4 (1984), 373 – 395.

[12] Khacian, L. G.: *Polynomial algorithms in linear programming.* Zh. vycisl. Mat. mat. Fiz. 20, No. 1 (1980), 51 – 68; translated in USSR Computational Mathematics and Mathematical Physics 20, No. 1 (1980), 53 – 72.

[13] Leichtweiss, K.: *Über die affine Exzentrizität konvexer Körper*. Arch. Math. 10 (1959), 187 – 199.

[14] Motzkin, T., Schoenberg, I. J.: *The relaxation method for linear inequalities*. Canadian Journal of Mathematics 6 (1954), 393 – 404.

[15] Nemirovsky, A. S., Yudin, D. B.: *Problem complexity and method efficiency in optimization*. John Wiley, Chichester (1983).

[16] Pogorelov, A. V.: *The Minkowski multidimensional problem*. John Wiley, New York (1978).

[17] Shor, N. Z.: *Minimization methods for non-differentiable functions*. Springer-Verlag Berlin, Heidelberg (1985).

[18] Sonnevend, G.: *A modified ellipsoid method for the minimization of convex functions with superlinear convergence (or finite termination) for well-conditioned C^3 smooth (or piecewise linear) functions*. In Demyanov, V. F. and Pallaschke, D. (eds.), "Nondifferentiable Optimization: Motivations and Applications", Lecture Notes in Economics and Mathematical Systems, No. 255, Springer-Verlag, Berlin (1984).

[19] Todd, M. J.: *Minimum volume ellipsoid containing a part of a given ellipsoid*. Mathematics of Operations Research 7 (1982), 253 – 261.

[20] Todd, M. J.: *Polynomial algorithms for linear programming*. SORIE Report 707, Cornell University, Ithaca, NY (1986).

[21] Todd, M. J., Burrell, B. P.: *An extension of Karmarkar's algorithm for linear programming using dual variables*. To appear in Algorithmica.

International Series of
Numerical Mathematics, Vol. 84
(c) 1988 Birkhäuser Verlag Basel

A general result of Farkas type.

J. Gwinner

Technische Hochschule Darmstadt

Fachbereich Mathematik

Schloßgartenstr. 7

6100 Darmstadt, West Germany

Abstract. A general result of Farkas type is established, which includes recent generalizations of the Farkas lemma, due to Shimizu - Aiyoshi - Katayama and Swartz.

1. Introduction

It is well known in mathematical programming [Bl-0e, Kr-1, Ma-1] that the Farkas lemma is a cornerstone in the derivation of necessary optimality conditions. During the development of modern optimization theory the original theorem of Farkas on linear homogeneous inequalities has been generalized from the linear to the convex case, from finite to infinite dimensions.

In this contribution a further extension is established. We replace the usual bilinear coupling $< y, g(x) >$ between the dual variable y and the constraint g by a convex/concave-positively homogeneous function F. More precisely, Theorem 2.2 in section 2 asserts that under certain convexity assumptions and an abstract closedness hypothesis the following two statements are equivalent:

$$x \in X, \ (\forall y \in Y) \, F(x,y) \leq 0 \Rightarrow f(x) \geq 0, \tag{1.1}$$

$$\exists y \in Y, \ (\forall x \in X) \, f(x) + F(x,y) \geq 0. \tag{1.2}$$

We note that if 0 is the optimal value of the general program

$$\begin{aligned} &\text{(P) minimize } f(x), \\ &\text{subject to } x \in X \text{ and } (\forall y \in Y) F(x,y) \leq 0, \end{aligned} \tag{1.3}$$

then (1.1) holds and (1.2) can be interpreted as a general form of the Karush-Kuhn-Tucker condition with the multiplier y in convex programming [Bl-0e]. If the closedness hypothesis is not satisfied, then instead of (1.2) an asymptotic conclusion holds (Theorem 2.1).

In section 3 we employ our result to deduce a recent generalization of the Farkas lemma, due to Shimizu, Aiyoshi and Katayama [S-A-K] in the infinite dimensional versions given by Swartz [Sw-1, Sw-2]. For other known infinite dimensional results of Farkas type and their integration into a single theory we refer to [Gw-1].

It is rather straightforward to derive from our Theorems 2.1 and 2.2 optimality conditions for the general program (P). For the details and for more specific classes of (P) we refer to [Gw-2] where optimality conditions and duality are studied for quadratic, homogeneous and fractional programs under constraints of the type (1.3).

2. The general results

Let X be a convex set, Y be a convex cone (i.e. $Y + Y \subset Y$ and $\mathbb{R}_+ Y \subset Y$ hold) in some linear spaces. Let f be a real-valued convex function on X, F be a real-valued function on $X \times Y$ such that for every $y \in Y$, $F(\cdot, y)$ is convex on X, and for every $x \in X$, $F(x, \cdot)$ is convex and positively homogeneous on Y. Let V denote the linear topological space of all real-valued functions on X, endowed with the product topology π [Ke-Na]. In this setting the following general asymptotic result of Farkas type can be established.

Theorem 2.1. *The system*

$$x \in X, f(x) < 0, \ (\forall y \in Y) \, F(x, y) \leq 0 \tag{2.1}$$

is inconsistent, if and only if there exist nets $\{y_\imath : \imath \in J\}$ *in* Y *and* $\{v_\imath : \imath \in J\}$ *in* V *such that*

$$f = \pi - \lim_{\imath \in J} v_\imath \tag{2.2}$$

and

$$(\forall x \in X) v_\imath(x) + F(x, y_\imath) \geq 0 \tag{2.3}$$

holds.

Proof. To prove the trivial part let the nets $\{y_\imath : \imath \in J\}$ in Y and $\{v_\imath : \imath \in J\}$ in V satisfy (2.2) and (2.3). The consistency of (2.1) leads to the contradiction

$$0 \leq \liminf_{\imath \in J}[-F(x, y_\imath)] \leq \limsup_{\imath \in J}[-F(x, y_\imath)] \leq \lim_{\imath \in J} v_\imath(x) = f(x) < 0.$$

Now assume, nets $\{y_\imath : \imath \in J\}$ in Y and $\{v_\imath : \imath \in J\}$ in V that satisfy (2.2) and (2.3) do not exist. This means, f does not belong to the π-closure of the set C in V given by

$$C = \{v \in V \mid (\exists y \in Y)(\forall x \in X) \, v(x) + F(x, y) \geq 0\}. \tag{2.4}$$

By definition of the π-topology there exist $\varepsilon > 0$ and $x_\kappa \in X$ for $\kappa = 1, \cdots, k$ for some positive integer k such that the π-neighborhood U of f given by

$$U = \{v \in V \mid |v(x_\kappa) - f(x_\kappa)| < \varepsilon \ (\kappa = 1, \cdots, k)\}$$

does not meet C. We set

$$K = \{1, \cdots, k\},$$

and introduce in the finite dimensional vector space $\mathbb{R}^k$

$$f^{(k)} = \begin{pmatrix} f(x_1) \\ \cdots \\ f(x_k) \end{pmatrix},$$

$$C^{(k)} = \{z \in \mathbb{R}^m \mid (\exists y \in Y)(\forall \kappa \in K) \, z_\kappa \geq -F(x_\kappa, y)\},$$

and the open ball $B^{(k)} = B(f^{(k)}, \varepsilon)$ centered at $f^{(k)}$ with radius ε. Then we can conclude that $C^{(k)} \cap B^{(k)} = \emptyset$; otherwise we could define a function v on X by

$$v(x) = \begin{cases} z_\kappa & \text{if } x = x_\kappa \; (\kappa \in K) \\ -F(x, y) & \text{else} \end{cases}$$

that belongs to $C \cap U$. By separation in the finite dimensional euclidean space $\mathbb{R}^k$ we obtain $a \in \mathbb{R}^k$, $a \neq 0$ and $\alpha \in \mathbb{R}$ such that

$$(\forall w \in B^{(k)}, z \in C^{(k)}) a^T z \geq \alpha \geq a^T w, \tag{2.5}$$

where $a^T w = \sum_{\kappa \in K} a_\kappa w_\kappa$ denotes the inner product on $\mathbb{R}^k$. By construction of $C^{(k)}$, all components a_κ are nonnegative and their sum is positive, since $a \neq 0$. We can assume $\sum a_\kappa = 1$; otherwise we divide the separating inequalities (2.5) by this sum. Since $F(x, \cdot)$ is positively homogeneous on the cone Y, α in (2.5) is nonpositive and

$$(\forall y \in Y) \sum_{\kappa \in K} a_\kappa F(x_\kappa, y) \leq 0$$

holds. Moreover

$$\sum_{\kappa \in K} a_\kappa f(x_\kappa) < 0,$$

since $a \neq 0$. By convexity we arrive with

$$\overline{x} = \sum_{\kappa=1}^{k} a_\kappa x_\kappa$$

at

$$\overline{x} \in X, f(\overline{x}) < 0, \; (\forall y \in Y) F(\overline{x}, y) \leq 0,$$

a solution to (2.1).   q.e.d

   We remark that the proof above only relies on the separation in *finite dimensional* spaces and is therefore different from the proof in [Gw-1, §2] where strong separation in the space V is employed. - The proof above shows also that if we impose the π-closedness of the set C given by (2.4) we obtain the nonasymptotic Farkas type result, already announced in the introduction.

Theorem 2.2. *Suppose the set*

$$C = \{v \in V \mid (\exists y \in Y)(\forall x \in X)\, v(x) + F(x, y) \geq 0\}$$

is π-closed. Then the system

$$x \in X, \; f(x) < 0, \; (\forall y \in Y)F(x, y) \leq 0 \tag{2.6}$$

is inconsistent, if and only if there exists a solution y to the system

$$y \in Y, \; (\forall x \in X)f(x) + F(x, y) \geq 0. \tag{2.7}$$

There are more concrete sufficient conditions in general linear topological spaces for the π-closedness of the set C [see Gw-1, Proposition 3.1]. Since we do not need this result here, we omit the details.

3. The Farkas type result of Shimizu - Aiyoshi - Katayama and Swartz

In this section we derive from Theorem 2.2 the Farkas type results of Swartz [Sw-1, Sw-2] which extend a recent generalization of the Farkas lemma, due to Shimizu, Aiyoshi, and Katayama [S-A-K, Theorem 2.1] to infinite dimensions. When using the nonasymptotic existence result of Theorem 2.2 we are faced with a closedness problem. Therefore we first settle this closedness problem in the special situation encountered with Swartz.

Lemma 3.1 Let E and E' be two real locally convex spaces in duality, denoted by $< \cdot, \cdot >$. Let Y be a nonempty subset of E', closed with respect to the weak topology $\sigma(E', E)$. Then the set

$$C = \{v \in V \mid (\exists y \in Y)(\forall x \in E)\, v(x) + < x, y > \geq 0\} \tag{3.1}$$

is closed in the space V of all real-valued functions on E with respect to the product topology π.

Proof. Consider a net $\{v_\iota : \iota \in J\}$ in C, π-convergent to $\hat{v}$. Then there exist $y_\iota \in Y$ $(\iota \in J)$ such that for any $x \in E = -E$

$$-v_\iota(x) \leq < x, y_\iota > \leq v_\iota(-x) \tag{3.2}$$

holds. These estimates together with the convergence of $v_\iota(x)$ and $v_\iota(-x)$ imply that the net $\{y_\iota : \iota \in J\}$ is pointwise bounded on E. In virtue of Tychonoff's theorem [Ke-Na, Theorem 4.1] there exists a subnet of $\{y_\iota : \iota \in J\}$, convergent to some $\hat{y} \in V$

with respect to π. Now the relative topology of π on E' is just the weak topology $\sigma(E', E)$, and by hypothesis, Y is weakly closed. Hence $\hat{y} \in Y$ and (3.2) gives in the limit for any $x \in E$

$$< x, \hat{y} > + \hat{v}(x) \geq 0,$$

thus finally $\hat{v} \in C$.   q.e.d.

Now we can derive the following result of Swartz [Sw-1, Theorem 2.2]. Here $cl\, A$, $co\, A$, respectively cone A denotes topological closure, convex hull, respectively conical hull of A (with vertex at the origin) in a linear topological space; $c(A) := co$ cone A is then the convex cone generated by A.

Corollary 3.2 Let E and E' be two real locally convex spaces in duality. Suppose, A and B are nonempty subsets of E such that A and $cl\, co\, A$ are compact with respect to $\sigma(E, E')$. Then the following statements are equivalent.

$$\xi \in E', \ (\forall y \in B) \ < \xi, y > \leq 0 \Rightarrow \max\{< \xi, x > \mid x \in A\} \geq 0; \tag{3.3}$$

$$(\exists x_0 \in cl\, co\, A, \ y_0 \in cl\, c(B)) \ x_0 + y_0 = 0. \tag{3.4}$$

Proof. We define on E', respectively on $E' \times E$

$$f(\xi) = \max\{< \xi, x > \mid x \in A\},$$
$$F(\xi, x) = < \xi, x >,$$

set

$$Y = cl\, c(B),$$

and note

$$(\forall y \in B) \ < \xi, y > \leq 0 \leftrightarrow (\forall y \in Y) \ < \xi, y > \leq 0,$$
$$f(\xi) = \max\{< \xi, x > \mid x \in cl\, co\, A\}.$$

Therefore (3.4) $\Rightarrow$ (3.3) is evident. On the other hand, (3.3) is equivalent to (2.6). In virtue of Lemma 3.1, Theorem 2.2 applies. It yields

$$(\exists y_0 \in Y)(\forall \xi \in E') f(\xi) + < \xi, y_0 > \geq 0.$$

Now fix $y_0 \in Y$, and we have the implication

$$\xi \in E', \ (\forall x \in cl\, co\, A) \ < \xi, x > \leq 0 \Rightarrow < \xi, y_0 > \geq 0.$$

Again we apply Lemma 3.1 and Theorem 2.2 to obtain

$$(\exists x_0 \in cl\, co\, A)(\forall \xi \in E') \ < \xi, x_0 > + < \xi, y_0 > \geq 0,$$

hence, finally $x_0 + y_0 = 0$.   q.e.d.

Remark 3.1 In contrast to the version in [Sw-1, Theorem 2.2] we do not need to assume B to be compact. On the other hand, if B is convex, compact and $0 \notin B$, then the cone generated by B is closed [Kr-1, IV.2.1]. So in this case, the statement $y_0 \in c\ell c(B)$ can be replaced by $y_0 \in \text{cone } B$. Also, if E is quasi-complete, in particular if E is a Banach space, then the closed convex hull of a weakly compact set is weakly compact [Ho-1, 11B, Theorem]. Therefore, in this case, the assumption on A can be relaxed. Finally in finite dimensions, the convex hull of a compact set is compact. Therefore in this case the assumption B is compact and $0 \notin co\, B$ leads to the statement $y_0 \in c(B)$. Thus, in the finite dimensional case, Corollary 6.2 contains Theorem 2.1 of [S-A-K]. If A is a singleton and B is finite, Corollary 3.2 reduces to the classical Farkas lemma.

Now we turn to the basic Farkas type result in another paper of Swartz [Sw-2, Theorem 2], which also extends the basic theorem of Shimizu, Aiyoshi and Katayama [S-A-K, Theorem 2.1] to infinite dimensions. In addition to the convex function f, let $h : E \to \mathbb{R}$ be another convex function such that for some fixed $x_0 \in E$, $h(x_0) = 0$ and the subdifferential $\partial h(x_0)$ is not empty. To the level set

$$\Omega = \{x \in E \mid h(x) \leq 0\}$$

one can associate the cone of feasible directions to Ω at x_0 [Ho-1, 14E], defined by

$$\mathcal{F}(\Omega, x_0) := \{e \in E \mid (\exists \alpha > 0)(\forall t \in [0, \alpha])x_0 + te \in \Omega\}.$$

Since Ω is convex,

$$\mathcal{F}(\Omega, x_0) = \{t(x - x_0) \mid t \geq 0, x \in \Omega\} = \mathbb{R}_-(x_0 - \Omega)$$

and in the topological dual of E,

$$\mathcal{F}(\Omega, x_0)^+ \supset \mathbb{R}_- \partial h(x_0)$$

holds always. Now the function h is defined to be *regular* at x_0, if and only if

$$\mathcal{F}(\Omega, x_0)^+ = \mathbb{R}_- h(x_0) \tag{3.5}$$

is valid. A sufficient condition for h to be regular at x_0 is that h satisfies Slater's condition; that is, there exists $x_1 \in \Omega$ such that $h(x_1) < 0$ [Ho-1, 14E].   .

Now we can state

Corollary 3.3 Let the convex function h on the real locally convex space E be regular at x_0 and let the convex lower semicontinuous function f on E possess a non-void weak* compact subdifferential $\partial f(x_0)$. Then the following assertions are equivalent.

$$h(x) \leq 0 \Rightarrow f(x) \geq f(x_0); \tag{3.6}$$

$$(\exists \xi_0 \in \partial f(x_0), \eta_0 \in \partial h(x_0), t \leq 0)\ \xi_0 = t\eta_0. \tag{3.7}$$

For the proof of this result we insert the subsequent

Lemma 3.4 The implication (3.6) holds, if and only if x_0 minimizes the convex lower semicontinuous function f on $x_0 + cl\mathcal{F}(\Omega, x_0)$.

Proof of the lemma. Obviously (3.6) means that x_0 minimizes f on Ω. Consider an arbitrary $\tilde{x} \in x_0 + \mathcal{F}(\Omega, x_0)$; that is $\tilde{x} = x_0 + t(x - x_0)$ for some $x \in \Omega$ and $t \geq 0$. We claim that $f(\tilde{x}) \geq f(x_0)$. For $t \leq 1$ this is immediate by the convexity of Ω. So let us consider $t > 1$ and suppose $f(\tilde{x}) < f(x_0)$. This gives for any $s \in (0, 1)$

$$f(s\tilde{x} + (1 - s)x_0) < f(x_0).$$

But we can choose $s = t^{-1}$ and

$$x = t^{-1}\tilde{x} + (1 - t^{-1})x_0$$

lies in Ω. This contradiction proves our claim. By the lower semicontinuity of f, this extends to

$$(\forall \tilde{x} \in x_0 + cl\, \mathcal{F}(\Omega, x_0))f(\tilde{x}) \leq f(x_0).$$

The reverse statement is trivial, since $\Omega \subset x_0 + cl\mathcal{F}(\Omega, x_0)$.   q.e.d.

Proof of Corollary 3.3. By the preceding lemma and by the bipolar theorem [see e.g. Ho-1, 12C], (3.6) is equivalent to

$$x \in E, (\forall y \in Y) < x, y > \leq 0 \Rightarrow f(x + x_0) - f(x_0) \geq 0, \tag{3.8}$$

where by the regularity of h at x_0,

$$Y := \mathcal{F}(\Omega, x_0)^- = \mathbb{R}_+ \partial h(x_0)$$

is a weak* closed cone. In virtue of Lemma 3.1, Theorem 2.2 applies to the functions

$$\tilde{f}(x) := f(x + x_0) - f(x_0),$$
$$F(x, y) = < x, y > .$$

It yields

$$(\exists y_0 \in Y)(\forall x \in E) < x, y_0 > + f(x + x_0) - f(x_0) \geq 0,$$

what is equivalent to (3.7) by the definitions of Y and $\partial f(x_0)$.   q.e.d.

Remark 3.2 Let A, B be two nonempty convex weak* compact subsets in the dual space E' and define

$$f(x) = \max\{< x, \xi > | \xi \in A\},$$
$$h(x) = \max\{< x, \xi > | \xi \in B\}.$$

Then the assumption $0 \notin B$ implies Slater's condition for h and by Corollary 3.3, (3.6) is equivalent to

$$(\exists s \leq 0,\ a \in A,\ b \in B)\ a = sb.$$

Thus we again arrive at the Farkas type result of Shimizu - Aiyoshi - Katayama.

Remark 3.3 If we redefine h to be regular at x_0, if and only if $h(x_0) = 0$ implies (3.5), we can replace the assumption of $h(x_0) = 0$ by the more general and natural assumption of feasibility, i.e. $x_0 \in \Omega$. Namely if $h(x_0) < 0$ holds, then $\mathcal{F}(\Omega, x_0) = E$ and $\mathcal{F}(\Omega, x_0)^+ = \{0\}$ are evident. Therefore in view of Lemma 3.4, in this case the conclusion (3.7) holds with $t = 0$. Thus in any case we arrive for the program

$$\text{minimize } f(x), \text{ such that } h(x) \leq 0 \tag{3.9}$$

and for its optimal solution x_0 to the multiplier rule - a mere restatement of (3.7) -

$$(\exists \mu \geq 0) : 0 \in \partial f(x_0) + \mu \partial h(x_0) \tag{3.10}$$

with the multiplier μ and to the complementary slackness condition

$$\mu h(x_0) = 0. \tag{3.11}$$

This result is of course not new; it can e.g. be found with Holmes [Ho-1, 12C] under Slater's regularity condition. As already noted there, the program (3.9) extends to a finite number of constraints $h_1, \cdots, h_m$ by using the known subdifferential rule for $h = \max\{h_1, \cdots, h_m\}$.

Finally let us mention that the preceding results of Shimizu - Aiyoshi - Katayama and Swartz along with many other known infinite dimensional Farkas type results are integrated into one theory in [Gw-1], based upon our general Farkas results, here Theorems 2.1 and 2.2.

References.

[Bl-Oe] Blum, E., Oettli, W.: *Mathematische Optimierung - Grundlagen und Verfahren.* (Springer, 1975).

[Gw-1] Gwinner, J.: *Results of Farkas type.* (submitted).

[Gw-2] Gwinner, J.: *A general Farkas lemma and applications in duality.* 11. Symposium über Operations Research, TH Darmstadt 1986 (submitted).

[Ho-1] Holmes, R. B.: *Geometric functional analysis and its applications.* (Springer, 1975).

[Ke-Na] Kelley, J. L., Namioka, I. et al.: *Linear topological spaces.* (Van Nostrand, 1963).

[Kr-1] Krabs, W.: *Optimierung und Approximation*. (Teubner, 1975).

[Ma-1] Mangasarian, O. L.: *Nonlinear programming*. (McGraw-Hill, 1969).

[S-A-K] Shimizu, K.; Aiyoshi, E.; Katamaya, R.: *Generalized Farkas' theorem and optimization of infinitely constrained problems*. Journal of Optimization Theory and Applications 40 (451 – 462).

[Sw-1] Swartz, C.: *A general Farkas lemma*. Journal of Optimization Theory and Applications 46 (1985), 237 – 244.

[Sw-2] Swartz, C.: *The Farkas lemma of Shimizu, Aiyoshi and Katayama*. Bulletin of the Australian Mathematical Society 31 (1985), 445 – 450.

International Series of
Numerical Mathematics, Vol. 84
(c) 1988 Birkhäuser Verlag Basel

Parametric semi-infinite optimization in certain lattices: Continuity of the feasible set.

Siegfried Helbig
Johann-Wolfgang-Goethe-Universität
Fachbereich Mathematik
Robert-Mayer-Straße 6-10
6000 Frankfurt/Main, West Germany

Abstract.
Let $(F, \oplus, \circ)$ be a complete, extremal, fully-ordered group with zero-element (introduced in HELBIG [5]). The aim of this paper is to consider optimization problems in $(F^n, \oplus, \circ)$ described by functions, which are linear with respect to $\oplus$ and $\circ$, and to investigate their continuous dependence on the restriction vector. We derive necessary and sufficient conditions for the lower- and upper-semi-continuity and the closedness of the feasible-set-mapping. Finally, an application of such problems in some scheduling problems is given.

I. Introduction.

Let F be a set with a binary relation "$\leq$" and a binary operation "$\circ$".

Definition I.1.: $(F, \oplus, \circ)$ is called *extremal, fully-ordered group with zero-element* $\bar{0}$, if

i) $(F \setminus \{\bar{0}\}, \leq)$ is a fully-ordered set
ii) $(F \setminus \{\bar{0}\}, \circ)$ is a group
iii) $(F, \circ)$ is a semi-group with $x \circ \bar{0} = \bar{0} \circ x = \bar{0}$ for $x \in F$.
iv) The binary operation "$\oplus$" is induced by the relation "$\leq$":

$$x \oplus y = y \qquad \Leftrightarrow x \leq y \qquad \text{for } x, y \in F, \ x, y \neq \bar{0}$$
$$x \oplus \bar{0} = x \qquad \qquad \qquad \text{for } x \in F$$

Because our aim is to introduce optimization problems over $(F, \oplus, \circ)$, it is convenient to assume the completeness of F, i.e. that every non-empty subset of F bounded from above has a least upper bound in F. For that reason, let $(F, \oplus, \circ)$ be a
complete, extremal, fully-ordered group with zero-element.

Let F^n be the cartesian product of F. We introduce a partial ordering in F^n by

$$x \leq y \Leftrightarrow x_i \leq y_i \text{ for } i = 1, \cdots, n, \ x, y \in F^n$$

and extend the operations $\oplus$ and $\circ$ by:
let $x,\, y \in F^n$, and $\alpha \in F$; then define

$$\alpha \circ x := (\alpha \circ x_1, \cdots, \alpha \circ x_n) \in F^n$$
$$x \oplus y := (x_1 \oplus y_1, \cdots, x_n \oplus y_n) \in F^n$$
$$x \circ y := (x,y) := \sum_{i=1}^{n} {}^{\oplus} x_i \circ y_i \in F.$$

Then

    i) $(F^n, \circ)$ and $(F^n, \oplus)$ are semi-groups with neutral-elements $(\bar{1}, \cdots, \bar{1}) \in F^n$, resp. $(\bar{0}, \cdots, \bar{0}) \in F^n$, where $\bar{1}$ is the neutral-element in $(F, \circ)$ and $\bar{0}$ is the zero-element.

    ii) $(F, \leq)$ is a lattice.

The expression $(.,.)$ is called *extremal-inner-product*, because it satisfies all properties of an inner-product.

By a theorem of Hölder, $(F \setminus \{\bar{0}\}, \circ)$ is isomorph to the additive group of real numbers with the natural ordering (for a proof see for instance KOKORIN and KOPYTOV [6], p. 110). Especially, this theorem implies

    a) the isomorphism φ preserves the order

    b) the operation $\circ$ is commutative.

This result can be strengthened:
we endow F with the so-called *open-interval-topology* $\mathcal{T}$ (see for instance KOKORIN and KOPYTOV [6], p. 108). The sets

$$U_a := \{x \in F \,|\, a < x\} \quad \text{for } a, b \in F$$

and

$$L_b := \{x \in F \,|\, x < b\} \quad \text{for } a, b \in F$$

and the set F itself are a subbasis of this topology. In this way, an element of the basis of neighbourhoods of some $x \in F$ is denoted by

$$U_{ab} := \{z \in F \,|\, a < z < b\} \quad \text{if } x \neq \bar{0}$$

resp.

$$U_{\bar{0}b} := \{z \in F \,|\, \bar{0} \leq z < b\} \quad \text{if } x = \bar{0}$$

with $a,\, b \in F$ (see [5]). F^n is equipped with the product topology $\mathcal{T}^n$.
If we extend the isomorphism φ (again denoted by φ) by

$$\varphi(\bar{0}) := -\infty,$$

we obtain

$$(F, \circ) \cong (\mathbb{R} \cup \{-\infty\}, +)$$

and moreover

Lemma I.2: The isomorphism φ is a topological mapping, i.e. φ is a homeomorphism.

Proof: see HELBIG [5], Lemma II.2. $\qquad\qquad\qquad\qquad\qquad\qquad\qquad\qquad$ □

So we obtain the following topological properties of F^n:
  a) $(F^n, \mathcal{T}^n)$ satisfies the first axiom of countability.
  b) The closed and bounded sets in $(F^n, \mathcal{T}^n)$ are compact.
  c) Every bounded sequence in F^n has a cluster point.
     Remark: Every sequence in F is bounded from below, since $\bar{0}$ is the least element in F.
  d) The extremal-inner-product is a continuous function from $F^n \times F^n$ to F.

We give some examples of $(F, \oplus, \circ)$ and the homeomorphism φ:

Example I.3.: (see [5]) Denote by $\mathbb{R}$ the real numbers, by $\mathbb{R}^+$ the non-negative real numbers, and by $\mathbb{R}^>$ the positive real numbers.

$(F, \oplus, \circ)$	$\bar{0}$	$\bar{1}$	homeomorphism φ
$(\mathbb{R} \cup \{-\infty\}, \max, +)$	$-\infty$	0	$\varphi(x) = x$
$(\mathbb{R} \cup \{\infty\}, \min, +)$	∞	0	$\varphi(x) = -x$
$(\mathbb{R}^+, \max, \cdot)$	0	1	$\varphi(x) = \begin{cases} \ln x & \text{if } x \neq 0 \\ -\infty & \text{if } x = 0 \end{cases}$
$(\mathbb{R}^> \cup \{\infty\}, \min, \cdot)$	∞	1	$\varphi(x) = \begin{cases} -\ln x & \text{if } x \neq \infty \\ -\infty & \text{if } x = \infty \end{cases}$

$\qquad\qquad\qquad\qquad\qquad\qquad\qquad\qquad\qquad\qquad\qquad\qquad\qquad\qquad\qquad\qquad\qquad$ □

For the following we need the useful

Lemma I.4: Let $a, b \in F^k$ with $a_i < b_i$ for $i = 1, \cdots, k$, $k \in \mathbb{N}$.
  Then there exists $c \in F^k$ such that

$$a_i < c_i < b_i \qquad \text{for } i = 1, \cdots, k.$$

Remark: This lemma was first proved for 'extremal algebras' with an additional property by K. ZIMMERMANN (see [7], Lemma 1h).
For our case, a proof is in [5], Lemma III.3.

In the next section, we introduce an extremally-linear optimization problem (linear with respect to $\oplus$ and $\circ$) in $(F^n, \oplus, \circ)$ depending on the restriction vector and give some examples and lemmata. The continuous dependence of the feasible set of the optimization problem on the restriction vector is studied in section III. The last section deals with an application of such optimization problems in some scheduling problems.

II. The extremally-linear optimization problem

Let $(F, \oplus, \circ)$ be a complete, extremal, fully-ordered group with zero-element $\bar{0}$. Furthermore, let T be a compact Hausdorff-space, $n \in \mathbb{N}$, $p \in F^n$, and let $B : T \to F^n$ be a continuous mapping.

For each $b \in EC[T] := \{h : T \to F \,|\, h \text{ continuous } \}$, we consider

$$ELP(b) \qquad \min(p, x)$$

$$\text{subject to}$$

$$(B(t), x) \geq b(t) \text{ for } t \in T,$$

where $(.,.)$ denotes the extremal-inner-product.

In advance, some remarks to the above optimization problem:

i) To minimize the function $(p, .)$ means to minimize it with respect to the relation "$\leq$" in F.

ii) We consider only "$\geq$"-inequalities, neither "$\leq$"- nor "$=$"-restrictions.

iii) In [5], HELBIG investigates the extremally-linear optimization problem in dependence on the objective function p.

iv) K. ZIMMERMANN [8] and U. ZIMMERMANN [9], p. 205ff, consider optimization problems of type ELP with a finite number of restrictions and give algorithms for solving the problem.

For $b \in EC[T]$, we define feasible set, optimal value, and optimal set of $ELP(b)$ by:

$$Z_b := \{x \in F^n \,|\, (B(t), x) \geq b(t) \text{ for } t \in T\}$$

$$E_b := \inf_{x \in Z_b} (p, x)$$

$$P_b := \{x \in Z_b \,|\, (p, x) = E_b\}.$$

Example II.1.: Let $(F, \oplus, \circ) = (\mathbb{R}^+, \max, \cdot)$ and $n = 2$.

a) Let $T = \{1, 2\}$, $B(1) = (1, 1/2)$, $B(2) = (1/2, 1)$, $p = (1, 1)$.

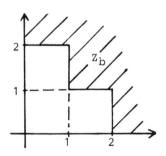

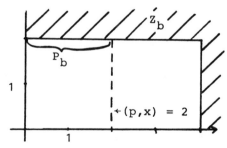

Fig. 1: $b(1) = b(2) = 1$
$E_b = 1$, $P_b = \{(1,1)\}$

Fig. 2: $b(1) = 1$, $b(2) = 2$
$E_b = 2$

b) Let $T = [0, \pi/2]$, $B(t) = (\sin t, \cos t)$ for $t \in T$, $p = (1,0)$.

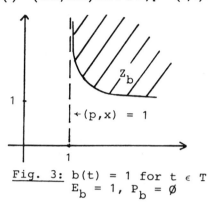

Fig. 3: b(t) = 1 for t ϵ T
$E_b = 1$, $P_b = \emptyset$

c) Let $T = [0, 1]$, $B(t) = (t, t)$ for $t \in T$.

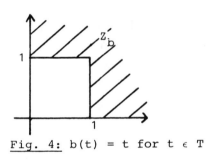

Fig. 4: b(t) = t for t ϵ T

For the following, the Slater-condition is important.

Definition II.2.: Let $b \in EC[T]$; Z_b satisfies the *Slater-condition*, if there exists $x \in Z_b$ with $(B(t), x) > b(t)$ for $t \in T$. x is called *Slater-element* of Z_b.

On account of the structure of the extremal-inner-product, we obtain the following necessary and sufficient criterion for the Slater-condition:

Lemma II.3: Let $b \in EC[T]$. Z_b satisfies the Slater-condition, if and only if

$$\forall_{t \in T} \exists_{i \in \{1, \cdots, n\}} B(t)_i \neq \bar{0}.$$

Proof: $\Rightarrow$: Let x be Slater-element of Z_b; then we have for $t \in T$

$$\bar{0} \leq b(t) < (B(t), x) = B(t)_i \circ x_i$$

for some $i \in \{1, \cdots, n\}$. This implies $B(t)_i \neq \bar{0}$.

$\Leftarrow$: Since $\sum_{i=1}^{n} {}^{\oplus}B(t)_i \neq \bar{0}$ by assumption, there exists

$$\alpha := \max_{t \in T} b(t) \circ (\sum_{i=1}^{n} {}^{\oplus}B(t)_i)^{-1}.$$

Let x_i be in F such that $x_i > \alpha$ for $i = 1, \cdots, n$. Because

$$b(t) = b(t) \circ (\sum_{i=1}^{n} {}^{\oplus}B(t)_i)^{-1} \circ (\sum_{i=1}^{n} {}^{\oplus}B(t)_i)$$

$$\leq \alpha \circ \sum_{i=1}^{n} {}^{\oplus}B(t)_i < \sum_{i=1}^{n} {}^{\oplus}B(t)_i \circ x_i = (B(t), x),$$

x is Slater-element of Z_b. $\qquad \square$

We see that the feasible sets in Examples II.1.a) and b) satisfy the Slater-condition.

Corollary II.4.: Let $b \in EC[T]$ such that Z_b satisfies the Slater-condition. Then Z_h satisfies the Slater-condition for all $h \in EC[T]$.

Proof: With Lemma II.3., we have $\sum_{i=1}^{n} {}^{\oplus}B(t)_i > \bar{0}$. Hence, there exists

$$\alpha^h := \max_{t \in T} h(t) \circ (\sum_{i=1}^{n} {}^{\oplus}B(t)_i)^{-1}.$$

Define $x_i > \alpha^h$ for $i = 1, \cdots, n$ and conclude like in the sufficient part of the above lemma. $\qquad \square$

III. Continuity properties of the feasible set

In this section, we ask for continuity properties of the *feasible-set-mapping*

$$Z : Z_{Bp} \to POW(F^n)$$
$$b \mapsto Z_b,$$

where $Z_{Bp} := \{b \in EC[T] | Z_b \neq \emptyset\}$ and $POW(F^n)$ denotes the power set of F^n. For this, we endow $EC[T]$ with the topology of uniform convergence like follows:

In the case of $(\mathbb{R}^+, \max, \circ)$, we define a metric by

$$\hat{d}(a, b) := \max_{t \in T} |a(t) - b(t)|,$$

where a, b are continuous mappings from T to $\mathbb{R}^+$. With Example I.3., an arbitrary $(F, \oplus, \circ)$ is homeomorph to $(\mathbb{R}^+, \max, \cdot)$. Let φ be this homeomorphism. Then we obtain a metric in F by

$$d(x, y) := \hat{d}(\varphi(x), \varphi(y))$$

for x, $y \in EC[T]$. This metric induces the topology of uniform convergence in $EC[T]$.

In the following, we use the notions of closedness, lower- and upper-semi-continuity of a set-valued-mapping in the sense of HAHN [4].

With the continuity of the extremal-inner-product, it follows immediately

Theorem III.1.: The mapping $Z : Z_{Bp} \to POW(F^n)$ is a closed mapping. $\qquad \square$

The next theorem gives a sufficient condition for the upper-semi-continuity (u.s.c.) of Z.

Theorem III.2.: If for all $t \in T$ and for all $i \in \{1, \cdots, n\}$ we have $B(t)_i \neq \bar{0}$, then $Z : Z_{Bp} \to POW(F^n)$ is an u.s.c. mapping.

Proof: If Z is not u.s.c. in $b \in Z_{Bp}$, then there exist an open set W with $Z_b \subset W$ and a sequence (b_k) in Z_{Bp} with $b_k \to b$ and $Z_{b_k} \setminus W \neq \emptyset$. Choose $v^k \in Z_{b_k} \setminus W$. Since v^k is not feasible for $ELP(b)$, there exists $t \in T$ with

$$B(t)_i \circ v_i^k \leq (B(t), v^k) < b(t) \leq \max_{s \in T} b(s) =: c.$$

By assumption, we obtain

$$v_i^k \leq c \circ B(t)_i^{-1} \leq c \circ \max_{s \in T} B(s)_i^{-1} =: d$$

for $i = 1, \cdots, n$. Since d is independent of k, the last inequality holds for all $k \in \mathbb{N}$. Hence, the bounded sequence (v^k) has a subsequence, which converges to $v \in F^n$. With Theorem III.1., we have

$$v \in Z_b \setminus W$$

in contradiction to the assumption. $\qquad \square$

In semi-infinite linear optimization, FISCHER [3] shows the equivalence of the u.s.c. of the feasible-set-mapping and the compactness of the feasible set. Since Z_b is never compact (see Example II.1.), the condition in Theorem III.2. is weaker.

Lemma III.3.: Let $b \in EC[T]$ such that $b(t) > \bar{0}$ for all $t \in T$. Then the condition

$$(*) \qquad \qquad \forall_{t \in T} \exists_{i \in \{1, \cdots, n\}} B(t)_i \neq \bar{0}$$

holds, if and only if the boundary $\partial Z_b := Z_b \setminus \text{int} Z_b$ is compact and non-empty. ($\text{int} Z_b$ denotes the topological interior of Z_b.)

Proof: $\Rightarrow$: Define

$$c_i := \max_{s \in T} b(s) \circ B(s)_i^{-1} \quad \text{for } i = 1, \cdots, n.$$

We claim that ∂Z_b is a subset of the compact set

$$K := \{x \in F^n | x_i \leq c_i \text{ for } i = 1, \cdots, n\}.$$

Let x be not in K, which implies $x_i > c_i$ for some $i \in \{1, \cdots, n\}$. Hence, it follows for $t \in T$

$$b(t) = B(t)_i \circ b(t) \circ B(t)_i^{-1}$$
$$\leq B(t)_i \circ c_i < B(t)_i \circ x_i \leq (B(t), x).$$

With the continuity of B and b, it follows $x \in \text{int}Z_b$, which implies $x \notin \partial Z_b$. Thus, ∂Z_b is closed subset of K and within a compact set. If ∂Z_b is an empty set, then $Z_b = \text{int}Z_b$ is an open set. According to the definition of Z_b, this is only the case if $Z_b = F^n$. Especially, this means $b(t) = \bar{0}$ for all $t \in T$ in contradition to the assumption.

$\Leftarrow$: First, we show that

$$\partial Z_b = R := \{x \in Z_b | (B(t), x) = b(t) \text{ for some } t \in T\}.$$

The inclusion $\partial Z_b \subset R$ is trivial. Conversely, let x be in the interior of Z_b. This implies the existence of a neighbourhood U_{ac} of x with $U_{ac} \subset \text{int}Z_b$. Let y be in U_{ac} with $y_i < x_i$ for $i \in I := \{y \in \{1, \cdots, n\} | x_i \neq \bar{0}\}$. Since $b(t) \neq \bar{0}$ and y is feasible, it follows

$$b(t) \leq (B(t), y) = \sum_{i \in I} {}^{\oplus} B(t)_i \circ y_i < (B(t), x)$$

for $t \in T$ and hence $x \notin R$.

To proof the assertion, assume that there exist $t \in T$ and $j \in \{1, \cdots, n\}$ with $B(t)_j = \bar{0}$. Then we define for $x \in R$ and $s \in F$

$$y_i^s := \begin{cases} x_i & \text{if } i \neq j \\ s & \text{if } i = j. \end{cases}$$

This implies

$$(B(t), y^s) = \sum_{i \neq j} {}^{\oplus} B(t)_i \circ x_i = b(t)$$

for all $s \in F$. Hence, $y^s \in R$ for all $s \geq x_j$ in contradiction to the boundedness of ∂Z_b. $\quad\square$

If we make further assumptions, the condition $(*)$ is necessary for the u.s.c. of Z. For this purpose, we call the restriction $s \in T$ *redundant* for Z_b, if

$$Z_b = \{x \in F^n | (B(t), x) \geq b(t) \text{ for } t \in T \setminus \{s\}\}.$$

Theorem III.4.: Let T be a finite set and $b \in Z_{Bp}$ such that no restriction is redundant for Z_b. If $Z : Z_{Bp} \to POW(F^n)$ is u.s.c. in $b \in Z_{Bp}$, then the condition $(*)$ holds.

Proof: If condition $(*)$ fails, then there exist $s \in T$ and $j \in \{1, \cdots, n\}$, such that $B(s)_j = \bar{0}$. Let

$$L := \{i \in \{1, \cdots, n\} | B(s)_i \neq \bar{0}\}$$

and let CL be the complement set of L. Furthermore, let (s^k) be a strictly increasing sequence converging to $\bar{1}$ and let

$$b_k(t) := b(t) \qquad \text{for } t \in T, t \neq s$$
$$b_k(s) := s^k \circ b(s)$$

be a sequence, which converges to b. Since no restriction is redundant for Z_b, we obtain especially

$$b_k(s) \neq \bar{0} \qquad \text{for } k \in \mathbb{N}.$$

Let $k_0 \in \mathbb{N}$ be such that the s-th restriction is not redundant for Z_{b_k} for $k \geq k_0$. Choose $w^k \in Z_{b_k}$ with $(B(s), w^k) = b_k(s)$ and define an element $v^k \in Z_{b_k}$ like follows

$$v_i^k := \begin{cases} s^k \circ b(s) \circ B(s)_i^{-1} \oplus w_i^k & \text{if } i \in L \\ w_i^k \oplus (r^k)^{-1} & \text{if } i \in CL, \end{cases}$$

where (r^k) is a strictly decreasing sequence converging to $\bar{0}$. Furthermore, define an open set W by

$$W := \cup_{l \in \mathbb{N}} W_l := \cup_{l \in \mathbb{N}} \{x \in F^n | (B(t), x) > s^l \circ b(s),$$
$$x_i < (r^l)^{-1} \text{ if } i \in CL\}.$$

We claim that:
  i) $Z_b \subset W$
  ii) $v^k \in Z_{b_k} \setminus W$.
<u>To i)</u>: For $v \in Z_b$, we have for sufficiently large l

$$v_i < (r^l)^{-1} \qquad \text{for } i \in CL$$

and

$$(B(s), v) \geq b(s) > s^l \circ b(s).$$

<u>To ii)</u>: If $l \geq k$, we obtain

$$(B(s), v^k) = \sum_{i \in L} {}^{\oplus} B(s)_i \circ s^k \circ b(s) \circ B(s)_i^{-1} \oplus \sum_{i \in L} {}^{\oplus} B(s)_i \circ w_i^k$$
$$= s^k \circ b(s) \oplus s^k \circ b(s) \leq s^l \circ b(s).$$

Hence, $v^k \notin W_l$ for $l \geq k$. In the case $k > l$, we have

$$(r^l)^{-1} < (r^k)^{-1} \leq v_i^k \quad \text{for } i \in CL,$$

which implies $v^k \notin W_l$ for $k > l$. This completes the proof of ii).

Therefore, Z is not u.s.c. in $b \in Z_{Bp}$ in contradiction to the assumption. $\qquad\square$

The assumption of no reduncancy in the last theorem is essential, because of

Example III.5.: Let $(F, \oplus, \circ) = (\mathbb{R}^+, \max, \cdot)$ and $n = 2$. Furthermore, let $T = \{1, 2\}$, $B(1) = (1, 1)$, $B(2) = (1, 0)$, and $b(1) = 1$, $b(2) = 0$. The second restriction is redundant.

Let W be an open set with $Z_b \subset W$. We claim that there exists $\alpha > 1$, such that

$$Z_{\alpha \circ b} \subset W.$$

Suppose that for all $\alpha < 1$ there exists $w^\alpha \in Z_{\alpha \circ b} \setminus W$. Choose a sequence (α^k) converging increasingly to 1. The sequence $(w^k) := (w^{\alpha^k})$ is bounded, since

$$a^k \circ b(1) \leq (B(1), w^k) = w_1^k \oplus w_2^k \leq b(1) = 1.$$

Since Z is a closed mapping and W is an open set, we obtain

$$w^k \rightarrow w \in Z_b \setminus W.$$

This is a contradiction to the assumption.

Let U_{ac} be a neighbourhood of b with $a_1 = \alpha \circ b(1)$, $a_2 = 0$, $c_1 = \alpha^{-1} \circ b(2)$, $c_2 > 0$. We have $Z_h \subset W$ for all $h \in U_{ac}$, which implies the u.s.c. of Z. But condition $(*)$ fails. $\qquad\square$

Similar to semi-infinite linear optimization (see FISCHER [3], Theorem 4.1.), the Slater-condition is sufficient for the lower-semi-continuity (l.s.c.) of Z.

Theorem III.6.: Let $b \in Z_{Bp}$ such that Z_b satisfies the Slater-condition. Then $Z : Z_{Bp} \rightarrow POW(F^n)$ is l.s.c. for all $h \in Z_{Bp}$.

Proof: Because of Corollary II.4., it suffices to show the assertion for some $b \in Z_{Bp}$. Let W be an open set such that $v \in W \cap Z_b$. We claim that there exists a point $w \in W \cap Z_b$ with $w_i > v_i$ for $i = 1, \cdots, n$. For this, let U_{ac} be a neighbourhood of v with $U_{ac} \subset W$ and let $s \in F$ with $s > \bar{1}$. Define $w^s \in F^n$ by

$$w_i^s := \begin{cases} s^{-1} \circ c_i & \text{if } v_i = \bar{0} \\ s \circ v_i & \text{if } v_i \neq \bar{0}. \end{cases}$$

Since $w_i^s \geq v_i$ for $i = 1, \cdots, n$, w^s is feasible for $ELP(b)$. W.l.o.g. let w^s be not in U_{ac}. Put

$$q := \sum_{i=1}^{n} {}^{\oplus} v_i \circ c_i^{-1} < \bar{1}.$$

q is unequal $\bar{0}$, since otherwise it follows $v_i = \bar{0}$ for $i = 1, \cdots, n$, which implies $w^s \in U_{ac}$. Since $v_i^{-1} \circ c_i \leq s$ for some $i \in \{1, \cdots, n\}$ with $v_i \neq \bar{0}$, $q^{-1} \leq s$. Choose $\beta \in F$ such that

$$s^{-1} < \beta < q^{-1} \circ s^{-1} \leq \bar{1}.$$

Then $w := v \oplus \beta \circ w^s$ has the required property: we show that $w \in U_{ac}$ which implies the assertion since $w_i \geq v_i$ for $i = 1, \cdots, n$. If $v_i \neq \bar{0}$, we have

$$a_i < v_i < \beta \circ w_i^s = w_i < q^{-1} \circ s^{-1} \circ s \circ v_i \leq c_i \circ v_i^{-1} \circ v_i = c_i.$$

If $v_i = \bar{0}$, we obtain

$$\bar{0} = v_i < \beta \circ w_i^s = w_i < w_i^s < c_i.$$

With the last two inequalities, it follows $w_i = \beta \circ w_i^s > v_i$ for $i = 1, \cdots, n$. For $t \in T$, the Slater-condition implies $B(t)_i \neq \bar{0}$ for some $i \in \{1, \cdots, n\}$ (see Lemma II.3.). Hence,

$$b(t) \leq (B(t), v) = B(t)_i \circ v_i < B(t)_i \circ w_i \leq (B(t), w)$$

for suitable i. Therefore, w is even a Slater-element of Z_b. Since $(B(t), w) > \bar{0}$ for $t \in T$, we can choose $s \in F$ such that

$$\max_{t \in T} b(t) \circ (B(t), w)^{-1} < s < \bar{1}.$$

Then $w \in Z_h$ for all $h \in U_{\bar{0}c_t}$ with $c_t := s \circ (B(t), w)$. To proof this, let h be in $U_{\bar{0}c_t}$ and let t be in T. It follows

$$h(t) < s \circ (B(t), w) < (B(t), w),$$

which implies the l.s.c. of Z in b. $\quad\square$

It should be remarked, that there is the open question, whether the lower-semicontinuity of Z does imply the Slater-condition or not.

IV. An application in scheduling problems

Let n machines be given. We assume that the machines work interdependent, i.e. there exist technological correlations between the machines. For instance, a product is required on machine j for further treatment, which was fabricated before on machine i $(i \neq j)$.

Denote by x_j the starting time of machine j and by a_{ij} the time, machine i has to wait for a restart after the start of machine j. If there is no relation between machines i and j, put $a_{ij} = -\infty$. Then the fastest restart of machine i after its start is given by

$$\max_{j=1,\cdots,n} (a_{ij} + x_j).$$

For a more detailed discussion of this problem see **CUNINGHAME-GREEN** [2], p. 6ff. Assume a prescribed, earliest finishing time $b \in F^n$ is given. This means that the machines have to start such that

$$\max_{j=1,\cdots,n} (a_{ij} + x_j) \geq b_i \quad \text{for } i = 1, \cdots, n.$$

If we write these last inequalities in the notation of the previous sections, we obtain

$$A \circ x \geq b,$$

if we set $(F, \oplus, \circ) = (\mathbb{R} \cup \{-\infty\}, \max, +)$. Then consider the minimization problem

$$EMP(b) \qquad \min(p, x)$$
$$\text{subject to}$$
$$A \circ x \geq b,$$

which of course is of type $ELP(b)$. Now, we give some interpretations of the objective function:

1.) (see U. ZIMMERMANN [9], p. 204ff)
Assume that a preparation procedure to start machine i takes time c_i. Then the next start of machine i is not possible before $x_i + c_i$. Let $p_i = c_i$ for $i = 1, \cdots, n$; then a solution of $EMP(b)$ is a vector of starting times such that a restart of the whole process is as early as possible.

2.) If $c_i = 0$ for $i = 1, \cdots, n$, then the duration of one cycle will be minimized by $EMP(b)$.

3.) (see BURKARD [1])
Let $d_i (i = 1, \cdots, n)$ be prescribed starting times of the machines. Define $p_i = -d_i \triangleq d_i^{-1}$ in F for $i = 1, \cdots, n$ and add the restrictions $x_i \geq d_i$ for $i = 1, \cdots, n$ to $EMP(b)$. Then a solution of $EMP(b)$ minimizes the maximal lateness.

With the results of section III., we can investigate the dependence of the starting time x on the prescribed finishing time b.

References:

[1] BURKARD, R. E.: *Über eine Anwendung algebraischer Transportprobleme bei Reihenfolgenproblemen.* In: Collatz, Meinardus, Wetterling (Eds.), Numerische Methoden bei graphentheoretischen und kombinatorischen Problemen 2, Birkhäuser Verlag, Basel, 1979, 22 – 36.

[2] CUNINGHAME-GREEN, R.: *Minimax Algebra.* Springer-Verlag, Berlin, Heidelberg, 1979.

[3] FISCHER, T.: *Contributions to semi-infinite linear optimization.* In: Brosowski and Martensen (Eds.), Approximation and optimization in mathematical physics, Peter Lang-Verlag, Frankfurt, 1983, 175 – 199.

[4] HAHN, H.: *Reelle Funktionen.* Chelsea Publishing Company, New York, 1948.

[5] HELBIG, S.: *Parametric optimization in certain lattice-ordered groups: variable objective function.* To appear in: Proceedings of the conference "Parametric optimization and related topics", Plaue, GDR, 1985.

[6] KOKORIN, A. I. and KOPYTOV, V. M.: *Fully ordered groups.* John Wiley & Sons, New York, London, 1974.

[7] ZIMMERMANN, K.: *A general separation theorem in extremal algebras.* Ekonomicko-matematický-obzor 13, 1977, 179 – 201.

[8] ZIMMERMANN, K.: *Solution of some optimization problems on the extremal algebra.* In: Prékopa (Ed.), Studies on mathematical programming, Mathematical Methods of Operations Research 1 (1980), 179 – 185.

[9] ZIMMERMANN, U.: *Linear and combinatorical optimization in ordered algebraic structures.* Annals of Discrete Mathematics 10, North Holland, Amsterdam, 1981.

International Series of
Numerical Mathematics, Vol. 84

Inverse Problems.

Andreas Kirsch

Universität Göttingen

Institut für Numerische und Angewandte Mathematik

Lotzestr. 16 – 18

3400 Göttingen, West Germany

1. Introduction

Following Keller [A6] we call two problems inverses of one another, if the formulations of each involves all or part of the solution of the other. From this definition it is arbitrary which one of the two problems we call the *direct* and which one the *inverse* problem. However, for historical - or other - reasons one of the two problems has been studied extensively for some time and is better understood than the other. This one we would call the direct problem.

Let us consider some first examples (Keller [A6]):

1. Find a polynomial p of degree n with roots $x_1, \cdots, x_n$. This task is inverse to the direct problem of finding the roots $x_1, \cdots, x_n$ of a given polynomial p. In this case the inverse problem is easier, having the solution $p(x) = c(x - x_1) \cdots (x - x_n)$ which is not unique since c is an arbitrary constant.

2. Find a polynomial p of degree n with given values $y_1, \cdots, y_n$ at $x_1, \cdots, x_n$. The corresponding direct problem is to find the values $y_1, \cdots, y_n$ of a given polynomial p at given points $x_1, \cdots, x_n$. The inverse problem is called the Lagrange interpolation problem, while the direct problem is that of evaluation of a polynomial.

3. Given a real symmetric matrix A of order n, and n real numbers $\lambda_1, \cdots, \lambda_n$, find a diagonal matrix D so that $A + D$ has eigenvalues $\lambda_1, \cdots, \lambda_n$. This is inverse to the direct problem of finding the eigenvalues $\lambda_1, \cdots, \lambda_n$ of a given real symmetric matrix $A + D$.

4. This inverse problem is used on intelligence tests: Given the first few members a_1, a_2, a_3, a_4 of a sequence, find the law of formation of the sequence, i.e. find a_n for all $n \in \mathbb{N}$. Usually only the next few members a_5, a_6, a_7 are asked for evidence that the law of formation has been found. The direct problem is to evaluate the first few members of a sequence a_n, given the law of formation. It is clear that such inverse problems have many solutions, and for this reason their use on intelligence tests has been criticized.

5. (Weck [B3])
   Let $\Omega \subset \mathbb{R}^3$ be bounded (the earth) and $u(z) = \frac{1}{4\pi} \int \int \int_\Omega \frac{\mu(z')}{|z - z'|} dz'$ be the volume potential with density μ (gravitational potential with mass density). Now, given u on a sphere ∂K outside of Ω, find μ. The direct problem is that of evaluating the volume potential u for given μ.

6. Find the shape of scattering object, given the intensity (and phase) of sound waves it scatters in any direction. The direct problem is that of calculating the scattered sound wave from a given object in any direction.

We formulate the direct problem as the evaluation of an operator A acting on a known "model" x, and the inverse problem as the solution of an equation:

Direct problem: given x (and A), evaluate $A(x)$

Inverse problem: given y (and A), solve $A(x) = y$ for x.

The examples above obviously fit into this general concept.

In order to formulate an inverse problem, the definition of the operator A including its domain and range has to be given. The formulation as an operator equation allows us to distinguish between finite, semifinite and infinite dimensional, linear and nonlinear problems. (Examples 1.-4. are finite and nonlinear, Example 5. is linear and infinite, and Example 6. is nonlinear and infinite dimensional.)

My paper is organized as follows: In the next section I will formulate some of the classical linear inverse problems and briefly recall some general aspects concerning the Tikhonov regularization method. Section 3 deals with Example 6. above which has received much attention in various areas such as remote sensing, nondestructive testing, ultra sound medicine, seismic imaging etc. For each of the examples in this talk there exists an enormous amount of literature, and it is impossible for me to give a complete list of references. But for every example I will quote some of the literature which - in my opinion and to my knowledge - can serve as an introduction and overview on the subject.

I start mentioning the survey articles by Anger [A1], Keller [A6] and Parker [A8] and the introductions to the proceedings edited by Anger [A2] and Sabatier [A10] which concentrate on some of the general aspects of inverse theory. A monograph by Baumeister on inverse problems contains several different topics in this field and will appear shortly.

2. Linear Theory

Naturally, linear inverse problems have received most attention, and their theory seems to be fairly complete. This is one reason why I start my talk with the linear theory. The other is that the concept developed in the linear theory applies almost directly in the (local) nonlinear theory via linearization.

Thus, in this section we consider an equation of the type

$$Ax = y$$

where $A : X \to Y$ denotes a linear and bounded operator between Hilbertspaces X and Y with $\dim X = \infty$ where $y \in Y$ is a given element.

Examples

5. Inverse Potential Problem (see above): $X = L^2(\Omega)$, $Y = L^2(\partial K)$

$$A\mu(z) = \frac{1}{4\pi} \int \int_\Omega \int \frac{\mu(z')}{|z-z'|} dz', \; z \in \partial K, \; \mu \in L^2(\Omega).$$

7. Differentiation: $X = Y = L^2(0,1)$

$$Ax(t) = \int_0^t x(s)ds, \; \text{i.e.} \; Ax = y \; \text{is equivalent to:} \; x = \frac{d}{dt}y \; \text{and} \; y(0) = 0$$

8. Radon Transform: The most spectacular application of the Radon transform is in medical imaging. For example, consider a fixed plane through a human body. Let $f(x,y)$ denote the density at the point (x,y) and let L be any line in the plane. Suppose we direct a thin beam of X-rays into the body along L, and measure how much the intensity is attenuated by going through the body. Then the logarithm of the attenuation factor is given approximately by

$$P_f(L) = \int_L f(x,y)ds, \; s = \; \text{arclength along} \; L.$$

We describe L by $\{t\omega + s\omega^\perp : s \in \mathbb{R}\}$ where $t \in \mathbb{R}$, ω denotes a unit vector and $\omega^\perp$ an orthogonal unit vector to ω. Then $P_f(L)$ is given by the *Randon transform*

$$R(f)(t,\omega) = \int_{-\infty}^{+\infty} f(t\omega + s\omega^\perp)ds, t \in \mathbb{R}, |\omega| = 1.$$

For X we choose - as suggested by Natterer [C5] - the Sobolev space $H_0^{\frac{1}{2}+\epsilon}(\Omega)$ of order $\frac{1}{2} + \epsilon$ for some small $\epsilon > 0$. Here, Ω denotes the unit disc. Furthermore, $Y = L^2(\mathbb{R} \times S^1)$ with $S^1 = \partial\Omega$. Now, $f \in H_0^{\frac{1}{2}+\epsilon}(\Omega)$ has to be identified with its extension to zero outside of Ω as a function on $\mathbb{R}^2$. As an introduction into this field of computer tomography I suggest the articles by Herman and Lewitt [C2], Roberts [C7] and Sheep and Kruskal [C8]. Soon there will appear a monograph by F. Natterer on this subject.

9. Heat equation backwards in time: Let $u(x,t)$ be the heat distribution at time t and location $x \in [0,\pi]$. Then, under normalized conditions, u satisfies the differential equation:

$$\frac{\partial u}{\partial t} = \frac{\partial^2 u}{\partial x^2}, \; t > 0, \; 0 < x < \pi,$$

with boundary conditions

$$u(0,t) = u(\pi,t) = 0, \; t \geq 0,$$

and initial condition

$$u(x,0) = u_0(x), \ 0 \le x \le \pi.$$

Separation of variables leads to the formal solution

$$u(x,t) = \sum_{n=1}^{\infty} a_n e^{-n^2 t} \sin(nx)$$

with Fourier coefficients $a_n = \frac{2}{\pi} \int_0^\pi u_0(y) \sin(ny) dy$. For $u_0 \in L^2(0,\pi)$ the series for u converges uniformly on compact subsets of $[0,\pi] \times \mathbb{R}^+$ and is called the mild solution of the initial boundary value problem.

The direct problem is: Given the final time T and initial distribution $u_0 \in L^2(0,\pi)$, find $u(\cdot, T)$.

The inverse problem is: Given T and a "measured" temperature distribution $u(\cdot, T)$, find the initial temperature $u(\cdot, T)$. If we denote by A the operator

$$A\psi(x) = \int_0^\pi k(x,y)\psi(y) dy, \ \text{ with kernel } \ k(x,y) = \frac{2}{\pi} \sum_{n=1}^{\infty} e^{-n^2 T} \sin(nx) \sin(ny),$$

then the inverse problem is equivalent to solving

$$A\psi = u(\cdot, T) \ \text{ for } \ \psi.$$

Here we choose $X = Y = L^2(0,\pi)$.

10. Abel's Equation: As another example we consider an inverse problem which is of importance in seismology. One is interested in the velocity distribution c of the (longitudinal or transversal) seismic waves. The following derivation is known as the Herglotz-Wiechert formula (and well-known to every student of geophysics). We assume for simplicity a flat Earth in which the velocity $c(z)$ depends only on the depth z. Let us assume that you measure travel times $T(X)$ as a function of distance X between a seismic source (e.g. an earthquake) and a receiver (measured along the Earth's surface). The analogy of Snell's law of geometrical optics states that the ratio $\frac{\sin \varphi(z)}{c(z)}$ is constant ($= \rho$) for every ray. Here $\varphi(z)$ denotes the angle between the ray path and the vertical (c.f. Fig. 1). Then it is easily seen that for a given ray with ray parameter ρ the horizontal distance $X(\rho)$ that the ray travels before reaching the surface is given by

$$X = X(\rho) = 2 \int_0^{Z(\rho)} \frac{\rho}{\sqrt{c(z)^{-2} - \rho^2}} dz$$

where $Z(\rho)$ is the depth of the deepest point characterized by $\frac{\sin(\pi/2)}{c(Z(\rho))} = \rho$). A change of variables $s = c(z)^{-2}$ (assuming c is monotonously increasing) leads to

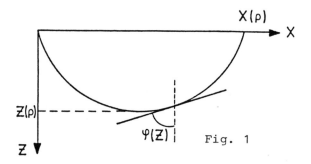

Fig. 1

$$\frac{X(\rho)}{2\rho} = \int_{c_0^{-2}}^{\rho^2} \frac{f(s)}{\sqrt{s - \rho^2}} ds \text{ where } f(s) = \left(\frac{dc(z)^{-2}}{dz}\right)^{-1}\Big|_{z=c_0^{-1}(\frac{1}{\sqrt{s}})}$$

where c_0 is the velocity at $z = 0$ (which is known). Actually, the travel time T is measured in dependence of the distance X. But as is easily seen from Fig. 1 for $z = 0$ the ray parameter is given by the derivative of X with respect to T : $\frac{dX}{dT} = c_0^2\rho$. This gives the function $X = X(\rho)$. Thus we are led to an integral equation of *Abel's type* for g of the form

$$r(t) = Ag(t) := \int_0^t \frac{g(s)}{\sqrt{t - s}} ds$$

where

$$t = c_0^{-2} - \rho^2, \ g(s) = f(c_0^{-1} - s), \ r(t) = \frac{X(\rho)}{2\rho}\Big|_{\rho=\sqrt{c_0^{-2}-t}} .$$

Then A maps $L^2(0, t_0)$ continuously into itself. This example is taken from Kerz [I3]. For further readings I suggest [E4] and the preprints by R. Gorenflo [E2], [E3] where some other nice applications of Abel's equation are formulated.

The common feature of all these examples is that X and Y are spaces of functions and (except Example 8) A is an integral operator with continuous or weakly continuous kernel. Then it is well known that A is a *compact* operator (also for Example 8, c.f. [C5]).

The basic reason why equations of the form $Ax = y$ with a compact operator A are improperly posed is given in the following lemma:

2.1 Lemma. Let $A : X \to Y$ be compact and injective. Then $A^{-1} : A(X) \to X$ is bounded if and only if X is finite dimensional.

Proof:

(i) A^{-1} bounded $\Rightarrow I = A^{-1} \circ A : X \to X$ compact $\Rightarrow \dim X < \infty$.

(ii) $\dim X < \infty \Rightarrow \dim A(X) < \infty \Rightarrow A^{-1}$ bounded.

Thus in our case ($\dim X = \infty$) A^{-1} is unbounded. This means that small errors in the data $y \in Y$ could (and usually do!) lead to large errors in x - if a solution to the perturbed equation exists at all. We demonstrate this with the following simple example

$$A : L^2(0,1) \to L^2(0,1) \text{ is given by}$$

$$Ax(t) = \int_0^1 e^{ts} x(s) ds, \ 0 \le t \le 1, \text{ and}$$

$$y(t) = \frac{1}{1+t}(e^{1+t} - 1), \ 0 \le t \le 1.$$

Then A is one-to-one (Laplace transform!), and the solution to $Ax = y$ is given by $x(t) = e^t$. For the numerical study of $Ax = y$ we replace the integral by the trapezoidal rule with knots $t_j = j\frac{2\pi}{N}$, $j = 0, \cdots, N$. We get the following disastrous results - even for an exact right hand side (the condition is taken with respect to the sup-norm):

N	error	condition	Figure
4	.87 − 2	.14 + 7	2a
8	.29	.13 + 16	2b
16	.28	.22 + 20	2c
32	.14 + 8	.40 + 22	

We see that the condition of the resulting $N \times N$-system of equations explodes. This comes from the fact that the matrix A_N approximates A which has an unbounded inverse. (The eigenvalues of A tend to zero, thus the smallest eigenvalue of A_N is very small).

The notion of "improper posedness" has been introduced by Hadamard [I1]. An equation $Ax = y$ is *improperly posed* if at least one of the following three properties fails to hold:

  i) uniqueness,
  ii) existence,
  iii) stability (i.e. the unique solution depends continuously on the right hand side)
of a solution. Proper - or improper posedness depends on the spaces X, Y and the operator A.

Let now the equation $Ax = y$ be improperly posed. The nonuniqueness can be removed by changing the space X (replacing X by the direct complement of the kernel of A). In deriving existence - and stability properties, however, one has to change the space Y. But this space is often "given" and depends on the norm of the errors of measurements. We can only assume - what we do from now on - that the range $A(X)$ is dense in Y, and that A is one-to-one.

A first way to treat equations $Ax = y$ with compact operators A has been proposed by Tikhonov [H9]. He replaced the equation $Ax = y$ by

(2.1) $$(\alpha I + A^* A)x_\alpha = A^* y$$

where $\alpha > 0$ is a given parameter, $A^* : Y \to X$ denotes the adjoint of A and I the identity in X. Thus we have replaced an equation of the first kind by one of the second kind (A compact $\Rightarrow A^*A$ compact) to which Fredholm's alternative applies (i.e. $\alpha I + A^*A$ one-to-one $\Rightarrow \alpha I + A^*A$ onto).

Those who are familiar with optimization theory immediately notice that (2.1) describes the necessary and suffcient condition for the following three optimization problems

(a) $\alpha > 0$ given: Min $\alpha \|x\|^2 + \|Ax - y\|^2$ s.t. $x \in X$ (penalty method)

(b) $\rho > 0$ given: Min $\|Ax - y\|^2$ s.t. $\|x\| \leq \rho$ (quasi solution)

(c) $\delta > 0$ given: Min $\|x\|^2$ s.t. $\|Ax - y\| \leq \delta$ (min-norm solution for given discrepancy).

In case (b) we assume $y \notin A(X)$. Then α relates to ρ through the condition $\|x_\alpha\| = \rho$. In case (c) we assume $\|y\| > \delta$. Then α relates to δ through the condition $\|Ax_\alpha - y\| = \delta$.

From these interpretations we see that (2.1) admits a unique solution for every $y \in Y$. We consider now equation (2.1), and the question arises how to choose α. To answer this question we assume further that the equation $Ax = y$ admits a (unique) solution x_0, but we have only "measured" data y^δ at hand with $\|y - y^\delta\| \leq \delta$. Thus, instead of (2.1), we solve

$$(2.2) \qquad (\alpha I + A^*A)x_\alpha^\delta = y^\delta.$$

Then one can prove (c.f. Groetsch [H3]):

2.2 Theorem (Convergence)   Let $\alpha = \alpha(\delta)$ with $\frac{\delta^2}{\alpha(\delta)} \to 0(\delta \to 0)$. Then $x_{\alpha(\delta)}^\delta \to x_0(\delta \to 0)$.

2.3 Theorem (Rate of convergence)   Let $y \in A(A^*A)^\gamma(X)$ for some $\gamma \in (0, 1]$, (i.e. $x_0 \in (A^*A)^\gamma(X)$) and $\alpha(\delta) \approx \delta^{\frac{2}{1+2\gamma}}$. Then

$$\|x_{\alpha(\delta)}^\delta - x_0\| = \mathcal{O}(\delta^{\frac{2\gamma}{1+2\gamma}}) \text{ for } \delta \to 0.$$

Thus the best order is obtained for $\gamma = 1$ and yields an order of $\delta^{2/3}$.

The assumption $x_0 \in (A^*A)^\gamma(X)$ is a smoothness assumption on x. In practical cases however, the range of A^*A can almost never be characterized. The choice of α is *a-priori* and depends on the error of the right hand side.

A different approach is known under the name of the *discrepancy principle* and is of a-posteriori type: (Morozov [H7], Ivanov [H4], see also Groetsch [H3]) Choose $\alpha = \alpha(\delta)$ such that $\|Ax_\alpha^\delta - y^\delta\| = \delta$ and x_α^δ solves (2.2). Thus x_α^δ is the minimum norm solution for given discrepancy (c.f. interpretation (c) for y^δ replacing y). It can be shown (c.f. [H3]) that this choice of $\alpha(\delta)$ is possible provided $\|y - y^\delta\| \leq \delta\|y^\delta\|$ holds. Furthermore, we have

2.4 Theorem (Convergence)

$$x^\delta_{\alpha(\delta)} \to x_0(\delta \to 0)$$

2.5 Theorem (Rate of convergence) *If $y \in (AA^*)(Y)$, i.e. $x_0 \in A^*(Y)$, then $\|x^\delta_{\alpha(\delta)} - x_0\| = \mathcal{O}(\sqrt{\delta})$, $\delta \to 0$ and this order is optimal, i.e. if $\|x^\delta_{\alpha(\delta)} - x_0\| = o(\sqrt{\delta})$ then A has finite rank.*

This order of convergence is not as good as the a-priori choice. But: If we measure the discrepancy in stronger norms we are led to an optimal order of $\delta^{2/3}$ (Engl and Neubauer [H1]).

Additional Remarks

(a) The computation of a quasi solution or a solution by the discrepancy principle uses the ordinary one dimensional Newton method applied to the function

$$f(\alpha) = \|x^\delta_\alpha\|^2 - \rho^2$$

or

$$f(\alpha) = \|Ax^\delta_\alpha - y^\delta\|^2 - \delta^2 \text{ resp.}$$

where x^δ_α denotes the unique solution to (2.2).

(b) Instead of minimizing $\|Ax - y^\delta\|^2 + \alpha\|x\|^2$ one could minimize $\|Ax - y^\delta\|^2 + \alpha|x|_1^2$ where $|\cdot|_1$ is a seminorm on a densely imbedded space $X_1 \subset X$. For example, Tikhonov [H9] used $X_1 = H^1(0,1) \subset L^2(0,1) =: X$ and $|x|_1 = \sqrt{\int_0^1 |\frac{dx(t)}{dt}|^2 dt}$.

(c) Analogously, convergence in stronger norms can be derived.

(d) A third influence on the convergence is given by a finite dimensional approximation of Tikhonov's equation (2.2), e.g. by Galerkin - or collocation methods.

(e) Besides Tikhonov's regularization other regularization techniques can be treated (e.g. Landweber-Fridman iteration [H2], [H5], spectral cut off [H8]). It is possible to subsume these regularization techniques under a general theory.

For further readings we again refer to Groetsch [H3].

Numerical Example (c.f. the example above)

$$\int_0^1 e^{ts} x(s) ds = y(t), \quad x(t) = e^t$$

α	condition	error		Figure
		$\delta = 0$	$\delta = 0.5$	
10^{-9}	$.78 + 10.$	$72 - 6$	$.78 + 3$	
10^{-7}	$.74 + 8$	$.42 - 6$	7.5	
10^{-5}	$.62 + 6$	$.16 - 4$	1.4	
10^{-3}	$.63 + 4$	$.33 - 3$	$.82 - 3$	$3c$
10^{-2}	$.53 + 3$	$.88 - 2$	$.94 - 2$	
$.1$	54	$.40 - 1$	$.40 - 1$	$3b$
$.2$	19	$.1$	$.1$	$3a$

From this table we observe clearly that a small regularization parameter α does not "remove" the improper posedness while a large value of α decreases the condition but also changes the equation too much.

3. An Inverse Scattering Problem

One is far away from developing a similarly complete theory for nonlinear equations $A(x) = y$ as in the linear case. The questions, of course, are the same: Uniqueness, existence, stability and numerical calculations. Although it is possible to study these problems in a general context ($A : X \rightarrow Y$ being a completely continuous operator between Banach spaces) the specific features of the given problem under consideration have to be used in deriving the strongest possible results.

Since G. Chavent [G4] has spoken already on parameter identification problems for partial differential equations - which are typical nonlinear inverse problems - I want to concentrate myself on a specific *domain-identification* problem (which is mathematically closely related to the so called shape-design problem).

My example is taken from scattering theory for acoustic or electromagnetic waves. Before I come to the inverse problem let me present the mathematical formulation of the *direct* problem:

Given a bounded domain $D \subset \mathbb{R}^N$ (the scatterer, $N = 2$ or 3) and an *incident* plane wave $u^i(x) = e^{ikd \cdot x}$ ($k > 0$ the wave number, d a unit vector representing the direction), find the *scattered field* u^s with:

$$\Delta u^s + k^2 u^s = 0 \ \text{ in } \ \mathbb{R}^N \setminus \overline{D}$$

(BVP) $\qquad\qquad\qquad\qquad u^s = -u^i \ \text{ on } \ \partial D$

$$\frac{\partial u^s}{\partial r} - iku^s = \mathcal{O}(r^{(1-N)/2}) \ \text{ for } \ r = |x| \rightarrow \infty \ \text{ uniformly in } \ \frac{x}{|x|}.$$

$u := u^i + u^s$ denotes the *total field* which vanishes on ∂D. In acoustic scattering $(N = 3)$ $v(x, t) = u(x)e^{-i\omega t}$ describes the pressure and $k = \frac{\omega}{c}$ with speed of sound c. In electromagnetic scattering $(N = 2)$ u is the z-component of the electric field and k is related to the electric permittivity ε and the magnetic permeability μ via $k = \sqrt{\varepsilon\mu}\omega$. Again, ω denotes the frequency.

Under certain assumptions on ∂D existence, uniqueness and stability of this direct problem can be assured (in the weak [F9] - or classical [F3]-sense). We assume in the following $\partial D \in C^2$ although for many results this assumption can be weakened. Then a unique classical solution to (BVP) exists (c.f. Colton and Kress [F3]).

Also, u^s admits a unique asymptotic expansion with first coefficient u_∞:

$$u^s(x) = \frac{e^{ik|x|}}{|x|^{\frac{N-1}{2}}} u_\infty\left(\frac{x}{|x|}; d\right) + o\left(|x|^{\frac{1-N}{2}}\right), \ |x| \to \infty \ \text{ uniformly in } \ \frac{x}{|x|}.$$

u_∞ is called *far field pattern* of u^s. Thus the operator (far field operator) F which maps ∂D onto u_∞ is well defined on a sufficiently large class of boundaries. Here, the incident wave u^i and the wave number k are fixed.

The *inverse scattering problem* is now: Given the incident field, the wave number k and the far field pattern u_∞ (measured!), find the scatterer D. Formulated with operator F we have:

Find ∂D which solves $F(\partial D) = f$, where f is given.

The uniqueness question is not yet completely answered. We have the following theorem which is due to Schiffer (c.f. Lax and Phillips [F8]):

3.1 Theorem *The scattered obstacle D is uniquely determined by a knowledge of the far field pattern u_∞ for x on some surface patch of the unit sphere and k on any interval of the positive real axis.*

It is not known whether uniqueness holds for one single fixed value of k.

Also, it is impossible to answer the question of existence, i.e. to describe the range of the far field operator F. Even a characterisation of the range of the much simpler - since linear - operator $u^i \mapsto u_\infty$ for fixed scatterer D is unknown. A necessary condition for u_∞ being a far field pattern is given by the following

3.2 Theorem *For each fixed value of $k > 0$ the far field pattern u_∞ is an entire function of its independent (complex) variables.*

The proof of this - and many more (e.g. existence- and stability)-results uses representation theorems which are in analogy to those in classical potential theory (c.f. Colton and Kress [F3]):

$$\int_{\partial D} \left[u(y)\frac{\partial}{\partial n(y)}\gamma(x, y) - \gamma(x, y)\frac{\partial u(y)}{\partial n}\right]ds(y) = u^s(x), \ x \notin \overline{D},$$

where

$$\gamma(x,y) = \begin{cases} \frac{i}{4}H_0^{(1)}(k|x-y|) & \text{if } N = 2 \\[2mm] \frac{e^{ik|x-y|}}{4\pi|x-y|} & \text{if } N = 3 \end{cases}$$

denotes the fundamental solution to the Helmholtz equation $\Delta u + k^2 u = 0$ and $n(y)$ the outer unit normal vector to ∂D.

The asymptotic behaviour of γ as $|x| \to \infty$ yields the assertion of Theorem 3.2. The jump conditions as x tends to a point on ∂D yield integral equations of the first - or second kinds on ∂D which can be combined and yield existence theorems (via Fredholm's alternative). From this representation theorem and a suitable parametrisation of ∂D one can show that the equation $F(\partial D) = f$ is improperly posed in any topology which is of practical interest, i.e. small errors in f can lead to large errors in ∂D - if a scatterer exists at all.

To solve the *inverse problem* $F(\partial D) = f$ for fixed and finite wavenumber k essentially two methods are under investigation among mathematicians. The first one is the analogy to the linear general case: We replace the equation $F(\partial D) = f$ by one of the minimization problems:
(a) Minimize $\|F(\partial D) - f\|^2$ s.t. $\partial D \in U_{ad}$, or
(b) Minimize $\alpha\|\partial D\|^2 + \|F(\partial D) - f\|^2$, $\partial D \in X$.

Here, by $\partial D \in X$ we mean a suitable parametrisation of ∂D, e.g. polar coordinates (if $N = 2$): $x_1 = \rho(t)\cos t$, $x_2 = \rho(t)\sin t$, $0 \le t \le 2\pi$, with $\rho \in X := C_{per}^2[0, 2\pi]$, $\rho > 0$. U_{ad} denotes an admissible set of boundaries which includes a-priori information on ∂D (and is compact in X).

Problems (a) and (b) are then treated by Quasi-Newton- or conjugate gradient methods. Computations with these methods were done by Roger [F10] and Kirsch [F7]. Due to the high nonlinearity in the operator F these methods work satisfactory only if a sufficiently good intial boundary is chosen.

In Fig. 4a-e and 5a,b) the following two dimensional examples are considered:
(a) Here, an ellipse $x_1^2 + (\frac{3}{2}x_2)^2 = 1$ had to be identified from measurements of u_∞ for $|x| = 1$. The wave number k is 1 or 3, the direction of the incoming wave is given by the angle $\theta = 30^o$ (i.e. $d = (\cos 30^o, \sin 30^o)^T$). The circle with radius 1.2 was taken as the initial curve and a BFGS method (implemented by Herbst [I2], with Goldstein Armijo as stepsize strategy) was applied to $J(\rho) = \alpha\|\rho\|_{L^2(0,2\pi)}^2 + \|F(\rho) - f\|_{L^2(0,2\pi)}^2$ with $\alpha = 10^{-3}$ where $F(\rho)$ denotes the far field pattern corresponding to the curve parameterized by $\rho(t)(\cos t, \sin t)^T$. ρ was taken from the $(2M + 1)$-dimensional space span$\{1, \cos(nt), \sin(nt) : 1 \le n \le M\}$ for $M = 2, 3$ or 4.
(b) Here, a pinched ellipse $\rho_0(t)(\cos t, \sin t)^T$ with $\rho_0(t) = 1 - \frac{1}{2}\cos(2t)$ had to be identified.

An obvious disadvantage of these methods is certainly, that each function call requires the solution of a (direct) scattering problem.

The second, somehow dual, method was recently proposed by Colton and Monk [F4-6]. They assumed the knowledge of the far field pattern corresponding to incident plane waves of several different directions. The wave number k is still fixed.

Then the following remarkable theorem is of importance which we formulate only for $N = 2$:

3.3 Theorem (Colton, Kirsch, Monk [F2], [F4]) *Let $\mathcal{F}$ be the set of far field patterns corresponding to incident plane waves of any direction. Let $k > 0$ be no Dirichlet eigenvalue of the Laplacian in D.*
(a) Then span $\mathcal{F}$ is dense in $L^2(S^1)$, where S^1 denotes the unit circle in $\mathbb{R}^2$.
(b) If D is a so called "Herglotz-domain" (c.f. [F2]), then

$$L^2(S^1) = \text{span}\{\psi\} \oplus \quad closure \ \text{span}\{\mathcal{F} - f_0\},$$

where f_0 is any element from $\mathcal{F}$. Furthermore, the sum is orthogonal, and
$v(x) = \int_{S^1} \psi(y) e^{ikx^T y} ds(y)$ *solves*

$$\Delta v + k^2 v = 0 \quad in \ \mathbb{R}^2$$

and

$$v(x) = H_0^{(2)}(k|x|), \quad on \ \partial D.$$

The idea of Colton and Monk's method is first to determine (approximately) the function ψ as the orthogonal complement of span$\{\mathcal{F} - f_0\}$ and, second, to determine ∂D as that curve where $v(x)$ and $H_0^{(2)}(k|x|)$ coincide. In fact, they treat both steps simultaneously and minimize the functional

$$J(\rho, \psi) = \sum_{n=1}^{P} \{ \int_{S^1} [f_n(x) - f_0(x)] \overline{\psi(x)} ds(x) \}^2$$

$$+ \alpha \int_0^{2\pi} |v(\rho(t), t) - H_0^{(2)}(k\rho(t))|^2 dt$$

subject to certain constraints on ρ and ψ which are taken from finite dimensional subspaces. Here, $\{f_0, f_1, \cdots, f_P\}$ are the measured far field patterns corresponding to different incident plane waves.

The advantage of this method is its simplicity: Every function call consists in the evaluations of some integrals. The disadvantage lies in the fact that it needs much more information than the first method. The numerical results seem to be as good - or bad, depending on the choice of the scatterer - as the results for the first method.

This second method shows how important it is to characterize the range of the far field operator - or at least to give strong necessary conditions for elements being in the range. It would be highly desirable to derive similar results for the case when the wave number changes instead of the direction of the incident field. Some ideas into these directions are presently under investigation. In any case however, it seems to me that more a-priori information about the geometry of the scatterer is needed in order to derive better numerical results. This may sound disappointing, but:

Everybody working on inverse problem should always keep in mind the following remark by Lanczos [14]:

"A lack of information cannot be
remedied by any mathematical trickery".

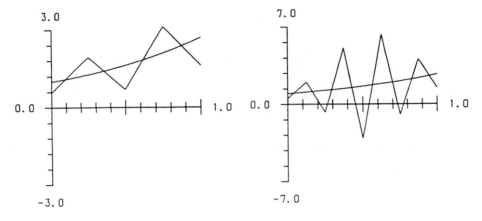

Fig.2a: N=4

Fig.2b: N=8

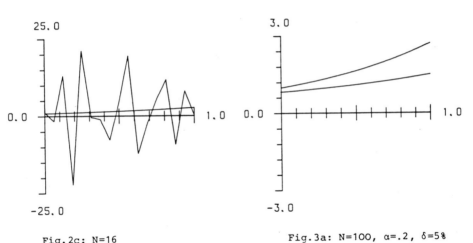

Fig.2c: N=16

Fig.3a: N=100, α=.2, δ=5%

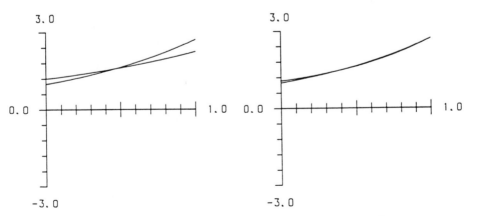

Fig.3b: N=100, α=.1, δ=5%

Fig.3c: N=100, α=10^{-3}, δ=5%

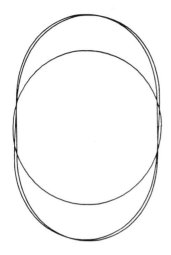

Fig. 4a : M = 2, k = 1

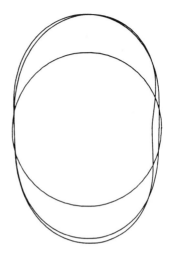

Fig. 4b : M = 3, k = 1

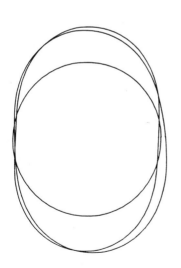

Fig. 4c : M = 2, k = 3

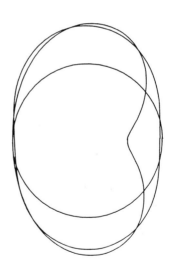

Fig. 4d : M = 3, k = 3

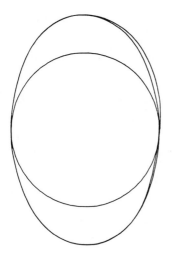

Fig. 4e : M = 4, k = 3

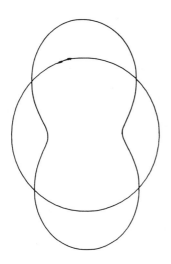

Fig. 5a : M = 2, k = 1

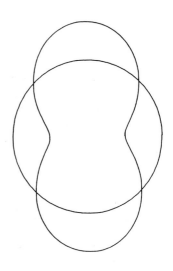

Fig. 5b : M = 3, k = 1

References.

(A) General Aspects for Improperly-Posed- and Inverse Problems

[A1] Anger, G.: *Einige Betrachtungen über inverse Probleme, Identifikationsprobleme und inkorrekt gestellte Probleme.* In: Jahrbuch Überblicke Mathemtik 1982, Springer, New York etc., 55 – 71 .

[A2] Anger, G.(ed.): *Inverse and improperly posed problems in differential equations.* Akademie Verlag, Berlin, 1979.

[A3] Deuflhard, E. and Hairer, E.(eds.): *Numerical treatment of inverse problems in differential and integral equations.* Birkhäuser, Boston, etc., 1983.

[A4] Gorenflo, R.(ed.): *Inkorrekt gestellte Probleme I, II.* Conference Proceedings. Free University of Berlin, Berlin, 1977/78.

[A5] Hämmerlin, G. and Hoffmann, K.-H.(eds.): *Improperly posed problems and their numerical treatment.* ISNM 63, Birkhäuser, Basel etc., 1983.

[A6] Keller, J. B.: *Inverse problems.* Amer. Math. Monthly 83 (1976), 107 – 118.

[A7] Lavrientiev, M. M. et al.: *Some improperly posed problems of mathematical physics.* Springer, New York etc., 1967.

[A8] Parker, R. L.: *Understanding inverse theory.* Ann. Rev. Earth. Planet. Sci. (1977), 35 – 64.

[A9] Payne, L. E.: *Improperly posed problems in partial differential equations.* Regional conference series in applied mathematics. SIAM, Philadelphia, 1975.

[A10] Sabatier, P. C.(ed.): *Applied inverse problems.* Lecture Notes in Physics 85, Springer, New York etc., 1978.

[A11] Tikhonov, A. M. and Arsenin, V. Y.: *Solutions of ill-posed problems.* Winston & Sons, Washington, 1977.

(B) Inverse Potential Problem

[B1] Anger, G.: *Uniquely determined mass distributions in inverse problems.* In: Veröffentlichungen des Zentralinstituts für Physik der Erde 52,2, Potsdam, 1977.

[B2] Brodsky, M. A.: *On the uniqueness of the inverse potential problem for homogeneous polyhedrons.* SIAM J. Appl. Math. 46 (1986), 345 – 350.

[B3] Weck, N.: *Inverse Probleme der Potentialtheorie.* Appl. Anal. 2 (1972), 195 – 204.

(C) Computer Tomography

[C1] Herman, G. T.(ed.): *Image reconstruction from projections.* Topics in Applied Physics 32 (1979), Springer, New York etc.

[C2] Herman, G. T. and Lewitt, R. M.: *Overview of image reconstruction from projections.* In: Image reconstruction from projections (Hermann, G. T. ed.). Topics in Applied Physics 32 (1979), Springer, New York etc.

[C3] Herman, G. T. and Natterer, F.(eds.): *Mathematical aspects of computerized tomography.* Lecture Notes in Medical Informatics 8 (1981), Springer, New York etc.

[C4] Natterer, F.: *Numerical inversion of the Radon transform.* Numer. Math. 30 (1978), 81 – 91.

[C5] Natterer, F.: *A Sobolev space analysis of picture reconstruction.* SIAM J. Appl. Math. 39 (1980), 402 – 411.

[C6] Natterer, F.: *Einige Beiträge der Mathematik zur Computer-Tomographie.* ZAMM 64 (1984), T252 – T260.

[C7] Roberts, A. J.: *An introduction to the technique of reconstruction.* SIAM J. Math. Anal. 16 (1985), 1243 – 1257.

[C8] Sheep, L. A. and Kruskal, J. B.: *Computerized tomography: The new medical X-ray technology.* Math. Monthly (1978), 420 – 439.

[C9] Schomberg, H. and Tasto, M.: *Computer-Tomographie mit Ultraschall.* Phys. Bl. 36 (1980), 311 – 313.

(D) Backwards Heat Equation

[D1] Buzbee, B. L. and Carasso, A.: *On the numerical computation of parabolic problems for preceeding times.* Math. of Comp. 27 (1973), 237 – 266.

[D2] Carasso, A.: *Error bounds in the final value problem for the heat equation.* SIAM J. Math. Anal. 7 (1976), 195 – 199.

[D3] Colton, D. S.: *The approximation of solutions to the backwards heat equation in a nonhomogeneous medium.* J. Math. Anal. Appl. 72 (1979), 418 – 429.

[D4] Elden, L.: *Regularization of the backwards solution of parabolic problems.* In: Inverse and improperly posed problems in differential equations (Anger, G. ed.). Berlin, 1979.

[D5] Ewing, R. E.: *The approximation of certain parabolic equations backwards in time by Sobolev equations.* SIAM J. Math. Anal. 6 (1975), 283 – 294.

[D6] Höhn, W.: *Finite elements for parabolic equations backwards in time.* Preprint no. 556, Technische Hochschule Darmstadt, 1980.

[D7] Kobayashi, T.: *Initial state determination for distributed parameter systems.* SIAM J. Control and Optim. 14 (1976), 934 – 944.

[D8] Miller, K.: *Efficient numerical methods for backward solution of parabolic problems with variable coefficients.* In: Improperly posed problems (Carasso, A. ed.), Pitman, Boston etc., 1975.

[D9] Showalter, R. E.: *The final value problem for evolution equations.* J. Math. Anal. Appl. 47 (1974), 563 – 572.

(E) Abel's Equation

[E1] Brunner, H.: *A survey of recent advances in the numerical treatment of Volterra integral and integro-differential equations.* J. Comput. Appl. Math. 8 (1982), 213 – 229.

[E2] Gorenflo, R.: *Abel integral equations: Applications-motivated solution concepts.* Preprint No. 209, Freie Universität Berlin, 1986.

[E3] Gorenflo, R. and Vessella, S.: *Basic theory and some applications of Abel integral equations.* Preprint Consiglio Nazionale delle Ricerche, Istituto di Analisi Globale e Applicazioni, Firenze 1984.

[E4] Krasnov, M. L., Kissélev, A. I. and Makarenko, G. I.: *Equations intégrales: problèmes et exércices.* Editions Mir, Moscow, 1977.

[E5] Tsalyuk, Z. B.: *Volterra integral equations.* J. Soviet Mathematics 12 (1979), 715 – 758.

[E6] Zabreyko, P. P. et al: *Integral equations - A reference text.* Noordhoff, Leiden, 1975.

(F) Inverse Problem for the Helmholtz Equation

[F1] Colton, D.: *The inverse scattering problem for time-harmonic acoustic waves.* SIAM Review 26 (1984), 323 – 350.

[F2] Colton, D. and Kirsch, A.: *Dense sets and far field pattern in acoustic wave propagation.* SIAM J. Math. Anal. 15 (1984), 996 – 1006.

[F3] Colton, D. and Kress, R.: *Integral equation methods in scattering theory.* Wiley, New York etc., 1983.

[F4] Colton, D. and Monk, P.: *A novel method for solving the inverse scattering problem for time-harmonic acoustic waves in the resonance region.* SIAM J. Appl Math. 45 (1985), 1039 – 1053.

[F5] Colton, D. and Monk, P.: *A novel method for solving the inverse scattering problem for time-harmonic acoustic waves in the resonance region II.* SIAM J. Appl. Math. 46 (1986), 506 – 523.

[F6] Colton, D. and Monk, P.: *The numerical solution of the three dimensional inverse scattering problem for time-harmonic acoustic waves.* University of Delaware, Technical Report.

[F7] Kirsch, A.: *Generalized boundary value and control problems for the Helmholtz equation.* Göttingen, Habilitationsschrift 1984.

[F8] Lax, P. D. and Phillips, R. S.: *Scattering theory.* Academic Press, New York etc., 1967.

[F9] Leis, R.: *Zur Dirichletschen Randwertaufgabe des Aussenraums der Schwingungsgleichung.* Math. Zeitschrift 90 (1965), 205 – 211.

[F10] Roger, A.: *Newton Kantorovich algorithm applied to an electromagnetic inverse problem.* IEEE Trans. Ant. Prop. AP-29 (1981), 232 – 238.

[F11] Sleeman, B. D.: *The inverse problem of acoustic scattering.* IMA J. Appl. Math. 29 (1982), 113 – 142.

(G) Identification of Parameters in Parabolic and Elliptic Equations

[G1] Åstrom, K. J. and Eykhoff, P.: *Systems identification - A survey.* Automatica 7 (1971), 123 – 162.

[G2] Banks, H. T.: *A survey of some problems and recent results for parameter estimation and optimal control in delay and distributed parameter systems.* In: Volterra and Functional differential Equations, (Hannsgen, K. B. et al. eds.), Marcel Dekker, New York, 1982, 3 – 24.

[G3] Banks, H. T. and Kunisch, K.: *An approximation theory for nonlinear partial differential equations with applications to identification and control.* SIAM J. Control and Optim. 20 (1982), 815 – 849.

[G4] Chavent, G.: *Optimization problems in the inversion of the 2-D wave equation.* (To appear).

[G5] Hoffmann, K.-H.: *Identifikationsprobleme bei partiellen Differentialgleichungen.* In: Numerische Behandlung von Differentialgleichungen, Vol. 3 (Albrecht and Collatz eds.), ISNM 56 (1981), 97 – 116.

[G6] Kubrusly, C. S.: *Distributed parameter system identifications.* Int. J. Control 26 (1977), 509 – 535.

[G7] Nguyen, V. V. and Wood, E. F.: *Review and unification of linear identifiability concepts.* SIAM Rev. 24 (1982), 34 – 51.

[G8] Polis, M. P. and Goodson, R. E.: *Parameter identification in distributed systems: A synthesizing overview.* Proc. IEEE 64 (1976), 43 – 61.

[G9] Ray, W. H.: *Some recent applications of distributed parameter systems theory - A survey.* Automatica 14 (1978), 281 – 287.

(H) General Theory for Equations of the First Kind

[H1] Engl, H. and Neubauer, A.: *Optimal discrepancy principles for the Tikhonov regularization of integral equations of the first kind.* In: Constructive Methods for the Practical Treatment of Integral Equations (Hämmerlin, G. and Hoffmann, K.-H. eds.), ISNM 73, Birkhäuser, Basel etc., 1985.

[H2] Friedman, V.: *Method of successive approximations for Fredholm integral equations of the first kind.* Uspehi Mat. Nauk 11 (1956), 233 – 234 (in Russian).

[H3] Groetsch, C. W.: *The theory of Tikhonov regularization for Fredholm equations of the first kind.* Pitman, Boston etc., 1984.

[H4] Ivanov, V. K.: *Approximate solution of operator equations of the first kind.* U.S.S.R. Comput. Math. and Math. Phys. 6 (1966), 197 – 205.

[H5] Landweber, L.: *An iteration formula for Fredholm integral equations of the first kind.* Amer. J. Math. 73 (1951), 615 – 624.

[H6] Morozov, V. A.: *On the solutions of functional equations by the method of regularization.* Soviet Math. Doklady 7 (1966), 414 – 417.

[H7] Morozov, V. A.: *The error principle in the solution of operational equations by the regularization method.* U.S.S.R. Comput. Math. and Math. Phys. 8 (1968), 63 – 87.

[H8] Strand, O. N.: *Theory and methods related to the singular function expansion and Landweber's iteration for integral equations of the first kind.* SIAM J. Numer. Anal. 11 (1974), 789 – 825.

[H9] Tikhonov, A. N.: *Regularization of incorrectly posed problems.* Soviet Doklady 4 (1963), 1624 – 1627.

(I) Other References

[I1] Hadamard, J.: *Lectures on the Cauchy problem in linear partial differential equations.* Yale University Press, New Haven, 1923.

[I2] Herbst, O.: *Konstruktion von Quasi-Newton Verfahren mit Hilfe konjugierter Richtungen.* PhD Thesis, Göttingen, 1984.

[I3] Kerz, W.: *Einführung in die Geophysik I, II.* Bibliographisches Institut Mannheim, 1985.

[I4] Lanczos, C.: *Linear differential operators.* Van Nostrand, New York, 1961.

International Series of
Numerical Mathematics, Vol. 84
(c) 1988 Birkhäuser Verlag Basel

Shorted operators through convex analysis

Marie-Laurence Mazure
Université Paul Sabatier
Laboratoire d'Analyse Numérique
118, route de Narbonne
31062 Toulouse Cedex, France

Abstract. Let A be a (bounded) symmetric positive semi-definite operator and S a (closed) subspace of a finite-dimensional (infinite-dimensional) real Hilbert space. Then, the shorted operator of A with respect to S, A_S, is defined as the greatest symmetric positive semi-definite operator among those which are bounded above by A and whose image is contained in S. Using classical operations of convex analysis leads us to easy and natural proofs, firstly of the existence of A_S, and secondly of all the known properties of the shorted operation.

Key words: Shorted operator, convex partially quadratic form, conjugacy operation, infimal convolution.

Introduction

Given a symmetric positive semi-definite operator A on the finite-dimensional vector space $X = \mathbb{R}^n$, and a subspace S of X, we can define a new symmetric positive semi-definite operator whose range is contained in S, denotes A_s and usually called *"the shorted operator of A with respect to S"*.

This construction has a physical meaning which we explain in the first section.

Using, especially, the conjugacy operation for convex quadratic forms, we give in the second section an interpretation, through convex analysis, of the construction of the operator A_s. We shall see in the third section how this interpretation enables us to find again easily all the known properties of the operation $(A, S) \rightarrow A_s$ previously established by several authors.

Finally, we show in the last section how the concept of shorted operators can be extended to infinite-dimensional Hilbert spaces, although it is not clear whether there is a physical meaning.

I. Preliminary Notions.

I.1. Convex (partially) quadratic forms and their conjugate functions.

It is equivalent to give a quadratic form q on the space $X = \mathbb{R}^n$, endowed with its usual Euclidean inner-product denoted by $< ., . >$, or to give the unique symmetric operator A on X - that we shall call the operator associated with q - defined by the relation:

$$q(x) = \frac{1}{2} < Ax, x > \quad \forall x \in X. \tag{$*$}$$

Throughout the paper, we shall denote by Ker A and Im A the kernel and the image of a symmetric operator A respectively; the operator A will be said to be symmetric positive semi-definite (s.p.s.d.) if the quadratic form q_A, defined as in (∗), satisfies: $q_A(x) \geq 0$ for all $x \in X$, or, in other terms, if q_A is a convex function. We recall that an order relationship on the set of all s.p.s.d. operators on X is defined by:

$$A \leq B \quad \text{if and only if} \quad q_A \leq q_B.$$

Let us recall that, given a function $f : X \to \overline{\mathbb{R}} = \mathbb{R} \cup \{-\infty, +\infty\}$, the conjugate (function) of f is the function $f^* : X \to \overline{\mathbb{R}}$ defined by ([10]):

$$f^*(x^*) = \sup_{x \in X} \{< x^*, x > -f(x)\} \quad \forall x^* \in X.$$

When A is a s.p.s.d. operator on X, the conjugate of the convex quadratic (c.q.) form q_A associated with A is written as ([13]):

$$q_A^*(x^*) = \begin{cases} \frac{1}{2} < A^+ x^*, x^* > & \text{if } x^* \in \text{Im } A, \\ +\infty & \text{otherwise,} \end{cases} \tag{I.1}$$

where A^+ denotes the *Moore-Penrose generalized inverse* of A, which is defined according to the following diagram:

$$X \xrightarrow{\quad P \quad} \text{Im } A \underset{A^+}{\overset{(A/\text{Im } A)^{-1}}{\xrightarrow{\hspace{2cm}}}} \text{Im } A \xrightarrow{\quad i \quad} X \ .$$

Here P is the orthogonal projection on the subspace Im A and i the canonical embedding of Im A in X.

From (I.1), we can derive in particular:

$$\text{dom } q_A^* = \text{Im } A. \tag{I.2}$$

Moreover, since the generalized inverse of a s.p.s.d. operator is s.p.s.d. itself, the conjugate of a c.q. form is clearly a convex partially quadratic form, where a convex partially quadratic (c.p.q.) form is any function $h : X \to \mathbb{R} \cup \{+\infty\}$ whose domain, denoted by dom h (dom $h = \{x \in X/h(x) < +\infty\}$), is a subspace of X, and which becomes a c.q. form when restricted to its domain.

Any c.p.q. form h on X, with dom $h = H$, may be written, in the following form:

$$h(x) = \begin{cases} \frac{1}{2} < Bx, x > & \text{if } x \in H, \\ +\infty & \text{otherwise,} \end{cases}$$

where B is a s.p.s.d. operator. This representation is not necessarily unique.

The conjugate function of f is then given by ([9]):

$$h^*(x^*) = \begin{cases} \frac{1}{2} < (\pi B \pi)^+ x^*, x^* >, & \text{if } x^* \in \text{Im } B + H^\perp, \\ +\infty & \text{otherwise,} \end{cases} \qquad (I.3)$$

where π is the orthogonal projection on H and $H^\perp$ the subspace of X orthogonal to H. Again, h^* is a c.p.q. form.

I.2. A possible underlying physical model leading to the definition of shorted operators ([3]).

Let us consider a n-port network, that is to say a system of n "input-output" couples, called ports, that we shall represent as below:

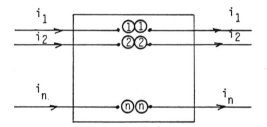

If v_k $(k = 1, \cdots, n)$ denotes the voltage at the k-th port with the corresponding current i_k, this network satisfies the generalized Ohm's law:

$$V = AI, \text{ with } V = \begin{pmatrix} v_1 \\ \vdots \\ v_n \end{pmatrix}, \quad I = \begin{pmatrix} i_1 \\ \vdots \\ i_n \end{pmatrix} \text{ and where } A \text{ is}$$

a s.p.s.d. matrix, called the *generalized resistance* of the network.

Let us denote by S the subspace of $\mathbb{R}^n$ generated by the s first vectors of the canonical basis $(1 \le s \le n)$ and consider the new situation obtained by *shorting* the last $(n - s)$ ports. To short some ports of a network gives to the current more paths, so that, for a given current I, the corresponding dissipated power decreases, i.e.:

$$< QI, I > \le < AI, I >,$$

or, equivalently, $Q \le A$. Moreover, across a short-circuit the voltage is always zero; thus, whatever the current I may be, $v_{s+1} = v_{s+2} = \cdots = v_n = 0$, so that:

$$\text{Im } Q \subset S.$$

Finally, provided these two conditions are satisfied, the dissipated power must be the largest possible. The generalized resistance A_s of the new network is therefore the maximum s.p.s.d. matrix among those which satisfy $Q \leq A$ and $\operatorname{Im} Q \subset S$.

More generally speaking, given a s.p.s.d. operator A and a subspace S of X, we shall denote by $\mathcal{M}(A, S)$ the following set of operators:

$$\mathcal{M}(A, S) = \{Q \text{ s.p.s.d. } /Q \leq A, \operatorname{Im} Q \subset S\}. \qquad (I.4)$$

Using algebraic arguments, Anderson and Trapp ([1] and [3]) proved the existence of a maximum element in $\mathcal{M}(A, S)$, precisely denoted A_s: this is the *shorted operator of A with respect to the subspace S*.

As a consequence of this definition, Anderson and Trapp proved that the associated quadratic form satisfies the following variational property ([3, Th. 6]):

$$< A_s x, x >= \operatorname{Inf}\{< A(x + y), x + y >, y \in S^\perp\} \ \forall x \in S.$$

The construction of the shorted operator A_s and the expression of the c.q. form q_{A_s} can be interpreted through convex analysis, using, in particular, the results recalled in I.1. We shall use, for that purpose, the basic properties of the conjugacy operation and of the infimal convolution (operation), as displayed in [10], [13] and [7] for instance.

II. Construction of A_S through convex analysis.

Let us first recall that the conjugacy operation defines an involutive and decreasing one-to-one correspondence from the set $\Gamma_0(X)$ onto itself, where, by $\Gamma_0(X)$, we mean the set of all *convex* functions on X, which are *lower semi-continuous* (l.s.c.) and *proper* (that is to say, whose domain is nonempty and which takes the value$-\infty$ nowhere).

Given a subspace S and a s.p.s.d. operator A on X, we now consider the set $\mathcal{M}(A, S)$ defined in (I.4).

For any s.p.s.d. operator Q, the two conditions $Q \leq A$ and $q_Q^* \geq q_A^*$ are equivalent, while the condition $\operatorname{Im} Q \subset S$ may be written, in view of (I.2): $\operatorname{dom} q_Q^* \subset S$. Accordingly, if $Q \in \mathcal{M}(A, S)$, the function q_Q^* belongs to the following set of c.p.q. forms on X:

$$\mathcal{H}(A, S) = \{h \text{ c.p.q., } h \geq q_A^*, \operatorname{dom} h \subset S\}.$$

Conversely, if $h \in \mathcal{H}(A, S)$, its conjugate is finite everywhere since it is bounded above by q_A: hence, it is a c.q. form. Moreover, since $h \in \Gamma_0(X)$, h is the conjugate of h^*, so that the symmetric operator Q associated with h^* is the only s.p.s.d. operator satisfying $q_Q^* = h$, and it clearly belongs to $\mathcal{M}(A, S)$.

Thus the correspondence $Q \to q_Q^*$ is decreasing and one-to-one from $\mathcal{M}(A, S)$ onto $\mathcal{H}(A, S)$.

From (I.1), we obtain the following necessary and sufficient condition for a c.p.d. form h to be in $\mathcal{H}(A, S)$:

$$h \in \mathcal{H}(A, S) \leftrightarrow \begin{cases} 1) \operatorname{dom} h \subset \operatorname{Im} A \cap S \\ 2) \forall x^* \in \operatorname{dom} h \ h(x^*) \geq \frac{1}{2} < A^+ x^*, x^* > . \end{cases}$$

The existence of a minimum element h_0 in $\mathcal{H}(A, S)$ follows immediately. This element is defined as follows:

$$h_0(x^*) = \begin{cases} \frac{1}{2} < A^+ x^*, x^* > & \text{if } x^* \in \operatorname{Im} A \cap S, \\ +\infty & \text{otherwise.} \end{cases} \qquad (II.1)$$

Therefore, $\mathcal{M}(A, S)$ has a maximum element, namely the symmetric operator associated with h_0^*: it will be denoted by A_S and called the *"shorted operator of A with respect to S."* This operator is s.p.s.d. and uniquely defined by relation $q_{A_S}^* = h_0$, which may be written like this:

$$q_{A_S}^* = q_A^* + \psi_S, \qquad (II.2)$$

where ψ_S is the indicator function of $S(\psi_S(x) = 0$ if $x \in S$, $\psi_S(x) = +\infty$ elsewhere).

Moreover, this construction leads us to the previously announced expression of the quadratic form $< A_S x, x >$, according to the following theorem:

Theorem I.1.

(i) for all $x \in X$, $< A_S x, x >= \operatorname{Inf}_{y \in S^\perp} < A(x - y), x - y >$ \qquad (II.3)

(ii) for all $x \in X$, there exists $x_0 \in S^\perp$ such that:

$$< A_S x, x >=< A(x - x_0), x - x_0 >$$

(iii) for all $x \in X$ and all $y \in S^\perp$, the equality

$$< A_S x, x >=< A(x - y), x - y >$$

holds if and only if $A(x - y) \in S$, in which case $A_S(x) = A(x - y)$.

Proof. Since the functions q_A^* and ψ_S have domains the relative interiors of which overlap (namely in 0), it follows ([13, Th. 16.4]), that the conjugate of the sum $q_A^* + \psi_S$ is the infimal convolution of the conjugates of q_A^* and ψ_S:

$$(q_A^* + \psi_S)^* = q_A^{**} \square \psi_S^*,$$

which may be written as:

$$q_{A_S} = q_A \square \psi_{S^\perp}. \qquad (II.4)$$

Moreover, this infimal convolution is exact. Equality (II.4) gives, for all x:

$$q_{A_S}(x) = \operatorname*{Inf}_{y \in X} \{q_A(x - y) + \psi_{S^\perp}(y)\},$$

whence (II.3). The assertion (ii) merely expresses the exactness of the infimal convolution, i.e., that the infimum in (II.3) is actually attained at some point $x_0 \in S^\perp$.

Furthermore, since any c.q. form is everywhere differentiable, if $y \in S^\perp$, the infimal convolution is exact at $x = (x - y) + y$ if and only if $\partial q_A(x - y) \cap \partial \psi_{S^\perp}(y) \neq \emptyset$ ([7, Th. 6.6.5]). As $\partial q_A(x-y) = \{A(x-y)\}$ and $\partial \psi_{S^\perp}(y) = S$, this condition is equivalent to: $A(x - y) \in S$.

Moreover, when this holds true, we know that ([7, Prop. 6.6.4]):

$$\partial q_{A_S}(x) = \partial q_A(x - y) \cap \partial \psi_{S^\perp}(y),$$

that is to say $A_S(x) = A(x - y)$, and (iii) is proved. $\qquad\square$

An example. If A is invertible, and if $\pi^\perp$ denotes the orthogonal projection onto $S^\perp$, the relation:

$$(\pi^\perp A)(\pi^\perp A \pi^\perp)^+ A = \pi^\perp A.$$

gives, with (iii), the following expression for A_S:

$$A_S = A - A(\pi^\perp A \pi^\perp)^+ A. \qquad (II.5)$$

The very construction of the operator A_S leads us to the next results, where (i) is proved by considering the domains in (II.2), and (ii) is a consequence of (I.3):

Proposition II.2.

$$(i) \quad \mathrm{Im}\ A_S = \mathrm{Im}\ A \cap S. \qquad (II.6)$$

$$(ii) \quad A_S = (\pi A^+ \pi)^+, \qquad (II.7)$$

where π denotes the orthogonal projection on $\mathrm{Im}\ A \cap S$.

III. Properties of the shorted operation $(A, S) \to A_S$.

Throughout this section, A, B, C will denote s.p.s.d. operators, while S and T are subspaces of X.

Proposition III.1. *The shorted operation $(A, S) \to A_S$ is monotone with respect to the operator and to the subspace, i.e.:*

$$A \leq B \quad \text{and} \quad S \subset T \Longrightarrow A_S \subset B_T.$$

Proof. Assumptions $A \leq B$ and $S \subset T$ are equivalent to $q_A \leq q_B$ and $\psi_{S^\perp} \leq \psi_{T^\perp}$ respectively. Thus the monotonicity of the infimal convolution operation implies:

$$q_A \,\square\, \psi_S \leq q_B \,\square\, \psi_T.$$

By the definition (II.4) of shorted operators, this inequality means $A_S \leq B_T$. $\qquad\square$

Proposition III.2.

$$(A_S)_T = (A_T)_S = A_{S \cap T}.$$

Proof. *This results from the associativity of the infimal convolution operation which allows us to write:*

$$(q_A \,\square\, \psi_{S\perp}) \,\square\, \psi_{T\perp} = q_A \,\square\, (\psi_{S\perp} \,\square\, \psi_{T\perp}) = q_A \,\square\, \psi_{(S\cap T)\perp}.$$

$\square$

Proposition III.3. *If the operator A is the orthogonal projection on a subspace H; then A_S is the projection on $H \cap S$.*

Proof. From (I.1) and (II.2), we get:

$$q_{A_S}^*(x^*) = \begin{cases} \frac{1}{2}\|x^*\|^2 & \text{if } x^* \in H \cap S, \\ +\infty & \text{otherwise} \end{cases}$$

and this is exactly, according to (I.1), the expression of the conjugate of the c.q. form associated with the orthogonal projection onto $H \cap S$. $\square$

Proposition III.4.
(i) $(A+B)_S \geq A_S + B_S$.
(ii) $(A+B)_S = A_S + B_S$ if and only if Im $(A - A_S + B - B_S) \cap S = \{0\}$.

Proof. (i) results from the following property of the infimal convolution operation:

$$(q_A + q_B) \,\square\, \psi_{S\perp} = (q_A + q_B) \,\square\, (\psi_{S\perp} + \psi_{S\perp}) \geq (q_A \,\square\, \psi_{S\perp}) + (q_B \,\square\, \psi_{S\perp}).$$

Taking (i) into account, (ii), is an immediate consequence of the next lemma, applied to the equality $A + B = A_S + B_S + (A - A_S + B - B_S)$.

Lemma: *If $A = B + C$, with $B \leq A_S$ (i.e., Im $B \subset S$), then $B = A_S$ iff $C_S = 0$ (i.e., Im $C \cap S = \{0\}$).* $\square$

Proposition III.5. *([11])*

$$(A^2)_S \leq (A_S)^2.$$

Proof. Given any $x \in X$, Theorem II.1 guarantees the existence of some $x_0 \in S^\perp$ such that $A_S(x) = A(x - x_0)$. Hence:

$$< (A_S)^2 x, x > \; = \; < A_S x, A_S x > \; = \; < A(x - x_0), A(x - x_0) >$$
$$= < A^2(x - x_0), x - x_0 > \; \geq \; \underset{y \in S^\perp}{\text{Inf}} < A^2(x - y), x - y >$$

which proves, applying (II.3) to the operator A^2:

$$< (A_S)^2 x, x > \; \geq \; < (A^2)_S x, x > .$$

$\square$

Proposition III.6. *If A and B commute, then:*

$$(AB)_S = B^{1/2} A_{(B^{1/2})^{-1}(S)} B^{1/2} = A^{1/2} B_{(A^{1/2})^{-1}(S)} A^{1/2}. \qquad (III.7)$$

Proof. According to Theorem II.1, when $x \in X$, there exists some x_0 in $S^\perp$ such that:

$$(AB)_S(x) = AB(x - x_0).$$

Since the operator A and B commute, so do A and $B^{1/2}$. Thus:

$$(AB)_S(x) = B^{1/2}A[B^{1/2}x - B^{1/2}x_0].$$

The equality above proves, in particular, that $A(B^{1/2}x - B^{1/2}x_0) \in (B^{1/2})^{-1}(S)$. Furthermore, the inclusion $B^{1/2}(S) \subset [(B^{1/2})^{-1}(S)]^\perp$ implies that $B^{1/2}x_0$ belongs to $[(B^{1/2})^{-1}(S)]^\perp$. By (iii) in Theorem II.1, these two conditions are sufficient to ensure that:

$$A(B^{1/2}x - B^{1/2}x_0) = A_{(B^{1/2})^{-1}(S)}(B^{1/2}x),$$

from which the result readily follows. $\qquad\square$

Remark: When applies to $B = I$ (identity map on X), (III.7) allows us to find again the first formulation of A_S, such as given by Krein ([6]):

$$A_S = A^{1/2}PA^{1/2}, \qquad\qquad (III.8)$$

where P is the orthogonal projection on the subspace $(A^{1/2})^{-1}(S)$.

Proposition III.7. *Let $(A_n)_n$ be a decreasing sequence of s.p.s.d. operators, and A its limit. Then the sequence $(A_n)_S$ converges to A_S.*

Proof. Since the operators are symmetric, the hypothesis means that q_A is the pointwise limit of the decreasing sequence of functions $(q_{A_n})_n$. This implies, for any $x \in X$:

$$
\begin{aligned}
q_{A_S}(x) &= \inf_{y \in S^\perp} q_A(x - y) = \inf_{y \in S^\perp} \inf_{n \in \mathbb{N}} q_{A_n}(x - y) \\
&= \inf_{n \in \mathbb{N}} \inf_{y \in S^\perp} q_{A_n}(x - y) = \inf_{n \in \mathbb{N}} q_{(A_n)_S}(x).
\end{aligned}
$$

The monotonicity of the shorted operation (cf. Proposition III.1) implies that the sequence $(A_n)_S$ is decreasing; therefore $\inf_{n \in \mathbb{N}} q_{(A_n)_S}(x) = \lim_{n \to \infty} q_{(A_n)_S}(x)$, which completes the proof. $\qquad\square$

Remark: We could also state an analogous result with an increasing sequence of s.p.s.d. operators $(A_n)_{n \in \mathbb{N}}$ assumed to converge to A. But in this case, the fact that X is finite-dimensional becomes essential to carry out the proof.

Proposition III.8.

$$(A//B)_S = A_S//B = A//B_s. \qquad\qquad (III.9)$$

Proof. Let us first recall that $A//B$ denotes the so-called *parallel sum of A and B*, namely the s.p.s.d. operator associated with the c.q. form $q_A \,\square\, q_B$, the infimal convolution of the c.q. forms q_A and q_B associated with the two s.p.s.d. operators A and B respectively ([9]).

Taking into account the equality $\psi_{S\perp} \,\square\, \psi_{S\perp} = \psi_{S\perp}$, form the associativity and commutativity properties of the infimal convolution, we can deduce:

$$(q_A \,\square\, q_B) \,\square\, \psi_{S\perp} = (q_A \,\square\, \psi_{S\perp}) \,\square\, q_B = q_A \,\square\, (q_B \,\square\, \psi_{S\perp})$$
$$= (q_A \,\square\, \psi_{S\perp}) \,\square\, (q_B \,\square\, \psi_{S\perp}).$$

In terms of associated operators, these equalities prove (III.9). $\qquad\square$

Proposition III.9. *If P denotes the orthogonal projection onto S, then:*

$$A_S = \lim_{n \to +\infty} A//nP. \qquad\qquad (III.10)$$

Proof. The monotonicity of the parallel addition implies that $(A//nP)_n$ is an increasing sequence; we have thus to verify that $q_{A_S} = \sup_n q_{A//nP}$. Let us now consider the sequence of conjugate functions:

$$q_{A//nP}^* = (q_A \,\square\, q_{nP})^* = q_A^* + q_{nP}^* = q_A^* + \frac{1}{n}q_P^*.$$

The decreasing sequence $(\frac{1}{n}q_P^*)_n$ converges pointwise to the indicator function of $\mathrm{dom}\, q_p^*$, that is to say to ψ_S. Hence:

$$\mathrm{Inf}_n\, q_{A//nP}^* = \lim_{n \to +\infty} (q_A^* + \frac{1}{n}q_P^*) = q_A^* + \psi_S.$$

Taking the conjugate in both sides, and using (II.2), we get:

$$(\mathrm{Inf}_n\, q_{A//nP}^*)^* = q_{A_S}.$$

Since the left-hand side may be rewritten as $\mathrm{Sup}_n(q_{A//nP}^{**}) = \mathrm{Sup}_n\, q_{A//nP}$, (III.10) follows immediately. $\qquad\square$

IV. Extensions to an infinite-dimensional Hilbert space context.

From now on, we shall assume that X is an infinite-dimensional Hilbert space; as before, the inner product on X will be denoted by $< \cdot, \cdot >$.

IV.1. Preliminary remarks.

A quadratic form on X is no longer necessarily continuous: this makes an essential difference with the finite-dimensional case. The correspondence $A \to q_A$ is now one-to-one from the set of all symmetric bounded operators on X onto the set of all continuous quadratic forms on X.

Moreover, a c.q. form q is continuous on X if and only if it is continuous at 0, that is to say if and only if there exists a positive number M such that:

$$q(x) \le M\|x\|^2 \quad \forall x \in X.$$

In other words, a necessary and sufficient condition for a c.q. form to be continous is to be bounded above by a continuous c.q. form.

Let now A be a bounded s.p.s.d. operator on X. If Im A is a closed subspace, the existence of the orthogonal projection on Im A is still guaranteed, so that we can define the generalized inverse A^+ of A exactly as in the finite-dimensional case, and A^+ is a bounded operator (according to the closed graph theorem). In that case, the conjugate of q_A is still given by (I.1).

If we do not assume Im A to be closed, the restiction $A/\overline{\text{Im } A}$ of A to $\overline{\text{Im } A} =$ (Ker $A)^\perp$ is one-to-one from $\overline{\text{Im } A}$ onto Im A. We shall still denote its inverse by A^+ (although abusively): A^+ is a linear one-to-one correspondence from Im A onto $\overline{\text{Im } A}$, which cannot be extended to a bounded operator on X.

From the equality Ker A = Ker $A^{1/2}$, it clearly results that:

$$\text{Im } A \subset \text{Im } A^{1/2} \subset \overline{\text{Im } A^{1/2}} = \overline{\text{Im } A}.$$

These inclusions may be strict; assume, for instance, that X is the space ℓ^2 of all the square-summable real sequences and consider the operator A defined as follows: $A\xi = (\frac{1}{i}x_i)_{i \ge 1}$ for any $\xi = (x_i)_{i \ge 1}$ in X. It is quite obvious to prove that Im A is a dense subspace of X. Furthermore, if ξ is defined by $\xi = (\frac{1}{i^\alpha})_{i \ge 1}$, then $\xi \in$ Im $A^{1/2}$ if and only if $\alpha > 1$, while $\xi \in$ Im A if and only if $\alpha > \frac{3}{2}$. Thus, inclusions Im $A \subset$ Im $A^{1/2}$ and Im $A^{1/2} \subset X$ are strict.

In fact, for any s.p.s.d. operator A, the three subspaces Im A, Im $A^{1/2}$ and $\overline{\text{Im } A}$ are equal if and only if any two of them are equal ([4]).

Given any bounded s.p.s.d. operator A, the quadratic form q_A may be written as $q_A = q_I \circ A^{1/2}$. As proved in [5], since q_I is a convex finite everywhere and continuous function, the conjugate q_A^* of q_A is the function $A^{1/2}$. q_I^*, called the *image of q_I^* under* $A^{1/2}$, defined by:

$$A^{1/2}.q_I^*(x^*) = \text{Inf}\{q_I^*(y^*)/A^{1/2}y^* = x^*\} \quad \forall x^* \in X.$$

The expression below follows easily:

$$q_A(x) = \begin{cases} \frac{1}{2}\|A^{1/2} + x^*\|^2 & \text{if } x^* \in \text{Im } A^{1/2}, \\ +\infty & \text{otherwise.} \end{cases} \tag{IV.1}$$

In particular:
$$\operatorname{dom} q_A^* = \operatorname{Im} A^{1/2}. \qquad (IV.2)$$

Finally, let us mention that, as proved by S. Maury [8], the conjugate of any c.p.q. form is still a c.p.q. form, although there exists no general explicit formula for such a conjugate, contrary to the finite-dimensional case.

IV.2. Extended definition of the shorted operation.

Given a *closed* subspace S of X, we can define the shorted operator of a bounded s.p.s.d. operator A to S: it is the maximum element A_S of the set $\mathcal{M}(A, S)$, now defined as below:
$$\mathcal{M}(A, S) = \{Q \text{ bounded}, \text{ s.p.s.d.} /Q \le A, \operatorname{Im} Q \subset S\}. \qquad (IV.3)$$

Since every c.p.q. form bounded above by a continuous c.q. form is a continuous c.q. form itself, the application $A \to q_A^*$ is now a one-to-one correspondence between $\mathcal{M}(A, S)$ and $\mathcal{H}(A, S)$, where:

$$\mathcal{H}(A, S) = \{h \text{ c.p.q., l.s.c.} /h \ge q_A^*, \operatorname{dom} h \subset S\}. \qquad (IV.4)$$

Therefore, the bounded s.p.s.d. operator A_S is again uniquely determined by formula (II.2):
$$q_{A_S}^* = q_A^* + \psi_S,$$

from which, we get immediately, using (IV.2):

$$\operatorname{Im} A_S^{1/2} = \operatorname{Im} A^{1/2} \cap S. \qquad (IV.5)$$

Since the functions q_A^* and $\psi_{S^\perp}$ belong to $\Gamma_0(x)$ and q_A is continuous and finite everywhere, we may apply proposition 9.b of [10] to get:

$$(q_a \,\square\, \psi_{S^\perp})^{**} = q_A \,\square\, \psi_{S^\perp}.$$

Since the left-hand side of the equality above is $(q_A^* + \psi_S)^*$, the relation (II.4) still holds:
$$q_{A_S} = q_A \,\square\, \psi_{S^\perp}.$$

Exactly as in the finite-dimensional case, statements (i) and (iii) of theorem II.1. follow; this proves, in particular, the inclusion (which may be strict):

$$\operatorname{Im} A \cap S \subset \operatorname{Im} A_S. \qquad (IV.6)$$

On the other hand, the infimal convolution $q_A \,\square\, \psi_{S^\perp}$ will generally not be exact.

A special case. When A is invertible, $q_A^* = q_{A^{-1}}$ is finite everywhere and continuous, which implies the exactness of $q_A \,\square\, \psi_{S^\perp}$ (see for instance th. 6.5.8 in [7]).

IV.3. Properties.

Most of the results and proofs in III do not depend on the assumptions on the dimension of X and therefore remain unchanged, provided the operators are supposed to be bounded and the subspaces considered to be closed. We shall now turn our attention to those which must be modified.

Proposition III.4. (new statement):

The condition $C_S = 0$ in lemma (in the proof of the earlier Prop. III.4) is now equivalent to Im $C^{1/2} \cap S = \{0\}$. The assertion (ii) of Proposition III.4. thus becomes:

$$(A + B)_S = A_S + B_S \text{ if and only if } \text{Im } (A - A_S + B - B_S)^{1/2} \cap S = \{0\}.$$

Proposition III.5. (new proof):

We can approximate the operator A by a decreasing sequence of invertible operators:

$$A = \lim_{n \to +\infty} A_n, \qquad A_n = A + \frac{1}{n}I,$$

where the convergence (here weak or strong convergence) of symmetric operators is still equivalent to the pointwise convergence of associated quadratic forms ([12]).

Using Proposition III.7, the convergence of the two decreasing sequences $(A_n)_n$ and $(A_n^2)_n$ to A and A^2 respectively, implies that of $(A_n)_S$ to A_S and that of $(A_n^2)_S$ to $(A^2)_S$. Moreover, since $(A_n)_S$ converges to A_S, so does $[(A_n)_S]^2$ to $(A_S)^2$. As each A_n satisfies condition (ii) of theorem II.1, we get:

$$(A_n^2)_S \leq \left[(A_n)_S\right]^2.$$

Taking the limits in the above inequality, we obtain $(A^2)_S \leq (A_S)^2$ as required. □

Proposition III.6. (new proof):

When the two operators A and B commute, we may write:

$$q_{AB} = q_A \circ B^{1/2},$$

which gives, by taking the conjugate functions: $q_{AB}^* = B^{1/2}.q_A^*$. Consequently:

$$
\begin{aligned}
q_{(AB)_S}^*(x^*) &= \text{Inf}\{q_A^*(y^*) + \psi_S(x^*), B^{1/2}y^* = x^*\} \\
&= \text{Inf}\{q_A^*(y^*) + \psi_{(B^{1/2})^{-1}(S)}(y^*), B^{1/2}y^* = x^*\} \\
&= B^{1/2}.[q_A^* + \psi_{(B^{1/2})^{-1}(S)}](x^*).
\end{aligned}
$$

This is exactly the conjugate of the c.q. form $q_C \circ B^{1/2}$, where C stands for the operator $A_{(B^{1/2})^{-1}(S)}$, which proves (III.7). □

IV.4. The explicit formulation of the shorted operator.

For any bounded s.p.s.d. operator A, formula (II.7) still holds provided Im A is supposed to be closed. If not, for a given $x \in X$, (II.3) means that:

$$< A_S x, x > = < Ax, x > + \operatorname*{Inf}_{y \in S^\perp} \{ < Ay, y > -2 < Ax, y > \},$$

which is exactly the same as:

$$q_A(x) - q_{A_S}(x) = \sup_{y \in X} \{ < \pi^\perp Ax, y > -q_{\pi^\perp A \pi^\perp}(y) \},$$

where $\pi^\perp$ denotes, as before, the orthogonal projection on $S^\perp$. In other words, we get:

$$q_A - q_{A_S} = q^*_{\pi^\perp A \pi^\perp} \circ \pi^\perp A.$$

It follows, on the one hand, that Im $\pi^\perp A \subset$ Im $(\pi^\perp A \pi^\perp)^{1/2}$, and, on the other hand, that $q_A - q_{A_S}$ is the c.q. form associated with the bounded s.p.s.d. operator $\Omega^* \Omega$, where $\Omega = (\pi^\perp A \pi^\perp)^{1/2^+} \pi^\perp A$. Therefore, we finally obtain the following expression for A_S:

$$A_S = A - \Omega^* \Omega, \qquad \Omega = (\pi A \pi)^{1/2^+} A, \tag{IV.7}$$

or, as an equivalent, since Im $A_S \subset S$:

$$A_S = \pi A \pi - \omega^* \omega, \qquad \omega = (\pi A \pi)^{1/2^+} A \pi, \tag{IV.8}$$

where π is the orthogonal projection on S.

Final remarks: (IV.8) is the expression Anderson and Duffin obtained in [3, Th. 3]. Moreover, when X is finite-dimensional, or when Im $(\pi^\perp A \pi^\perp)$ is supposed to be closed, (IV.7) is nothing else than formula (II.5), already obtained for invertible operators.

References.

[1] Anderson, W. N. Jr.: *Shorted operators.* SIAM J. Appl. Math. 20 (1971), 520 – 525.

[2] Anderson, W. N. Jr. and Duffin, R. J.: *Series and parallel addition of matrices.* J. Math. Analysis and Applications 26 (1969), 576 – 594.

[3] Anderson, W. N. Jr. and Trapp, G. E.: *Shorted operators II.* SIAM J. Appl. Math. 28 (1975), 60 – 71.

[4] Anderson, W. N. Jr. and Schreiberg, M.: *The infimum of two projections.* Acta Sci. Math. (Szeged) 33 (1972), 165 – 168.

[5] Castaing, C. and Valadier, M.: *Convex analysis and measurable multifunctions.* Springer-Verlag, Lecture notes no. 580 (1977).

[6] Krein, M. G.: *The theory of self-adjoint extensions of semibounded hermitian operators and its applications.* Math. Sb. 20 (62) (1947), 431 – 495.

[7] Laurent, P. J.: *Approximation et optimisation.* Hermann, Paris (1972).

[8] Maury, S.: *Formes quadratiques généralisées.* Comptes-Rendus 271, série A (1970), 1054 – 1057.

[9] Mazure, M. L.: *L'addition parallèle d'opérateurs interprètée comme inf-convolution de formes quadratiques convexes.* Modélisation Mathématique et Analyse Numérique 3 (1986).

[10] Moreau, J. J.: *Fonctionnelles convexes.* Collège de France, (1966 - 1967).

[11] Nishio, K. and Ando, T.: *Characterization of operations derived from network connections.* J. Math. Analysis and Applications 53 (1976), 539 – 549.

[12] Riesz, F. and Nagy, B. Sz.: *Functional Analysis.* Frederich Ungar, New York, 1965.

[13] Rockafellar, R. T.: *Convex Analysis.* Princeton University Press, New Jersey, 1970.

International Series of
Numerical Mathematics, Vol. 84
(c) 1988 Birkhäuser Verlag Basel

About the finite convergence of the proximal point algorithm

O. Lefebvre and C. Michelot

Université de Bourgogne

Département de Mathématiques

Laboratoire d'Analyse Numérique, B.P. 138

21004 Dijon Cedex, France

Abstract. We study the finite convergence property of the proximal point algorithm applied to the partial inverse, with respect to a subspace, of the subdifferential of a polyhedral convex function. Using examples we show how sufficient conditions providing the finite convergence can be realized and we give a case with non finite termination.

Key words: Partial inverse method, proximal point algorithm.

1. Introduction.

In recent years J. E. Spingarn [12] has introduced the concept of partial inverse T_A, with respect to a subspace A, of a maximal monotone multifunction T and developed what he called the method of partial inverses. This procedure amounts to applying the proximal point algorithm to the partial inverse T_A of T. Applications (particularly to give new decomposition algorithms) of this method in the framework of mathematical programming are various and of great interest, see for instance Auslender [1], Spingarn [12], [13], [14].

In this paper by means of a really suited tool, the Diff-Max property, we study the finite convergence of the proximal point algorithm applied to the partial inverse of the subdifferential of a polyhedral convex function.

The paper is organized as follows:

- In section 2 we give the formulation of the problem and recall the partial inverse method which yields the description of the algorithm.
- In section 3 we study the finite convergence in the polyhedral case.
- In section 4 we give two examples of applications.

2. Problem formulation and algorithm.

Let Z be the space $\mathbb{R}^n$ with inner product $< .,. >$. We consider a lower-semicontinuous convex function $f : Z \to \mathbb{R} \cup \{+\infty\}$ with a nonempty domain and let A be a subspace of Z.

The orthogonal subspace of A will be denoted by $A^\perp$. If $z \in Z$, z_A (resp. $z_{A^\perp}$) refers to the projection of z onto A (resp. onto $A^\perp$).

Let $K \subset Z$ be a convex set. We denote respectively by $N_A(K, z)$, $Int_A(K)$, $Bd_A(K)$, the normal cone to K at z, the interior of K and the boundary of K with respect to A. We also will write $N(K, z)$ the normal cone to K at z relative to the whole space Z.

Consider the pair of dual optimization problems

$$P \begin{cases} Min\ f(x) \\ x \in A \end{cases}$$

$$D \begin{cases} Min\ f^*(x) \\ y \in A^\perp \end{cases}$$

where f^* is the conjugate of f. We denote by SP (resp. SD) the set of optimal solutions to P (resp. to D). Problem P is a linear constrained problem. However other constraints can be taken into account in the objective function since f takes its values in $\mathbb{R} \cup \{+\infty\}$.

It is classical to associate with P and D the following optimality conditions problem which may be written as:

$$\begin{cases} \text{find} \quad x \in A,\ y \in A^\perp \\ \text{such that} \quad y \in T(x) \end{cases}$$

where T denotes the subdifferential of f.

From the work of Spingarn [12] this problem is equivalent to

$$\begin{cases} \text{find} \quad x \in A,\ y \in A^\perp \\ \text{such that} \quad o \in T_A(x + y) \end{cases}$$

where T_A is a maximal monotone multifunction, the partial inverse of T with respect to A. T_A is defined [12] via its graph by

$$\Gamma(T_A) = \{(x_A + y_{A^\perp}; y_A + x_{A^\perp}),\ y \in T(x)\}.$$

To solve simultaneously P and D we have to find a zero z of T_A (i.e. a point z verifying $o \in T_A(z)$) and after to project z onto A (resp. onto $A^\perp$) which provides a primal solution x (resp. a dual solution y).

It is well known that a possible iterative process to approach a zero z of a maximal monotone multifunction S is given by the proximal point algorithm [8], [11] which generates from any starting point $z^0 \in Z$, the sequence $\{z^k\}$ defined by

$$z^{k+1} = (I + S)^{-1}(z^k). \tag{2.1}$$

For our problem, we obtain with $S = T_A$ the following algorithm

$$z^{k+1} = (I + T_A)^{-1}(z^k) \tag{2.2}$$

$$x^k = z_A^k \tag{2.3}$$

$$y^k = z_{A^\perp}^k \tag{2.4}$$

$$\text{Putting} \quad y'^k = x^k - x^{k+1} + y^{k+1} \tag{2.5}$$

$$x'^k = y^k - y^{k+1} + x^{k+1} \tag{2.6}$$

and using the definitions (see also [13]) we obtain the following properties of (ALG) which will be useful in the next section

$$x^k + y^k = x'^k + y'^k \tag{2.7}$$

$$x^{k+1} = (x'^k)_A \tag{2.8}$$

$$y^{k+1} = (y'^k)_{A^\perp} \tag{2.9}$$

$$x^{k+1} = x^k - (y'^k)_A \tag{2.10}$$

$$y^{k+1} = y^k - (x'^k)_{A^\perp} \tag{2.11}$$

$$y'^k \in T(x'^k) \tag{2.12}$$

3. Finite convergence of algorithm (ALG).

In this section we assume that f is a polyhedral convex function. Following papers of Martinet [7] and Opial [9] the convergence of the proximal point algorithm applied to a maximal monotone multifunction S has been carefully studied by R. T. Rockafellar [11] who stated the following theorem

Theorem 3.1 [11]. *Let $\{z^k\}$ be any sequence generated by the proximal point algorithm (2.1) and suppose that there exists at least one solution to $o \in S(z)$ Then*
 (i) The sequence $\{z^k\}$ converges to a point z^∞ satisfying $o \in S(z^\infty)$.
 (ii) If $S = \partial g$ with g polyhedral convex, the convergence is reached in a finite number of iterations.

Consequently any sequence $\{z^k\}$ generated by (ALG) converges to a zero z^∞ of T_A and the limits x^∞ and y^∞ of the sequences $\{x^k\}$ and $\{y^k\}$ are respectively an optimal solution to P and an optimal solution to D.

Unfortunately, even when g is polyhedral convex, the partial inverse of T_A of $T = \partial g$ does not coincide with the subdifferential of a polyhedral convex function and we cannot conclude by this way to the finite termination of algorithm (ALG).

Actually the finite convergence of (ALG) is based on the concept of Diff-Max convex function [2], [4].

Definition 3.1 [4].
A convex function g is Diff-Max if for each x, there exists a neighbourhood $V(x)$ of x such that $\partial g(y) \subset \partial g(x)$ for each $y \in V(x)$.

In finite dimension this property is a characterization of locally-polyhedral convex functions [2] and it is an efficient tool to work with polyhedral functions. For instance, it allows in [4] to obtain a geometrical description of various kinds of efficient points in the framework of multiobjective location theory.

To emphasize the interest of Diff-Max property we give here a new and very simple proof of the second part of Theorem 3.1.

The function g being polyhedral, its conjugate is also polyhedral, hence Diff-Max [2]. This means that for each y there exists a neighbourhood $V(y)$ of y such that for $z \in V(y)$ we have $S^{-1}(z) \subset S^{-1}(y)$. Then we conclude that, for each x, we have

$$\begin{cases} \text{either} & S(x) \cap V(y) = \emptyset \\ \text{or} & x \in S^{-1}(y), \text{ i.e. } y \in S(x) \end{cases}$$

Putting $y = 0$ we obtain

$$\forall x \begin{cases} \text{either} & S(x) \cap V(o) = \emptyset \\ \text{or} & o \in S(x) \end{cases}$$

The relation $z^k - z^{k+1} \in S(z^{k+1})$, deduced from (2.1), and the convergence of $\{z^k\}$ imply that $S(z^{k+1}) \cap V(o) \neq \emptyset$ for large values of k, so we have $o \in S(z^{k+1})$ which gives $z^{k+m} = z^{k+1}$ for each $m \geq 1$ and the result follows.

Now to study the convergence of (ALG) we need some technical lemmas.

Lemma 3.1

Let H be a closed half-space and let $x \in A \cap H$. We have

$$\text{Proj}_A N(H, x) = N_A(A \cap H, x)$$

where $\text{Proj}_A(.)$ denotes the projection onto A.

This result, easy to be obtained, is given without proof. While it fails for a general convex set Ω, it can be generalized in the polyhedral case. So we have

Lemma 3.2

Let Ω be a polyhedron and let $x \in \Omega \cap A$. We have

$$\text{Proj}_A(N(\Omega, x)) = N_A(A \cap \Omega, x).$$

Proof. The polyhedron Ω is an intersection of a finite family I of closed half-spaces H_i, $i \in I$.

By Corollary 23.8.1 of [10], we have

$$N(\Omega, x) = \sum_{i \in I} N(H_i, x)$$

The operator projection $\text{Proj}_A(.)$ is linear, so we obtain

$$\text{Proj}_A N(\Omega, x) = \sum_{i \in I} \text{Proj}_A(H_i, x).$$

Using again Corollary 23.8.1 of [10] and Lemma 3.1 we deduce that

$$\text{Proj}_A N(\Omega, x) = \sum_{i \in I} N_A(A \cap H_i, x)$$
$$= N_A(\cap_i (A \cap H_i), x)$$
$$= N_A(A \cap \Omega, x)$$

$\square$

The following Lemmas show that the sequences $\{z^k\}$, $\{x^k\}$ and $\{y^k\}$ generated by (ALG) enjoy three important properties.

Lemma 3.3

For k sufficiently large, we have
(i) $x^k - x^{k+1} \in N_A(SP, x^\infty)$
(ii) $y^k - y^{k+1} \in N_{A\perp}(SD, y^\infty)$.

Proof. By relation (2.5) we have:

$$x^k - x^{k+1} = y'^k - y^{k+1}.$$

Let $x \in SP$. We obtain

$$< x^k - x^{k+1}, x - x^\infty > = < y'^k - y^\infty, x - x^\infty > + < y^\infty - y^{k+1}, x - x^\infty >$$
$$= < y'^k - y^\infty, x - x^\infty > .$$

Now, by the Diff-Max property of f, there exists $k_0 > 0$ such that for $k \geq k_0$, we have

$$y'^k \in T(x'^k) \subset T(x^\infty)$$

and consequently the monotony of T implies

$$< y'^k - y^\infty, x - x^\infty > \leq o.$$

Then we have $< x^k - x^{k+1}, x - x^\infty > \leq o$ for each $x \in SP$ and the first part of the result follows.

Finally the second part can be obtained in the same way using the Diff-Max property of f^* and by exchanging the role of y^k and x^k on one hand, x'^k and y'^k on the other hand. $\square$

The set $N_A(SP, x^\infty)$ (resp. $N_{A\perp}(SD, y^\infty)$) being a closed convex cone, we deduce easily the following result.

Corollary 3.1

For k sufficiently large, we have
(i) $x^k - x^\infty \in N_A(SP, x^\infty)$

(ii) $y^k - y^\infty \in N_{A\perp}(SD, y^\infty)$.

Lemma 3.4

For k sufficiently large, we have

$$< z^k - z^{k+1}, z^{k+1} - z^\infty >= o.$$

Proof. By (2.10) and (2.11) we have

$$z^k - z^{k+1} = (x'^k)_{A\perp} + (y'^k)_A.$$

Using (2.8) and (2.9) we also have

$$z^{k+1} - z^\infty = (x'^k)_A - x^\infty + (y'^k)_{A\perp} - y^\infty.$$

So we deduce the following equality

$$< z^k - z^{k+1}, z^{k+1} - z^\infty >=< x'^k - x^\infty, y'^k - y^\infty >.$$

By the Diff-Max property of f and f^*, we respectively find that for k sufficiently large, $y'^k \in T(x^\infty)$ and $y^\infty \in T(x'^k)$.

Then we obtain $< y'^k - y^\infty, x^\infty - x'^k >\geq o$ by the monotony of T.

Moreover we have $y'^k \in T(x'^k)$ and $y^\infty \in T(x^\infty)$, hence $< y'^k - y^\infty, x'^k - x^\infty >\geq o$ and the stated equality is obtained. $\qquad\square$

Lemma 3.5

Suppose that $\text{Int}_A(SP) \neq \emptyset$, $x^\infty \in Bd_A(SP)$ and $x^k \neq x^\infty$ for each k (resp. $\text{Int}_{A\perp}(SD) \neq \emptyset$, $y^\infty \in Bd_{A\perp}(SD)$ and $y^k \neq y^\infty$ for each k).

Then there exists a linear function $l : Z \to \mathbb{R}$ such that the sequence $\{l(z^k)\}$ is strictly increasing.

Proof. By symmetry we only need to prove the result with the assumptions relative to the primal problem P.

As $\text{Int}_A(SP) \neq \emptyset$ and $x^\infty \in Bd_A(SP)$, there exists [5] $\eta \in N_A(SP, x^\infty)$, $\eta \neq o$, such that $< \eta, x >> o$ for all $x \in N_A(SP, x^\infty)$, $x \neq o$. Observe that SP is a polyhedron which can be defined, using optimality conditions, by

$$SP = A \cap T^{-1}(\hat{y}), \forall \hat{y} \in SD.$$

Using Lemma 3.2. with $\Omega = T^{-1}(y^\infty)$, there exists $\xi \in N(\Omega, x^\infty)$, $\xi \neq o$, such that $\xi_A = \eta$.

Then we construct l as $l(z) =< \xi, x_{A\perp} >$ and we have by relations (2.11) and (2.8):

$$l(z^{k+1} - z^k) = l(y^{k+1} - y^k) = -l((x'^k)_{A\perp})$$
$$= l(x^{k+1} - x'^k)$$
$$=< \eta, x^{k+1} - x^\infty > - < \xi, x'^k - x^\infty >.$$

Finally for large values of k, we have on one hand $< \eta, x^{k+1} - x^\infty >> o$ since $x^{k+1} \in N_A(SP, x^\infty)$ and $x^k \neq x^\infty$, on the other hand $< \xi, x'^k - x^\infty >\leq o$ since $\xi \in N(\Omega, x^\infty)$ and $x'^k \in T^{-1}(y^\infty) = \Omega$ by the Diff-Max property of f^*. $\qquad\square$

Now we can state the main theorem:

Theorem 3.1 *Assume that* $\text{Int}_A(SP) \neq \emptyset$ *and* SD *is a singleton (resp.* $\text{Int}_{A^\perp}(SD) \neq \emptyset$ *and* SP *is a singleton). Then algorithm (ALG) converges in a finite number of steps.*

Proof. First of all, let us assume that $x^\infty \in \text{Int}_A(SP)$. In this case $N_A(SP, x^\infty) = \{o\}$, then by Corollary 3.1 there exists k_0 such that $x^{k_0+m} = x^\infty$ for $m \geq o$. Therefore relation (2.10) gives $(y'^{k_0+m})_A = o$ which means that y'^{k_0+m} is dual feasible. But for m sufficiently large we have $y'^{k_0+m} \in T(x^\infty)$ by means of the Diff-Max property of f, then the pair $(x^\infty; y'^{k_0+m})$ solves the system of optimality conditions. We get that y'^{k_0+m} is a dual solution, hence $y'^{k_0+m} = y^\infty$ since SD is a singleton. Using (2.5) we easily conclude that $y^{k_0+m} = y^\infty$ for large values of m.

In the case where x^∞ belongs to the boundary $Bd_A(SP)$ of the set of optimal solutions to P, let us assume that for some k_0, $x^k \neq x^\infty$ for all $k \geq k_0$.

J. E. SPINGARN proved in [13] that the proximal point algorithm with respect to a maximal monotone multifunction cannot generate a sequence $\{z^k\}$ satisfying

(1) $z^k \to z^\infty$

(2) $< z^k - z^{k+1}, z^{k+1} - z^\infty > = o$

(3) there exists a linear function $l : Z \to \mathbb{R}$ such that $\{l(z^k)\}$ is strictly increasing.

By means of Lemma 3.4 and 3.5 we get our assumption fails, in other words, there exists k_1 sufficiently large according to Lemma 3.3, 3.4, 3.5 and Corollary 3.1 such that $x^{k_1} = x^\infty$.

So we deduce (Lemma 3.3)

$$x^\infty - x^{k_1+1} \in N_A(SP, x^\infty)$$

and (Corollary 3.1)

$$x^{k_1+1} - x^\infty \in N_A(SP, x^\infty)$$

As $\text{Int}_A(SP) \neq \emptyset$, the normal cone $N_A(SP, x^\infty)$ only contains the subspace $\{o\}$ (see [5]), thus $x^{k_1+1} = x^\infty$ and by induction we find that $x^{k_1+m} = x^\infty$ for every $m \geq 1$. We conclude in the same way as in the first part of the proof. $\square$

4. Examples.

As an illustration of Theorem 3.2 we give two examples. The first example, which is the problem of finding a point in a polyhedron, has been developed by J. E. Spingarn in [13]. In this paper the finite convergence is obtained without using the concept of Diff-Max property. The second example deals with the location problem, or Fermat-Weber problem, and is described in detail in [6].

Example 1 [12]
We consider

$$Z = (\mathbb{R}^p)^m$$

$$A = \{x \in Z, x_1 = x_2 = \cdots = x_m; x_i \in \mathbb{R}^p\}$$

$$f(x) = \sum_{i=1}^m \delta(x_i, C_i)$$

where C_i is a closed half-space of $\mathbb{R}^p$ and $\delta(., C_i)$ denotes the indicator function of C_i.

Problem P amounts to finding a point of $K = \cap_{i=1}^m C_i$ and problem D can be written as

$$D \begin{cases} \text{Sup} - \sum_{i=1}^m \delta^*(y_i, C_i) \\ \sum_{i=1}^m y_i = o \end{cases}$$

where $\delta^*(., C_i)$ is the support function of C_i.

It is easy to see that if $\text{Int}_{\mathbb{R}^p}(K) \neq \emptyset$, the single optimal solution to D is $y = o$.

Example 2 [6]

We consider

$$Z = (\mathbb{R}^p)^m$$

$$A = \{x \in Z, x_1 = x_2 = \cdots = x_m; x_i \in \mathbb{R}^p\}$$

$$f(x) = \sum_{i=1}^m \gamma_i(x_i - a_i)$$

where $\{a_i, i = 1, 2, \cdots, m\}$ is a finite set of different points of $\mathbb{R}^p$ which represents a set of existing facilities, the function γ_i are a family of polyhedral gauges of convex compact polyhedra $B_i \subset \mathbb{R}^p$ such that $o \in \text{Int}_{\mathbb{R}^p}(B_i)$.

Problem P amounts to placing a new facility in order to minimize the sum of transportation costs between new and existing facilities. For an economical justification of considering polyhedral gauges, see for instance [3].

The dual D of this location problem can be written as

$$D \begin{cases} \text{Sup} - \sum_{i=1}^m < a_i, y_i > \\ \gamma_i^0(y_i) \leq 1 \\ \sum_{i=1}^m y_i = o \end{cases}$$

where γ_i^0 is the polar gauge of γ_i, the unit ball of which is denoted by B_i^0.

It $\hat{y}$ is any solution to D, it is stated in [3] that the set of optimal solutions to P can be geometrically described as

$$SP = \{(x, x, \cdots, x), x \in C = \cap_i(a_i + N_{\mathbb{R}^p}(B_i^0, \hat{y}_i))\}.$$

When $\text{Int}_A SP \neq \emptyset$, i.e. $\text{Int}_{\mathbb{R}^p} \neq \emptyset$, it can be easily seen that the dual variables $\hat{y}_i$ are necessarily extreme points of B_i^0 and therefore SD is a singleton.

Moreover, observe that the finite convergence of $\{z^k\}$ in Theorem 3.2 may fail if $\mathrm{Int}_A(SP) = \emptyset$. A counterexample with three existing facilities and where the distances are measured by the l^1-norm is given in [6].

References.

[1] Auslender, A.: *Two general methods for computing saddle points with applications for decomposing convex programming problems.* Applied Mathematics and Optimization 13 (1985), 79 – 95.

[2] Durier, R.: *On locally polyhedral convex functions.* Working Paper, Université de Dijon (1986).

[3] Durier, R. and Michelot, C.: *Geometrical properties of the Fermat-Weber problem.* European J. Oper. Res. (1985), 332 – 343.

[4] Durier, R. and Michelot, C.: *Sets of efficient points in a normed space.* Journal of Mathematical Analysis and Applications 116 (1986).

[5] Eckhardt, U.: *Theorems on the dimension of convex sets.* Linear Algebra and its Applications 12 (1975), 63 – 76.

[6] Lefebvre, O. and Michelot, C.: *A primal-dual algorithm for the Fermat-Weber problem involving mixed gauges.* Working paper, Université de Dijon (1986).

[7] Martinet, B.: *Détermination approchée d'un point fixe d'une application pseudo-contractante. Cas de l'application prox.* Comptes Rendus de l'Académie des Sciences de Paris, t. 274 (1972), 163 – 165.

[8] Moreau, J. J.: *Proximité et dualité dans un espace hilbertien.* Bull. Soc. Math. France 93 (1965), 273 – 299.

[9] Opial, Z.: *Weak convergence of the successive approximations for nonexpansive mappings in Banach spaces.* Bull. Amer. Math. Soc. 73 (1967), 591 – 597.

[10] Rockafellar, R. T.: *Convex Analysis.* Princeton University Press, Princeton 1970.

[11] Rockafellar, R. T.: *Monotone operators and the proximal point algorithm.* SIAM Journal on Control and Optimization 14, No. 5 (1976), 877 – 898.

[12] Spingarn, J. E.: *Partial inverse of a monotone operator.* Applied Mathematics and Optimization 10 (1983), 247 – 265.

[13] Spingarn, J. E.: *A primal-dual projection method for solving systems of linear inequalities.* Linear Algebra and its Applications 65 (1985), 45 – 62.

[14] Spingarn, J. E.: *Applications of the method of partial inverses to convex programming: decomposition.* Mathematical Programming 32 (1985), 199 – 223.

International Series of
Numerical Mathematics, Vol. 84
(c) 1988 Birkhäuser Verlag Basel

Coupling optimization methods and variational convergence

B. Lemaire
University Montpellier II
Place E. Bataillon
34060 Montpellier, France

Abstract. It is shown on a prototype of standard iterative method for solving convex optimization problems, that the variational convergence theory allows to explain some stability properties of such methods for a large class of perturbation.

Key words: Convex optimization, Mosco convergence, penalization, perturbation, proximal regularization, variational approximation, variational convergence.

Introduction

This paper deals with approximation methods for solving convex optimization problems, obtained by coupling a standard iterative method with a data perturbation (or approximation) by variational convergence. The objective is to show that the variational convergence (or epi-convergence) theory enables to explain the stability of some iterative methods with respect to a large class of perturbations, in the sense that the perturbed method has the same convergence properties than the original one.

The basic iterative method used here as a prototype is the gradient and proximal regularization method. In §1, we recall this method and introduce a perturbed version. §2 is devoted to the tools of the variational convergence theory used to get the general results which are given in §3. In §4, some applications are made, essentially to penalty methods in convex programming.

1. The perturbed gradient with proximal regularization method

1.1. The problem

Let U be a real Hilbert space, $J : U \to \mathbb{R}$ a Gâteaux differentiable convex function, and $\varphi : U \to]-\infty, +\infty]$ a proper closed convex function. We consider the convex optimization problem

$$(P) \qquad (J + \varphi)(u) = \inf_U (J + \varphi).$$

It is well known that u is a solution of (P) if and only if it is a solution of the monotone inclusion

$$(Q) \qquad -A(u) \in \partial\varphi(u)$$

where $A(u)$ is the G-derivative $J'(u)$ of J at u and $\partial\varphi$ denotes the subdifferential operator associated to φ. In fact some results given here (see §3), only use the monotonicity properties of J', and then can be applied to monotone inclusions which do not arise from optimization problems.

1.2. The basic iterative method

For solving (P), we consider the gradient and proximal regularization method. Starting from an arbitrary point of U, it generates a sequence $\{u^n\}$ by the iteration scheme

$$(R) \qquad u^n = (I + \lambda_n \partial\varphi)^{-1}(u^{n-1} - \lambda_n J'(u^{n-1}))$$

where $(I + \lambda_n \partial\varphi)^{-1}$ denotes the resolvant operator associated to φ with the given parameter $\lambda_n > 0$. An equivalent formulation of (R) is

$$(F) \qquad u^n = Arg\min\{\frac{1}{2\lambda_n}\|. - u^{n-1} + \lambda_n J'(u^{n-1})\|^2 + \varphi\}.$$

In other words, following the terminology of J. J. Moreau ([14]), u^n is the proximal point of $u^{n-1} - \lambda_n J'(u^{n-1})$ associated to the function $\lambda_n \varphi$. When φ is the indicator function of a nonempty closed convex subset C of U, the method reduces to the classical gradient and projection (onto C) method. If J' is identically zero we recover the proximal regularization method of Martinet ([12]) or Rockafellar ([17]). This justifies the terminology taken here. This method has been studied by Cohen ([7]) under the name of "Auxiliary problem principle".

Remark 1. The iteration scheme (R) (or (F)) can be rewritten as

$$\frac{u^{n-1} - u^n}{\lambda_n} \in J'(u^{n-1}) + \partial\varphi(u^n)$$

and can be seen as a discretization scheme (explicit on J' and implicit on $\partial\varphi$) of the differential inclusion

$$-\frac{du}{d\lambda} \in J'(u) + \partial\varphi(u), \ \lambda > 0.$$

1.3. Perturbation

One way of perturbing the scheme (R) is to add in the right-hand side an error term e^n for taking into account a possible inexact computation of the proximal point and, because the resolvant is non-expansive, also an inexact computation of the gradient $J'(u^{n-1})$. In the (F) setting this can be done by adding to the gradient an error term g^{n-1} and by defining u^n no more as an exact minimizer but as an ε_n-minimizer, with some $\varepsilon_n > 0$. The two settings (R) and (F) remain no more equivalent. Nevertheless, it can be shown, from the strong unicity of the proximal point (as remarked by Auslender [4]) and the nonexpansiveness of the resolvant, that the (F) (functional) one implies the (R) (resolvant) one with

$$\|e^n\| \leq \lambda_n \|g^{n-1}\| + \sqrt{2\lambda_n \varepsilon_n}.$$

This inexact version has yet been considered by Martinet ([13]) in the particular case of the gradient method and by Martinet ([12]), Rockafellar [17] and Auslender [4], for the proximal regularization method. Moreover, in [4], is given an implementable algorithm for computing an ε-proximal point in a finite number of steps when $\operatorname{dom} \varphi = U = \mathbb{R}^N$ and $\varepsilon > 0$.

Here we shall consider, in addition, an other perturbation by replacing, in the iteration scheme, φ by φ^n, where the sequence $\{\varphi^n\}$ approximates φ (this will be precised in §2). Finally we get the new iteration schemes

$$(R') \qquad u^n = (I + \lambda_n \partial \varphi^n)^{-1}(u^{n-1} - \lambda_n J'(u^{n-1})) + e^n$$

$$(F') \qquad u^n \in \varepsilon_n - Arg\min\{\frac{1}{2\lambda_n}\|. - u^{n-1} + \lambda_n(J'(u^{n-1}) + g^{n-1})\|^2 + \varphi^n\}.$$

Remark 2. The method defined by (F') (then by (R') as noted above) can be seen as a diagonal iterative method for solving the approximate problems

$$(P_n) \qquad (J + \varphi^n)(u^n) \leq \inf_U (J + \varphi^n) + \varepsilon_n.$$

Such a diagonal method has been introduced and studied by Boyer ([6]), Martinet ([13]), Sonntag ([18]), in the particular case of an indicator function for φ, by coupling the gradient method with an approximation of (P) by discretization. In the context of convex programming, the same idea has been used by Auslender ([4]), Auslender-Crouzeix-Fedit ([5]) and Alart ([1]), by coupling the proximal regularization method with an approximation of problem (P) by unconstrained problems. As we shall see in the following, the variational convergence theory enables to give a unified point of view of these different works.

Remark 3. Following the remark 1, the iteration scheme (R'), with $e^n = 0$, can be seen as a discretization scheme of the differential inclusion

$$-\frac{du}{d\lambda} \in J'(u) + \partial \varphi(\lambda, u), \ \lambda > 0$$

where φ is defined on $\mathbb{R}^+ \times U$, and $\varphi^n = \varphi(\lambda_n, .)$. Proofs of convergence of $\{u^n\}$ may be derived from proofs of asymptotic behaviour of the solution of the differential inclusion given, for instance, in [9]).

2. Variational convergence theory

In this section some basic results from variational convergence theory derived from [2] and [3] are stated.

Let $\{\varphi^n : U \to]-\infty, +\infty], \ n = 1, 2, \cdots\}$ a sequence of proper closed convex functions.

Definition 1. φ^n *converges to φ in the sense of Mosco (which is noted $\varphi^n \overset{M}{\rightarrow} \varphi$), if and only if the two following sentences hold*

$\forall u \in U, \forall \{u^n\}$ such that $u = w - \lim u^n$, then $\varphi(u) \leq \liminf \varphi^n(u^n)$

$\forall u \in U, \exists \{u^n\}$ such that $u = s - \lim u^n$, and $\varphi(u) \geq \limsup \varphi^n(u^n)$

The Mosco-convergence is connected to the simple convergence of the Moreau-Yosida approximates* and of the resolvants by the following proposition

Proposition 1.

(i) $\varphi^n \overset{M}{\rightarrow} \varphi \Leftrightarrow \quad \forall \lambda > 0, \forall u \in U, \varphi_\lambda^n(u) \rightarrow \varphi_\lambda(u)$

(ii) $\varphi^n \overset{M}{\rightarrow} \varphi \Rightarrow \quad$ let $\lambda_n > 0$, $u^n \in U$, $n \in \mathbb{N}$, $\lambda > 0$, $u \in U$
$\qquad$ such that $\lambda_n \rightarrow \lambda$, $u^n \overset{s}{\rightarrow} u$, then
$\qquad (I + \lambda_n \partial \varphi^n)^{-1}(u^n) \overset{s}{\rightarrow} (I + \lambda \partial \varphi)^{-1}(u)$

Proof.

(i) see [2] (theorem 3.26, p. 305)

(ii) improve the proof of [2] theorem 3.26, (i) $\Rightarrow$ (ii). $\qquad\qquad\qquad$ □

Let us consider the semi-distances between φ^1 and φ introduced in [3].

Definition 2. $\forall \lambda > 0, \forall \rho \geq 0$

$$d_{\lambda,\rho}^n = \sup_{\|u\| \leq \rho} |\varphi_\lambda^n(u) - \varphi_\lambda(u)|$$

$$\delta_{\lambda,\rho}^n = \sup_{\|u\| \leq \rho} \|(I + \lambda \partial \varphi^n)^{-1}(u) - (I + \lambda \partial \varphi)^{-1}(u)\|$$

Proposition 2. *If there exists $\lambda > 0$ such that $\forall \rho \geq 0$, $d_{\lambda,\rho}^n \rightarrow 0$, then $\varphi^n \overset{M}{\rightarrow} \varphi$. The converse being true if U is finite dimensional.*

Proof. see [3] theorem 2.51. $\qquad\qquad\qquad\qquad\qquad\qquad\qquad\qquad\qquad$ □

Proposition 3. *Assume $0 < \underline{\lambda} \leq \lambda_n \leq \overline{\lambda} < +\infty$ and $\forall \rho \geq 0$, $\lim_{n \rightarrow \infty} d_{\underline{\lambda},\rho}^n = 0$. Then $\forall \rho \geq 0$, $\exists \rho_1 > \rho$ such that*

$$\forall n, \delta_{\lambda_n,\rho}^n \leq (1 + \overline{\lambda})(2 d_{\underline{\lambda},\rho_1}^n)^{1/2}.$$

---

* Let us recall the definition of the Moreau-Yosida approximates of a proper closed convex function $f : U \rightarrow]-\infty, +\infty]$:

$$\forall \lambda > 0, \forall u \in U, f_\lambda(u) = \inf_{v \in U} \{\frac{1}{2\lambda}\|v - u\|^2 + f(v)\}.$$

Proof. From [3] theorem 2.33, for a given $\rho \geq 0$,

$$\delta^n_{\lambda_n,\rho} \leq (1 + \lambda_n)(2d^n_{\lambda_n,\rho_0})^{1/2}$$

for any ρ_0 such that

$$\rho_0 \geq (1 + \lambda_n^{-1})\rho + \lambda_n^{-1}\theta^n_{\lambda_n}$$

where

$$\theta^n_{\lambda_n} = \|(I + \lambda_n\partial\varphi)^{-1}(0)\| + \|(I + \lambda_n\partial\varphi^n)^{-1}(0)\|.$$

By proposition 2, the assumption implies $\varphi^n \xrightarrow{M} \varphi$. Then improving the proof of [2] (theorem 3.26, (i) $\Rightarrow$ (ii)) it follows that $\theta^n_{\lambda_n}$ is bounded and we can take

$$\rho_0 = (1 + \underline{\lambda}^{-1})\rho + \underline{\lambda}^{-1}\sup_n \theta^n_{\lambda_n}.$$

Then, from [3] (lemma 2.46),

$$d^n_{\lambda_n,\rho_0} \leq d^n_{\underline{\lambda},\rho_1}$$

for any ρ_1 such that

$$\rho_1 \geq \rho_0 + (\lambda_n - \underline{\lambda})\underline{\lambda}^{-1}\gamma^n_{\lambda_n}$$

where $\gamma^n_{\lambda_n} = \max\{\|(I + \lambda_n\partial\varphi)^{-1}(0)\|, \|(I + \lambda_n\partial\varphi^n)^{-1}(0)\|\}.$

As above $\gamma^n_{\lambda_n}$ is bounded and we can take

$$\rho_1 = \rho_0 + (\overline{\lambda} - \underline{\lambda})\underline{\lambda}^{-1}\sup_n \gamma^n_{\lambda_n}.$$

Then the result is immediate. $\qquad\qquad\qquad\qquad\qquad\qquad\qquad\qquad\square$

3. Main results

Along this section, the following common assumption is made: J' is Lipschitz continuous, with constant $M \geq 0$, on the union of the effective domains of the φ^n and φ.

Theorem 1. Assume $M > 0$, J' strongly monotone with constant $\alpha > 0$ on $\cup_n \text{dom}\,\varphi^n \cup \text{dom}\,\varphi$, $0 < \underline{\lambda} \leq \lambda_n \leq \overline{\lambda} < 2\alpha/M^2$, $\lambda_n \to \lambda$, $\varphi^n \xrightarrow{M} \varphi$, $\{u^n\}$ generated by (R') with $\|e^n\| \to 0$. Then u^n converges strongly to the unique solution of (P).

Proof. Classically, the inclusion (Q) has a unique solution u. This solution is characterized by

$$u = (I + \lambda\partial\varphi)^{-1}(u - \lambda J'(u)).$$

First, by introducing the term $(I + \lambda_n \partial \varphi^n)^{-1}(u - \lambda_n J'(u))$ in the difference $u^n - u$, and from the nonexpansiveness of the resolvent, we get the inequality

$$\|u^n - u\| \leq \sigma(\lambda_n)\|u^{n-1} - u\| + \theta_n$$

where $\sigma(\lambda) = (1 - 2\alpha\lambda + M^2\lambda^2)^{1/2}$, and

$$\theta^n = \|(I + \lambda_n \partial\varphi^n)^{-1}(u - \lambda_n J'(u)) - (I + \lambda\partial\varphi)^{-1}(u - \lambda J'(u))\| + \|e^n\|.$$

Then $\|u^n - u\| \leq \sigma^n\|u^n - u\| + \sum_{j=0}^{n-1} \sigma^j \theta_{n-j}$, where $\sigma = \max\{\sigma(\underline{\lambda}), \sigma(\overline{\lambda})\} < 1$.

The result follows from [15] (NR 12, 2.3, p. 399), because, by proposition 1, (ii), $\lim_{n\to\infty} \theta_n = 0$. $\qquad\square$

Remark 4. This theorem 1 is, in some sense, an extension of a result of Sonntag ([18]), theorem 5.1, p. V6). The fact that the operator J' is a derivative does not play any role.

Theorem 2. Assume $0 < \underline{\lambda} \leq \lambda_n \leq \overline{\lambda} < 2/M$, φ^n decreases and φ is the closure of $\inf_n \varphi^n$ or $\forall \rho \geq 0$ $\lim_{n\to\infty} d_{\underline{\lambda},\rho}^n = 0$, $\{u^n\}$ generated by (R') with $\lim_{n\to\infty} \|e^n\| = 0$, $\{u^n\}$ bounded.

Then every weak cluster point of $\{u^n\}$ is a solution of (P). If, in addition, $\{u^n\}$ is generated by (F') with $\lim_{n\to\infty} \varepsilon_n = 0$ and $\lim_{n\to\infty} \|g^n\| = 0$, then

$$\lim_{n\to\infty} J(u^n) + \varphi^n(u^n) = \inf(P)$$

Proof.

$1°$ *Every weak cluster point is a solution.*

  a) We first treat the case of $\{\varphi^n\}$ decreasing, following the method of proof of Martinet ([13]). Let

$$v^n = u^n - e^n.$$

We have $v^n \in \operatorname{dom} \varphi^n$, $\lim_{n\to\infty} \|u^n - v^n\| = 0$ and

$$\forall v \in U, \varphi^n(v) \geq \varphi^n(v^n) + \left(\frac{u^{n-1} - v^n}{\lambda_n} - J'(u^{n-1}), v - v^n\right). \qquad (1)$$

On the other hand

$$J(v^n) - J(v^{n-1}) - (J'(v^{n-1}), v^n - v^{n-1})$$

$$= \int_0^1 (J'(v^{n-1} + t(v^n - v^{n-1})) - J'(v^{n-1}), v^n - v^{n-1})dt$$

$$\leq \frac{M}{2}\|v^n - v^{n-1}\|^2$$

which, with (1) where we take $v = v^{n-1}$ and because φ^n decreases, gives

$$(\frac{1}{\lambda} - \frac{M}{2})\|v^n - v^{n-1}\|^2 + s_n \leq s_{n-1} + (\frac{1}{\lambda} + M)\|e^{n-1}\|\|v^n - v^{n-1}\| \qquad (2)$$

where $s_n = J(v^n) + \varphi^n(v^n)$. Applying the inequality

$$2ab \leq \alpha a^2 + \frac{1}{\alpha}b^2, \ \alpha > 0, \ \text{with}$$

$a = \|e^{n-1}\|$, $b = \|v^n - v^{n-1}\|$, we derive from (2)

$$\beta\|v^n - v^{n-1}\|^2 + s_n \leq s_{n-1} + \mu_n \qquad (3)$$

where $\beta = (\frac{1}{\lambda} - \frac{M}{2}) - \frac{1}{\alpha}(\frac{1}{\lambda} + M)$ is positive for α large enough, and
$\mu_n = \alpha(\frac{1}{\lambda} + M)\|e^{n-1}\|^2$.
Now let $S = \{n \in \mathbb{N}, s_n > s_{n-1}\}$

(i) S *is not finite.*
From (3) and because $\lim_{n \to \infty} \mu_n = 0$, we get

$$\lim_{n \in S} \|v^n - v^{n-1}\| = 0 \qquad (4)$$

From (1) and the convexity of J, it follows

$$\forall v \in U, (J + \varphi^n)(v) \geq s_n + (\frac{u^{n-1} - v^n}{\lambda_n} + J'(v^n) - J'(u^{n-1}), v - v^n). \qquad (5)$$

On the other hand ([2], theorem 3.20, p. 298), $\varphi^n \overset{M}{\to} \varphi$. Let $w \in U$. By the second sentence of definition 1, we can take in (5), $v = w^n$ where $w^n \overset{s}{\to} w$ and $\limsup \varphi^n(w^n) \leq \varphi(w)$. Passing to the limit, we get

$$\limsup_{n \in S} s_n \leq \inf(P). \qquad (6)$$

If S has an empty or finite complement, we get trivially

$$\limsup_{n \to \infty} s_n \leq \inf(P). \qquad (7)$$

Otherwise, for every $n \in \mathbb{N}$ define $i(n) \in S$ by

$$i(n) = \begin{cases} n, & \text{if } n \in S \\ \max\{\ell; \ell < n, \ell \in S\}, & \text{if } n \notin S \end{cases}$$

We have $\lim_{n \to \infty} i(n) = +\infty$ and $s_n \leq s_{i(n)}$, which, with (6), gives (7).

(ii) *S is empty or finite.*

For every n large enough we have

$$s_n \leq s_{n-1}$$

so $\{s_n\}$ converges in $\overline{\mathbb{R}}$. If $\lim_{n \to \infty} s_n = -\infty$, then, because $\{\varphi^n\}$ decreases, $\lim_{n \to \infty} s_n = \inf(P)$ $(= -\infty)$.

Otherwise, from (3) we get

$$\lim_{n \to \infty} \|v^n - v^{n-1}\| = 0,$$

and, as in the previous case for deriving (6), we get directly (7). In all cases we have proved (7). In fact, because $\{\varphi^n\}$ decreases we have

$$\lim_{n \to \infty} s_n = \inf(P). \tag{8}$$

Let u be a weak cluster point of $\{u^n\}$. It is also a weak cluster point of $\{v^n\}$. There exists a subsequence $\{u^\nu\}$ such that $w - \lim_{\nu \to \infty} u^\nu = u$. From the first sentence of definition 1 and the weak lower semicontinuity of J, we get

$$J(u) + \varphi(u) \leq \liminf_{\nu \to \infty} s_\nu = \inf(P)$$

b) Now consider the case of the other assumption: $\forall \rho \geq 0$, $\lim_{n \to \infty} d^n_{\underline{\lambda}, \rho} = 0$. Following an idea due to H. Attouch, define the sequence $\{\tilde{u}^n\}$ by

$$\tilde{u}^n = (I + \lambda_n \partial \varphi)^{-1}(u^{n-1} - \lambda_n J'(u^{n-1})).$$

As in the proof of theorem 1, we get

$$\|u^n - \tilde{u}^n\| \leq \delta^n_{\lambda_n, \rho} + \|e^n\| \tag{9}$$

where, $\forall n$, $\rho \geq \|u^{n-1} - \lambda_n J'(u^{n-1})\|$ which has sense because J' is Lipschitz continuous and $\{u^n\}$ and $\{\lambda_n\}$ are bounded sequences, and

$$\tilde{u}^n = (I + \lambda_n \partial \varphi)^{-1}(\tilde{u}^{n-1} - \lambda_n J'(\tilde{u}^{n-1})) + \tilde{e}^n$$

where $\|\tilde{e}^n\| \leq (1 + \overline{\lambda} M)(\delta^{n-1}_{\lambda_{n-1}, \rho} + \|e^{n-1}\|)$.

By proposition 3, $\lim_{n \to \infty} \|u^n - \tilde{u}^n\| = 0$ and $\lim_{n \to \infty} \|\tilde{e}^n\| = 0$. So we reduce to the previous case ($\tilde{\varphi}^n \equiv \varphi$).

$2°$ $\{u^n\}$ *is generated by* (F')

As noted in 1.3 this is a particular case of (R') generating. Moreover, $u^n \in \text{dom } \varphi^n$. From the definition of $\{u^n\}$ and the convexity of J, we derive

$$\forall v \in U, (J(u^n) + \varphi^n(u^n) \leq J(v) + \varphi^n(v) + \frac{1}{2\lambda_n}\|v - u^{n-1}\|^2 + \varepsilon_n + \tag{10}$$
$$+ (J'(u^{n-1}) + g^{n-1} - J'(u^n), v - u^n).$$

Consider the sequence $\{v^n\}$ introduced in the first part of the proof. By (3) and (8), $\lim_{n\to\infty}\|v^n - v^{n-1}\| = 0$. Taking $v = v^n$ in (10) and passing to the limit, it follows

$$\limsup_{n\to\infty} J(u^n) + \varphi^n(u^n) \leq \inf(P). \tag{11}$$

Moreover, from every subsequence of $\{J(u^n) + \varphi^n(u^n)\}$ we can extract a subsequence $\{J(u^\nu) + \varphi^\nu(u^\nu)\}$ where $\{u^\nu\}$ is a subsequence of $\{u^n\}$ which, by the first part of the proof, converges weakly to some solution of (P). So, by the Mosco convergence of $\{\varphi^n\}$ to φ (see the first part and proposition 2)

$$\liminf_{\nu\to\infty} J(u^\nu) + \varphi^\nu(u^\nu) \geq \inf(P).$$

Therefore, with (11), the whole sequence converges to inf (P). $\qquad\square$

Remark 5. (i) If U is finite dimensional, by Proposition 2, we can replace the assumption on $d^n_{\underline{\lambda},\rho}$ by $\varphi^n \xrightarrow{M} \varphi$.
(ii) In the additional case, if $M = 0$, the result of theorem 2 remain true with $\overline{\lambda} = +\infty$ ([11]).
(iii) The assumption that $\{u^n\}$ is bounded is crucial in theorem 2 and must be verified in each application. Nevertheless we have the following general result.

Proposition 4. Assume $\{\varphi^n\}$ decreases and φ is the closure of $\inf_n \varphi^n$. Let $\{u^n\}$ be generated by (R'). $\{u^n\}$ is bounded if one of the following assumptions holds:
(i) dom φ is bounded and $\{e^n\}$ is bounded
(ii) $0 < \underline{\lambda} \leq \lambda_n \leq \overline{\lambda} < 2/M$, $J + \varphi$ is coercive and $\sum_n \|e^n\|^2 < +\infty$
(iii) U is finite dimensional, $0 < \underline{\lambda} \leq \lambda_n \leq \overline{\lambda} < 2/M$, $J + \varphi$ is coercive and $\lim_{n\to\infty}\|e^n\| = 0$.

Proof. Recall the proof of theorem 2, 1° a).
(i) $v \in \text{dom } \varphi^n \subset \text{dom } \varphi$. Then $\{v^n\}$ is bounded.
(ii) From (3) we easily derive

$$J(v^n) + \varphi(v^n) \leq s_n \leq s_0 + \sum_n \mu_n < +\infty$$

since $J + \varphi$ is coercive, $\{v^n\}$ is bounded.
(iii) We follow the method of proof of [4] (theorem 1.1).

If S (cf. proof of theorem 2, 1° a)) is finite, then for n large enough

$$J(v^n) + \varphi(v^n) \leq s_n \leq s_0.$$

Then $\{v^n\}$ is bounded.

If S is not finite, from (3) it follows

$$\lim_{n \in S} \|v^n - v^{n-1}\| = 0 \tag{12}$$

Let $w \in U$, in (5) take $v = w^n$ with $w^n \xrightarrow{s} w$ and $\limsup_{n \to \infty} \varphi^n(w^n) \leq \varphi(w)$ (Recall that $\varphi^n \xrightarrow{M} \varphi$). It follows from (1)

$$(J + \varphi)(v^n) \leq s_n \leq (J + \varphi^n)(w^n) - (z^n, w^n - v^n) \tag{13}$$

where, by (12), $\lim_{n \in S} \|z^n\| = 0$.

Assume $\{v^n\}_{n \in S}$ is not bounded. There exists a subsequence $\{v^\nu\}$ such that $\lim_{\nu \in S} \|v^\nu\| = +\infty$.

From (13) it follows

$$\limsup_{\nu \in S} \frac{(J + \varphi)(v^\nu)}{\|v^\nu\|} \leq 0. \tag{14}$$

Let $d_\nu = \frac{v^\nu}{\|v^\nu\|}$. There exists $d \neq 0$ and a subsequence $\{d_\mu\}$ converging to d. Let $\eta > 0$. For n large enough, $0 < \frac{\eta}{\|v^\mu\|} < 1$. Let $\bar{v} \in \operatorname{dom} \varphi$. By convexity, we get

$$(J + \varphi)(\bar{v} + \frac{\eta}{\|v^\mu\|}(v^\mu - \bar{v})) \leq (J + \varphi)(\bar{v}) + \frac{\eta}{\|v^\mu\|}(J + \varphi)(v^\mu) - (J + \varphi)(\bar{v})).$$

From (14) and the lower-semicontinuity of $J + \varphi$, we have

$$(J + \varphi)(\bar{v} + \eta d) \leq (J + \varphi)(\bar{v}) \tag{15}$$

This contradicts the coercivity of $J + \varphi$.

Because $\{v^n\}_{n \in S}$ is bounded, by (13), there exists $\theta > 0$ such that

$$s_n \leq \theta, \ \forall n \in S.$$

Let ℓ be the smaller integer such that $\ell \notin S$. Then we have

$$\forall n \geq \ell, \ (J + \varphi)(v^n) \leq s_n \leq \max\{\theta, (J + \varphi^\ell)(v^\ell)\}$$

and since $J + \varphi$ is coercive, $\{v^n\}$ is bounded.

Finally in the three cases $\{v^n\}$ is bounded and since $\|u^n - v^n\| \leq \|e^n\|$, $\{u^n\}$ is bounded too. $\qquad \square$

Theorem 3. *Assume $M = 0$ (i.e. J is affine), (P) has at least one solution, $0 < \lambda \leq \lambda_n \leq \overline{\lambda} < +\infty$, $\forall \rho \geq 0$, $\lim_{n \to \infty} d_{\overline{\lambda}, \rho}^n = 0$, $\{u^n\}$ generated by (R') with $\sum_n \|e^n\| < +\infty$ or by (F') with $\sum_n \|g^n\| < +\infty$ and $\sum_n \sqrt{\varepsilon_n} < +\infty$. Let u be any solution of (P), $f \in U$ defining the linear part of J and $\rho_1(u)$ associated to $\rho = \|u\| + \overline{\lambda}\|f\|$ in proposition 3. Assume further $\sum_n (d_{\overline{\lambda}, \rho_1(u)}^n)^{1/2} < +\infty$. Then u^n converges weakly to one solution of (P).*

Proof. As noted in 1.3, it suffices to prove the result in the case of $\{u^n\}$ generated by (R'). We have

$$\forall n, \ u = (I + \lambda_n \partial \varphi)^{-1} (u - \lambda_n f).$$

Form the non-expansiveness of $(I + \lambda_n \partial \varphi^n)^{-1}$ and definition 2, we derive

$$
\begin{aligned}
\|u^n - u\| &\leq \|u^{n-1} - u\| + \|(I + \lambda_n \partial \varphi^n)^{-1}(u - \lambda_n f) - u\| + \|e^n\| \\
&\leq \|u^{n-1} - u\| + \delta_{\lambda_n, \|u\| + \overline{\lambda}\|f\|}^n + \|e^n\|
\end{aligned}
\tag{16}
$$

This implies, by proposition 3,

$$\|u^n - u\| \leq \|u^{n-1} - u\| + \theta_n(u), \quad \text{with} \quad \sum_n \theta_n(u) < +\infty. \tag{17}$$

The end of the proof is classical ([10], [12] chap. V, [17]). It follows from (17) that $\{u^n\}$ is bounded and, for each solution u of (P),

$$\lim_{n \to \infty} \|u^n - u\|^2 = \ell(u). \tag{18}$$

By theorem 2, we know that every weak cluster point of $\{u^n\}$ is a solution of (P). It remains to show that there is no more than one weak cluster point. This is a consequence of (18): let u^1 and u^2 be two weak cluster points of $\{u^n\}$, and $\{u^\nu\}$ a subsequence weak converging to u^2. We have

$$
\begin{aligned}
\ell(u^1) - \ell(u^2) &= \lim_{n \to \infty} (\|u^n - u^1\|^2 - \|u^n - u^2\|^2) \\
&= \lim_{\nu \to \infty} (2u^\nu - u^2 - u^1, u^2 - u^1) = \|u^2 - u^1\|^2
\end{aligned}
$$

Exchanging the role of u^1 and u^2 we get $u^1 = u^2$. $\qquad \square$

Remark 6. Assume $\{\varphi^n\}$ increases (then, [2], theorem 3.20, p. 298, $\varphi^n \xrightarrow{M} \varphi = \sup_n \varphi^n$) or $\varphi^n \equiv \varphi$ on dom φ. Let $\lambda > 0$. By the strong unicity of the proximal point, we get

$$\frac{1}{2\lambda} \|(I + \lambda \partial \varphi^n)^{-1}(v) - (I + \lambda \partial \varphi^{-1}(v)\|^2 \leq \varphi_\lambda(v) - \varphi_\lambda^n(v), \ \forall v \in U.$$

This implies $\varphi_\lambda(v) \geq \varphi_\lambda^n(v), \ \forall v \in U$.

If u is a solution of (P), it follows

$$\|(I + \lambda\partial\varphi^n)^{-1}(u - \lambda f) - u\| \le (2\lambda[\varphi_\lambda(u - \lambda f) - \varphi_\lambda^n(u - \lambda f)]^{1/2}. \tag{19}$$

Doing again the proof of theorem 3 from the inequality (16), we see that we may replace the assumption $\sum_n d_{\underline{\lambda},\rho_1(u)}^n < +\infty$ by

$$\sum_n (\lambda_n[\varphi_{\lambda_n}(u - \lambda_n f) - \varphi_{\lambda_n}^n(u - \lambda_n f)])^{1/2} < +\infty \tag{20}$$

without making use of proposition 3.

Moreover, in the case of $\{u^n\}$ generated by (F'), following remark 5 (ii), we can take $\bar{\lambda} = +\infty$ with $\sum_n \lambda_n\|g^n\| < +\infty$ and $\sum_n \sqrt{\lambda_n \varepsilon_n} < +\infty$. As already mentioned (remark 5, (i)) if U is finite dimensional the assumption $\forall\rho \ge 0$ $\lim_{n\to\infty} d_{\underline{\lambda},\rho}^n = 0$ is nothing else than the Mosco convergence of φ^n to φ. For instance, the context of [5] appears as a particular of the present one. It is not difficult to see that the technical assumption H introduced there implies (20) above, and therefore, that theorem 5 of [5] is a consequence of our theorem 3.

Remark 7. A similar result to theorem 3 can be obtained for the fixed-point problem $u = Pu$ where P is a steady nonexpansive (i.e. $\|Pu - Pv\|^2 \le (Pu - Pv, u - v)$, $\forall u, v \in U$) mapping from U to U (here $P = (I + \lambda\partial\varphi)^{-1}$) and $\{u^n\}$ generated by the iteration scheme

$$u^n = P_n u^{n-1} + e^n,$$

where P_n is a nonexpansive mapping from U to U, by introducing the semi-distance

$$\delta_\rho^n = \sup_{\|v\|\le\rho} \|P_n v - Pv\|,$$

and reducing to [12] (chap. V).

4. Applications

4.1. Variational approximation

Let $\{C_n\}$ be an increasing sequence of nonempty closed convex subsets of U. Then ([2]), $\varphi^n \xrightarrow{M} \varphi$ decreasingly, where φ^n (resp. φ) is the indicator function of C_n (resp. C) with $C = \overline{\cup_n C_n}$. So, we recover the diagonal method of Boyer-Martinet-Sonntag for the problem $\inf_C J$ approximated by $\inf_{C_n} J$. Results of convergence can be derived from theorem 1, theorem 2 and theorem 3.

4.2. Exterior penalization

Let $\varphi = \varphi_0 + \psi_C$ with $\varphi_0 : U \to \mathbb{R}$ a continuous convex function and ψ_C the indicator function of the nonempty closed convex subset C assumed to be described by

$$C = \{v \in U; Bv \le 0\}$$

where B is a continuous convex mapping from U to Y, a normed vector lattice ([16]) the norm of which is non decreasing on the positive cone Y_+.

Define the two continuous convex functions

$$\Phi_i : U \to \mathbb{R}^+, \ i = 1, 2,$$

by

$$\Phi_1(v) = \|(Bv)^+\|_Y, \quad \Phi_2(v) = \frac{1}{2}\|(Bv)^+\|_Y^2.$$

Then, we have

$$C = \Phi_i^{-1}(0), \quad i = 1, 2.$$

Let

$$\varphi_i^n = \varphi_0 + r_n \Phi_i, \quad i = 1, 2, \ r_n > 0.$$

Then, φ and $\{\varphi_i^n\}$, $i = 1, 2$, agree with remark 6. In particular $\varphi_\lambda \ge (\varphi_i^n)_\lambda$, $\forall \lambda > 0$, $\forall n$.

We assume that Y_+ has a non-empty interior $\overset{\circ}{Y}_+$ and that

$$\left.\begin{array}{l} \text{for each } \overline{y} \in -\overset{\circ}{Y}_+, \text{ there exists } c > 0 \text{ such that for} \\ \text{every } p \in Y_+' \text{ (dual positive cone)}, \ < p, \overline{y} > \le -c\|p\|_* \end{array}\right\} \tag{21}$$

Examples of such a space Y satisfying all the above conditions are:

(i) the space $\mathbb{R}^N$ ordered by the order product of $\mathbb{R}$ and equipped with the ℓ_p-norm, $1 \le p \le +\infty$.

(ii) the space of real continuous functions over a compact space equipped with the norm of uniform convergence, and ordered by the cone of non-negative functions.

(iii) the space $L^\infty(\Omega, \Sigma, \mu)$ of measurable and bounded functions over a measured space Ω, equipped with the essential-sup norm, and ordered by the cone of μ-almost everywhere non negative functions.

We assume moreover the Slater condition satisfied: there exists $\overline{u} \in C$ such that $-B\overline{u} \in \overset{\circ}{Y}_+$.

Proposition 5. Assume $\inf(P) > -\infty$.

1°   Take $\varphi^n = \varphi_1^n$

(i) $\forall \lambda > 0$, $\forall u \in U$, $\exists r(\lambda, u) \ge 0$ such that

$$\varphi_\lambda(u) \le \varphi_\lambda^n(u) \ \forall n, r_n \ge r(\lambda, u)$$

(ii) $\forall \underline{\lambda} > 0$, $\forall \rho \ge 0$, $\exists r \ge 0$ such that

$$d_{\lambda, \rho}^n = 0 \quad \forall n, r_n \ge r, \forall \lambda \ge \underline{\lambda}.$$

    2°   Take $\varphi^n = \varphi_2^n$

(i) $\forall \lambda > 0, \forall u \in U, \exists \mu(\lambda, u) \geq 0$ such that

$$\varphi_\lambda(u) \leq \varphi_\lambda^n(u) + \mu(\lambda, u)/r_n, \quad \forall n$$

(ii) $\forall \underline{\lambda} > 0, \forall \rho \geq 0, \exists \mu \geq 0$ such that

$$d_{\lambda,\rho}^n \leq \mu/r_n \quad \forall n, \forall \lambda \geq \underline{\lambda}.$$

Proof.

There exists ([8] chap. III, theorem 5.1), $p(\lambda, u) \in Y_+'$ such that

$$\forall v \in U, \; \varphi_\lambda(u) \leq \frac{1}{2\lambda}\|v - u\|^2 + \varphi_0(v) + \; < p(\lambda, u), Bv > \tag{22}$$

it follows from assumption (21) and the Slater condition that

$$\|p(\lambda, u)\|_* \leq (\frac{1}{2\lambda}\|\overline{u} - u\|^2 + \varphi_0(\overline{u}) - \inf(P))/c.$$

1°   We have

$$\forall v \in U, \; < p(\lambda, u), Bv > \; \leq \; < p(\lambda, u), (Bv)^+ > \; \leq \|p(\lambda, u)\|_* \|(Bv)^+\|.$$

So, (i) is satisfied with $r(\lambda, u) = \|p(\lambda, u)\|_*$ and (ii), with

$$r = (\frac{1}{\underline{\lambda}}\|\overline{u}\|^2 + \rho^2) + \varphi_0(\overline{u}) - \inf(P))/c.$$

2°   We have

$$\forall v \in U, \; < p(\lambda, u), Bv > \; \leq \frac{1}{2r_n}\|p(\lambda, u)\|_*^2 + \frac{r_n}{2}\|(Bv)^+\|^2.$$

So, (i) is satisfied with $\mu(\lambda, u) = \frac{1}{2}r(\lambda, u)^2$ and (ii), with $\mu = \frac{1}{2}r^2$. $\square$

If $r_n \to \infty$, it can be easily verified that $\varphi_i^n \xrightarrow{M} \varphi$ (this is also a consequence of proposition 2 and the above estimates). So theorem 1 can be applied, but also theorem 2 and theorem 3 (if $\sum \sqrt{\varepsilon_n} < +\infty$ and $\sum \frac{1}{\sqrt{r_n}} < +\infty$ for φ_2^n).

Remark 8. Incidentally, proposition 3, and the above estimate (ii) enable us to estimate the error on the (unique) solution of the problem

$$\inf_C \{\frac{1}{2\lambda}\|\cdot\|^2 + \varphi_0\}, \; \lambda > 0$$

approximated by the solution u^n of the problem

$$\inf_U \{\frac{1}{2\lambda}\|.\|^2 + \varphi_0 + r_n \Phi_2\}.$$

In fact, we get $\|u^n - u\| = \delta_{\lambda,0}^n = 0 \,(\frac{1}{\sqrt{r_n}})$.

Remark 9. (i) In the context of convex programming

$$C = \{v \in \mathbb{R}^n; f_i(v) \leq 0, \; i = 1, \cdots, m\}.$$

If $Y = \mathbb{R}^n$ is equipped with the l_1-norm, then Φ_1 is the classical exact penalty function $\sum_i f_i^+$. With the l_2-norm, $\Phi_2 = \frac{1}{2}\sum_i (f_i^+)^2$ is the classical differentiable penalty function.

(ii) With $\varphi^n = \varphi_1^n$, $\forall \rho \geq 0$, $d_{\lambda,\rho}^n = 0$ for n large enough.
So theorem 1, 2, 3 can be applied.
Moreover by proposition 3, $\delta_{\lambda_n,\rho}^n = 0$ for n large enough (depending on ρ). Therefore, if $\{u^n\}$ and $\{\lambda_n\}$ are bounded, for n large enough,

$$u^n - e^n = (I + \lambda_n \partial \varphi)^{-1}(u^{n-1} - \lambda_n J'(u^{n-1}))$$

i.e. the perturbation holds only in the error term. In particular, $u^n - e^n \in \operatorname{dom} \varphi$ for n large enough. Another result of [5] (theorem 6), about the finite convergence of the penalty-proximal method in the case of linear programming, appears as a particular case of this remark.

4.3. A non-monotone penalization

Here $U = \mathbb{R}^N$. We assume that φ is bounded above on its effective domain C which is described by

$$C = \{v \in \mathbb{R}^N, g(v) \leq 0\},$$

where $g : \mathbb{R}^N \to \mathbb{R}$ is a given convex function. Assume the interior of C, $\overset{\circ}{C} = \{v \in \mathbb{R}^N, g(v) < 0\}$ nonempty. Let $M > \sup_C \varphi$ (if $\varphi = \varphi_0 + \psi_C$) with φ_0 everywhere finite, replace g by $\max\{g, \varphi_0 - \varphi_0(v_0)\}$ where $v_0 \in C$, $\varphi_0(v_0) > \inf \varphi$, and take $M > \varphi_0(v_0)$). Let

$$\tilde{\varphi} = \begin{cases} \varphi & \text{on } C \\ M & \text{otherwise} \end{cases}.$$

We note that $\tilde{\varphi}$ is everywhere finite, lower-semicontinuous, but no more convex. Finally, let

$$\varphi^n = \max\{\tilde{\varphi}, r_n g + M\}, \quad r_n > 0.$$

This type of penalization, which is not monotone, has been studied by Alart ([1]) outside the context of variational convergence.

He proved that φ^n is an everywhere finite *convex* function and the convergence of the perturbed penalty-proximal method (iteration (F')) if g is coercive and $\sum_n \varepsilon_n / r_n <$

$+\infty$. In fact ([11]) this result is a consequence of theorem 2 with an estimate of $d^n_{\lambda,\rho}$ like in proposition 5, (ii), and can be improved by applying theorem 3.

5. Conclusion

During the past twenty years, the variational convergence theory had had many applications in the limit analysis of sequences of variational problems (optimization, inequations, min-max, saddle-point). The aim of the present work was to prove its power in the study of perturbed iterative optimization methods. There is no doubt that the ideas presented here on a prototype method, could be successfully applied to other ones.

References.

[1] Alart, P. (1985): *Contribution à la résolution numérique des inclusions différentielles.* Thèse de 3ème cycle, Montpellier.

[2] Attouch, H. (1984): *Variational convergence for functions and operators.* Pitman Advance Publishing Program.

[3] Attouch, H., Wets R. J. B. (1984): *Isometries for the Legendre-Fenchel transform.* Transactions of the AMS, Vol. 296, 33 – 60.

[4] Auslender, A. (1985): *Numerical methods for non-differentiable convex optimization.* Math. Progr. Studies, No. 30, Ed. Vial, Cornet, Nguyen.

[5] Auslender, A., Crouzeix, J. P., Fedit, P. (1986): *Penalty-proximal methods in convex programming.* To appear in JOTA.

[6] Boyer, R. (1974): *Quelques algorithmes diagonaux en optimisation convexe.* Thése de 3ème cycle, Université de Provence.

[7] Cohen, G. (1980): *Auxiliary problem principle and decomposition of optimization problems.* JOTA 32, No. 3, 277 – 305.

[8] Ekeland, I., Temam, R. (1974): *Analyse convexe et problèmes variationnels.* Dunod, Gauthier-Villars.

[9] Furuya, H., Miyashiba, K., Kenmochi, N. (1986): *Asymptotic behaviour of solutions to a class of non linear equations.* Journal Diff. Eq. 62, No. 1, 73 – 94.

[10] Lemaire, B. (1977): *Approximations successives pour certains problèmes périodiques.* Séminaire d'Analyse Convexe, Montpellier, exposé No. 21.

[11] Lemaire, B., Alart, P.: *Perturbation of the proximal regularization method.* To appear.

[12] Martinet, B. (1972): *Algorithmes pour la résolution de problèmes d'optimisation et de minimax.* Thèse d'Etat. Université de Grenoble.

[13] Martinet, B. (1978): *Perturbation des méthodes d'optimisation*. R.A.I.R.O., Analyse Numérique 12, No. 2, 153 – 171.

[14] Moreau, J. J. (1965): *Proximité et dualité dans un espace hilbertien*. Bull. Soc. Math. France 93, 273 – 299.

[15] Ortega, J. M., Rheinboldt, W. C. (1970): *Iterative solution of nonlinear equations in several variables*. Acad. Press.

[16] Peressini, A. R. (1967): *Ordered topological vector spaces*. Harper's series in modern Math.

[17] Rockafellar R. T. (1976): *Monotone operators and the proximal point algorithm*. SIAM J. Control and Optimization 14, No. 5, 877 – 898.

[18] Sonntag, Y. (1982): *Convergence au sens de U. Mosco: théorie et applications à l'approximation des solutions d'inéquations*. Thèse d'Etat. Université de Provence.

International Series of
Numerical Mathematics, Vol. 84
(c) 1988 Birkhäuser Verlag Basel

Approximate solutions for two-level optimization problems

P. Loridan
Université de Bourgogne
Département de Mathématiques
Laboratoire d'Analyse Numérique
B. P. 138
21004 Dijon Cedex, France

J. Morgan
Dipartimento di Matematica e Applicazioni
Via Mezzocannone 8
80134 Napoli, Italia

Abstract. This paper is devoted to general results for approximating two-level optimization problems in which the set of solutions to the lower level problem is not a singleton.

In particular, we give sufficient conditions for upper semicontinuity of ε-Stackelberg solutions by using the notions of convergence presented at "Journées Fermat: Mathematics for Optimization" (Toulouse). ([8]).

Key words: Two level optimization problem, approximate solution, Stackelberg solution, Stackelberg equilibrium pair, asymptotically Stackelberg approximating sequence, Γ-convergence, variational convergence.

1. Introduction.

We are concerned with two-level optimization problems corresponding to two-player Stackelberg games in which player 1 has the leadership in playing the game whereas player 2 knows only the strategy decided by player 1.

More precisely, the aim of the two players is to minimize their objective functionals with the following rules:

- player 1 (called the leader) knows the objective functional of player 2 and chooses firstly his optimal strategy knowing that player 2 reacts by playing optimally.
- for the announced strategy of player 1, player 2 (called the follower) selects one strategy in order to minimize his own objective and his choice cannot be affected by the leader.

In the case where the optimal reaction set of the follower to the strategy announced by the leader is a singleton, we have a two-level optimization problem which can be stated in the following way:

let X and Y be two topological spaces and f_i, $i = 1, 2$, two functionals defined on $X \times Y$ and valued in $\overline{\mathbb{R}}$ (with $\overline{\mathbb{R}} = \mathbb{R} \cup \{+\infty\} \cup \{-\infty\}$), find $\overline{x} \in X$ such that

$$f_1(\overline{x}, \hat{y}(\overline{x})) = \inf_{x \in X} f_1(x, \hat{y}(x)),$$

where $\hat{y}(x)$ is the solution to the parametric lower level problem $P(x)$:

$$\inf_{y \in Y} f_2(x, y).$$

In this formulation, constraints can be included in the objective functionals by using indicator functionals since f_1 and f_2 are valued in $\overline{\mathbb{R}}$.

The optimal solution $\hat{y}(x)$ is also called the rational response of the follower to the strategy x announced by the leader. Any optimal strategy chosen by the leader for minimizing $f_1(x, \hat{y}(x))$ is called a Stackelberg solution.

This concept has been introduced for the first time by Von Stackelberg ([14]) for static economic problems and a dynamic version has also been studied with optimal control problems (see, for example, [12], [13]).

In the case where the set of solutions to the lower level problem $P(x)$ is not a singleton, we consider the optimal set:

$$M_2(x) = \{\hat{y} \in Y / f_2(x, \hat{y}) = \inf_{y \in Y} f_2(x, y)\}.$$

Since the leader cannot force the choice of the follower among his optimal strategies in $M_2(x)$, he has to provide himself against the possible worst choice of the follower by minimizing $\text{Sup}_{y \in M_2(x)} f_1(x, y)$.

In the sequel, we shall deal with this last case. The main purpose of our paper is to give some results for approximate solutions by adapting a theoretical approximation scheme that we have presented in [8].

In section 2, we begin with a description of the two-level problem and some definitions concerning, in particular, approximate solutions: ε-Stackelberg solutions, ε-Stackelberg equilibrium pairs. In section 3, we present the theoretical framework for approximating the two-level problem and we state the main assumptions.

Sections 4 and 5 are devoted to approximation results. In particular, we prove that any accumulation point of a sequence of ε-solutions to the approximate problems defined in the previous sections, is an ε-solution to the considered two-level optimization problem, providing that a rather strong additional assumption is satisfied. In the next section, we give some sufficient conditions for verifying such an assumption. Finally, in section 7, we present a result for asymptotically Stackelberg approximating sequences generalizing the one given in [8].

The paper is organized as follows:

2 – The two-level optimization problem: description and definitions
3 – A theoretical approximation scheme: description and main assumptions
4 – Approximation results for the lower level problems
5 – Approximations results for the problem (S)
6 – Sufficient conditions for verifying (H)
7 – Asymptotically Stackelberg approximating sequences.

2. The two-level optimization problem: Description and definitions.

Let X and Y be two topological spaces and f_i, $i = 1, 2$, two functionals defined on $X \times Y$ and valued in $\overline{\mathbb{R}}$. We consider the following two-level optimization problem (S) corresponding to a Stackelberg game:

$$(S) \begin{cases} \text{Find } \overline{x} \in X \text{ such that:} \\[2mm] \qquad \sup_{y \in M_2(x)} f_1(\overline{x}, y) = \inf_{x \in X} \sup_{y \in M_2(x)} f_1(x, y) \\[2mm] \text{where } M_2(x) \text{ is the set of optimal solutions to the lower level problem } P(x): \\[2mm] \qquad P(x) \begin{cases} \text{Minimize } f_2(x, y) \\ \text{subject to } y \in Y \end{cases} \end{cases}$$

Let us introduce the following notations:

$$w_1(x) = \sup_{y \in M_2(x)} f_1(x, y) \qquad v_1 = \inf_{x \in X} w_1(x).$$

Definition 2-1
Any $\overline{x} \in X$ verifying $v_1 = w_1(\overline{x})$ is called a Stackelberg solution to (S).

Definition 2-2
Any pair $(\overline{x}, \overline{y}) \in X \times Y$ verifying $v_1 = w_1(\overline{x})$ and $y \in M_2(\overline{x})$ is called a Stackelberg equilibrium pair.

Remark 2-1
A Stackelberg solution does not necessarily exist, even if the objective functionals are continuous and X and Y are compact spaces. For example (see [2]), let us choose $X = Y = [0, 1]$, $f_1(x, y) = -xy$, $f_2(x, y) = (x - \frac{1}{2})y$. With the previous notations, we have:

$$M_2(x) = \{0\}, w_1(x) = 0, \text{ for any } x, \frac{1}{2} < x \leq 1$$

$$M_2(x) = [0, 1], w_1(x) = 0, \text{ if } x = \frac{1}{2}$$

$$M_2(x) = \{1\}, w_1(x) = -x, \text{ for any } x, 0 \leq x < \frac{1}{2}$$

We have $v_1 = -\frac{1}{2}$ but w_1 is not lower semicontinuous at $x = \frac{1}{2}$ and the corresponding two-level optimization problem has no solution.

In the sequel, *we shall assume that v_1 is a finite number*, for the sake of simplicity. We introduce the definitions concernng approximate solutions.

Definition 2-3
Let $\varepsilon > 0$ be a given number. We shall say that $\overline{x}$ is an ε-Stackelberg solution if and only if $\overline{x} \in X$ and $w_1(\overline{x}) \leq v_1 + \varepsilon$.

Definition 2-4

We shall say that a pair $(\overline{x}, \overline{y})$ is an ε-Stackelberg equilibrium pair if and only if $\overline{x}$ is an ε-Stackelberg solution and $\overline{y} \in M_2(\overline{x})$.

Now, we present a general framework for approximating (S). This approach has been firstly introduced in [8], in the case where the lower level problem has an unique solution.

3. A theoretical approximation scheme: Description and main assumptions.

We consider a general approach for approximating (S) by a sequence of two-level optimization problems (S_n), $n \in \mathbb{N}$, corresponding to approximate Stackelberg games:

$$(S_n) \begin{cases} \text{Find } \overline{x}_n \in X \text{ such that:} \\[2mm] \displaystyle \sup_{y \in M_{2,n}(x)} f_{1,n}(\overline{x}_n, y) = \inf_{x \in X} \sup_{y \in M_{2,n}(x)} f_{1,n}(x, y) \\[2mm] \text{where } M_{2,n}(x) \text{ is the set of optimal solutions to the lower level problem } P_n(x): \\[2mm] \qquad P_n(x) \begin{cases} \text{Minimize } f_{2,n}(x, y) \\ \text{subject to } y \in Y \end{cases} \end{cases}$$

with $f_{1,n}$ and $f_{2,n}$ defined on $X \times Y$ and valued in $\overline{\mathbb{R}}$ for $n \in \mathbb{N}$.

In order to obtain our approximation results for approximate solutions, we impose the following main assumptions for the leader and the follower.

Main assumptions

(L1) For any $(x, y) \in X \times Y$, for any sequence (x_n, y_n) converging to (x, y) in $X \times Y$, we have:
$$\liminf_{n \to +\infty} f_{1,n}(x_n, y_n) \geq f_1(x, y)$$

(L2) For any $x \in X$, there exists a sequence x_n converging to x in X such that, for any $y \in Y$ and for any sequence y_n converging to y in Y:
$$\limsup_{n \to +\infty} f_{1,n}(x_n, y_n) \leq f_1(x, y)$$

(F1) For any $(x, y) \in X \times Y$, for any sequence (x_n, y_n) converging to (x, y) in $X \times Y$, we have:
$$\liminf_{n \to +\infty} f_{2,n}(x_n, y_n) \geq f_2(x, y)$$

(F2) For any $(x, y) \in X \times Y$, for any sequence x_n converging to x in X, there exists a sequence y_n such that
$$\limsup_{n \to +\infty} f_{2,n}(x_n, y_n) \leq f_2(x, y)$$

Remark 3-1

1. In [7], we have presented an application of assumptions (F1) and (F2) to penalty methods, with a generalization of some results given in [11].
2. Remarks related to other convergence concepts have been reported in [8].
3. For the convenience of the reader, we also mention the following observations:
   - if y_n is fixed equal to y for any n in (L1) and (L2), we get the definition of Γ-convergence (or epiconvergence) of the sequence $f_{1,n}(.,y)$ to $f_1(.,y)$ (see [3], [4], [1], [6])
   - if x_n is fixed equal to x for any n in (F1) and (F2), we get the variational convergence of the sequence $f_{2,n}(x,.)$ to $f_2(x,.)$. ([15])

4. Approximation results for the lower level problems.

In the sequel, we shall use the following notations:

$$v_2(x) = \inf_{y \in Y} f_2(x,y) \qquad v_{2,n}(x) = \inf_{y \in Y} f_{2,n}(x,y)$$
$$M_2(x) = \{\bar{y} \in Y / v_2(x) = f_2(x,\bar{y})\}$$
$$M_{2,n}(x) = \{\bar{y} \in Y / v_{2,n}(x) = f_{2,n}(x,\bar{y})\}.$$

For the sake of simplicity, we shall assume that $v_2(x)$ and $v_{2,n}(x)$ *are finite numbers and that* $M_2(x)$ *and* $M_{2,n}(x)$ *are nonempty*, for any $x \in X$ and any $n \in \mathbb{N}$.

Then, with assumptions (F1) and (F2) we have the following propositions:

Proposition 4-1

For any $x \in X$ and any sequence x_n converging to x in X, we have

$$\limsup_{n \to +\infty} M_{2,n}(x_n) \subset M_2(x), \quad \limsup v_{2,n}(x_n) \leq v_2(x).$$

Proposition 4-2

If, moreover, $\limsup M_{2,n}(x_n) \neq \emptyset$ for a sequence x_n converging to x in X, then, for some subsequence, we have $\lim_{n \to +\infty} v_{2,n}(x_n) = v_2(x)$.

If Y is compact, the result holds for the original sequence and for any sequence converging to x in X.

The proofs are rather straightforward. We give them for convenience sake.

Proof of proposition 4-1

a) Let $x \in X$ and x_n converging to x in X when $n \to +\infty$. If $\limsup M_{2,n}(x_n)$ is empty, there is nothing to prove. If $\bar{y} \in \limsup M_{2,n}(x_n)$, there exists a sequence $\bar{y}_n$, $n \in N' \subset \mathbb{N}$, such that $\bar{y}_n \in M_{2,n}(x_n)$ for any $n \in N'$ and $\lim_{\substack{n \to +\infty \\ n \in N'}} \bar{y}_n = \bar{y}$.

$$\text{From (F1),} \qquad \liminf_{\substack{n \to +\infty \\ n \in N'}} f_{2,n}(x_n, \bar{y}_n) \geq f_2(x, \bar{y}). \qquad (4-1)$$

From (F2), for any $y \in Y$, there exists a sequence y_n such that

$$\limsup_{n \to +\infty} f_{2,n}(x_n, y_n) \leq f_2(x, y). \tag{4-2}$$

Furthermore, $f_{2,n}(x_n, \bar{y}_n) \leq f_{2,n}(x_n, y_n)$ for any $n \in N'$. $\qquad (4-3)$

So, with inequalities (4-1), (4-2), (4-3), we get $f_2(x, \bar{y}) \leq f_2(x, y)$ for any $y \in Y$. Hence $\bar{y} \in M_2(x)$ and $\limsup M_{2,n}(x_n) \subset M_2(x)$.

b) Let $\varepsilon > 0$ be a given number. There exists $y_\varepsilon \in Y$ such that $f_2(x, y_\varepsilon) \leq v_2(x) + \varepsilon$. Let x_n be a sequence converging to x in X. From (F2), there exists a sequence y_n^ε such that:

$$\limsup_{n \to +\infty} v_{2,n}(x_n) \leq \limsup_{n \to +\infty} f_{2,n}(x_n, y_n^\varepsilon) \leq f_2(x, y_\varepsilon) \leq v_2(x) + \varepsilon.$$

Hence, for any $\varepsilon > 0$ and for any sequence x_n converging to x in X, we have $\limsup v_{2,n}(x_n) \leq v_2(x) + \varepsilon$.

Proof of proposition 4-2

a) Let x be an element of X and x_n a sequence converging to x in X. Let $\bar{y} \in \limsup M_{2,n}(x_n)$. There exists a subsequence $\bar{y}_n$, $n \in N' \subset \mathbb{N}$ verifying $\bar{y}_n \in M_{2,n}(x_n)$ for any $n \in N'$ and such that $\bar{y}_n$ converges to $\bar{y}$ when $n \to +\infty$, $n \in N'$.

$$\text{From (F1),} \qquad \liminf_{\substack{n \to +\infty \\ n \in N'}} f_{2,n}(x_n, \bar{y}_n) \geq f_2(x, \bar{y}).$$

But, we have $f_{2,n}(x_n, \bar{y}_n) = v_{2,n}(x_n)$ for any $n \in N'$ and $f_2(x, \bar{y}) = v_2(x)$ since $\bar{y} \in M_2(x)$ from Proposition 4-1.

Therefore, $v_2(x) \leq \liminf_{\substack{n \to +\infty \\ n \in N'}} v_{2,n}(x_n)$ and, with Proposition 4-1, we get $v_2(x) = \lim_{\substack{n \to +\infty \\ n \in N'}} v_{2,n}(x_n)$.

b) We have $\limsup_{n \to +\infty} v_{2,n}(x_n) \leq v_2(x)$ and it is assumed that $v_2(x)$ is a finite number. So the sequence $v_{2,n}(x_n)$ is bounded above and there exists a subsequence $v_{2,n}(x_n)$, $n \in N_1 \subset \mathbb{N}$, converging to $v^* \geq -\infty$. We have assumed that $M_{2,n}(x)$ is nonempty for any $x \in X$. So there exists $\bar{y}_n \in M_{2,n}(x_n)$ such that $v_{2,n}(x_n) = f_{2,n}(x_n, \bar{y}_n)$ for any $n \in N_1$. From the compactness of Y, there exists a subsequence $\bar{y}_n$, $n \in N_2 \subset \mathbb{N}$, converging to $\bar{y}$ in Y and by using Proposition 4-1, $\bar{y} \in M_2(x)$.

From (F1), $\liminf_{\substack{n \to +\infty \\ n \in N_2}} f_{2,n}(x_n, \bar{y}_n) \geq f_2(x, \bar{y})$, and, with the previous results, we get $v^* \geq v_2(x)$.

Since $v^* = \lim_{\substack{n \to +\infty \\ n \in N_1}} v_{2,n}(x_n) \leq \limsup_{n \to +\infty} v_{2,n}(x_n) \leq v_2(x)$, we deduce $v_2(x) = v^*$.

This result holds for any converging subsequence. Hence $v_2(x)$ is the limit of the sequence $v_{2,n}(x_n)$, $n \in \mathbb{N}$. Obviously, we have the same result for any sequence x_n converging to x in X and the proof is complete.

Remark 4-1

Let x_n be a sequence converging to x and let us denote by g_n and g the functionals defined by:

$$g_n(y) = f_{2,n}(x_n, y) \quad \text{and} \quad g(y) = f_2(x, y).$$

Then, from (F1) and (F2), the sequence g_n variationally converges to g and by adapting the results given in [16], we also have the following proposition:

Proposition 4-3

Let x_n be a sequence converging to x in X. If there exists a relatively compact sequence y_n in Y such that:

$$\lim_{n \to +\infty} [f_{2,n}(x_n, y_n) - v_{2,n}(x_n)] = 0$$

then we have: $\lim_{n \to +\infty} v_{2,n}(x_n) = v_2(x)$.

Let $\eta > 0$ be a given number. We define the sets of approximate solutions (up to η) for the lower level problems $P(x)$ and $P_n(x)$, $n \in \mathbb{N}$:

$$M_2(x, \eta) = \{\bar{y} \in Y / f_2(x, \bar{y}) \leq v_2(x) + \eta\}$$
$$M_{2,n}(x, \eta) = \{\bar{y} \in Y / f_{2,n}(x, \bar{y}) \leq v_{2,n}(x) + \eta\}.$$

With (F1) and (F2), we also get an extension of Proposition 4-1:

Proposition 4-4

For any $x \in X$ and any sequence x_n converging to x in X, we have

$$\limsup M_{2,n}(x_n, \eta) \subset M_2(x, \eta).$$

Proof

The proof is straightforward and analogous with the one given in Proposition 4-1. So, it will be omitted. The result can also be derived from the variational convergence of g_n to g ([16]).

5. Approximation results for the problem (S).

In the sequel, we shall consider the following notations:

$$w_1(x) = \sup_{y \in M_2(x)} f_1(x, y) \quad v_1 = \inf_{x \in X} w_1(x)$$
$$w_{1,n}(x) = \sup_{y \in M_{2,n}(x)} f_{1,n}(x, y) \quad v_{1,n} = \inf_{x \in X} w_{1,n}(x).$$

Recall we have assumed that $M_2(x)$ and $M_{2,n}(x)$ are nonempty for any $x \in X$ and any $n \in \mathbb{N}$, and that v_1 is a finite number, for the sake of simplicity.

Then, by using (F1), (F2) and (L2), we get:

Proposition 5-1

If Y is compact, then, for any $x \in X$, there exists a sequence x_n converging to x in X such that:

$$\limsup_{n \to +\infty} w_{1,n}(x_n) \leq w_1(x).$$

Furthermore, $\limsup_{n \to +\infty} v_{1,n} \leq v_1$.

Proof

We begin with the first part of the proposition. Let $x \in X$. If $w_1(x) = +\infty$, there is nothing to prove. Otherwise, $w_1(x)$ is a finite number since $v_1 > -\infty$.

From (L2), there exists a sequence x_n converging to x in X such that, for any $y \in Y$ and for any sequence y_n converging to y in Y,

$$\limsup_{n \to +\infty} f_{1,n}(x_n, y_n) \leq f_1(x, y).$$

If there exists $n_0 \in \mathbb{N}$ such that $w_{1,n}(x_n) = -\infty$ for any $n \geq n_0$, then we have obviously $\limsup_{n \to +\infty} w_{1,n}(x_n) \leq w_1(x)$. If this is not the case, there exists an infinite subsequence $w_{1,n}(x_n)$, $n \in N' \subset \mathbb{N}$, verifying $w_{1,n}(x_n) > -\infty$ for any $n \in N'$. For such a subsequence we have $_{1,n} \leq +\infty$, at least for n sufficiently large. Indeed, if not, for any $A > 0$, there would exist a sequence $y_n^* \in M_{2,n}(x_n)$ such that $f_{1,n}(x_n, y_n^*) \geq A$, for n sufficiently large. Then, since Y is compact, there would exist an infinite subsequence y_n^*, $n \in N''$, such that y_n^* converges to y^*, when $n \to +\infty$, $n \in N''$, and, from proposition 4-1, $y^* \in M_2(x)$. So, we should deduce:

$$A \leq \limsup_{\substack{n \to +\infty \\ n \in N''}} f_{1,n}(x_n, y_n^*) \leq f_1(x, y^*) \leq w_1(x).$$

Since $w_1(x) < +\infty$, we get a contradiction for A sufficiently large. Hence, $w_{1,n}(x_n) < +\infty$ for $n \in N'$ sufficiently large and, for any $\varepsilon > 0$, there exists a sequence y_n^ε, $n \in N'$, verifying $y_n^\varepsilon \in M_{2,n}(x_n)$, $n \in N'$, such that

$$w_{1,n}(x_n) \leq f_{1,n}(x_n, y_n^\varepsilon) + \varepsilon, \ n \in N'. \tag{5-1}$$

From the compactness of Y, there exists a subsequence y_n^ε, $n \in N_1$, converging to y^ε, and, as previously, $y^\varepsilon \in M_2(x)$.

By using inequality (5-1) and assumption (L2), we get:

$$\limsup_{\substack{n \to +\infty \\ n \in N_1}} w_{1,n}(x_n) \leq \limsup_{\substack{n \to +\infty \\ n \in N_1}} f_{1,n}(x_n, y_n^\varepsilon) + \varepsilon$$

$$\leq f_1(x, y^\varepsilon) + \varepsilon \leq w_1(x) + \varepsilon$$

Finally, we have proved that, for any $\varepsilon > 0$, there exists a sequence x_n converging to x in X, such that:

$$\limsup_{n \to +\infty} w_{1,n}(x_n) \leq w_1(x) + \varepsilon.$$

Now, let us prove the second part of propositon 5-1.
For any $\varepsilon > 0$, there exists $x_\varepsilon \in X$ such that:

$$w_1(x_\varepsilon) \leq v_1 + \varepsilon. \tag{5-2}$$

From the first part, there exists a sequence x_n^ε converging to x_ε in X such that $\limsup_{n \to +\infty} w_{1,n}(x_n^\varepsilon) \leq w_1(x_\varepsilon)$ and by using (5-2), we get:

$$\limsup_{n \to +\infty} v_{1,n} \leq v_1 + \varepsilon.$$

So, the proof is complete.

Remark 5-1

Let us denote by $M_1(\varepsilon)$ the set of ε-Stackelberg solutions to (S): $M_1(\varepsilon) = \{x \in X / w_1(x) \leq v_1 + \varepsilon\}$ and $M_{1,n}(\varepsilon) = \{x_n \in X / w_{1,n}(x) \leq v_{1,n} + \varepsilon\}$ the set of ε-solutions to (S_n). In order to obtain approximation results for approximate solutions to (S), we introduce an additional (strong! ...) assumption:

(H) For any $x \in X$ and any sequence x_n converging to x in X we have

$$M_2(x) \subset \liminf M_{2,n}(x_n).$$

Then, by using (L1) and (H), we get:

Proposition 5-2

For any $x \in X$ and any sequence x_n converging to x in X we have
$\liminf_{n \to +\infty} w_{1,n}(x_n) \geq w_1(x)$.

Proof

Let $x \in X$ and $x_n \to x$ when $n \to +\infty$.
Let $z \in M_2(x)$. There exists a sequence $z_n \to z$ verifying $z_n \in M_{2,n}(x_n)$ for all $n \geq n_0$ (assumption (H)).
We have $w_{1,n}(x_n) \geq f_{1,n}(x_n, z_n)$ and by using (L1):

$$\liminf_{n \to +\infty} w_{1,n}(x_n) \geq \liminf_{n \to +\infty} f_{1,n}(x_n, z_n) \geq f_1(x, z).$$

Hence $\liminf_{n \to +\infty} w_{1,n}(x_n) \geq f_1(x, z) \; \forall z \in M_2(x)$ that is to say:
$\liminf_{n \to +\infty} w_{1,n}(x_n) \geq w_1(x)$.

By using proposition 5-1 and proposition 5-2 we get an approximation result for ε-Stackelberg solutions:

Proposition 5-3
With the assumptions (L1), (L2), (F1), (F2), (H) and if Y is compact, we have

$$\limsup M_{1,n}(\varepsilon) \subset M_1(\varepsilon).$$

Proof
With propositions 5-1 and 5-2, we observe that $w_{1,n}$ Γ–converges to w_1. Then, the conclusion is a well-known result ([1]).

Remarks 5-2
1) From Γ–convergence, w_1 is lower semicontinuous on X. So if X is compact, we get a result for the existence of Stackelberg solutions to (S).
2) Let us consider the sets of ε-Stackelberg equilibrium pairs:

$$E(\varepsilon) = \{(x,y) \in X \times Y / x \in M_1(\varepsilon), y \in M_2(x)\}$$
$$E_n(\varepsilon) = \{(x,y) \in X \times Y / x \in M_{1,n}(\varepsilon), y \in M_{2,n}(x)\}.$$

Then, with proposition 4-1 and proposition 5-3 we have also:

Proposition 5-4
$$\limsup E_n(\varepsilon) \subset E(\varepsilon)$$

Proof
The proof is straightforward. Let $(\bar{x}, \bar{y}) \in \limsup E_n(\varepsilon)$. Then, there exists a sequence $(\bar{x}_n, \bar{y}_n)$, $n \in N' \subset \mathbb{N}$, such that $\bar{y}_n \in M_{2,n}(\bar{x}_n)$, $\bar{x}_n \in M_{1,n}(\varepsilon)$, for any $n \in N'$, and $\bar{x}_n$ converges to $\bar{x}$, $\bar{y}_n$ converges to $\bar{y}$ when $n \to +\infty$, $n \in N'$.
From proposition 4-1, we have $\bar{y} \in M_2(\bar{x})$. From proposition 5-3, we have $\bar{x} \in M_1(\varepsilon)$. Hence $(\bar{x}, \bar{y}) \in E(\varepsilon)$ and the proof is complete.

Remarks 5-3
1) What can be said when (H) is not satisfied? Let us introduce the sets of lower Stackelberg equilibrium pairs:

$$A = \{(x,y) \in X \times Y / y \in M_2(x), f_1(x,y) \leq v_1\}$$
$$A_n = \{(x,y) \in X \times Y / y \in M_{2,n}(x), f_{1,n}(x,y) \leq v_{1,n}\}$$

Then, from the previous results, we have easily:

$$\limsup A_n \subset A.$$

We also have a similar result for the sets of (ε, η)-lower Stackelberg equilibrium pairs:

$$A(\varepsilon, \eta) = \{(x,y) \in X \times Y / y \in M_2(x,\eta), f_1(x,y) \leq v_1 + \varepsilon\}$$
$$A_n(\varepsilon, \eta) = \{(x,y) \in X \times Y / y \in M_{2,n}(x,\eta), f_{1,n}(x,y) \leq v_{1,n} + \varepsilon\}$$

2) We notice that if $(\overline{x}, \overline{y})$ is a Stackelberg equilibrium pair, then $(\overline{x}, \overline{y}) \in A$. Besides, the set A also contains the concept of solution defined in [9].

3) Other results can also be obtained with $v_1(\eta) = \sup_{y \in M_2(x, \eta)} f_1(x, y)$.

6. Sufficient conditions for verifying (H).

From the previous section, assumption (H) is fundamental for obtaining approximation results. We now present two results in order to verify such an assumption.

6-1 First Result

With the previous notations, we assume that (F1) is satisfied as well as a modification of condition (F2) that we shall denote (F$\tilde{2}$):

(F$\tilde{2}$) For any $(x, y) \in X \times Y$, for any sequence x_n converging to x in X, there exists a sequence y_n converging to y in Y such that

$$\limsup_{n \to +\infty} f_{2,n}(x_n, y_n) \leq f_2(x, y).$$

Furthermore, we assume:

(H1) $M_{2,n}(x)$ is nonempty for any $x \in X$ and any $n \in N$

(H2) Y is a metric compact space

(H3) For any sequence $(x_n, y_n) \in X \times Y$ verifying
$\lim_{n \to +\infty}[f_{2,n}(x_n, y_n) - v_{2,n}(x_n)] = 0$, we have:
$\lim_{n \to +\infty} d(y_n, M_{2,n}(x_n)) = 0$ (where d denotes the distance on Y).

Then, with the conditions (F1), (F$\tilde{2}$), (H1), (H2), (H3), we have the following proposition:

Proposition 6-1

For any $x \in X$ and any sequence x_n converging to x in X, $\liminf M_{2,n}(x_n) \supset M_2(x)$.

Proof

Since Y is compact, we have $\limsup M_{2,n}(x_n) \neq \emptyset$ and with proposition 4-1, we deduce $M_2(x) \neq \emptyset$. Let $\overline{y} \in M_2(x)$.

From (F$\tilde{2}$), if x_n converges to x in X, there exists a sequence y_n converging to $\overline{y}$ in Y such that

$$\limsup_{n \to +\infty} f_{2,n}(x_n, y_n) \leq f_2(x, \overline{y}) = v_2(x)$$

and, by using (F1), we get $\lim_{n \to +\infty} f_{2,n}(x_n, y_n) = v_2(x)$.

But, from proposition 4.2, we also have $\lim_{n \to +\infty} v_{2,n}(x_n) = v_2(x)$, so $\lim_{n \to +\infty}[f_{2,n}(x_n, y_n) - v_{2,n}(x_n)] = 0$ and, by using (H3), we have $\lim_{n \to +\infty} d(y_n, M_{2,n}(x_n)) = 0$.

Finally, let us consider $\overline{y}_n \in M_{2,n}(x_n)$ such that

$$d(\overline{y}_n, y_n) \leq \frac{1}{n} + d(y_n, M_{2,n}(x_n)).$$

It is easy to prove that $\lim_{n \to +\infty} d(\overline{y}_n, \overline{y}) = 0$.

So, for $\overline{y} \in M_2(x)$, there exists a sequence $\overline{y}_n$ verifying $\overline{y}_n \in M_{2,n}(x_n)$ for any $n \in N$ and $\overline{y}_n \to \overline{y}$ when $n \to +\infty$.

This result means that (H) is satisfied and the proof is complete.

Remark 6-1

Similar results can be found in [5] for classical optimization problems.

6-2 Second Result

A motive for doing our second result is a paper of Robinson and Day [10] in which the authors have studied the continuity of solution sets for maximization problems:

$$\text{Maximize } \{\Theta(x, w) / x \in \Gamma(w)\}$$

where Γ is a multivalued function from a topological space W into a topological space X and the objective function Θ is defined from $X \times W$ into the set of real numbers by letting

$$\Theta(x, w) = \text{Min}\{\mu(x, w), \sigma(w)\}$$

where μ is strictly quasiconcave in x for each w and σ is continuous on W.

With such a definition of Θ, the solution set $M(w)$ defined by $M(w) = \{\overline{x} \in \Gamma(w) / \Theta(\overline{x}, w) = \text{Max}_{x \in \Gamma(w)} \Theta(x, w)\}$ is not necessarily a singleton. Furthermore, it is easy to observe that, in such a case, $\overline{x} \in M(w)$ if and only if $\overline{x} \in \Gamma(w)$ and $\Theta(\overline{x}, w) = \sigma(w)$.

In our case we shall consider:

$$f_2(x, y) = \text{Max}\{h_2(x, y), \sigma(x)\}$$
$$f_{2,n}(x, y) = \text{Max}\{h_{2,n}(x, y), \sigma_n(x)\}, \ n \in N$$

where: h_2 and $h_{2,n}$ are defined on $X \times Y$

σ and σ_n are defined on X.

First, it is easy to prove the following proposition:

Proposition 6-2

If h_2 and the sequence $h_{2,n}$ satisfy the conditions (F1) and (F2) (respectively (F1) and (F$\tilde{2}$)), if σ_n continuously converges to σ (that is to say, for any sequence x_n converging to x in X, $\sigma_n(x_n)$ converges to $\sigma(x)$), then f_2 and $f_{2,n}$ satisfy the conditions (F1) and (F2) (respectively (F1) and (F$\tilde{2}$)).

Remark 6-2

With proposition 6-1, we see that f_2 and $f_{2,n}$ satisfy the conditions of our general approach described in section 3. Now, from the previous observations, we introduce the following assumptions.

Assumptions

(A1) h_2 and the sequence $h_{2,n}$ verify (F1) and (F$\tilde{2}$) and σ_n continuously converges to σ.

(A2) h_2 is strictly quasiconvex in y for each x and $M_2(x)$ is not a singleton (so, $M_2(x) = \{y \in Y/f_2(x, y) = \sigma(x)\}$) for any $x \in X$.

(A3) $M_{2,n}(x) = \{y \in Y/f_{2,n}(x, y) = \sigma_n(x)\}$ and $M_{2,n}(x) \neq \emptyset$ for any $x \in X$ and any $n \in N$.

(A4) Y is a metric space.

Then, we have:

Proposition 6-3

For any $x \in X$ and any sequence x_n converging to x in X,

$$\liminf M_{2,n}(x_n) \supset M_2(x).$$

(that is to say: the assumption (H) is satisfied).

Proof

Let $y \in M_2(x)$. First, assume $\sigma(x) > h_2(x, y)$. From $(\tilde{F2})$, there exists a sequence y_n converging to y in Y such that:

$$\limsup_{n \to +\infty} h_{2,n}(x_n, y_n) \leq h_2(x, y).$$

Then, $y_n \in M_{2,n}(x_n)$ for n sufficiently large. Otherwise, with (A3), there would exist an infinite subset $N' \subset N$ such that:

$$f_{2,n}(x_n, y_n) = h_{2,n}(x_n, y_n) > \sigma_n(x_n) \text{ for any } n \in N'$$

and $h_2(x, y) \geq \limsup_{n \to +\infty} h_{2,n}(x_n, y_n) \geq \limsup_{\substack{n \to +\infty \\ n \in N'}} \sigma_n(x_n) = \sigma(x)$, which contradicts $\sigma(x) > h_2(x, y)$. So, for the considered case, we have $y_n \in M_{2,n}(x_n)$ for n sufficiently large and (H) is satisfied. Now, we consider the case where $y \in M_2(x)$ verify $\sigma(x) = h_2(x, y)$. We know that $M_2(x)$ is not a singleton and, besides, $M_2(x)$ is convex ([10]).

Let $y^* \in M_2(x)$ verifying $y \neq y^*$.

Let us consider $y_p^* = y + \frac{1}{p}(y^* - y)$, $p \in N$, $p \geq 1$. Then $y_p^* \in M_2(x)$ and from the strict quasiconvexity of $h_2(x, .)$ we get $h_2(x, y_p^*) < \sigma(x)$ (otherwise, $M_2(x)$ would be a singleton).

From $(\tilde{F2})$, there exists a sequence z_n converging to y_p^*, such that $\limsup h_{2,n}(x_n, z_n) \leq h_2(x, y_p^*)$ and, from the first part of the proof, we deduce $z_n \in M_{2,n}(x_n)$ for n sufficiently large. Let $\varepsilon > 0$. There exists $p(\varepsilon) \in \mathbb{N}$ such that $p \geq p(\varepsilon)$ implies $d(y_p^*, y) \leq \frac{\varepsilon}{2}$ and, for a fixed $p \geq p(\varepsilon)$, there exists $n(\varepsilon)$ such that $n \geq n(\varepsilon)$ implies $d(z_n, y_p^*) \leq \frac{\varepsilon}{2}$. Finally, for any $\varepsilon > 0$ there exists $n(\varepsilon)$ such that $d(z_n, y) \leq \varepsilon$ for any $n \geq n(\varepsilon)$, with $z_n \in M_{2,n}(x_n)$ for n sufficiently large, which means that $\liminf M_{2,n}(x_n) \supset M_2(x)$.

7. Asymptotically Stackelberg approximating sequences

Definition 7-1

A sequence (x_n, y_n) in $X \times Y$ is an asymptotically Stackelberg approximating sequence if and only if:

(1) $w_{1,n}(x_n) - v_{1,n} \to 0$

(2) $f_{2,n}(x_n, y_n) - v_{2,n}(x_n) \to 0$ when $n \to +\infty$

Remark 7-1

If $M_{2,n}(x_n)$ is a singleton for all $n \in N$, we get the definition that we have introduced in [8].

Proposition 7-1

With (L1), (L2), (F1), (F2) and (H), let us assume that X and Y are compact. If there exists an asymptotically Stackelberg approximating sequence, then any accumulation point $(\bar{x}, \bar{y})$ is a Stackelberg equilibrium pair. Moreover, for any subsequence (x_n, y_n), $n \in N'$, converging to $(\bar{x}, \bar{y})$ in $X \times Y$, we have

$$\lim_{\substack{n \to +\infty \\ n \in N'}} f_{2,n}(x_n, y_n) = f_2(\bar{x}, \bar{y})$$

$$\lim_{\substack{n \to +\infty \\ n \in N'}} w_{1,n}(x_n) = v_1.$$

Proof

From proposition 4-3 and definition 7-1, we have:

$$\lim_{\substack{n \to +\infty \\ n \in N'}} f_{2,n}(x_n) = v_2(\bar{x}). \qquad (7-1)$$

$$\text{From (F1), } \lim_{\substack{n \to +\infty \\ n \in N'}} f_{2,n}(x_n, y_n) \geq f_2(\bar{x}, \bar{y}) \geq v_2(\bar{x}) \qquad (7-2)$$

and, with (7-1), we get:

$$\lim_{\substack{n \to +\infty \\ n \in N'}} f_{2,n}(x_n) = v_2(\bar{x}) = f_2(\bar{x}, \bar{y}) \quad (\text{so, } \bar{y} \in M_2(\bar{x})).$$

With proposition 5-1 and proposition 5-2, we have, by using definition 7-1

$$v_1 \leq w_1(\bar{x}) \leq \liminf_{\substack{n \to +\infty \\ n \in N'}} w_{1,n}(x_n) \leq \limsup_{\substack{n \to +\infty \\ n \in N'}} w_{1,n}(x_n) \leq \limsup_{\substack{n \to +\infty \\ n \in N'}} v_{1,n} \leq v_1.$$

So $v_1 = w_1(\bar{x})$ and the proof is complete.

References.

[1] Attouch, H.; Wets, R.: *Approximation and convergence in nonlinear optimization.* Nonlinear Programming 4, Mangasarian O., Meyer, R., Robinson, S. (eds.), Academic Press 1981, 367 – 394.

[2] Basar, T.; Olsder, G. J.: *Dynamic noncooperative game theory.* Academic Press, New York, 1982.

[3] de Giorgi, E.; Franzoni, T.: *Su un tipo di convergenza variazionale.* Atti Accad. Naz. Lincei, Vol. 58, No. 8 (1975), 842 – 850.

[4] de Giorgi, E.; Franzoni, T.: *Su un tipo di convergenza variazionale.* Rendiconti del Seminario Matematico di Brescia, Vol. 3 (1979), 63 – 101.

[5] del Prete, I.; Lignola, M. B.: *On the variational properties of $\Gamma^-(d)$-convergence.* Pubblicazioni dell'Istituto di Matematica, Napoli, 1981.

[6] Dolecki, S.: *Tangency and Differentiation: some applications of convergence theory.* Ann. Mat. Pura Appl., Vol. 130 (1982), 223 – 255.

[7] Loridan, P.; Morgan, J.: *Approximation results for a two-level optimization problem and application to penalty methods.* Submitted for Publication to Mathematical Programming 1985.

[8] Loridan, P.; Morgan, J.: *A general approach for the Stackelberg problem and applications.* Journées Fermat: Mathematics for Optimization, Toulouse, 1985.

[9] Papavassilopoulos, G.; Cruz, J.: *Nonclassical control problems and Stackelberg games.* IEEE Transactions on Automatic Control, Vol. AC-24, No. 2 (1979), 155 – 165.

[10] Robinson, S.; Day, R.: *A sufficient condition for continuity of optimal sets in mathematical programming.* Journal of Mathemtical Analysis and Applications 45 (1974), 506 – 511.

[11] Shimizu, K.; Aiyoshi, E.: *A new computational method for Stackelberg and minmax problems by use of a penalty method.* IEEE Transactions on Automatic Control, Vol. AC-26, No. 2 (1981), 460 – 466.

[12] Simaan, M.; Cruz, J.: *On the Stackelberg strategy in nonzero-sum games.* Journal of Optimization Theory and Applications 11, No. 5 (1973), 533 – 555.

[13] Simaan, M.; Cruz, J.: *Additional aspects of the Stackelberg strategy in nonzero-sum games.* Journal of Optimization Theory and Applications 11, No. 6 (1973), 613 – 626.

[14] von Stackelberg, H.: *The theory of market economy.* Oxford University Press, Oxford 1952.

[15] Zolezzi, T.: *On convergence of minima*. Bollettino U.M.I., Vol. 8 (1973), 246 – 257.

[16] Zolezzi, T.: *On stability analysis in mathematical programming*. Mathematical Programming Study 21 (1984), 227 – 242.

International Series of
Numerical Mathematics, Vol. 84
(c) 1988 Birkhäuser Verlag Basel

On lower subdifferentiable functions

J. E. Martínez-Legaz
Departamento de Matemática Aplicada y Análisis
Universidad de Barcelona, Spain

Abstract. This paper studies the notion of lower subdifferentiability from the view-point of generalized conjugation. By this method the main properties of lower sub-differentiable functions are analysed. A related conjugation theory for Hölder and Lipschitz functions is developed, which is used to characterize those functions which can be expressed as a supremum of Hölder functions. Some applications to quasiconvex optimization and optimal control theory are examined.

Key words: Lower subdifferentiable functions, generalized conjugation, quasiconvex functions, Hölder functions, Lipschitz functions, duality, optimality conditions, minimal time function.

Subject Classification: AMS (MOS): 26B25, 26B35, 90C30, 49E99.

1. Introduction.

Lower subdifferentiable (l.s.d.) functions were introduced by Plastria [26]. He proved that the cutting plane algorithm of Kelley for convex programming problems can be adapted to the minimization of a boundedly lower subdifferentiable (b.l.s.d.) function subject to linear constraints and established that a l.s.d. function on a closed convex set is quasiconvex and lower semicontinuous (l.s.c.). Plastria also obtained that a function is b.l.s.d. on $\mathbb{R}^n$ if and only if it is Lipschitz and quasiconvex.

The theory of generalized conjugation of Moreau [24] is a useful tool in the analysis of optimization problems. In this framework, one has a notion of generalized subdifferentiablity (see [1]). The natural question arises whether the concept of lower subdifferentiability is a particular case of the more abstract definition of Balder. The main purpose of this paper is to answer this question, in order to understand better the meaning of lower subdifferentiablity. Thanks to the existence of a coupling function from which the concept of lower subdifferential can be derived, one can obtain, in a natural way, the fundamental properties of l.s.d. functions and develop some applications.

In Section 2 a conjugation theory for Hölder functions is given. Section 3 uses a modification of this theory, which is applied to suprema of Hölder functions. In Section 4 we show that, for a certain coupling function, the notions of generalized subdifferentiability and lower subdifferentiability coincide. The relationship existing between l.s.d. functions and quasiconvex functions is examined in detail. By restricting that coupling function, we obtain in Section 5 a conjugation notion, appropriate for b.l.s.d. functions.

Some applications of the above theory are outlined in the last sections: duality and optimality conditions in quasiconvex optimization (Section 6) and study of the minimal time function of linear control processes (Section 7).

We shall use the following notation. By $\overline{\mathbb{R}}$ we shall denote the extended real line $[-\infty, +\infty]$; $\mathbb{R}_+$ will be the set of nonnegative real numbers; the order relation $\leq$ for vectors will be understood in the componentwise sense. The Euclidean scalar product will be represented by $< \cdot, \cdot >$, the Euclidean norm by $\|\cdot\|$ and the ball centered at the origin with radius N by $B(0; N)$. For square matrices A, we shall consider the norm subordinated to the Euclidean vector norm, that is,

$$\|A\| = \max_{\|x\|=1} \|Ax\| = \sqrt{\rho(A^T A)},$$

where ρ denotes spectral radius and the superscript^T means transpose. Given a set F of extended real functions, the family of their suprema (resp. infima) will be represented by $s(F)$ (resp. $i(F)$). We shall use some basic concepts of convex analysis: epigraph, conjugate function, subdifferential, etc., for which we adopt the standard notation (epi f, f^*, ∂f, etc.) of [27]. The gradient and the lower semicontinuous hull of a function f will be respectively denoted by $\bigtriangledown f$ and $\overline{f}$. The level sets (resp. strict level sets) of f are:

$$S_\lambda(f) = \{x \in \mathbb{R}^n / f(x) \leq \lambda\} \qquad (\lambda \in \mathbb{R})$$
$$\dot{S}_\lambda(f) = \{x \in \mathbb{R}^n / f(x) < \lambda\} \qquad (\lambda \in \mathbb{R}).$$

When the level sets (equivalently, the strict level sets) of f are convex, f is said to be quasiconvex (see, e.g., [19]). By a cone we mean a set $C \subset \mathbb{R}^n$ such that $\lambda x \in C$ whenever $x \in C$ and $\lambda > 0$. Thus, its vertex is the origin, although it does not necessarily belong to C. The smallest convex set (resp. closed set, convex cone, closed convex set, closed cone) which contains $S \subset \mathbb{R}^n$ will be represented by conv S (resp. $\overline{S}$, conv cone S, $\overline{\text{conv}}\,S$, $\overline{\text{cone}}\,S$).

2. A conjugation theory for Hölder and Lipschitz functions

We recall the generalized conjugation theory of Moreau [24]. Given two sets X, Y and a "coupling" function $c : X \times Y \to \mathbb{R}$, the conjugate function of $f : X \to \overline{\mathbb{R}}$ is $f^c : Y \to \overline{\mathbb{R}}$ defined by

$$f^c(y) = \sup_{x \in X} \{c(x,y) - f(x)\}.$$

In the same way, for every $g : Y \to \overline{\mathbb{R}}$, its conjugate function $g^c : X \to \overline{\mathbb{R}}$ is defined by

$$g^c(x) = \sup_{y \in Y} \{c(x,y) - g(y)\}.$$

An elementary function on X is a function of the form $c(.,b) + \beta$, with $b \in Y$ and $\beta \in \mathbb{R}$. The elementary functions on Y are defined analogously. The set of functions from X into $\overline{\mathbb{R}}$ (resp. from Y into $\overline{\mathbb{R}}$) which are a supremum of elementary functions is denoted by $\Gamma(X,Y)$ (resp. $\Gamma(Y,X)$).

The Γ-regularized of $f : X \to \overline{\mathbb{R}}$ is the supremum of the elementary functions which are a minorant of f. It coincides with f^{cc} (see [24, p. 123]). In particular,

$$f = f^{cc} \Leftrightarrow f \in \Gamma(X,Y).$$

We shall apply the above theory to the case in which $X = Y = \mathbb{R}^n$ and $c = c_{\alpha,N} : X \times Y \to \mathbb{R}$ is given by

$$c_{\alpha,N}(x,y) = -N\|x-y\|^\alpha,$$

where α, N are fixed real numbers such that $0 < \alpha \le 1$, $N > 0$. This coupling function has been considered previously by Dolecki and Kurcyusz (see [6, p. 288]). Thus, in our case, $f^{c_{\alpha,N}} : \mathbb{R}^n \to \overline{\mathbb{R}}$ is given by

$$f^{c_{\alpha,N}}(y) = \sup_{x \in \mathbb{R}^n} \{-N\|x-y\|^\alpha - f(x)\}$$

and the elementary functions on $\mathbb{R}^n$ are of the form $-N\|\cdot - y\|^\alpha + b$. The set $\Gamma(X,Y)$, which coincides with $\Gamma(Y,X)$ due to the fact that $X = Y$ and $c_{\alpha,N}$ is symmetric, will be denoted by $\Gamma_{\alpha,N}(\mathbb{R}^n)$.

Proposition 2.1. For every $f : \mathbb{R}^n \to \mathbb{R}$, $f^{c_{\alpha,N}} \ge -f$.

Proof. Take $x = y$ in the definition of $f^{c_{\alpha,N}}$. $\qquad\square$

Proposition 2.2. The following statements are equivalent:
a) $f^{c_{\alpha,N}} = -f$
b) $f \in \Gamma_{\alpha,N}(\mathbb{R}^n)$
c) either $f(\mathbb{R}^n) \subset \mathbb{R}$ and f is α-Hölder continuous with constant N or $f \equiv \pm\infty$.

Proof. a) $\Rightarrow$ b)

One has

$$f^{c_{\alpha,N}c_{\alpha,N}} = (-f)^{c_{\alpha,N}} \ge -(-f) = f \ge f^{c_{\alpha,N}c_{\alpha,N}},$$

whence $f = f^{c_{\alpha,N}c_{\alpha,N}} \in \Gamma_{\alpha,N}(\mathbb{R}^n)$.

b) $\Rightarrow$ c)

Let us assume that $f \not\equiv \pm\infty$. Let $x_1, x_2 \in \mathbb{R}^n$. We have

$$f(x_1) = f^{c_{\alpha,N}c_{\alpha,N}}(x_1) = \sup_{y \in \mathbb{R}^n} \{-N\|x_1 - y\|^\alpha - f^{c_{\alpha,N}}(y) \ge$$

$$\ge \sup_{y \in \mathbb{R}^n} \{-N\|x_1 - x_2\|^\alpha + \|x_2 - y\|\alpha) - f^{c_{\alpha,N}}(y)\} =$$

$$= \sup_{y \in \mathbb{R}^n} \{-N\|x_2 - y\|^\alpha - f^{c_{\alpha,N}}(y)\} - N\|x_1 - x_2\|^\alpha =$$

$$= f^{c_{\alpha,N}c_{\alpha,N}}(x_2) - N\|x_1 - x_2\|^\alpha = f(x_2) - N\|x_1 - x_2\|^\alpha.$$

From this it follows that if there was some $x_1 \in \mathbb{R}^n$ such that $f(x_1) = -\infty$, then $f(x_2) = -\infty$ for every $x_2 \in \mathbb{R}^n$, which is a contradiction. Analogously, the existence of $x_2 \in \mathbb{R}^n$ such that $f(x_2) = +\infty$ would imply $f \equiv +\infty$. This proves that f is finite. Moreover, the above inequality shows that f is α-Hölder continuous with constant N.

c) $\Rightarrow$ a)

Obviously, if $f \equiv \pm\infty$ then $f^{c_{\alpha,N}} = -f$. Let us assume that f is a finite function which is α-Hölder continuous with constant N. For every $y \in \mathbb{R}^n$ one has $f^{c_{\alpha,N}}(y) = \sup_{x \in \mathbb{R}^n}\{-N\|x - y\|^\alpha - f(x)\} = -f(y)$, since the above supremum is attained at $x = y$, due to the Hölder continuity assumption on f. Thus, also in this case, $f^{c_{\alpha,N}} = -f$. $\qquad\square$

Corollary 2.3. For every $f : \mathbb{R}^n \to \overline{\mathbb{R}}$,

$$-(f^{c_{\alpha,N}}) = f^{c_{\alpha,N}c_{\alpha,N}} \le f \le (-f)^{c_{\alpha,N}}.$$

Moreover, one of the above inequalities holds with the equal sign if and only if $f \in \Gamma_{\alpha,N}(\mathbb{R}^n)$, in which case both inequalities hold with the equal sign.

Proof. Since $f^{c_{\alpha,N}} \in \Gamma_{\alpha,N}(\mathbb{R}^n)$, by Prop. 2.2 one has $f^{c_{\alpha,N}c_{\alpha,N}} = -(f^{c_{\alpha,N}})$. From the general theory of Moreau [24] it follows that $f^{c_{\alpha,N}c_{\alpha,N}} \le f$. Prop. 2.1 applied to $-f$ gives $(-f)^{c_{\alpha,N}} \ge -(-f) = f$.

It is clear that $f^{c_{\alpha,N}c_{\alpha,N}}$ is equivalent to $f \in \Gamma_{\alpha,N}(\mathbb{R}^n)$. If $f = (-f)^{c_{\alpha,N}}$, then $f \in \Gamma_{\alpha,N}(\mathbb{R}^n)$, whence $f = f^{c_{\alpha,N}c_{\alpha,N}}$. Conversely, if $f \in \Gamma_{\alpha,N}(\mathbb{R}^n)$, by the equivalence b) $\leftrightarrow$ c) in Prop. 2.2 one has $-f \in \Gamma_{\alpha,N}(\mathbb{R}^n)$. Now, by the implication b) $\leftrightarrow$ a) in Prop. 2.2 applied to $-f$ one obtains $(-f)^{c_{\alpha,N}} = -(-f) = f$. $\qquad\square$

The above results imply that $-(f^{c_{\alpha,N}}) = f^{c_{\alpha,N}c_{\alpha,N}}$ is the greatest α-Hölder continuous function with constant N which is a minorant of f. Of course, when $\alpha = 1$ we obtain in this way the greatest Lipschitz function with constant N majorized by f. By reversing the sign in the above statement one obtains that $f^{c_{\alpha,N}}$ is the smallest α-Hölder function with constant N which majorizes $-f$. This applied to $-f$, gives that the smallest α-Hölder majorant of f with constant N is just $(-f)^{c_{\alpha,N}}$. Prop. 2.2 also shows that the zero function is the only one which is invariant under $c_{\alpha,N}$-conjugation.

Corollary 2.4. For every $f : \mathbb{R}^n \to \overline{\mathbb{R}}$ and $x_0 \in \mathbb{R}^n$,

$$f^{c_{\alpha,N}c_{\alpha,N}}(x_0) = \inf_{x \in \mathbb{R}^n}\{f(x) + N\|x - x_0\|^\alpha\}.$$

Proof. It is an immediate consequence of the equality $f^{c_{\alpha,N}c_{\alpha,N}} = -(f^{c_{\alpha,N}})$ and the definition of $f^{c_{\alpha,N}}$. $\qquad\square$

From the above considerations it follows that the formula in Cor. 2.4, gives an expression for the lower α-Hölder envelope with constant N of f. In the same way, a formula for the corresponding upper envelope is provided by

$$(-f)^{c_{\alpha,N}}(x_0) = \sup_{x \in \mathbb{R}^n}\{f(x) - N\|x - x_0\|^\alpha\} \qquad (x \in \mathbb{R}^n).$$

This expression appears in [20] in the general context of metric spaces (see also [34]). McShane proved that it can be used to obtain an extension of an α-Hölder function with constant N which is defined on a subset of a metric space. In our case, given $g : S \subset \mathbb{R}^n \to \overline{\mathbb{R}}$, this extension is $(-f)^{c_{\alpha,N}}$, where f is the extension of g to the whole of $\mathbb{R}^n$ obtained by letting $f(x) = +\infty$ for $x \in \mathbb{R}^n \setminus S$. When $\alpha = 1$, the above expressions for the α-Hölder envelopes of f have been studied by Hiriart-Urruty [15], who has proved that they give, respectively, the minimal and the maximal extensions of g. In his work, $f^{c_{\alpha,N}c_{\alpha,N}}$ appears as $f \triangledown (N\|\ \|)$, where $\triangledown$ denotes the inf-convolution operation of convex analysis. Also in the case $\alpha = 1$, the characterization of the functions belonging to $\Gamma_{\alpha,N}(\mathbb{R}^n)$ has been obtained by Evers and van Maaren [7, p. 65]. In their paper, our elementary functions have been called "anti-cone functionals".

Proposition 2.5. For every $N > 0$,

$$\cup_{0 < N' < N} \Gamma_{\alpha,N'}(\mathbb{R}^n) \not\subseteq s\left(\cup_{0 < N' < N} \Gamma_{\alpha,N'}(\mathbb{R}^n)\right) \not\subseteq \Gamma_{\alpha,N}(\mathbb{R}^n)$$

$$\Gamma_{\alpha,N}(\mathbb{R}^n) = \cap_{N' > N} \Gamma_{\alpha,N'}(\mathbb{R}^n)$$

Proof. The first inclusion is obvious, while the second follows from $\Gamma_{\alpha,N'}(\mathbb{R}^n) \subset \Gamma_{\alpha,N}(\mathbb{R}^n)(N' < N)$ and the fact that $\Gamma_{\alpha,N}(\mathbb{R}^n)$ is closed under supremum. Let us denote by $f_N : \mathbb{R}^n \to \mathbb{R}$ the function defined by $f_N(x) = N\|x\|^\alpha$, for fixed $N > 0$. Since $f_N = \sup_{0 < N' < N} f_{N'}$, the first inclusion is strict. It is also easy to see that $-f_N$, which is an α-Hölder function with constant N, cannot be expressed as a supremum of α-Hölder functions with constants smaller than N. Finally, the equality in the statement is obvious. $\square$

The above proposition shows that $\Gamma_{\alpha,N}(\mathbb{R}^n)$ cannot be obtained from $\cup_{0 < N' < N} \Gamma_{\alpha,N'}(\mathbb{R}^n)$ simply by taking suprema. Thus, the question arises how to obtain one set from the other. The answer is given in the next proposition.

Proposition 2.6. For every $N > 0$,

$$\Gamma_{\alpha,N}(\mathbb{R}^n) = i\left(s\left(\cup_{0 < N' < N} \Gamma_{\alpha,N'}(\mathbb{R}^n)\right)\right).$$

Proof. The inclusion $\supset$ follows from Cor. 2.4 and the fact that $\Gamma_{\alpha,N}(\mathbb{R}^n)$ is closed under infimum. Conversely, let $f \in \Gamma_{\alpha,N}(\mathbb{R}^n)$. Then, by $f = f^{c_{\alpha,N}c_{\alpha,N}}$ and Cor. 2.4 we have

$$f = \inf_{x \in \mathbb{R}^n} \{f(x) + N\|x - .\|^\alpha\} = \inf_{x \in \mathbb{R}^n} \sup_{0 < N' < N} \{f(x) + N'\|x - .\|^\alpha\},$$

which shows that $f \in i(s(\cup_{0 < N' < N} \Gamma_{\alpha,N'}(\mathbb{R}^n)))$. $\square$

It is easy to see that, in Prop. 2.5 and 2.6, s and i can be interchanged. This requires to interchange also f_N and $-f_N$ in the proof of Prop. 2.5 and to use $f = (-f)^{c_{\alpha,N}}$, instead of $f = f^{c_{\alpha,N}c_{\alpha,N}}$, in the Proof of Prop. 2.6. It follows that there is no inclusion relation between $s(\cup_{0<N'<N}\Gamma_{\alpha,N'}(\mathbb{R}^n))$ and $i(\cup_{0<N'<N}\Gamma_{\alpha,N'}(\mathbb{R}^n))$. Indeed, if, let us say, $s(\cup_{0<N'<N}\Gamma_{\alpha,N'}(\mathbb{R}^n)) \subset i(\cup_{0<N'<N}\Gamma_{\alpha,N'}(\mathbb{R}^n))$, by Prop. 2.6 and Prop. 2.5 (with s replaced by i) we should obtain $\Gamma_{\alpha,N}(\mathbb{R}^n) = i(s(\cup_{0<N'<N}\Gamma_{\alpha,N'}(\mathbb{R}^n))) \subset i(\cup_{0<N'<N}\Gamma_{\alpha,N'}(\mathbb{R}^n))$, which contradicts the second strict inclusion in Prop. 2.5 (with s replaced by i). Alternatively, it is also easy to observe that for $f_N : \mathbb{R}^n \to \mathbb{R}$, defined by $f_N(x) = N\|x\|^\alpha$, one has

$$f_N \in s(\cup_{0<N'<N}\Gamma_{\alpha,N'}(\mathbb{R}^n)) \setminus i(\cup_{0<N'<N}\Gamma_{\alpha,N'}(\mathbb{R}^n))$$
$$- f_N \in i(\cup_{0<N'<N}\Gamma_{\alpha,N'}(\mathbb{R}^n)) \setminus s(\cup_{0<N'<N}\Gamma_{\alpha,N'}(\mathbb{R}^n)).$$

By specializing the definition of Balder [1] to the case $c = c_{\alpha,N}$, we shall say that $f : \mathbb{R}^n \to \overline{\mathbb{R}}$ is $c_{\alpha,N}$-subdifferentiable at $x_0 \in \mathbb{R}^n$ if $f(x_0) \in \mathbb{R}$ and there exists $y \in \mathbb{R}^n$ such that $f(x) - f(x_0) \geq c_{\alpha,N}(x,y) - c_{\alpha,N}(x_0,y)$ for every $x \in \mathbb{R}^n$. An element y verifying this property will be called a $c_{\alpha,N}$-subgradient of f at x_0. The $c_{\alpha,N}$-subdifferential of f at x_0 will be the set

$$\partial_{c_{\alpha,N}}f(x_0) = \{y/y \text{ is a } c_{\alpha,N} \text{-subgradient of } f \text{ at } x_0\}.$$

Proposition 2.7. Let $f : \mathbb{R}^n \to \overline{\mathbb{R}}$ and $x_0 \in \mathbb{R}^n$ be such that $f(x_0) \in \mathbb{R}$. The following statements are equivalent:

a) $f^{c_{\alpha,N}c_{\alpha,N}}(x_0) = f(x_0)$.
b) $f + N\|\cdot -x_0\|^\alpha$ attains its minimum at x_0.
c) $x_0 \in \partial_{c_{\alpha,N}}f(x_0)$.
d) f is $c_{\alpha,N}$-subdifferentiable at x_0.

Proof. The equivalence a) $\Leftrightarrow$ b) follows immediately from Cor. 2.4. The equivalence b) $\Leftrightarrow$ c) follows directly from the definition of a $c_{\alpha,N}$-subgradient. The implication c) $\Rightarrow$ d) is obvious. Finally, the implication d) $\Rightarrow$ a) is only a particular case of a general result in the generalized conjugation theory (see [1, p. 332, (2.2)]). $\square$

Corollary 2.8. Let $f : \mathbb{R}^n \to \overline{\mathbb{R}}$, $x_0 \in \mathbb{R}^n$. Then,

$$\partial_{c_{\alpha,N}}f(x_0) \neq \phi \text{ implies } \partial_{c_{\alpha,N'}}f(x_0) \neq \phi \qquad (N' > N).$$

Proof. It is direct consequence of Prop. 2.7, equivalence d) $\Leftrightarrow$ b). $\square$

The last corollary does not mean that $\partial_{c_{\alpha,N}}f(x_0)$ is a subset of $\partial_{c_{\alpha,N'}}f(x_0)$ whenever $N' > N$. For example, consider $f : \mathbb{R} \to \mathbb{R}$ given by $f(x) = x^2$. It is easy to check that $2 \in \partial_{c_{1,2}}f(1)$ but $2 \notin \partial_{c_{1,N}}f(1)$ for every $N > 2$.

The $c_{1,N}$-subdifferentiability is also related to the standard subdifferentiability of convex analysis, as shown in the following proposition.

Proposition 2.9. Let $f : \mathbb{R}^n \to \overline{\mathbb{R}}$ be a proper convex function, $x_0 \in \mathbb{R}^n$. Then, f is $c_{1,N}$-subdifferentiable at x_0 if and only if $\partial f(x_0) \cap NB(0;1) \neq \phi$.

Proof. By Prop. 2.7, equivalence d) ↔ b), the $c_{1,N}$-subdifferentiability of f at x_0 is equivalent to x_0 to be a minimum point for $f + N\|\cdot - x_0\|$, which is in turn equivalent to $0 \in \partial(f + N\|\cdot - x_0\|)(x_0)$. Since $\partial(f + N\|\cdot - x_0\|)(x_0) = \partial f(x_0) + N\partial\|\cdot - x_0\|(x_0)$ (see [27, p. 223, Th. 23.8]) and $\partial\|\cdot - x_0\|(x_0) = B(0;1)$ (see 27, p. 215]), by the symmetry of the unit ball it is equivalent to the nonemptiness of $\partial f(x_0) \cap NB(0;1)$. ☐

Remark. The above proposition does not mean that $\partial_{c_{1,N}} f(x_0) = \partial f(x_0) \cap NB(0;1)$. This, together with Prop. 2.7, equivalence d) ↔ c), would imply that $\partial f(x_0) \cap NB(0;1) \neq \phi$ only if $x_0 \in \partial f(x_0) \cap NB(0;1)$, which is obviously false.

Corollary 2.10. Let $f : \mathbb{R}^n \to \overline{\mathbb{R}}$ be a proper convex function, $x_0 \in \mathbb{R}^n$. If f is differentiable at x_0, then f is $c_{1,N}$-subdifferentiable at x_0 if and only if $\|\nabla f(x_0)\| \leq N$.

Proof. It is an immediate consequence of Prop. 2.9 and $\partial f(x_0) = \{\nabla f(x_0)\}$ (see [26, p. 242, Th. 25.1]). ☐

The above corollary also follows from Prop. 2.7, equivalence d) ↔ b), and Prop. 2.3. in [16].

3. The suprema of Hölder and Lipschitz functions

In this section we shall apply the generalized conjugation theory of Moreau to the case in which $X = \mathbb{R}^n$, $Y = \mathbb{R}^n \times (\mathbb{R}_+ \setminus \{0\})$ and the coupling function $c_\alpha : X \times Y \to \mathbb{R}$ is defined by

$$c_\alpha(x, (y, N)) = -N\|x - y\|^\alpha,$$

where α is a fixed number such that $0 < \alpha \leq 1$. In this way, we have $c_\alpha(x, (y, N)) = c_{\alpha,N}(x, y)$, with $c_{\alpha,N}$ being the coupling function used in Section 2. The conjugation theory associated to c_α has been considered by Dolecki and Kurcyusz (see [6, p. 288]). The c_α-conjugate function of $f : \mathbb{R}^n \to \overline{\mathbb{R}}$ is now $f^{c_\alpha} : \mathbb{R}^n \times (\mathbb{R}_+ \setminus \{0\}) \to \overline{\mathbb{R}}$, defined by

$$f^{c_\alpha}(y, N) = \sup_{x \in \mathbb{R}^n} \{-N\|x - y\|^\alpha - f(x)\}.$$

Thus, one has $f^{c_\alpha}(y, N) = f^{c_{\alpha,N}}(y)$, where $f^{c_{\alpha,N}}$ is the conjugate of f in the sense of Section 2. The elementary functions are again those of the form $-N\|\cdot - y\|^\alpha$, but now N is an arbitrary (not fixed) positive real number. The set of their suprema will now be denoted by $\Gamma_\alpha(\mathbb{R}^n)$. The c_α-conjugate of $g : Y \to \overline{\mathbb{R}}$, following the general theory of Moreau, is $g^{c_\alpha} : \mathbb{R}^n \to \overline{\mathbb{R}}$, given by

$$g^{c_\alpha}(x) = \sup_{(y,N) \in Y} \{-N\|x - y\|^\alpha - g(y, N)\}.$$

In order to give a characterization of functions belonging to $\Gamma_\alpha(\mathbb{R}^n)$, we introduce the following notion: a function $f : \mathbb{R}^n \to \overline{\mathbb{R}}$ will be said to satisfy the α-growth condition if there exists some strictly positive real number N such that the function $f + N\|\cdot\|^\alpha$

is bounded below. In the case $\alpha = 2$ one obtains the quadratic growth condition of Rockafellar [28, p. 273, 3.2]. For f to satisfy the α-growth condition it is necessary that $\liminf_{\|x\| \to \infty} \frac{f(x)}{\|x\|^\alpha} > -\infty$. This is also sufficient if f is lower semicontinuous, but not in general (consider, for example, $f : \mathbb{R} \to \mathbb{R}$ given by $f(x) = -\frac{1}{|x|}$ if $x \neq 0$ and $f(0) = 0$). It is clear that a function which is bounded below satisfies the α-growth condition for every α. Note that a function satisfying the α-growth condition does not take the value $-\infty$ at any point.

Proposition 3.1. Let $f : \mathbb{R}^n \to \overline{\mathbb{R}}$ and $x_0 \in \mathbb{R}^n$ be such that $f(x_0) > -\infty$. Then, $f^{c_\alpha c_\alpha}(x_0) = f(x_0)$ if and only if f is l.s.c. at x_0 ans satisfies the α-growth condition.

Proof. The second c_α-conjugate of f, $f^{c_\alpha c_\alpha}$, is a minorant of f which is l.s.c., since the elementary functions are continuous. Thus, $f^{c_\alpha c_\alpha} \leq \overline{f} \leq f$. Hence, if $f^{c_\alpha c_\alpha}(x_0) = f(x_0)$ then $\overline{f}(x_0) = f(x_0)$, which means that f is l.s.c. at x_0. Moreover, since $f^{c_\alpha c_\alpha}$ is the supremum of the elementary minorants of f, from $f^{c_\alpha c_\alpha}(x_0) = f(x_0) \geq -\infty$ we deduce that there are $y \in \mathbb{R}^n$, $N > 0$ and $b \in \overline{\mathbb{R}}$ such that $-N\| \cdot -y\|^\alpha + b$ is a minorant of f which takes a value greater than $-\infty$ at x_0. This means that $b > -\infty$ and $f + N\| \cdot -y\|^\alpha$ is bounded from below by b, which implies that $f + N\| \cdot \|^\alpha$ is bounded from below by $b - N\|y\|^\alpha$. Thus, f satisfies the α-growth condition.

The converse follows from a result of Dolecki and Kurcyusz [6, p. 286, Remark 4.10, (iii)]. ◻

The above proposition gives a complete characterization of the local c_α-regularity of a function. Note that when $f(x_0) = -\infty$, obviously $f^{c_\alpha c_\alpha}(x_0) = f(x_0)$, since $f^{c_\alpha c_\alpha}$ is a minorant of f. The next corollary gives the interpretation of the second c_α-conjugate.

Corollary 3.2. Let $f : \mathbb{R}^n \to \overline{\mathbb{R}}$. Then

$$f^{c_\alpha c_\alpha} = \begin{cases} \overline{f} & \text{if } f \text{ satisfies the } \alpha\text{-growth condition.} \\ -\infty & \text{otherwise.} \end{cases}$$

Proof. First, let us assume that f satisfies the α-growth condition. Since $f^{c_\alpha c_\alpha}$ is a l.s.c. minorant of f, we have $f^{c_\alpha c_\alpha} \leq \overline{f}$. By the assumption, there is $N > 0$ such that $f + N\| \cdot \|^\alpha$ is bounded below, say by b. Clearly, the same holds with f replaced by $\overline{f}$, which implies that $\overline{f}$ also satisfies the α-growth condition. Hence, by Prop. 3.1, $\overline{f}^{c_\alpha c_\alpha} = \overline{f}$. Since $\overline{f}^{c_\alpha c_\alpha} \leq f^{c_\alpha c_\alpha}$, we obtain that $f^{c_\alpha c_\alpha} = \overline{f}$.

If $f^{c_\alpha c_\alpha} \not\equiv -\infty$, there exists $x_0 \in \mathbb{R}^n$ such that $f^{c_\alpha c_\alpha}(x_0) > -\infty$. As in the proof of Prop. 3.1, we conclude that f satisfies the α-growth condition. ◻

Corollary 3.3. Let $f : \mathbb{R}^n \to \overline{\mathbb{R}}$. Then, $f \in \Gamma_\alpha(\mathbb{R}^n)$ if and only if either f is l.s.c. and satisfies the α-growth condition or $f \equiv -\infty$.

Proof. Since $f \in \Gamma_\alpha(\mathbb{R}^n)$ if and only if $f = f^{c_\alpha c_\alpha}$. ◻

The following proposition establishes the relation existing between $\Gamma_\alpha(\mathbb{R}^n)$ and the sets $\Gamma_{\alpha,N}(\mathbb{R}^n)$ (see Section 2).

Proposition 3.4.

$$\cup_{N>0}\Gamma_{\alpha,N}(\mathbb{R}^n) \not\subseteq \Gamma_\alpha(\mathbb{R}^n) = s\big(\cup_{N>0}\Gamma_{\alpha,N}(\mathbb{R}^n)\big).$$

Proof. The equality, and hence the inclusion, is an immediate consequence of the fact that the set of elementary functions corresponding to c_α is the union over $N > 0$ of the sets of elementary functions corresponding to $c_{\alpha,N}$. To see that the inclusion is strict it is enough to consider the function f defined by $f(x) = \|x\|^{2\alpha}$, which belongs to $\Gamma_\alpha(\mathbb{R}^n)$ (it is continuous and bounded from below) but it does not belong to $\cup_{N>0}\Gamma_{\alpha,N}(\mathbb{R}^n)$ since it is not α-Hölder continuous (see Prop. 2.2). $\qquad\square$

It is perhaps interesting to observe that, for the function f defined in the above proof, one has $f = \sup_{N>0}\{N\|\cdot\|^\alpha - \frac{N^2}{4}\}$. In this way we see that $f \in s(\cup_{N>0}\Gamma_{\alpha,N}(\mathbb{R}^n))$, as should happen following Prop. 3.4.

The next proposition relates the second c_α-conjugate of a function to its second $c_{\alpha,N}$-conjugates. Note that from Prop. 2.5 it follows that $f^{c_{\alpha,N'}c_{\alpha,N'}} \leq f^{c_{\alpha,N}c_{\alpha,N}}$ whenever $N' < N$.

Proposition 3.5. Let $f : \mathbb{R}^n \to \overline{\mathbb{R}}$,

$$f^{c_\alpha c_\alpha} = \sup_{N>0} f^{c_{\alpha,N}c_{\alpha,N}}.$$

Proof. Given $x_0 \in \mathbb{R}^n$, one has

$$f^{c_\alpha c_\alpha}(x) = \sup_{(y,N)\in Y}\{c(x,(y,N)) - f^{c_\alpha}(y,N)\} = \sup_{(y,N)\in Y}\{c_{\alpha,N}(x,y) - f^{c_{\alpha,N}}(y)\} =$$

$$= \sup_{N>0}\sup_{y\in\mathbb{R}^n}\{c_{\alpha,N}(x,y) - f^{c_{\alpha,N}}(y)\} = \sup_{N>0} f^{c_{\alpha,N}c_{\alpha,N}}(x).$$

Corollary 3.6. For every $f : \mathbb{R}^n \to \overline{\mathbb{R}}$ and $x_0 \in \mathbb{R}^n$,

$$f^{c_\alpha c_\alpha}(x_0) = \sup_{N>0}\inf_{x\in\mathbb{R}^n}\{f(x) + N\|x - x_0\|^\alpha\}.$$

Proof. It follows from Prop. 3.5 and Cor. 2.4. $\qquad\square$

By Cor. 3.2, the formula in Cor. 3.6 gives an expression of the lower semicontinuous hull of f when f satiesfies the α-growth condition. This can be compared with the formula

$$f(x_0) = \sup_{N>0}\inf\{f(x) \mid \|x - x_0\| \leq N\},$$

which follows from [17, p. 331, Prop. 6.2.5] and is valid for every function, although it presents the inconvenient of involving a constrained infimum.

Prop. 3.4 and 2.2 show that $\Gamma_\alpha(\mathbb{R}^n)$ is the set of extended real valued functions on $\mathbb{R}^n$ which can be expressed as a supremum of α-continuous Hölder functions.

By Cor. 3.3, these are just the l.s.c. functions which satisfy the α-growth condition. In particular, $\Gamma_1(\mathbb{R}^n)$ is the set of suprema of Lipschitz functions, which are those l.s.c. functions satisfying the 1-growth condition. In the following proposition we give a relation between the differents $\Gamma_\alpha(\mathbb{R}^n)$, when α varies. Note that there is no inclusion relation between the sets of α-Hölder and α'-Hölder functions when $\alpha \neq \alpha'$. Indeed, the function f defined by $f(x) = \|x\|^\alpha$ is α'-Hölder continuous only for $\alpha' = \alpha$.

Corollary 3.7. For $0 < a' \leq 1$,

$$\cup_{\alpha < \alpha'} \Gamma_\alpha(\mathbb{R}^n) = s\left(\cup_{\alpha < \alpha'} \Gamma_\alpha(\mathbb{R}^n)\right) \not\subseteq \Gamma_{\alpha'}(\mathbb{R}^n).$$

Proof. Let $f \in s(\cup_{\alpha < \alpha'} \Gamma_\alpha(\mathbb{R}^n))$. If $f \equiv -\infty$, it belongs to $\Gamma_\alpha(\mathbb{R}^n)$ for every α. Assume that $f \not\equiv -\infty$. Then, since f is a supremum of functions each of which belongs to some $\Gamma_\alpha(\mathbb{R}^n)$, with $\alpha < \alpha'$, there exists $f_0 \in \Gamma_\alpha(\mathbb{R}^n) \setminus \{-\infty\}$, for some $\alpha_0 < \alpha'$, such that f_0 is a minorant of f. By Cor. 3.3, f_0 satisfies the α_0-growth condition. Clearly, f also satisfies this condition. On the other hand, since the sets $\Gamma_\alpha(\mathbb{R}^n)$ consist of l.s.c. functions (see Cor. 3.3), f is also l.s.c. Hence, again by Cor. 3.3, $f \in \Gamma_\alpha(\mathbb{R}^n)$. This proves the equality.

To prove the inclusion, let $f \in \Gamma_\alpha(\mathbb{R}^n)$ for some $\alpha < \alpha'$. We only need to consider the case in which $f \not\equiv -\infty$. In this case, by Cor. 3.3 f is l.s.c. and satisfies the α-growth condition. Since the expression $\|x\|^{\alpha'} - \|x\|^\alpha$ is bounded below (it attains an absolute minimum for $\|x\| = (\alpha/\alpha')^{1/(\alpha'-\alpha)}$), it follows that f also satisfies the α'-growth condition, whence it belongs to $\Gamma_{\alpha'}(\mathbb{R}^n)$.

To see that the inclusion is strict, consider f given by $f(x) = -\|x\|^{\alpha'}$. It is a continuous function which satisfies the α'-growth condition but not the α-growth condition for any $\alpha < \alpha'$. $\square$

From Cor. 3.7, it follows that $\Gamma_\alpha(\mathbb{R}^n) \subset \Gamma_{\alpha'}(\mathbb{R}^n)$ whenever $\alpha < \alpha'$. This is equivalent to say that every α-Hölder function is a supremum of α'-Hölder functions. In particular, by considering the case $\alpha' = 1$, we obtain that every α-Hölder function is a supremum of Lipschitz functions. However, the converses of these statements are false, as the strict inclusion in Cor. 3.7 says.

Following the general definition of Balder [1], we shall say that $f : \mathbb{R}^n \to \overline{\mathbb{R}}$ is c_α-subdifferentiable at $x_0 \in \mathbb{R}^n$ if $f(x_0) \in \mathbb{R}$ and there exists $(y, N) \in Y$ such that $f(x) - f(x_0) \geq c_\alpha(x, (y, N)) - c_\alpha(x_0, (y, N))$ for every $x \in \mathbb{R}^n$. Such an element (y, N) will be called a c_α-subgradient of f at x_0. The set of all the c_α-subgradients of f at x_0, will be denoted by $\partial_{c_\alpha} f(x_0)$. From the relation existing between the coupling functions c_α and $c_{\alpha,N}$, one sees that $(y, N) \in \partial_{c_\alpha} f(x_0)$ if and only if $y \in \partial_{c_{\alpha,N}} f(x_0)$. Thus, Prop. 2.7, equivalencies d) $\leftrightarrow$ b) $\leftrightarrow$ c), can be restated as:

Proposition 3.8. Let $f : \mathbb{R}^n \to \overline{\mathbb{R}}$ and $x_0 \in \mathbb{R}^n$ be such that $f(x_0) \in \mathbb{R}$. The following statements are equivalent:

a) f is c_α-subdifferentiable at x_0.

b) There exists $N > 0$ such that $f + N\| \cdot - x_0\|^\alpha$ attains its minimum at x_0.

c) There exists $N > 0$ such that $(x_0, N) \in \partial_{c_\alpha} f(x_0)$.

In the same way, Prop. 2.9 gives:

Proposition 3.9. Let $f : \mathbb{R}^n \to \overline{\mathbb{R}}$ be a proper convex function and $x_0 \in \mathbb{R}^n$. Then, f is c_1-subdifferentiable at x_0 if and only if f is subdifferentiable at x_0. In particular, f is c_1-subdifferentiable at every point in the relative interior of the effective domain of f.

The above result on c_1-subdifferentiability of proper convex functions in the relative interior of their domain does not hold in the case of a nonconvex function. Consider, for example, the function $f : \mathbb{R}^n \to \mathbb{R}$ defined by $f(x) = -(1 - x^2)^{\alpha/2}$ if $-1 \leq x \leq 1$, $f(x) = 0$ if not (for $\alpha = 1$, this function has been used by Plastria [26, p. 39] as a counterexample in the context of lower subdifferentiable functions, which, as we shall see in the next section, are closely related to the c_1-subdifferentiable functions). Although this is a finite function, it is not c_1-subdifferentiable at $x_0 = \pm 1$ for any α. Indeed, by Prop. 3.8, equivalence a) $\Leftrightarrow$ b), the c_α-subdifferentiability of f at, say $x_0 = 1$, means that $f + N| \cdot - 1|^\alpha$ attains its minimum at 1 for some $N > 0$. However, for $x < 1$ close enough to 1, one has

$$f(x) + N|x - 1|^\alpha = -(1 - x^2)^{\alpha/2} + N(1 - x)^\alpha < 0 = f(1) + N|1 - 1|^\alpha,$$

which is a contradiction. Note that, since f is continuous and bounded from below, it belongs to $\Gamma_\alpha(\mathbb{R}^n)$ (see Cor. 3.3). Thus, it also shows that the relation $f^{c_\alpha c_\alpha}(x_0) = f(x_0) \in \mathbb{R}$ does not imply the c_α-subdifferentiability of f at x_0.

4. A conjugation theory for lower subdifferentiable functions

The notion of lower subdifferential has been introduced by Plastria [26]. A function $f : K \subset \mathbb{R}^n \to \overline{\mathbb{R}}$ is lower subdifferentiable (l.s.d.) at x_0 on K if there exists a vector $x^* \in \mathbb{R}^n$ such that $f(x) - f(x_0) \geq < x - x_0, x^* >$ for any $x \in K$ with $f(x) < f(x_0)$. The vector x^* is called a lower subgradient of f at x_0 on K. The set of all lower subgradients of f at x_0 is denoted by $\partial^- f(x_0)$. A function is l.s.d. on K if it admits at least one lower subgradient at each point on K.

The motivation for introducing these notions is that the cutting plane algorithm of Kelley for convex programming problems can be adapted to the minimization of a l.s.d. function (under a boundedness condition on its lower subgradients) subject to linear constraints. Plastria proved [26, Th. 2.1], that every l.s.d. function on K is quasiconvex and l.s.c. provided that K is convex and closed. In this section we will show that the concept of lower subdifferentiability can be obtained in the framework of the generalized conjugation theory of Moreau when an appropriate coupling function is taken.

Let $X = \mathbb{R}^n$, $Y = \mathbb{R}^n \times \mathbb{R}$ and $Q : X \times Y \to \mathbb{R}$ defined by

$$Q(x, (x^*, k)) = \min\{< x, x^* >, k\}.$$

This coupling function has been also used, independently and at the same time, by Penot and Volle [25] as an approach to l.s.d. functions. The Q-conjugates of $f : X \to \overline{\mathbb{R}}$ and $g : Y \to \overline{\mathbb{R}}$ are $f^Q : Y \to \overline{\mathbb{R}}$ and $g^Q : X \to \overline{\mathbb{R}}$, given by

$$f^Q(x^*, k) = \sup_{x \in \mathbb{R}^n} \{\min\{< x, x^* >, k\} - f(x)\}$$

$$g^Q(x) = \sup_{(x^*, k) \in Y} \{\min\{< x, x^* >, k\} - g(x^*, k)\}.$$

The elementary functions on $\mathbb{R}^n$ are those of the form $\min\{< ., x^* >, k\} + b$, with $x^* \in \mathbb{R}^n$, $k \in \mathbb{R}$ and $b \in \mathbb{R}$. These are the functions which can be expressed as the minimum of an affine function and a constant. The set of their suprema will be denoted by $\Gamma_Q(\mathbb{R}^n)$. The next lemma, which follows easily from the definition, gives a first characterization of functions belonging to $\Gamma_Q(\mathbb{R}^n)$.

Lemma 4.1. Let $f : \mathbb{R}^n \to \overline{\mathbb{R}}$. Then, $f \in \Gamma_Q(\mathbb{R}^n)$ if and only if for every $(x_0, \lambda) \in (\mathbb{R}^n \times \mathbb{R}) \setminus \mathrm{epi}\, f$ there exists $x^* \in \mathbb{R}^n$ such that $< x - x_0, x^* > + \lambda \leq f(x)$ for all $x \in \dot{S}_\lambda(f)$.

Proof. Let $f \in \Gamma_Q(\mathbb{R}^n)$ and $(x_0, \lambda) \in (\mathbb{R}^n \times \mathbb{R}) \setminus \mathrm{epi}\, f$. Since $\lambda < f(x_0)$, from the definition of $\Gamma_Q(\mathbb{R}^n)$ it follows the existence of an elementary minorant of f, $\min\{< ., x^* >, k\} + b$, such that $\min\{< x_0, x^* >, k\} + b \geq \lambda$. Let $x \in \dot{S}_\lambda(f)$. Since $< x_0, x^* > + b \geq \lambda$, one has $\lambda + < x - x_0, x^* > \leq < x, x^* > + b$. On the other hand, $f(x) < \lambda \leq k + b$. From this and the fact that $\min\{< ., x^* >, k\} + b$ is a minorant of f, it follows that $\lambda + < x - x_0, x^* > \leq f(x)$.

Let us now assume that f satisfies the condition in the statement. Given $x_0 \in \mathbb{R}^n$ and $\lambda < f(x_0)$, that is, $(x_0, \lambda) \in (\mathbb{R}^n \times \mathbb{R}) \setminus \mathrm{epi}\, f$, there exists $x^* \in \mathbb{R}^n$ such that $< x - x_0, x^* > + \lambda \leq f(x)$ for all $x \in \dot{S}_\lambda(f)$. Let $k = < x_0, x^* >$ and $b = \lambda - < x_0, x^* >$. For $x \in \dot{S}_\lambda(f)$, one has

$$\min\{< x, x^* >, k\} + b \leq < x, x^* > + b = < x - x_0, x^* > + \lambda \leq f(x).$$

For $x \in \mathbb{R}^n \setminus \dot{S}_\lambda(f)$, one has

$$\min\{< x, x^* >, k\} + b \leq k + b = \lambda \leq f(x).$$

This proves that $\min\{< ., x^* >, k\} + b$ is a minorant of f. Since it takes the value λ at the point x_0, we conclude that $f \in \Gamma_Q(\mathbb{R}^n)$. $\square$

In fact, the above proof shows that a necessary and sufficient condition for the equality $f(x_0) = f^{QQ}(x_0)$ is the existence, for every $\lambda < f(x_0)$, of x^* with the property stated in the Lemma.

Since the elementary functions corresponding to Q are quasiconvex and Lipschitz, the functions belonging to $\Gamma_Q(\mathbb{R}^n)$, which are their suprema, are also quasiconvex and lie in $\Gamma_1(\mathbb{R}^n)$ (see Prop. 3.4 and 2.2). However, the converse statement does not hold (for $n > 1$). Indeed, in [25, p. 10], Penot and Volle give an example of a continuous quasiconvex function $f : \mathbb{R}^2 \to \mathbb{R}$ which admits a finite elementary minorant but $f \notin \Gamma_Q(\mathbb{R}^2)$; by Prop. 2.2, 3.4 and Cor. 3.3, the elementary functions satisfy the 1-growth condition, whence, again by Cor. 3.3, $f \in \Gamma_1(\mathbb{R}^2)$. For $n = 1$, $\Gamma_Q(\mathbb{R}^n)$ is the intersection of the set of quasiconvex functions with $\Gamma_1(\mathbb{R}^n)$. In [25, p. 10], Penot and Volle have made the equivalent observation that $\Gamma_Q(\mathbb{R})$ is "the class of l.s.c. quasiconvex mappings bounded below by some subaffine function, augmented with the constant map with value$-\infty$" (their subaffine functions are our finite elementary functions corresponding to Q); in fact, it is very easy to prove that a quasiconvex function of one real variable has a "subaffine" minorant if and only if it satisfies the 1-growth condition.

Penot and Volle also proved [25, p. 11, Th. 2.4] that "each l.s.c. quasiconvex function defined on a locally convex space and minorized by a continuous affine functional coincides with the supremum of its subaffine minorants". This sufficient condition for a function to belong to $\Gamma_Q(\mathbb{R}^n)$ is not a necessary one (consider, for example, the elementary functions corresponding to Q). By adapting their proof, we have obtained the following characterizations of functions belonging to $\Gamma_Q(\mathbb{R}^n)$ (we recall that every function in $\Gamma_Q(\mathbb{R}^n)$ is l.s.c. and quasiconvex):

Proposition 4.2. Let $f : \mathbb{R}^n \to \overline{\mathbb{R}}$ be a l.s.c. quasiconvex function. The following statements are equivalent:

a) $f \in \Gamma_Q(\mathbb{R}^n)$.

b) (resp. c)). For every $\lambda < \sup_{x \in \mathbb{R}^n} f(x)$, there exists an affine function which minorizes f on $S_\lambda(f)$ (resp. $\dot{S}_\lambda(f)$).

d) For every $\lambda < \sup_{x \in \mathbb{R}^n} f(x)$, there exist $x_\lambda^* \in \mathbb{R}^n$ and $b_\lambda \in \mathbb{R}$ such that the elementary function $\min\{< ., x_\lambda^* > +b_\lambda, \lambda\}$ minorizes f.

e) $\sup_{x \in \mathbb{R}^n} f(x) = \sup_{x \in \mathbb{R}^n} f^{QQ}(x)$.

Proof. Since a) is equivalent to the equality $f = f^{QQ}$, the implication a) $\Rightarrow$ e) is obvious.

e) $\Rightarrow$ d)

Let $\lambda < \sup_{x \in \mathbb{R}^n} f(x) = \sup_{x \in \mathbb{R}^n} f^{QQ}(x)$. Then, there exists $x_0 \in \mathbb{R}^n$ such that $\lambda < f^{QQ}(x_0)$. Since f^{QQ} is the supremum of the elementary minorants of f, there are $x_\lambda^* \in \mathbb{R}^n$ and $k_\lambda, b_\lambda' \in \mathbb{R}$ such that the function $\min\{< ., x_\lambda^* >, k_\lambda\} + b_\lambda'$ minorizes f and $\min\{< x_0, x_\lambda^* >, k_\lambda\} + b_\lambda' > \lambda$. The last inequality implies that $k_\lambda + b_\lambda' > \lambda$, whence $\min\{< ., x_\lambda^* > +b_\lambda, \lambda\}$, with $b_\lambda = \lambda - k_\lambda$, minorizes f.

The equivalence d) $\leftrightarrow$ c) follows from the simple observation that, for any function $g : \mathbb{R}^n \to \overline{\mathbb{R}}$, g minorizes f on $\dot{S}_\lambda(f)$ if and only if $\min\{g, \lambda\} \leq f$.

The equivalence c) $\leftrightarrow$ b) is obvious.

c) $\Rightarrow$ a)

The following proof of this implication is along the lines of that of Lemma 2.5 in [25, p. 11]. Let $(x_0, \lambda) \in (\mathbb{R}^n \times \mathbb{R}) \setminus$ epi f. Then, $x_0 \notin S_\lambda(f)$. Since f is l.s.c. and quasiconvex, $S_\lambda(f)$ is closed and convex, whence, by a classical separation theorem there are $y^* \in \mathbb{R}^n$ and $t \in \mathbb{R}$ such that, for every $x \in S_\lambda(f)$, $< x, y^* > \leq t << x_0, y^* >$. By the assumption, there exist $z^* \in \mathbb{R}^n$ and $b \in \mathbb{R}$ such that $< ., z^* > +b$ minorizes f on $\dot{S}_\lambda(f)$. Let $x^* = \gamma y^* + z^*$, with $\gamma \geq \max\{\frac{\lambda - <x_0, z^*> - b}{<x_0, y^*> - t}, 0\}$. If $x \in \dot{S}_\lambda(f)$, we have

$$\lambda + < x - x_0, x^* > = \lambda + < x - x_0, \gamma y^* + z^* > =$$
$$= \lambda + \gamma < x - x_0, y^* > + < x, z^* > - < x_0, z^* > \leq$$
$$\leq \lambda + \gamma < x - x_0, y^* > + f(x) - b - < x_0, z^* > \leq$$
$$\leq \gamma(< x_0, y^* > -t) + \gamma < x - x_0, y^* > + f(x) =$$
$$= \gamma(< x, y^* > -t) + f(x) \leq f(x).$$

Thus, by Lemma 4.1, $f \in \Gamma_Q(\mathbb{R}^n)$. $\square$

Remark. The assumption on f have been used only to prove the implication c) $\Rightarrow$ a). Moreover, the implication d) $\Rightarrow$ e) can be proved directly with the only additional assumption that $x_\lambda^* \neq 0$. Since any constant function is a supremum of nonconstant elementary functions, by a minor modification of the proof of e) $\Rightarrow$ d) one obtains that, for any $f : \mathbb{R}^n \to \overline{\mathbb{R}}$, e) is equivalent to each one of b'), c') and d'), where b'), c') and d') are the conditions obtained by replacing the words "an affine function" by "a nonconstant affine function" and "$x_\lambda^* \in \mathbb{R}^n$" by "$x_\lambda^* \in \mathbb{R}^n \setminus \{0\}$" in b), c), d), respectively.

By Prop. 4.2, $\Gamma_Q(\mathbb{R}^n)$ is the set of l.s.c. quasiconvex functions satisfying the equivalent conditions e), b'), c'), d'). A function satisfying these conditions will be said to have property (L). Clearly, property (L) is stronger than the 1-growth condition.

The above proposition shows that, although the sufficient condition, given by Penot and Volle, for a function to belong to $\Gamma_Q(\mathbb{R}^n)$ consisting in the existence of an affine minorant, is not a necessary one, there is a closely related necessary and sufficient condition: the existence of an affine minorant on each level set which is different from the whole space. In the same way, in spite of the fact that the (obvious) necessary condition for $f \in \Gamma_Q(\mathbb{R}^n) \setminus \{-\infty\}$ consisting in the existence of a finite elementary minorant is not sufficient (as the example of Penot and Volle shows), there is a closely related necessary and sufficient condition: the existence, for each $\lambda < \sup_{x \in \mathbb{R}^n} f(x)$, of an elementary minorant whose supremum is λ. By the definition of $\Gamma_Q(\mathbb{R}^n)$ and by Lemma 4.1, Prop. 4.2 shows that the existence of the minorants stated in d) and c), which depend only on λ, is sufficient for the existence of minorants of these types, approaching the value of the function at any given point. It is also interesting the fact that, according to the implication e) $\Rightarrow$ a), the equality $\sup_{x \in \mathbb{R}^n} f(x) = \sup_{x \in \mathbb{R}^n} f^{QQ}(x)$ is a sufficient condition for $f = f^{QQ}$.

Using the fact that $\Gamma_Q(\mathbb{R})$ is the intersection of the set of quasiconvex functions with $\Gamma_1(\mathbb{R})$, one can easily prove that, for $f : \mathbb{R} \to \overline{\mathbb{R}}$, one has:

$$f^{QQ} = \begin{cases} f_{\bar{q}} & \text{if } f_{\bar{q}} \text{ satisfies the 1-growth condition} \\ -\infty & \text{otherwise} \end{cases}$$

where $f_{\bar{q}}$ denotes the greatest l.s.c. quasiconvex minorant of f [4,p. 11]. This is false for $f : \mathbb{R}^n \to \overline{\mathbb{R}}$, $n > 1$, as the example of Penot and Volle in [25, p. 10] shows. Since the elementary functions corresponding to Q are continuous and quasiconvex, Th. 2.4 in [25, p. 11] is equivalent to say that if f is minorized by an affine function, then $f^{QQ} = f_{\bar{q}}$. Let

$$\lambda_f = \sup\{\lambda| \text{ there exists a nonconstant affine function which minorizes } f \text{ on } \dot{S}_\lambda(f)\}.$$

By means of λ_f one can express the relation existing between f^{QQ} and $f_{\bar{q}}$, for a general function:

Corollary 4.3. Let $f : \mathbb{R}^n \to \overline{\mathbb{R}}$. Then,

$$f^{QQ} = \min\{f_{\bar{q}}, \lambda_f\}.$$

Moreover, f^{QQ} coincides with $f_{\bar{q}}$ if and only if $f_{\bar{q}}$ has property (L).

Proof. First, let us observe that $\lambda_f = \sup_{x \in \mathbb{R}^n} f^{QQ}(x)$. Indeed, as we have already mentioned (see the proof of Prop. 4.2), a function g minorizes f on $\dot{S}_\lambda(f)$ if and only if $\min\{g, \lambda\} \leq f$; hence, the above equality follows from

$$\sup_{x \in \mathbb{R}^n} f^{QQ}(x) = \sup_{x \in \mathbb{R}^n} \sup_{g \in M(f)} g(x) = \sup_{x \in \mathbb{R}^n} \sup_{g \in M'(f)} g(x) = \sup_{g \in M'(f)} \sup_{x \in \mathbb{R}^n} g(x),$$

where

$$M(f) = \{g : \mathbb{R}^n \to \overline{\mathbb{R}}|g \text{ is an elementary minorant of } f\}$$

and

$$M'(f) = M(f) \setminus \{g : \mathbb{R}^n \to \overline{\mathbb{R}}|g \text{ is constant}\},$$

and the fact that, for $x^* \neq 0$, $b \in \mathbb{R}$ and $\lambda \in \mathbb{R}$,

$$\sup_{x \in \mathbb{R}^n} \min\{<x, x^*> +b, \lambda\} = \lambda.$$

Let

$$g = \min\{f_{\bar{q}}, \sup_{x \in \mathbb{R}^n} f^{QQ}(x)\}.$$

Clearly, g is a l.s.c. quasiconvex minorant of f. Moreover, since f^{QQ} is l.s.c. and quasiconvex, one has

$$f^{QQ} \leq g \leq \sup_{x \in \mathbb{R}^n} f^{QQ}(x),$$

whence

$$f^{QQ} \le g^{QQ} \le g \le \sup_{x \in \mathbb{R}^n} f^{QQ}(x).$$

Therefore, $\sup_{x \in \mathbb{R}^n} g^{QQ}(x) = \sup_{x \in \mathbb{R}^n} g(x)$, which, by Prop. 4.2, implies that $g \in \Gamma_Q(\mathbb{R}^n)$. Since g is a minorant of f, it follows that $g \le f^{QQ}$. Thus, the first assertion is proved. To prove the second one, it is enough to observe that, according to Prop. 4.2, f^{QQ} is the greatest l.s.c. quasiconvex minorant of f which has property (L). □

Remark. One can replace $\dot{S}_\lambda(f)$ by $S_\lambda(f)$ in the definition of λ_f.

From the preceding corollary, it follows that, for any $f : \mathbb{R}^n \to \overline{\mathbb{R}}$ and $x_0 \in \mathbb{R}^n$,

$$f^{QQ}(x_0) = f(x_0) \Leftrightarrow f_{\bar{q}}(x_0) = f(x_0) \le \lambda_f.$$

The lower semicontinuity and quasiconvexity of the functions belonging to $\Gamma_Q(\mathbb{R}^n)$ implies that:

$$(f_{\bar{q}})^{QQ} = f^{QQ} \le f_{\bar{q}} \le f.$$

Thus, according to the proof of Cor. 4.3,

$$\lambda_{f_{\bar{q}}} = \sup_{x \in \mathbb{R}^n} (f_{\bar{q}})^{QQ}(x) = \sup_{x \in \mathbb{R}^n} f^{QQ}(x) = \lambda_f.$$

The above chain of inequalities also shows that

$$f \text{ has property (L)} \Rightarrow f_{\bar{q}} \text{ has property (L)}.$$

The converse implication does not hold, (consider, e.g. f defined by $f(x) = 0$ for $x \ne 0$, $f(0) = 1$). The preceding considerations remain true when one replaces $f_{\bar{q}}$ by f_q or $\bar{f}$. Moreover, since $\sup_{x \in \mathbb{R}^n} f_{\bar{q}}(x) = \sup_{x \in \mathbb{R}^n} f_q(x)$,

$$f_{\bar{q}} \text{ has property (L)} \Leftrightarrow f_q \text{ has property (L)};$$

in other words, a quasiconvex function has property (L) if and only if its l.s.c. hull has it (see Cor. 3 in [5, p. 112]). Therefore, by the second part of Cor. 4.3, $f^{QQ} = f_q$ if and only if f_q has property (L).

Corollary 4.4. If $f : \mathbb{R}^n \to \overline{\mathbb{R}}$ is bounded below, then $f^{QQ} = f_{\bar{q}}$.

Proof. Since a lower bound for f is also a lower bound for its l.s.c. quasiconvex hull, $f_{\bar{q}}$ has an affine minorant, whence, by Th. 2.4 in [25, p. 11], $f_{\bar{q}} \in \Gamma_Q(\mathbb{R}^n)$. By Prop. 4.2, this means that $f_{\bar{q}}$ has property (L). Now, we can apply the second part of Cor. 4.3. □

Remark. By Cor. 4.4 and Prop. 4.2, any l.s.c. quasiconvex function which is bounded below has property (L). Consider any l.s.c. quasiconvex function $f : \mathbb{R}^n \to \overline{\mathbb{R}}$ which does not have property (L) (for example, that of Penot and Volle [25, p. 10]). Then,

$g = \min\{f_{\overline{q}}, \mu\}$, with μ such that $\sup_{x \in \mathbb{R}^n} f^{QQ}(x) < \mu < \sup_{x \in \mathbb{R}^n} f(x)$, is a l.s.c. quasiconvex function which is bounded above but does not have property (L).

For a quasiconvex function $f : \mathbb{R}^n \to \overline{\mathbb{R}}$, one has:

$$f^{QQ} = \min\{\overline{f}, \lambda_f\}.$$

This is an immediate consequence of Cor. 3 in [5, p. 112] and Cor. 4.3. Therefore, at any $x_0 \in \mathbb{R}^n$,

$$f^{QQ}(x_0) = f(x_0) \Leftrightarrow \overline{f}(x_0) = f(x_0) \leq \lambda_f.$$

Moreover, $f^{QQ} = \overline{f}$ if and only if f has the property (L). The next corollary establishes the relationship existing between f^{QQ} and $f^{c_1 c_1}$ (see Section 3).

Corollary 4.5. If $f : \mathbb{R}^n \to \overline{\mathbb{R}}$ is quasiconvex, then

$$f^{QQ} = \min\{f^{c_1 c_1}, \lambda_f\}.$$

Proof. If f satisfies the 1-growth condition, then, by Cor. 3.2, $f^{c_1 c_1} = \overline{f}$. If not, f has no finite elementary minorant (since every elementary function satisfies the 1-growth condition), whence $f^{QQ} \equiv -\infty \equiv f^{c_1 c_1}$ (by Cor. 3.2). □

By Cor. 4.5.and 3.2, for a quasiconvex function $f : \mathbb{R}^n \to \overline{\mathbb{R}}$,

$$f^{QQ} \neq f^{c_1 c_1} \Leftrightarrow f \text{ satisfies the 1-growth condition but it does not have property (L).}$$

An example of such a function is, again, that of Penot and Volle [25, p. 10]. Moreover,

$$f^{QQ}(x_0) = f(x_0) \Leftrightarrow f^{c_1 c_1}(x_0) = f(x_0) \leq \lambda_f.$$

Since $\Gamma_Q(\mathbb{R}^n)$ consists of quasiconvex functions, for any $f : \mathbb{R}^n \to \overline{\mathbb{R}}$ one has $f^{QQ} = (f_q)^{QQ}$. Therefore, by Cor. 4.5 and $\lambda_{f_q} = \lambda_f$, the following general formula holds:

$$f^{QQ} = \min\{(f_q)^{c_1 c_1}, \lambda_f\}.$$

Hence, by Cor. 3 in [5, p. 112], Cor. 3.2 and the second part of Cor. 4.3,
$f^{QQ} \neq (f_q)^{c_1 c_1} \Leftrightarrow f$ satisfies the 1-growth condition but it does not have property (L).

As we have already observed (see the comments following Lemma 4.1), the 1-growth condition is not sufficient for a l.s.c quasiconvex function to belong to $\Gamma_Q(\mathbb{R}^n)$. However, by imposing a not too restrictive condition on the level sets of f, it becomes a sufficient condition, as proved in the following proposition.

Proposition 4.6. Let $f : \mathbb{R}^n \to \overline{\mathbb{R}}$ be a quasiconvex function belonging to $\Gamma_1(\mathbb{R}^n)$. If for every $(x_0, \lambda) \in (\mathbb{R}^n \times \mathbb{R}) \setminus \text{epi } f$ there exist $y^* \in \mathbb{R}^n$ and $k > 0$ such that

$$< d, y^* > \geq k\|d\| \qquad (d \in \text{cone } (x_0 - S_\lambda(f))),$$

then $f \in \Gamma_Q(\mathbb{R}^n)$.

Proof. Let $(x_0, \lambda) \in (\mathbb{R}^n \times \mathbb{R}) \setminus \text{epi } f$. Since $f = f^{c_1 c_1}$, by Cor. 3.6 there exists $N > 0$ such that $f(x) + N\|x - x_0\| \geq \lambda$ for every $x \in \mathbb{R}^n$. Let x^* and k be as in the statement. For $x \in \dot{S}_\lambda(f)$, we have

$$\frac{\lambda - f(x)}{< x_0 - x, y^* >} \leq \frac{N\|x - x_0\|}{< x_0 - x, y^* >} \leq \frac{N}{k}.$$

Thus, $x^* = \frac{N}{k} y^*$ satisfies the condition in Lemma 4.1. $\square$

In fact, the above proof shows that a sufficient condition for $f(x_0) = f^{QQ}(x_0)$ is the existence, for every $\lambda < f(x_0)$, of y^* and k with the property described in the statement (see the comments after Lemma 4.1). However, this is not necessary (consider, for example, the elementary functions corresponding to Q).

The following proposition gives an expression of the second Q-conjugate of a function.

Proposition 4.7. Let $f : \mathbb{R}^n \to \overline{\mathbb{R}}$. Then, for every $x_0 \in \mathbb{R}^n$,

$$f^{QQ}(x_0) = \sup_{x^* \in \mathbb{R}^n} \inf_{x \in \mathbb{R}^n} \max\{f(x) - < x - x_0, x^* >, f(x)\}.$$

Proof. From the definition of Q-conjugate one has:

$$f^{QQ}(x_0) = \sup_{(x^*, k) \in Y} \{\min\{< x_0, x^* >, k\} - f^Q(x^*, k)\} =$$

$$= \sup_{(x^*, k) \in Y} \{\min\{< x_0, x^* >, k\} - \sup_{x \in \mathbb{R}^n} \{\min\{< x, x^* >, k\} - f(x)\}\} =$$

$$= \sup_{(x^*, k) \in Y} \inf_{x \in \mathbb{R}^n} \{\min\{< x_0, x^* >, k\} - \min\{< x, x^* >, k\} + f(x)\}.$$

Since the expression $\min\{< x_0, x^* >, k\} - \min\{< x, x^* >, k\}$, as a function of k, attains its maximum at $k = < x_0, x^* >$ (independently on x), we obtain:

$$f^{QQ}(x_0) = \sup_{x^* \in \mathbb{R}^n} \inf_{x \in \mathbb{R}^n} \{< x_0, x^* > - \min\{< x, x^* >, < x_0, x^* >\} + f(x)\} =$$

$$= \sup_{x^* \in \mathbb{R}^n} \inf_{x \in \mathbb{R}^n} \max\{f(x) - < x - x_0, x^* >, f(x)\}.$$

$\square$

By Cor. 4.3, the formula appearing in Prop. 4.7 provides an expression of the l.s.c. quasiconvex hull of f when this hull has property (L). This happens, for example, when f is bounded below (see Cor. 4.4). Some other expressions for the l.s.c. quasiconvex hull of a function have been obtained in [4], [20], [29] - [31] and [33] by using conjugation techniques. In [31], a generalized convexity theory is given from which formulas for $\overline{f}$, f_q $f_{\overline{q}}$ and the everly quasiconvex hull of f are derived (in fact, these approaches are essentially equivalent, as I. Singer has shown in [32]). All these expressions are valid for every function; however, they are more complicated or involve a constrained infimum. The formula given in Prop. 4.7 can be compared with the well-known formula for the second convex conjugate of f:

$$f^{**}(x_0) = \sup_{x^* \in \mathbb{R}^n} \inf_{x \in \mathbb{R}^n} \{f(x) - <x - x_0, x^*>\}.$$

Following the pattern of Balder [1], we shall say that $f : \mathbb{R}^n \to \overline{\mathbb{R}}$ is Q-subdifferentiable at $x_0 \in \mathbb{R}^n$ if $f(x_0) \in \mathbb{R}$ and there are $x^* \in \mathbb{R}^n$ and $k \in \mathbb{R}$ such that $f(x) - f(x_0) \geq \min\{<x, x^*>, k\} - \min\{<x_0, x^*>, k\}$ for every $x \in \mathbb{R}^n$. The pair (x^*, k) will be said to be an Q-subgradient of f at x_0. The set of all of them, denoted $\partial_Q f(x_0)$, will be called the Q-subdifferential of f at x_0.

The following proposition gives a characterization of the Q-subgradients in terms of the lower subgradients of Plastria [26].

Proposition 4.8. Let $f : \mathbb{R}^n \to \overline{\mathbb{R}}$ and $x_0 \in \mathbb{R}^n$ be such that $f(x_0) \in \mathbb{R}$, $x^* \in \mathbb{R}^n$ and $k \in \mathbb{R}$. Then $(x^*, k) \in \partial_Q f(x_0)$ if and only if $x^* \in \partial^- f(x_0)$ and $\alpha(x^*) \leq k \leq \beta(x^*)$, where

$$\alpha(x^*) = f(x_0) + \sup\{<x, x^*> -f(x)|f(x) < f(x_0)\}$$

and

$$\beta(x^*) = <x_0, x^*> -f(x_0) + \inf\{f(x)| <x, x^*> -f(x) > <x_0, x^*> -f(x_0)\}.$$

Proof. Let $(x^*, k) \in \partial_Q f(x_0)$ and $x \in \mathbb{R}^n$ be such that $f(x) < f(x_0)$. We have $0 > f(x) - f(x_0) \geq \min\{<x, x^*>, k\} - \min\{<x_0, x^*>, k\} \geq \min\{<x, x^*>, k\} - k$, whence $k > \min\{<x, x^*>, k\}$. This means that $<x, x^*> < k$. Therefore $f(x) - f(x_0) \geq <x, x^*> - <x_0, x^*>$. Thus we have proved that $x^* \in \partial^- f(x_0)$. Moreover, $f(x_0) + <x, x^*> -f(x) < k$, whence $\alpha(x^*) \leq k$. Let $x \in \mathbb{R}^n$ be such that $<x, x^*> -f(x) > <x_0, x^*> -f(x_0)$. Assume that $<x, x^*> \leq k$. In this case, the condition $(x^*, k) \in \partial_Q f(x_0)$ means that $f(x) - f(x_0) \geq <x, x^*> - \min\{<x_0, x^*>, k\}$, which implies that $\min\{<x_0, x^*>, k\} \neq <x_0, x^*>$, whence $<x_0, x^*> > k \geq <x, x^*>$. From this and the definition of x we obtain $f(x) - f(x_0) < 0$. Since $x^* \in \partial^- f(x_0)$, this implies that $f(x) - f(x_0) \geq <x, x^*> - <x_0, x^*>$, which contradicts the definition of x. Thus we must have $<x, x^*> > k$. This and $(x^*, k) \in \partial_Q f(x_0)$ give $f(x) - f(x_0) \geq k - <x_0, x^*>$. Hence $k \leq <x_0, x^*> -f(x_0) + f(x)$, thus proving $k \leq \beta(x^*)$.

Conversely, assume that $x^* \in \partial^- f(x_0)$ and k is such that $\alpha(x^*) \leq k \leq \beta(x^*)$. Let $x \in \mathbb{R}^n$. If $f(x) < f(x_0)$, then $f(x) - f(x_0) \geq <x, x^*> - <x_0, x^*>$. Moreover, from $k \geq \alpha(x^*)$ it follows that $k \geq f(x_0) + <x, x^*> -f(x)$, i.e., $f(x) - f(x_0) \geq <x, x^*> -k$. Both inequalities give $f(x) - f(x_0) \geq \min\{<x, x^*>, k\} - \min\{<x_0, x^*>, k\}$. Assume now that $f(x) \geq f(x_0)$, i.e., $f(x) - f(x_0) \geq k - k$. If, moreover, $<x, x^*> -f(x) > <x_0, x^*> -f(x_0)$, then, by $k \leq \beta(x^*)$ one has $k \leq <x_0, x^*> -f(x_0) + f(x)$, that is, $f(x) - f(x_0) \geq k- < x_0, x^* >$. From both inequalities we obtain that $f(x) - f(x_0) \geq \min\{< x, x^* >, k\} - \min\{< x_0, x^* >, k\}$. If, instead, $< x, x^* > - f(x) \leq < x_0, x^* > - f(x_0)$, that is, $f(x) - f(x_0) \geq < x, x^* > - < x_0, x^* >$, we directly arrive to $f(x) - f(x_0) \geq \min\{< x, x^* >, k\} - \min\{< x_0, x^* >, k\}$. Thus, we have proved that $(x^*, k) \in \partial_Q f(x_0)$. $\qquad\square$

Corollary 4.9. If $f : \mathbb{R}^n \to \overline{\mathbb{R}}$ and $x_0 \in \mathbb{R}^n$ be such that $f(x_0) \in \mathbb{R}$. Then, $x^* \in \partial^- f(x_0)$ if and only if $(x^*, < x_0, x^* >) \in \partial_Q f(x_0)$.

Proof. The "if" part follows directly from Prop. 4.8. To prove the converse implication we have to demonstrate that $\alpha(x^*) \leq < x_0, x^* > \leq \beta(x^*)$ whenever $x^* \in \partial^- f(x_0)$. Let $x \in \mathbb{R}^n$ be such that $f(x) < f(x_0)$. By $x^* \in \partial^- f(x_0)$ we have $f(x) - f(x_0) \geq < x - x_0, x^* >$, that is, $< x_0, x^* > \geq f(x_0) + < x, x^* > - f(x)$. This proves that $\alpha(x^*) \leq < x_0, x^* >$. Now, let $x \in \mathbb{R}^n$ be such that $< x, x^* > - f(x) > < x_0, x^* > - f(x_0)$, that is, $f(x) < f(x_0) + < x - x_0, x^* >$. Since $x^* \in \partial^- f(x_0)$ we must have $f(x) \geq f(x_0)$. Thus we can write $< x_0, x^* > \leq < x_0, x^* > - f(x_0) + f(x)$, which proves that $< x_0, x^* > \leq \beta(x^*)$. $\qquad\square$

Corollary 4.10. Let $f : \mathbb{R}^n \to \overline{\mathbb{R}}$ and $x_0 \in \mathbb{R}^n$ be such that $f(x_0) \in \mathbb{R}$. Then, $\partial^- f(x_0)$ is the projection of $\partial_Q f(x_0)$ onto $\mathbb{R}^n$.

Corollary 4.11. Let $f : \mathbb{R}^n \to \overline{\mathbb{R}}$ and $x_0 \in \mathbb{R}^n$ be such that $f(x_0) \in \mathbb{R}$. Then, f is l.s.d. at x_0 on $\mathbb{R}^n$ if and only if f is Q-subdifferentiable at x_0.

The case in which f is l.s.d. at x_0 only on $K \subset \mathbb{R}^n$ reduces to the lower subdifferentiability of f at x_0 on $\mathbb{R}^n$, where f is the extension of f to the whole space obtained by letting $f(x) = +\infty$ for $x \in \mathbb{R}^n \setminus K$.

From Cor. 4.11 and [1, p. 332, (2.2) and (2.3)] one also obtains:

Corollary 4.12. Let $f : \mathbb{R}^n \to \overline{\mathbb{R}}$ and $x_0 \in \mathbb{R}^n$ be such that $f(x_0) \in \mathbb{R}$. Then, the following statements hold:

a) $\partial^- f(x_0) \neq \phi \Rightarrow f(x_0) = f^{QQ}(x_0)$
b) $f(x_0) = f^{QQ}(x_0) \Rightarrow \partial^- f(x_0) = \partial^- f^{QQ}(x_0)$.

The converses of these statements are false. Consider, for example, the function $f : \mathbb{R}^n \to \mathbb{R}$ defined by $f(x) = -\sqrt{1 - x^2}$ if $-1 \leq x \leq 1$, $f(x) = 0$ if not [26, p. 39]. One has $f \in \Gamma_Q(\mathbb{R}^n)$, however $\partial^- f(-1) = \partial^- f(1) = \phi$. Consider now $g : \mathbb{R}^n \to \mathbb{R}$ given by $g(x) = f(x)$ if $x \neq 1$, $g(1) = 1$. One has $g^{QQ} = f$ and $\partial^- g(1) = \phi = \partial^- g^{QQ}(1)$ but $g(1) \neq g^{QQ}(1)$.

The next corollary gives a characterization of the lower subgradients in terms of Q-conjugation.

Corollary 4.13. Let $f : \mathbb{R}^n \to \overline{\mathbb{R}}$, $x_0 \in \mathbb{R}^n$ be such that $f(x_0) \in \mathbb{R}$ and $x^* \in \mathbb{R}^n$. Then, $x^* \in \partial^- f(x_0)$ if and only if $f(x_0) + f^Q(x^*, < x_0, x^* >) = < x_0, x^* >$.

Proof. By (2.4) in [1, p. 332] and Cor. 4.9 we have $x^* \in \partial^- f(x_0)$ if and only if $f(x_0) + f^Q(x^*, < x_0, x^* >) = Q(x_0, (x^*, < x_0, x^* >))$. $\qquad\square$

In the context of quasiconvex analysis, there are two notions of subdifferential. One of them is the quasi-subdifferential of Greenberg and Pierskalla [8, p. 441], defined by (see [8, p. 442, Th. 6])

$$\partial^* f(x_0) = \{x^* \in \mathbb{R}^n | < x, x^* > \geq < x, x_0 > \text{ implies } f(x) \geq f(x_0)\};$$

The other one is the tangential of Crouzeix [3, p. 956]:

$$T f(x_0) = \{x^* \in \mathbb{R}^n | \sup_{x \in \mathbb{R}^n} \{< x - x_0, x^* > | f(x) \leq \lambda\} < 0 \forall \lambda < f(x_0)\}.$$

Crouzeix proved ([3, p. 956, Prop. 4.] and [4, p. 42, Prop. 12]) that

$$\partial f(x_0) \subset T f(x_0) \subset \partial^* f(x_0).$$

On the other hand, obviously $\partial f(x_0) \subset \partial^- f(x_0)$ (see [26, p. 38]). One also has:

Proposition 4.14. Let $f : \mathbb{R}^n \to \overline{\mathbb{R}}$ and $x_0 \in \mathbb{R}^n$ be such that $f(x_0) \in \mathbb{R}$. Then $\partial^- f(x_0) \subset T f(x_0)$.

Proof. Let $x^* \in \partial^- f(x_0)$, $\lambda < f(x_0)$ and $x \in \mathbb{R}^n$ be such that $f(x) \leq \lambda$. Then $f(x) < f(x_0)$, whence $< x - x_0, x^* > \leq f(x) - f(x_0) \leq \lambda - f(x_0)$. Hence,

$$\sup_{x \in \mathbb{R}^n} \{< x - x_0, x^* > | f(x) \leq \lambda\} \leq \lambda - f(x_0) < 0.$$

$$\square$$

Thus, the lower subdifferential is a set which lies between the standard subdifferential and the tangential. One has not, in general, $\partial^- f(x_0) = T f(x_0)$. Consider, for example, the function f given above, for which $\partial^- f(\pm 1) = \phi$ and, as is easily checked, $T f(\pm 1) = \mathbb{R} \setminus \{0\}$. However, by Prop. 14 in [4, p. 44], Prop. 4.14, Prop. 1.2 in [4, p. 42], the inclusion $\partial f(x_0) \subset \partial^- f(x_0)$ (see [26, p. 38]), Prop. 13' in [4, p. 43] and Th. 3.1 in [26, p. 42], the following holds:

Corollary 4.15. Let $f : \mathbb{R}^n \to \overline{\mathbb{R}}$ be a l.s.c. proper convex function and $x_0 \in \mathbb{R}^n$ be such that $\partial f(x_0) \neq \phi$. Then, $\overline{\text{cone}} \, \partial^- f(x_0) = \partial^* f(x_0)$. If, moreover, f is continuous at x_0, then cone $\partial^- f(x_0) = \partial^* f(x_0)$.

Corollary 4.16. Let $f : \mathbb{R}^n \to \overline{\mathbb{R}}$ be quasiconvex and differentiable at x_0, with $\nabla f(x_0) \neq 0$. Then

$$\partial^- f(x_0) \subset \{k \nabla f(x_0) | k \geq 1\}.$$

Proof. By Prop. 20 in [4, p. 53] and Prop. 4.14 we have $\partial^- f(x_0) \subset \{k \nabla f(x_0) | k > 0\}$. Let $k > 0$ be such that $k \nabla f(x_0) \in \partial^- f(x_0)$. By $\nabla f(x_0) \neq 0$, for sufficiently small $\lambda > 0$ one has $f(x_0 - \lambda \nabla f(x_0)) < f(x_0)$. Then, by $k \nabla f(x_0) \in \partial^- f(x_0)$ we have:

$$f(x_0 - \lambda \nabla f(x_0)) - f(x_0) \geq < -\lambda \nabla f(x_0), k \nabla f(x_0) > = -\lambda k \| \nabla f(x_0) \|^2,$$

whence $\frac{f(x_0 - \lambda \nabla f(x_0)) - f(x_0)}{\lambda} \geq -k\| \nabla f(x_0)\|^2$. By letting $\lambda \to 0^+$, we obtain $-\| \nabla f(x_0)\|^2 \geq -k\| \nabla f(x_0)\|^2$. Hence $k \geq 1$. $\quad\square$

The opposite inclusion in Cor. 4.16 does not generally hold. Consider, for example, $f : \mathbb{R} \to \mathbb{R}$ given by $f(x) = \sqrt{|x|}$, which verifies $\partial^- f(1) = [1, +\infty)$ and $f'(1) = 1/2$. Even one may have $\partial^- f(x_0) = \phi$, as it happens for $f : \mathbb{R} \to \mathbb{R}$ defined by $f(x) = x^3$ at every $x_0 \in \mathbb{R}$, although $f'(x_0) \neq 0$ if $x_0 \neq 0$.

Given a set $C \subset \mathbb{R}^n$, we shall denote by $P(C)$ the union of the projections of C onto the hyperplanes which meet C, i.e.,

$$P(C) = \bigcup_{\substack{H \; hyperplane \\ H \cap C \neq \phi}} \Pi_H(C),$$

where Π_H denotes projection onto H. The convexity assumption in Cor. 4.15 can be replaced by a Lipschitz condition on $P(S_{f(x_0)}(f) \cup \{x_0\})$.

Proposition 4.17. Let $f : \mathbb{R}^n \to \overline{\mathbb{R}}$ and $x_0 \in \mathbb{R}^n$ be such that $f(x_0) \in \mathbb{R}$. If f is Lipschitz on $P(\dot{S}_{f(x_0)}(f) \cup \{x_0\})$, then

$$\text{cone } \partial^- f(x_0) = Tf(x_0) = \partial^* f(x_0).$$

Proof. By Prop. 12, 13 and 13' in [4, pp. 42 - 43], which establish that $Tf(x_0) \subset \partial^*$ $f(x_0)$ and that they are convex cones, and by Prop. 4.14, we have

$$\text{cone } \partial^- f(x_0) \subset Tf(x_0) \subset \partial^* f(x_0).$$

Thus, it only remains to be proved that $\partial^* f(x_0) \subset \text{cone } \partial^- f(x_0)$. This is immediate when $f(x_0) = \min_{x \in \mathbb{R}^n} f(x)$, since in this case, by Prop. 13' in [4, p. 43] and Th. 3.1 in [26, p. 42], one has $\partial^* f(x_0) = \mathbb{R}^n = \partial^- f(x_0)$. Assume now that $f(x_0) > \inf_{x \in \mathbb{R}^n} f(x)$. The above mentioned results of Crouzeix and Plastria imply that $0 \notin \partial^* f(x_0)$. Let $x^* \in \partial^* f(x_0)$ and $x \in \mathbb{R}^n$ be such that $f(x) < f(x_0)$. Denote by x' the projection of x onto the hyperplane defined by the equation $< x, x^* > = < x_0, x^* >$ and by N the Lipschitz constant of f on $P(\dot{S}_{f(x_0)}(f) \cup \{x_0\})$. We have:

$$f(x) - f(x_0) \geq f(x) - f(x') \geq -N\|x - x'\| = < x - x', \frac{N}{\|x^*\|}x^* > = < x - x_0, \frac{N}{\|x^*\|}x^* >.$$

This proves that $\frac{N}{\|x^*\|}x^* \in \partial^- f(x_0)$, whence $x^* \in \text{cone } \partial^- f(x_0)$. $\quad\square$

Following Prop. 4.17, for a Lipschitz function on $\mathbb{R}^n$ one has cone $\partial^- f(x_0) = \partial^*$ $f(x_0)$ at every $x_0 \in \mathbb{R}^n$. In fact, under the assumption of inf-compactness it suffices that f be locally Lipschitz:

Lemma 4.18. If C is a bounded subset of $\mathbb{R}^n$, then $P(C)$ is also bounded.

Proof. Let us assume that $C \subset B(0; N)$. Let $x' \in \Pi_H(C)$ for some hyperplane H which meets C. There are $x^* \in \mathbb{R}^n$ and $x_0 \in C$ such that $\|x^*\| = 1$ and $H = \{x| < x, x^* > = < x_0, x^* >\}$. We have:

$$\|x' - < x_0, x^* > x^*\|^2 = \|x'\|^2 - 2 < x_0, x^* > < x', x^* > + (< x_0, x^* >)^2 =$$
$$= \|x'\|^2 - (< x_0, x^* >)^2 \geq \|x'\|^2 - \|x_0\|^2.$$

On the other hand, since $x' = \overline{x} + < x_0 - \overline{x}, x^* > x^*$ for some $\overline{x} \in C$ we obtain:

$$\|x' - < x_0, x^* > x^*\|^2 = \|\overline{x} - < \overline{x}, x^* > x^*\|^2 = \|\overline{x}\|^2 - (< \overline{x}, x^* >)^2 \leq \|\overline{x}\|^2,$$

whence, by combining both inequalities, we deduce:

$$\|x'\| \leq \sqrt{\|x\|^2 + \|x_0\|^2} \leq \sqrt{2}N.$$

$\square$

Thus we have proved that $P(C) \subset B(0; \sqrt{2}N)$.

Remark. In general, the radius of the ball contained in the above proof cannot be improved (when $n > 1$). For example, one has $P(B(0; N)) = B(0; \sqrt{2}N)$. Indeed, given $x' \in B(0; \sqrt{2}N) \setminus B(0; N)$, for any $y \in \mathbb{R}^n$ such that $\|y\| = 1$ and $< x', y > = 0$ one can construct the vectors $\overline{x} = (1 - (\frac{N}{\|x'\|})^2)x' - N\sqrt{1 - (\frac{N}{\|x'\|})^2}y$ and $x^* = \frac{N}{\|x'\|^2}x' + \sqrt{1 - (\frac{N}{\|x'\|})^2}y$. It is easy to check that $x \in B(0; N)$, $\|x^*\| = 1$ and x' is the projection of $\overline{x}$ onto the hyperplane defined by the equation $< x, x^* > = N$ (which meets $B(0; N)$). Therefore, $x' \in P(B(0; N))$. $\square$

Corollary 4.19. Let $f : \mathbb{R}^n \to \mathbb{R}$ be locally Lipschitz, $x_0 \in \mathbb{R}^n$. If $\dot{S}_{f(x_0)}(f)$ is bounded, then

$$\text{cone } \partial^- f(x_0) = Tf(x_0) = \partial^* f(x_0).$$

Proof. By Lemma 4.18, $P(\dot{S}_{f(x_0)}(f) \cup \{x_0\})$ is bounded, whence f is Lipschitz on it. $\square$

Corollary 4.20. If $f : \mathbb{R}^n \to \mathbb{R}$ is locally Lipschitz and inf-compact, then

$$\text{cone } \partial^- f(x_0) = Tf(x_0) = \partial^* f(x_0) \qquad (x_0 \in \mathbb{R}^n).$$

If, moreover, f is quasiconvex, then it is l.s.d. on $\mathbb{R}^n$.

Proof. The first part is an immediate consequence of Cor. 4.19. The second part follows from the fact that $\dot{S}_{f(x_0)}(f)$ is an open convex set excluding x_0, whence there exists $x^* \in \mathbb{R}^n$ such that $< x, x^* > < < x_0, x^* >$ whenever $x \in \dot{S}_{f(x_0)}(f)$, i.e., $x^* \in \partial^* f(x_0)$. $\square$

Let us consider now a function $f = \max_{i=1,\cdots,p} f_i$, with each $f_i : \mathbb{R}^n \to \overline{\mathbb{R}}$ being l.s.d. at x_0 on $\mathbb{R}^n$. It follows directly from the definition of the lower subdifferential that $\cup_{i|f_i(x_0)=f(x_0)}\partial^- f_i(x_0) \subset \partial^- f(x_0)$. In particular, f is l.s.d. at x_0 on $\mathbb{R}^n$. Even more, since the lower subdifferential is always a closed convex set [26, p. 42, Th. 3.1], one has

$$\overline{\mathrm{conv}}\ \cup_{i|f_i(x_0)=f(x_0)}\ \partial^- f_i(x_0) \subset \partial^- f(x_0).$$

In fact, this holds also for the maximum of an infinite family of functions $\{f_i\}_{i\in I}$ if $\sup_{i\in I} f_i(x_0) = f_{i_0}(x_0)$ for some $i_0 \in I$ (see [26, p. 43, Th. 3.2.]). The opposite inclusion does not generally hold. Consider, for example, the case $p = 2$, $n = 1$, $f_1 = \log_{10}(1 + |\cdot|)$, $f_2 \equiv 1$ and $x_0 = 99$. One has $\partial^- f(x_0) = [1/90, +\infty)$, while the left hand side in the above inclusion gives $[2/99, +\infty)$. In fact, this example shows that $\partial^- f(x_0)$ does not generally depend only on the lower subdifferentials of the functions which are "active" at x_0. However, in the next section we shall prove that, under some assumptions (which hold in the above example), $\partial^- f(x_0) \subset \mathrm{conv}$ cone $\cup_{i|f_i(x_0)=f(x_0)} \partial^- f_i(x_0)$.

Finally, to end this section we want to mention the notion of infragradient, introduced by Gutiérrez-Diez [9] as follows: $x^* \in \mathbb{R}^n$ is an infragradient of $f : \mathbb{R}^n \to \overline{\mathbb{R}}$ at $x_0 \in \mathbb{R}^n$ if $f(x) - f(x_0) \geq\ < x - x_0, x^* >$ for any $x \in \mathbb{R}^n$ with $f(x) \leq f(x_0)$. The property of possessing an infragradient at every point has been called strict lower subdifferentiability by Plastria [26]. Clearly, every infragradient is also a lower subgradient, but the converse is not true. For example, the function $f : \mathbb{R}^n \to \mathbb{R}$ given by $f(x) = \min\{< x, x^* >, < x_0, x^* >\}$, with $x_0 \in \mathbb{R}^n$ and $x^* \in \mathbb{R}^n \setminus \{0\}$, verifies $x^* \in \partial^- f(x_0)$, although f has no infragradient at x_0. However, one has:

Proposition 4.21. If $f : \mathbb{R}^n \to \overline{\mathbb{R}}$ and $x_0 \in \mathbb{R}^n$ are such that there is no local minimum for f in $f^{-1}(f(x_0))$, then $\partial^- f(x_0)$ coincides with the set of infragradients of f at x_0.

Proof. Let $x^* \in \partial^- f(x_0)$ and $x \in \mathbb{R}^n$ be such that $f(x) = f(x_0)$. Then x is not a local minimum of f. Hence, there exists a sequence x_n converging to x such that $f(x_n) < f(x) = f(x_0)$ for every n. Therefore, we have

$$f(x) - f(x_0) > f(x_n) - f(x_0) \geq\ < x_n - x_0, x^* > \qquad (n \in N).$$

By letting $n \to \infty$, we obtain $f(x) - f(x_0) \geq\ < x - x_0, x^* >$, which proves that x^* is an infragradient of f at x_0. □

Following Th. 3.1 in [26, p. 42], $\partial^- f(x_0) = \mathbb{R}^n$ when x_0 is a global minimum for f. On the other hand, one can easily check that the set of infragradients of f at a global minimum x_0 coincides with the normal cone to the set of global minima at this point. Therefore, at such a point, every lower subgradient is an infragradient if and only if it is the only global minimum. The case of a nonminimal point is considered in the next corollary.

Corollary 4.22. If any local minimum of $f : \mathbb{R}^n \to \overline{\mathbb{R}}$ is a local minimum, then, for every x_0 such that $f(x_0) > \inf_{x\in\mathbb{R}^n} f(x)$, $\partial^- f(x_0)$ coincides with the set of infragradients of f at x_0. If f is l.s.d. on $\mathbb{R}^n$, the converse also holds.

Proof. The first part is an immediate consequence of Prop. 4.21.

Conversely, assume that f is l.s.d. on $\mathbb{R}^n$ and that at every x_0 such that $f(x_0) > \inf_{x\in\mathbb{R}^n} f(x)$, the lower subdifferential of f coincides with the set of its infragradient. Let x_0 be a local minimum of f. Assume that $x \in \mathbb{R}^n$ is such that $f(x) < f(x_0)$. Then, for every $\lambda \in (0,1)$ one has $f((1 - \lambda)x_0 + \lambda x) \leq f(x_0)$. Since x_0 is a local minimum of f, this must be an equality for sufficiently small λ. Take one of such λ and $x^* \in \partial^- f((1 - \lambda)x_0 + \lambda x)$. By the hypothesis, x^* is also an infragradient of f at $(1 - \lambda)x_0 + x$, whence

$$0 = f(x_0) - f((1 - \lambda)x_0 + \lambda x) \geq\, < x_0 - ((1 - \lambda)x_0 + \lambda x), x^* > = \lambda < x_0 - x, x^* > .$$

This implies that $< x_0 - x, x^* > \leq 0$. On the other hand, by $f(x) < f(x_0) = f((1 - \lambda)x_0 + \lambda x)$ we have:

$$0 > f(x) - f((1 - \lambda)x_0 + \lambda x) \geq\, < x - ((1 - \lambda)x_0 + \lambda x), x^* > = (1 - \lambda) < x - x_0, x^* > .$$

This implies $< x_0 - x, x^* > > 0$, which is a contradiction. Thus, there is no $x \in \mathbb{R}^n$ with $f(x) < f(x_0)$, i.e., x_0 is a global minimum of f. $\qquad\square$

In fact, to prove the converse part in the above Corollary we have only used the existence of an infragradient at every point. Under this apparently weaker assumption, this result has been mentioned (without proof) by Plastria [26, p. 43]. It follows from the proof of Cor. 4.22, that the existence of an infragradient at every point implies the coincidence of the lower subdifferential with the set of infragradients at every nonminimal point. Moreover, the first statement obtained in Cor. 4.22 remains true when one replaces the words "global minimum" by "strict global minimum" and drops the condition "such that $f(x_0) > \inf_{x\in\mathbb{R}^n} f(x)$" (see the comments following Prop. 4.21).

5. Boundedly lower subdifferentiable functions

A function $f : K \subset \mathbb{R}^n \to \mathbb{R}$ is boundedly lower subdifferentiable (b.l.s.d.) on K if, at each point of K, there exists a lower subgradient of f of norm not exceeding a constant N, which is called a b.l.s.d.-bound of f [26, p. 39]. Plastria has proved [26, p. 39, Th. 2.2] that every b.l.s.d. function is a Lipschitz function. Moreover, if K is convex and closed then f is quasiconvex [26, p. 39, Th. 2.1]. Conversely, every quasiconvex function f on $\mathbb{R}^n$ satisfying a Lipschitz condition with constant N is b.l.s.d. on $\mathbb{R}^n$ with b.l.s.d.-bound N. For general $K \subset \mathbb{R}^n$, a bounded above function f defined on K is b.l.s.d. on K if and only if there exists a quasiconvex Lipschitz function $g : \mathbb{R}^n \to \mathbb{R}$ extending f [26, p. 41, Th. 2.4]. However, Plastria mentions as an open problem whether this result is valid for unbounded functions [26, p. 42]. In this section we give a conjugation theory for b.l.s.d. functions which among other things, gives an affirmative answer to this question.

Let $X = \mathbb{R}^n$, $Y_N = B(0; N) \times \mathbb{R}$ and $Q_N : X \times Y_N \to \mathbb{R}$ be defined by

$$Q_N(x, (x^*, k)) = \min\{< x, x^* >, k\},$$

where N is a fixed positive real number. Thus, $Q_N = Q_{|X \times Y_N}$, where Q is the coupling function we have used in the preceding section. The Q-conjugates of $f : X \to \overline{\mathbb{R}}$ and $g : Y \to \overline{\mathbb{R}}$ are $f^{Q_N} : Y \to \overline{\mathbb{R}}$ and $g^{Q_N} : X \to \overline{\mathbb{R}}$, given by

$$f^{Q_N}(x^*, k) = \sup_{x \in \mathbb{R}^n} \{\min\{< x, x^* >, k\} - f(x)\}$$

$$g^{Q_N}(x) = \sup_{(x^*, k) \in Y_N} \{\min\{< x, x^* >, k\} - g(x^*, k)\}.$$

The elementary functions on $\mathbb{R}^n$ are those of the form $\min\{< ., x^* >, k\} + b$, with $x^* \in B(0; N)$ and $b \in \mathbb{R}$. These are the functions which can be expressed as the minimum of an affine function with slope not exceeding N and a constant. The set of their suprema will be denoted by $B_N(\mathbb{R}^n)$. The following proposition establishes the relations existing between the different sets $B_N(\mathbb{R}^n)$, when N varies, and $\Gamma_Q(\mathbb{R}^n)$ (see Section 4).

Proposition 5.1.

(i) $\quad \cup_{0 < N' < N} B_{N'}(\mathbb{R}^n) \nsubseteq s(\cup_{0 < N' < N} B_{N'}(\mathbb{R}^n)) \nsubseteq B_N(\mathbb{R}^n) \qquad (N > 0)$.

(ii) $\quad\quad\quad B_N(\mathbb{R}^n) = \cap_{N' > N} B_{N'}(\mathbb{R}^n) \qquad (N > 0)$.

(iii) $\quad \cup_{N > 0} B_N(\mathbb{R}^n) \nsubseteq \Gamma_Q(\mathbb{R}^n) = s(\cup_{N > 0} B_N(\mathbb{R}^n))$.

Proof. (i) The first inclusion is evident, while the second is a consequence of the closedness under supremum of $B_N(\mathbb{R}^n)$. To see that the first inclusion is strict consider the function $f : \mathbb{R}^n \to \mathbb{R}$ given by $f(x) = \max\{< x, x^* >, 0\}$, with $\|x^*\| = N$. From $f(x) = \max\{\sup_{0 < \lambda < 1} < x, \lambda x^* >, 0\}$ it follows that $f \in s(\cup_{0 < N' < N} B_{N'}(\mathbb{R}^n))$ (note that $< ., \lambda x^* >$ and 0 are elementary functions with respect to $Q_{\lambda N}$; they correspond to $k = +\infty$, $b = 0$ and to $x^* = 0$, $k = b = 0$, respectively). However $f \notin \cup_{0 < N' < N} B_{N'}(\mathbb{R}^n)$, since every function in $B_{N'}(\mathbb{R}^n)$ must be Lipschitz with constant N' because the elementary functions corresponding to $Q_{N'}$ are. To see that the second inclusion is strict, consider a linear function $f = < ., x^* >$ with $\|x^*\| = N$. It obviously belongs to $B_N(\mathbb{R}^n)$, but it has no Lipschitz minorant with constant $N' < N$, whence $f \notin s(\cup_{0 < N' < N} B_{N'}(\mathbb{R}^n))$. (ii) will be an immediate consequence of Prop. 5.4. The inclusion in (iii) follows from the inclusion relation existing between the sets of elementary minorants corresponding to Q_N and to Q. To see that it is strict, consider f defined by $f(x) = \|x\|^2$. One has $f \in \Gamma_Q(\mathbb{R}^n)$ (see Prop. 4.2 and Cor. 3.3) but $f \notin \cup_{N > 0} B_N(\mathbb{R}^n)$, since f is not Lipschitz. Since $\Gamma_Q(\mathbb{R}^n)$ is closed under supremum, it includes $s(\cup_{N > 0} B_N(\mathbb{R}^n))$. The opposite inclusion follows from the fact that every elementary function corresponding to Q is also elementary with respect to Q_N for some $N > 0$. $\square$

The next proposition gives the formula of the second Q_N-conjugate:

Proposition 5.2. Let $f : \mathbb{R}^n \to \overline{\mathbb{R}}$. Then, for every $x_0 \in \mathbb{R}^n$,

$$f^{Q_N Q_N}(x) = \max_{x^* \in B(0;N)} \inf_{x \in \mathbb{R}^n} \max\{f(x) - <x - x_0, x^*>, f(x)\}.$$

Proof. It is identical to that of Prop. 4.7. Note that we can put "max" instead of "sup" because the infimum in the statement, as a function of x^*, is u.s.c. $\square$

The following corollary relates the second Q-conjugate of a function (see Section 4) to its second Q_N-conjugates. Note that from Prop. 5.1 (i) one has $f^{Q_{N'} Q_{N'}} \le f^{Q_N Q_N}$ whenever $N' < N$.

Corollary 5.3. For every $f : \mathbb{R}^n \to \overline{\mathbb{R}}$,

$$f^{QQ} = \sup_{N > 0} f^{Q_N Q_N}.$$

Proof. By Prop. 4.7 and 5.2. $\square$

Following the general scheme of Balder [1], we shall say that $f : \mathbb{R}^n \to \overline{\mathbb{R}}$ is Q_N-subdifferentiable at $x_0 \in \mathbb{R}^n$ if $f(x_0) \in \mathbb{R}$ and there are $x^* \in B(0;N)$ and $k \in \mathbb{R}$ such that $f(x) - f(x_0) \ge \min\{<x, x^*>, k\} - \min\{<x_0, x^*>, k\}$ for every $x \in \mathbb{R}^n$. The pair (x^*, k) will be said to be an Q_N-subgradient of f at x_0. They form the set $\partial_{Q_N} f(x_0)$, which will be called the Q_N-subdifferential of f at x_0. One has (see Section 4):

$$\partial_{Q_N} f(x_0) = \partial_Q f(x_0) \cap Y_N,$$
$$\partial_Q f(x_0) = \cup_{N > 0} \partial_{Q_N} f(x_0).$$

Moreover,

$$\cup_{0 < N' < N} \partial_{Q_{N'}} f(x_0) \subset \partial_{Q_N} f(x_0),$$

but here one has equality only if $\partial_{Q_N} f(x_0) = \phi$. Indeed, let us suppose that $\partial_{Q_N} f(x_0) \ne \phi$. Take $(x^*, k) \in \partial_Q f(x_0)$. By Prop. 4.8 one has $x^* \in \partial^- f(x_0)$. We can assume that $x^* \ne 0$, since otherwise $\partial^- f(x_0) = \mathbb{R}^n$ (see [26, p. 42, Th. 3.1]) and we can choose any other $x^* \in B(0;N) \setminus \{0\}$, which will satisfy $(x^*, <x_0, x^*>) \in \partial_Q f(x_0)$ (see Cor. 4.9). By [26, p. 42, Th. 3.1] one has $\frac{N}{\|x^*\|} x^* \in \partial^- f(x_0)$, whence, by Cor. 4.9, $(\frac{N}{\|x^*\|} x^*, \frac{N}{\|x^*\|} <x_0, x^*>) \in \partial_{Q_N} f(x_0)$. However, it is obvious that this point does not belong to $\cup_{0 < N' < N} \partial_{Q_{N'}} f(x_0)$. A similar argument can be used to prove that the equality $\partial_{Q_N} f(x_0) = \partial_Q f(x_0)$ holds only when $\partial_Q f(x_0) = \phi$.

Proposition 5.4. Let $f : \mathbb{R}^n \to \overline{\mathbb{R}}$. Then, $f \in B_N(\mathbb{R}^n)$ if and only if either $f(\mathbb{R}^n) \subset \mathbb{R}$ and f is b.l.s.d. on $\mathbb{R}^n$ with b.l.s.d. -bound N or $f \equiv \pm\infty$.

Proof. Assume that $f \in B_N(\mathbb{R}^n) \setminus \{\pm\infty\}$. Let $x_0 \in \mathbb{R}^n$. By Prop. 5.2. we have

$$f(x_0) = \max_{x^* \in B(0;N)} \inf_{x \in \mathbb{R}^n} \max\{f(x) - <x - x_0, x^*>, f(x)\},$$

whence there exists $x^* \in B(0;N)$ such that $f(x_0) = \inf_{x \in \mathbb{R}^n} \max\{f(x) - <x - x_0, x^*>, f(x)\}$. Let $y \in \mathbb{R}^n$ be such that $f(y) < f(x_0)$. We have

$$f(x_0) \leq \max\{f(y) - <y - x_0, x^*>, f(y)\} = f(y) - <y - x_0, x^*>.$$

If we had $f(x_0) = +\infty$, then, by $f \equiv +\infty$, there would exist some $y \in \mathbb{R}^n$ satisfying the above condition, that is, $f(y) < +\infty$, which gives $f(x_0) < +\infty$, a contradiction. On the other hand, if there was some $y \in \mathbb{R}^n$ such that $f(y) = -\infty$ then, by $f \not\equiv -\infty$, there would exist $x_0 \in \mathbb{R}^n$ with $f(x_0) > f(y)$, whence by the above inequality we obtain $f(x_0) = -\infty$, a contradiction. Thus we have $f(\mathbb{R}^n) \subset \mathbb{R}$ and $x^* \in \partial^- f(x_0)$, which proves that f is b.l.s.d. on $\mathbb{R}^n$.

The converse is an immediate consequence of (2.2) in [1, p. 332] and Cor. 4.9. $\square$

By Th. 2.2 and 2.3 in [26, p. 39], $B_N(\mathbb{R}^n)$ is the set of quasiconvex functions on $\mathbb{R}^n$ which satisfy a Lipschitz condition with constant N and the constants $\pm\infty$. Therefore, the equality in Prop. 5.1, (iii) means that $\Gamma_Q(\mathbb{R}^n)$ is the set of suprema of quasiconvex Lipschitz functions. In Section 4, we have observed that $\Gamma_Q(\mathbb{R}^n)$ is a proper subset of the intersection of the set of quasiconvex functions on $\mathbb{R}^n$ with $\Gamma_1(\mathbb{R}^n)$. Since $\Gamma_1(\mathbb{R}^n)$ is the set of functions which can be expressed as a supremum of Lipschitz functions (see Prop. 3.4 and 2.2), it follows that there are quasiconvex functions that can be expressed as a supremum of Lipschitz functions but not as a supremum of quasiconvex Lipschitz functions. The example given by Penot and Volle in [25, p. 10] provides one of such functions.

The next proposition says that Th. 2.4. in [26, p. 41] is valid for every function, not necessarily bounded above. This solves the problem posed by Plastria at the end of Section 2 in [26].

Proposition 5.5. Let $f : K \subset \mathbb{R}^n \to \mathbb{R}$, $N > 0$. Then, f is b.l.s.d. on K with b.l.s.d.-bound N if and only if there exists a quasiconvex Lipschitz function $g : \mathbb{R}^n \to \mathbb{R}$ with constant N extending f.

Proof. By Th. 2.4 in [26, p. 41.], we only have to prove the "only if" part. Let us assume that f is b.l.s.d. on K with b.l.s.d.-bound N. Let $\tilde{f}$ be the extension of f to the whole of $\mathbb{R}^n$ such that $f|_{\mathbb{R}^n \setminus K} \equiv +\infty$. Let $x_0 \in K$. Clearly, $\partial^- \tilde{f}(x_0) = \partial^- f(x_0)$. Hence, by the assumption, $\partial^- \tilde{f}(x_0) \cap B(0;N) \neq \phi$. By Cor. 4.9, this implies that there exists $x^* \in B(0;N)$ such that $(x^*, <x_0, x^*>) \in \partial_Q \tilde{f}(x_0)$ or, in other words, $\partial_{Q_N} \tilde{f}(x_0) = \partial_Q \tilde{f}(x_0) \cap Y_N \neq \phi$, whence, by (2.2) in [1, p. 332], $f(x_0) = \tilde{f}(x_0) = \tilde{f}^{Q_N Q_N}(x_0)$. Thus we have proved that $f = \tilde{f}^{Q_N Q_N}|_K$. Since $\tilde{f}^{Q_N Q_N}$ is finite on K and belongs to $B_N(\mathbb{R}^n)$, by Prop. 5.4. it must be finite everywhere and b.l.s.d. on

$\mathbf{R}^n$ with b.l.s.d.-bound N. Therefore, by Th. 2.1 and 2.2 in [26, p. 39], $\tilde{f}^{Q_N Q_N}$ is quasiconvex and Lipschitz with constant N. $\qquad\square$

In Section 4 we have observed that for a function $f = \max_{i=1,\cdots,p} f_i$, with each $f_i : \mathbf{R}^n \to \overline{\mathbf{R}}$ being l.s.d. at $x_0 \in \mathbf{R}^n$ on $\mathbf{R}^n$, one has

$$\overline{\operatorname{conv}} \cup_{i|f_i(x_0)=f(x_0)} \partial^- f_i(x_0) \subset \partial^- f(x_0).$$

Now we can prove a result of converse type, under some additional assumptions:

Proposition 5.6. Let $f_i : \mathbf{R}^n \to \overline{\mathbf{R}}$, $i = 1, \cdots, p$, be strictly quasiconvex and b.l.s.d. on $\mathbf{R}^n$, $f = \max_{i=1,\cdots,p} f_i$ and $x_0 \in \mathbf{R}^n$ be such that $f(x_0) \in \mathbf{R}$. Then,

$$\partial^- f(x_0) \subset \operatorname{conv} \operatorname{cone} \cup_{i|f_i(x_0)=f(x_0)} \partial^- f_i(x_0).$$

Proof. By Prop. 12 and 15 in [4, p. 42 and 81] and by Prop. 4.14, we have:

$$\partial^- f(x_0) \subset \partial^* f(x_0) = \sum_{i|f_i(x_0)=f(x_0)} \partial^* f_i(x_0).$$

Moreover, since the quasi-subdifferentials are convex cones (see [8, p. 442, Th. 6]) and every local minimum of an explicitly quasiconvex function in its domain is global, by Prop. 5.6 we obtain:

$$\sum_{i|f_i(x_0)=f(x_0)} \partial^* f_i(x_0) = \operatorname{conv} \cup_{i|f_i(x_0)=f(x_0)} \partial^* f_i(x_0) =$$

$$= \operatorname{conv} \cup_{i|f_i(x_0)=f(x_0)} \operatorname{cone} \partial^- f_i(x_0) =$$

$$= \operatorname{conv} \operatorname{cone} \cup_{i|f_i(x_0)=f(x_0)} \partial^- f_i(x_0).$$

$\qquad\square$

The opposite inclusion in Prop. 5.6. does not generally hold, since the lower subdifferential usually is not a cone.

6. Application to quasiconvex optimization

In this Section we shall apply the theory developed in the preceding paragraphs to the study of the following mathematical programming problem:

$$(P) \qquad\qquad \inf\{f(x)/g(x) \leq 0\},$$

where $f : \mathbf{R}^n \to \overline{\mathbf{R}}$ and $g : \mathbf{R}^n \to \mathbf{R}^m$. In order to obtain duality results, we shall consider the problem (P) embedded in a family of perturbed problems:

$$\inf\{f(x)/g(x) + w \leq 0\},$$

depending on a parameter $w \in \mathbb{R}^m$. We shall denote by p the perturbation function, which assigns to every $w \in \mathbb{R}^m$ the optimal value $p(w)$ corresponding to the perturbed problem associated with w. Thus, $p(0)$ represents the optimal value of problem (P). We shall consider the following dual problem:

$$(D) \qquad \sup\{Q(0, (w^*, k)) - p^Q(w^*, k)\},$$

whose variables are $(w^*, k) \in \mathbb{R}^m \times \mathbb{R}$. In this way, the optimal value of (D) is just $p^{QQ}(0) \leq p(0)$; so we have weak duality. A straightforward computation of this optimal dual value gives (see Prop. 4.7):

$$
\begin{aligned}
p^{QQ}(0) &= \sup_{w^* \in \mathbb{R}^m} \inf_{w \in \mathbb{R}^m} \{p(w) + \max\{- <w, w^*>, 0\}\} = \\
&= \sup_{w^* \in \mathbb{R}^m} \inf_{w \in \mathbb{R}^m} \{\inf_x\{f(x)/g(w) + w \leq 0\} + \max\{- <w, w^*>, 0\}\} = \\
&= \sup_{w^* \in \mathbb{R}^m} \inf_{w \in \mathbb{R}^m} \inf_x\{f(x) + \max\{- <w, w^*>, 0\}/g(x) + w \leq 0\} = \\
&= \sup_{w^* \in \mathbb{R}^m} \inf_{x \in \mathbb{R}^n} \inf_w\{f(x) + \max\{- <w, w^*>, 0\}/g(x) + w \leq 0\}.
\end{aligned}
$$

Since

$$
\begin{aligned}
\inf_w\{f(x) + \max\{- <w, w^*>, 0\}/g(x) + w \leq 0\} &= \\
= \begin{cases} f(x) + \max\{<g(x), w^*>, 0\} & \text{if } w^* \geq 0 \\ f(x) & \text{if } w^* \not\geq 0, \end{cases}
\end{aligned}
$$

one obtains:

$$p^{QQ}(0) = \sup_{w^* \geq 0} \inf_{x \in \mathbb{R}^n} \{f(x) + \max\{<g(x), w^*>, 0\}\}.$$

For this reason, the dual problem consists, equivalently, in maximizing the function of w^*

$$\inf_{x \in \mathbb{R}^n} \{f(x) + \max\{<g(x), w^*>, 0\}\},$$

under the restriction $w^* \geq 0$. This formulation of the dual problem can be compared with that of the classical convex dual, which is:

$$\sup_{w^* \geq 0} \inf_{x \in \mathbb{R}^n} \{f(x) + <g(x), w^*>\}.$$

In our case, the duality gap is zero if and only if $p(0) = p^{QQ}(0)$. Moreover, if the optimal value of (P) is finite, from Cor. 4.9 it follows that the set of optimal dual solutions is $\partial^- p^{QQ}(0) \cap \mathbb{R}^m_+$, which coincides with $\partial^- p(0) \cap \mathbb{R}^m_+$ if the duality gap is zero (see Cor. 4.12). Furthermore, by the above computation one can observe that $\partial^- p(0) \subset \mathbb{R}^m_+$ whenever $\inf\{f(x)/g(x) \leq 0\} > \inf_{x \in \mathbb{R}^n} f(x)$ and the duality gap is zero. Therefore, one has strong duality, i.e., the dual problem admits an optimal solution and the duality gap is zero if and only if p is l.s.d. at 0 on $\mathbb{R}^n$. In many cases, namely, when p_q has property (L), the dual problem is equivalent to the quasiconvex dual of Crouzeix [4], since in this case $p^{QQ} = p_{\bar{q}}$ (see Cor. 4.3). This happens, for example, when f is bounded below (see Cor. 4.4).

We can also prove a Kuhn-Tucker type theorem involving lower subdifferentials:

Proposition 6.1. Let $f, g_i : \mathbb{R}^n \to \mathbb{R}$, $i = 1, \cdots, m$, be strictly quasiconvex Lipschitz functions on $\mathbb{R}^n$ and $x_0 \in \mathbb{R}^n$. If $g = (g_1, \cdots, g_m)$ satisfies the Slater's condition, i.e., there exists $x \in \mathbb{R}^n$ such that $g_i(x) < 0$ $(i = 1, \cdots, m)$, then x_0 is an optimal solution of (P) if and only if there are nonnegative numbers λ_i, $i = 1, \cdots, m$, such that $\lambda_i g_i(x_0) = 0$ $(i = 1, \cdots, m)$ and $0 \in \partial^- f(x_0) + \sum_{i=1}^m \lambda_i \partial^- g_i(x_0)$.

Proof. If x_0 is a global minimum of f, the equivalence is true, since one can take $\lambda_i = 0$ $(i = 1, \cdots, m)$ (see Th. 3.1 in [26, p. 42]). Let us assume that $f(x_0) > \inf_{x \in \mathbb{R}^n} f(x)$. By the Th. of Karamardian [19, p. 138], the functions f, g_i are explicitly quasiconvex, whence by Prop. 13 in [4, p. 79], x_0 is an optimal solution of (P) if and only if there are $x_i^* \in \partial^* g_i(x_0)$, $i = 1, \cdots, m$, such that $-\sum_{i=1}^m x_i^* \in \partial^* f(x_0)$ and $g_i(x_0)$ whenever $x_i^* \neq 0$. By Prop. 4.17, this is equivalent to the existence of nonzero vectors $y_i^* \in \partial^- g_i(x_0)$, $y^* \in \partial^- f(x_0)$ and nonnegative numbers λ_i', λ such that $x_i^* = \lambda_i' y_i^*$, $\lambda_i' g_i(x_0) = 0$ $(i = 1, \cdots, m)$ and $-\sum_{i=1}^m x_i^* = \lambda y^*$. Since x_0 is not a global minimum of f, we have $\lambda > 0$ (see Prop. 13' in [4, p. 42]). Letting $\lambda_i = \frac{\lambda_i'}{\lambda}$ we can equivalently write $y^* + \sum_{i=1}^m \lambda_i y_i^* = 0$ (i.e., $0 \in \partial^- f(x_0) + \sum \lambda_i \partial^- g_i(x_0)$) and $\lambda_i g_i(x_0) = 0$ $(i = 1, \cdots, m)$. $\qquad \square$

Remarks. a) By Th. 3.1. in [26, p. 42] one can impose, in the above proposition the conditions $\lambda_i \leq 1$ $(i = 1, \cdots, m)$. Indeed, if $\lambda_i > 1$ then $\lambda_i y_i^* \in \partial^- g_i(x_0)$, whence, by redefining y_i^*, one can take $\lambda_i = 1$.
b) In the above proof we have only used the continuity of the functions and their Lipschitz character on some special subsets (see Prop. 4.17). By Cor. 19, it suffices to assume that f and the g_i's are locally Lipschitz and the sets $\dot{S}_{f(x_0)}(f)$ and $\dot{S}_{g_i(x_0)}(g_i)$ $(i = 1, \cdots, m)$ are bounded.

Gutiérrez-Diez has also proved a Kuhn-Tucker type theorem for convex optimization problems on locally convex spaces in terms of infragradients [10].

7. An application to optimal control theory

Let us consider a linear differential system

$$\dot{x} = A(t)x + B(t)u,$$

with $x \in \mathbb{R}^n$, $u \in \mathbb{R}^m$ and $A(t)$, $B(t)$ being real matrices of sizes $n \times b$ and $n \times m$, respectively, whose components are measurable on $\mathbb{R}$ and whose norms are locally integrable. For this system, an admissible control will be a bounded measurable function

$u : [0, t_1] \rightarrow \Omega \subset \mathbb{R}^m$, with t_1 being a nonfixed positive number and Ω being a set containing the origin. For a detailed study of these linear control processes see the books [18] and [14], from which the following definitions are taken.

The set of attainability at time t_1, denoted by $K_\Omega(t_1)$, is the set of all endpoints $x(t_1)$ corresponding to responses to admissible controls, initiating at $x(0) = 0$. More explicitly, by the variation of parameters formula,

$$K_\Omega(t_1) = \{\Phi(t_1) \int_0^t \Phi^{-1}(s) B(s) u(s) ds / u \text{ is an admissible control}\},$$

where $\Phi(t)$ is the fundamental matrix solution of the homogeneous system $\dot{x} = A(t)x$ with $\Phi(0) = I$ (the identity matrix). The reachable set at time t_1 is $R_\Omega(t_1) = \Phi^{-1}(t_1) K_\Omega(t_1)$. Its opposite, $-R_\Omega(t_1)$, is the set of points which can be controlled to the origin at time t_1 by an admissible control.

The minimal time function is $T_\Omega : \mathbb{R}^n \rightarrow \overline{\mathbb{R}}$ defined by:

$$T_\Omega(x) = \inf\{t / x \in -R_\Omega(t)\}.$$

If Ω is compact, by the existence theorem [18, p. 127] one can replace inf by min in the above definition for $x \in -R_\Omega$, where $R_\Omega = \cup_{t \geq 0} R_\Omega(t)$ ($-R_\Omega$ is the set of points which can be controlled to the origin by an admissible control). The properties of the minimal time function have been studied by several authors [12], [13], [23], [2], [11], [21].

A general result for the minimal time function, which does not require any condition for Ω (but $0 \in \Omega$) is:

Proposition 7.1.

$$\overline{T}_\Omega \in \Gamma_Q(\mathbb{R}^n).$$

Proof. The minimal time function is quasiconvex [21, Prop. 3.1] and bounded below by 0. Hence, by Cor. 3 in [5, p. 12] and Cor. 4.4 we have

$$\overline{T}_\Omega = \overline{(T_\Omega)_q} = (T_\Omega)_{\overline{q}} = T_\Omega^{QQ} \in \Gamma_Q(\mathbb{R}^n).$$

$\square$

Corollary 7.2. If Ω is compact, then

$$T_\Omega \in \Gamma_Q(\mathbb{R}^n).$$

Proof. Following Prop. 3.7 in [21], T_Ω is inf-compact, whence $T_\Omega = \overline{T}_\Omega$. $\square$

Under some restrictive assumptions one can prove the lower subdifferentiability of T_Ω.

Proposition 7.3. If $A(t) = A$ and $B(t) = B$ are constant, no eigenvalue of A has a positive real part, rank $B = n$ and $\Omega = [-1, 1]^m$, then T_Ω is l.s.d. on $\mathbb{R}^n$.

Proof. Since rank $B = n$, we have rank $(B, AB, \cdots, A^{n-1}B) = n$, whence, by Th. 17.3 and 17.6 in [14, pp. 74 and 79], T_Ω is finite everywhere. By Th. 3.1 in [26, p. 42], $\partial^- T_\Omega(0) = \mathbb{R}^n$. Let $x_0 \in \mathbb{R}^n \setminus \{0\}$. Since T_Ω is continuous [12, p. 340, Th. 1] and quasiconvex [21, Prop. 3.1], the strict level set $\dot{S}_{T_\Omega(x_0)}(T_\Omega)$ is an open convex set. Since $x_0 \notin \dot{S}_{T_\Omega(x_0)}(T_\Omega)$, by a well-known separation theorem there exists $x^* \in B(0; 1)$ such that $< x, x^* > << x_0, x^* >$ whenever $T_\Omega(x) < T_\Omega(x_0)$. Let $\bar{x}$ be such that $T_\Omega(\bar{x}) < T_\Omega(x_0)$. We have $< x, x^* > << x_0, x^* >$. Let x' be the projection of x onto the hyperplane H defined by the equation $< \bar{x}, x^* > = < x_0, x^* >$. Since $< x', x^* > = < x_0, x^* >$, it follows that $T_\Omega(x') \geq T_\Omega(x_0) > T_\Omega(\bar{x})$. By Th. 16 in [12, p. 348], there exists $\lambda > 0$ such that $|T_\Omega(x) - T_\Omega(y)| \leq \lambda e^{\|A\| \max\{T_\Omega(x), T_\Omega(y)\}} \|x - y\|$ for every $x, y \in \mathbb{R}^n$. Moreover, by Cor. 3 in [12, p. 34] and Th. 1A in [18, p. 164], the level set $S_{T_\Omega(x_0)}(T_\Omega) = R_\Omega(T_\Omega(x_0))$ is compact. Let Π_{x_0, x^*} be its projection onto H, $K = \max\{T_\Omega(x) | x \in \Pi_{x, x^*}\}$ and $N = \lambda e^{\|A\|K}$. We have (see [12, p. 348, Th. 16]):

$$T_\Omega(x') - T_\Omega(x) \leq \lambda e^{\|A\| \max\{T_\Omega(x'), T_\Omega(x)\}} \|x' - x\| \leq N \|x' - x\|.$$

Therefore,

$$T_\Omega(\bar{x}) - T_\Omega(x_0) \geq T_\Omega(\bar{x}) - T_\Omega(x') \geq -N\|\bar{x} - x'\| < \bar{x} - x', Nx^* > = < \bar{x} - x_0, Nx^* > .$$

Thus, we have proved that $Nx^* \in \partial^- T_\Omega(x_0)$. $\qquad\square$

Finally, we give two results which relate the Pontryagin maximum principle to the lower subdifferentials of the minimal time function.

Proposition 7.4. If co Ω is compact and $u^* : [0, T_\Omega(x_0)] \to \Omega$ is a control steering $x_0 \neq 0$ to the origin, then every solution $\eta(t)$ of the adjoint system $\dot{\eta} = -A^T(t)\eta$ such that $-\eta(0) \in \partial^- T_\Omega(x_0)$ is associated with u^* by the maximum principle, i.e.,

$$(*) \qquad \eta^T(t)B(t)u^*(t) = \max_{u \in \Omega} \eta^T(t)B(t)u \qquad \text{a.e. on } [0, T_\Omega(x_0)].$$

Proof. It is an immediate consequence of Prop. 3.17 in [21], Prop. 12 in [4, p. 42] and Prop. 4.14. $\qquad\square$

Proposition 7.5. Under the assumptions of Prop. 7.3, if $u^* : [0, T_\Omega(x_0)] \to \Omega$ is a control steering $x_0 \neq 0$ to the origin, then for every solution $\eta(t)$ of the adjoint system $\dot{\eta} = -A^T\eta$ which satisfies $(*)$ there exists a real number $\lambda \geq 1$ such that $-\lambda\eta(0) \in \partial^- T_\Omega(x_0)$.

Proof. Since rank $B = n$, we have rank $(B, AB, \cdots, A^{n-1}B) = n$, whence, by Prop. 3.17 in [21], $-\eta(0) \in \partial^* T_\Omega(x_0)$. Moreover, T_Ω is finite everywhere (see Th. 17.3 and 17.6 in [14, pp/ 74 - 79]) and inf-compact [21, Prop. 3.7]. By Lemma 4.18, the set

$$P(S_{T_\Omega(x_0)}) = \bigcup_{\substack{H \text{ hyperplane} \\ H \cap S_{T_\Omega(x_0)}(T_\Omega) \neq \phi}} \Pi_H(S_{T_\Omega(x_0)}(T_\Omega))$$

is bounded. Since T_Ω is continuous [21, Cor. 3.13], it is bounded above on P, say by K. By Th. 16 in [12, p. 348], there exists $\lambda > 0$ such that $|T_\Omega(x) - T_\Omega(y)| \leq \lambda e^{\|A\| \max\{T_\Omega(x),T_\Omega(y)\}}\|x - y\|$. Let $N = \lambda e^{\|A\|K}$. Since T_Ω is Lipschitz with constant N on $P(S_{T_\Omega(x_0)}(T_\Omega))$, from Prop. 4.17 it follows that $\partial^* T_\Omega(x_0) = \text{cone } \partial^- T_\Omega(x_0)$, whence there exists a positive number λ such that $-\lambda\eta(0) \in \partial^- T_\Omega(x_0)$. By Th. 3.1 in [26, p. 42], this holds for some $\lambda \geq 1$.

Acknowledgements. We would like to thank Prof. J. P. Penot for his many helpful comments, especially for discovering that the original statements of Prop. 4.2 and Cor. 4.22 were wrong. The present improved version of Cor. 4.15, with $\partial^* f(x_0)$ instead of $Tf(x_0)$, is also due to him. We are also indebted to Prof. I. Singer, for his interesting suggestions and remarks and for recommending several references.

References.

[1] Balder, E. J.: *An extension of duality-stability relations to non convex optimization problems.* SIAM J. Control. Optim. 15 (1977), 329 – 343.

[2] Carja, O.: *On the minimal time function for distributed control systems in Banach spaces.* J. Optim. Theory Appl. 44 (1984), 397 – 406.

[3] Crouzeix, J. P.: *Polares quasi-convexes et dualité.* C. R. Acad. Sc. Paris 279 (1974), 955 – 958.

[4] Crouzeix, J. P.: *Contributions a l'étude des fonctions quasiconvexes.* Thesis, Université de Clermont-Ferrand II (1977).

[5] Crouzeix, J. P.: *Continuity and differentiability properties of quasiconvex functions on $\mathbb{R}^n$.* Generalized concavity in Optimization and Economics, ed. by S. Schaible and W. T. Ziemba, Academic Press (1981), 109 – 130.

[6] Dolecki, S. and Kurcyusz S.: *On Φ-convexity in extremal problems.* SIAM J. Control Optim. 16 (1978), 277 – 300.

[7] Evers, J. J. M. and van Maaren, H.: *Duality principles in mathematics and their relations to conjugate functions.* Nieuw Arch. Wiskunde 3 (1985), 23 – 68.

[8] Greenberg, H. P. and Pierskalla, W. P.: *Quasiconjugate function and surrogate duality.* Cahier du Centre d'études de Rechn. Oper. 15 (1973), 437 – 448.

[9] Gutiérrez-Diez, J. M.: *Infragradients y direcciones de decrecimiento.* Rev. Real Acad. C. Ex., Fis. y Nat. Madrid 78 (1984), 523 – 532.

[10] Gutiérrez-Diez, J. M.: *Una caracterización dual de optimalidad para optimización convexa.* Trab. Est. Inv. Oper. 35 (1984), 293 – 304.

[11] Gyurkovics, E.: *Hölder condition for the minimum time function of linear systems.* System Modelling and Optimization, ed. by P. Thoft-Christensen, Springer-Verlag (1984), 383 – 392.

[12] Hájek, O.: *Geometric theory of time optimal control.* SIAM J. Control Optim. 9 (1971), 339 – 350.

[13] Hájek, O.: *On differentiability of the minimal time function.* Funkcialaj Ekvacioj 20 (1977), 97 – 114.

[14] Hermes, H. and la Salle, J. P.: *Functional analysis and time optimal control.* Academic Press (1969).

[15] Hiriart-Urruty, J. B.: *Extension of Lipschitz functions.* J. Math. Anal. Appl. 77 (1980), 539 – 554.

[16] Hiriart-Urruty, J. B.: *Lipschitz r-continuity of the approximate subdifferential of a convex function.* Math. Scand. 47 (1980), 123 – 134.

[17] Laurent, P. J.: *Approximation et optimisation.* Hermann (1972).

[18] Lee, E. B. and Markus, L.: *Foundations of optimal control theory.* John Wiley (1967).

[19] Mangasarian, O. L.: *Non linear programming.* Mc Graw Hill (1969).

[20] Martínez-Legaz, J. E.: *Conjugación asociada a un grafo.* Actas IX Jornadas Matemáticas Hispano-Lusas, Vol. II, Universidad de Salamanca (1982), 837 – 839.

[21] Martínez-Legaz, J. E.: *Level sets and the minimal time function of linear control processes.* Numer. Funct. Anal. Optimiz. (to appear).

[22] Mc Shane, E. J.: *Extension of range of functions.* Bull. Amer. Math. Soc. 40 (1934), 837 – 842.

[23] Mignanego, F. and Pieri, G.: *On a generalized Bellman equation for the optimal-time problem.* Systems & Control Letters 3 (1983), 235 – 241.

[24] Moreau, J. J.: *Inf-convolution, sous-additivité, convexité des fontions numériques.* J. Math. pures et appl. 49 (1970), 109 – 154.

[25] Penot, J. P. and Volle, M.: *Another duality scheme for quasiconvex problems.* Paper presented at the 4th French-German Conference on Optimization (1986).

[26] Plastria, F.: *Lower subdifferentiable functions and their minimization by cutting planes.* J. Optim. Theory Appl. 46 (1985), 37 – 53.

[27] Rockafellar, R. T.: *Convex analysis.* Princeton University Press (1970).

[28] Rockafellar, R. T.: *Augmented Lagrange multiplier functions and duality in non-convex programming.* SIAM J. Control Optim. 12 (1974), 268 – 285.

[29] Singer, I.: *The lower semi-continuous quasi-convex hull as a normalized second conjugate.* Nonlinear Anal. Theory, Meth. Appl. 7 (1983), 1115 – 1121.

[30] Singer, I.: *Surrogate conjugate functionals and surrogate convexity.* Applicable Anal. 16 (1983), 291 – 327.

[31] Singer, I.: *Generalized convexity, functional hulls and applications to conjugate duality in optimization.* Selected Topics in Operations Research and Mathematical Economics, ed. by G. Hammer and D. Pallaschke, Springer-Verlag (1984), 80 – 97.

[32] Singer, I.: *Some relations between dualities, polarities, coupling functionals and conjugations.* J. Math. Anal. Appl. 115 (1986), 1 – 33.

[33] Volle, M.: *Conjugaison par tranches.* Annali Mat. Pura Applicata 139 (1985), 279 – 311.

[34] Whitney, H.: *Analytic extensions of differentiable functions defined in closed sets.* Trans. Math. Soc. 36 (1934), 63 – 89.

International Series of
Numerical Mathematics, Vol. 84
(c) 1988 Birkhäuser Verlag Basel

On the Usage of Bundle Methods in Optimal Control of Nondifferentiable Systems.

J. V. Outrata

ÚTIA ČSAV

182 08 Prague 8

Pod vodárenskou vezi 4

Czechoslovakia

Abstract. Optimal control problems with nondifferentiable systems can often be numerically solved by means of subgradient or bundle methods, provided we are able to compute vectors from the generalized gradient of the objective with respect to the control. In the paper we propose several ways, how to perform this computation, depending on the description of the controlled system and the nature of the nondifferentiability in question.

1. Introduction.

Let us consider an optimal control problem of the general form

$$J(x, u) \to \inf$$

subj. to

$$A(x, u) = 0 \qquad\qquad (P)$$

$$u \in \omega \subset U$$

$$x \in X,$$

where X, U are the state and the control space, respectively; $J[X \times U \to \mathbb{R}]$ is the optimality criterion (cost, objective), the map $A[X \times U \to X]$ defines the system equation $A(x, u) = 0$ and ω is the set of admissible controls. As a *process* we denote a couple $(x, u) \in X \times U$, satisfying the system equation.

We suppose that eventual state-space constraints have been already augmented to the objective by a suitable penalty so that we do not need to take care about them. It is also assumed that the system equation defines a unique implicit function μ on U such that $A(\mu(u), u) = 0$ on U.

When solving problems of the type (P) numerically, we mostly transcribe them into the mathematical programming form

$$\theta(u) = J(\mu(u), u) \to \inf$$

subj. to $\qquad\qquad (MP)$

$$u \in \omega$$

and apply some suitable numerical technique of mathematical programming. If J and A are continuously differentiable and the structure of ω is sufficiently simple, we use mostly a gradient method and compute the gradients of θ using the well-known concept of adjoint equations. If J and/or A are nonsmooth locally Lipschitz, we may (under some further conditions) apply some bundle or subgradient method (cf. [13] for a survey) to the numerical solution of (MP); however, we must be able to compute at every admissible control u at least one point from $\partial\theta(u)$ - the generalized gradient of θ at u in the sense of Clarke.

This problem has been investigated in [7] for nonsmooth objectives of a special structure and in [8], [9] for some general classes of objectives. In the present paper we consider the case of a continuously differentiable cost and a nonsmooth system equation (in fact, most problems with nonsmooth terms appearing in both the system equation and the objective can be rewritten in such a form). Sect. 2 contains a complement to the implicit function theorem for locally Lipschitz maps from $\mathbb{R}^n \times \mathbb{R}^m$ into $\mathbb{R}^n$, indicating how to compute matrices of the generalized Jacobian of the implicit function. This assertion is then applied to (MP) and illustrated on an economic model. With respect to the definition of generalized Jacobians and the used implicit function theorem we confine ourselves in Sect. 2 to problems, where spaces X and U are finite-dimensional. In Sect. 3 we utilize the classical implicit function theorem and an extension of generalized Jacobians to maps from separable into reflexive separable Banach spaces. Then, however, we need a certain specific structure of A. Sect. 4 is devoted to a special class of systems, given by the elliptic variational inequalities in $\mathbb{R}^n$.

It is assumed that the reader is familiar with the definition and basic properties of the generalized gradient of Clarke and the generalized Jacobian as they are collected e.g. in [1], [2]. For the definition and basic properties of generalized derivatives of infinite-dimensional operators, used in Sect. 3, we refer to [4].

We use the following notation: $\mathcal{U}_x(a)(\mathcal{U}_n(a))$ is the filter of all (norm) neighbourhoods of a in a Banach space $X(\mathbb{R}^n)$, B^* is the adjoint operator of a continuous linear operator B, $f'(x,h)$ and $f^0(x;h)$ are the usual directional derivative and the directional derivative of Clarke of a function $f[X \to \mathbb{R}]$ at x in the direction h, respectively; ∂f is the generalized gradient of f at x or also the generalized Jacobian of f at x if $f[\mathbb{R}^n \to \mathbb{R}^m]$, $\partial_H A(x)$ is the generalized derivative of a map $A[X \to Y]$ with respect to a set $H \subset X$ (cf. [4] or [12]), plen $\{A\}$ is the plenary hull of a set A (cf. [4]). If $f[X \times U \to Z]$ is partially differentiable at a point (x,u), we use the notation $\nabla_1 f$, $\nabla_2 f$ for the partial derivatives with respect to the first and second variable. $\delta_\Gamma^*(h)$ is the support function of a set Γ in the direction h, for $\lambda \in \mathbb{R}$, $(\lambda)^+ = \max\{0, \lambda\}$ and x^j is the j-th coordinate of a vector $x \in \mathbb{R}^n$.

2. Generalized Jacobians of implicit functions

For convenience we recall the generalized implicit function theorem of [2]. Let the map $A[\mathbb{R}^n \times \mathbb{R}^m \to \mathbb{R}^n]$ be Lipschitz near $(x_0, u_0) \in \mathbb{R}^n \times \mathbb{R}^m$; by $P_x \partial A(x_0, u_0)$ we denote the set of all $[n \times n]$ matrices M such that, for some $[n \times m]$ matrix N, the $[n \times (n+m)]$ matrix $[M, N]$ belongs to $\partial A(x_0, u_0)$.

Theorem 2.1. *Suppose that for all $M \in P_x \partial A(x_0, u_0)$*

$$\operatorname{rank} M = n. \tag{2.1}$$

Then there exists a neighbourhood $O \in U_m(u_0)$ and a Lipschitz map $\mu[O \to \mathbb{R}^n]$ such that $\mu(u_0) = x_0$ and, for every $u \in O$

$$A(\mu(u), u) = 0.$$

Matrices from $\partial \mu(u_0)$ may be computed in some cases by using the following assertion:

Proposition 2.2. *Let A satisfy the condition (2.1) at (x_0, u_0). Denote by Γ_A the (open, possibly empty) set of points $(x, u) \in \mathbb{R}^n \times \mathbb{R}^m$ that have a neighbourhood $O \in U_{n \times m}(x, u)$, where the derivative ∇A is continuous. Furthermore, let*

$$(x_0, u_0) \in \overline{\Gamma}_A \tag{2.2}$$

and $\{(x_j, u_j)\}$ be a sequence converging to (x_0, u_0) and satisfying the inclusion

$$(x_j, u_j) \in \Gamma_A \cap \operatorname{graph}\mu \quad \text{for all } j. \tag{2.3}$$

Then, there exists a subsequence $\{(x_{j'}, u_{j'})\}$ of $\{(x_j, u_j)\}$ such that

$$-\left(\lim_{j \to \infty} \nabla_1 A(x_{j'}, u_{j'})\right)^{-1} \lim_{j \to \infty} \nabla_2 A(x_{j'}, u_{j'}) \in \partial \mu(u_0). \tag{2.4}$$

Proof. Note that

$$\lim_{j' \to \infty} \nabla A(x_{j'}, u_{j'}) = \lim_{j' \to \infty} \nabla_1 A(x_{j'}, u_{j'}), \lim_{j' \to \infty} \nabla_2 A(x_{j'}, u_{j'})]$$

exists due to the Lipschitz continuity and belongs to $\partial A(x_0, u_0)$ by the definition; hence the matrix $\lim_{j' \to \infty} \nabla_1 A(x_{j'}, u_{j'})$ is nonsingular because of the condition (2.1). The continuity of A on Γ_A implies furthermore the existence of a natural number k_0 such that for $j' > k_0$ $\nabla_1 A(x_{j'}, u_{j'})$ is nonsingular. Hence, for such j'

$$\nabla \mu(u_{j'}) = -(\nabla_1 A(x_{j'}, u_{j'}))^{-1} \nabla_2 A(x_{j'}, u_{j'})$$

due to the classical implicit function theorem. Consequently,

$$\lim_{j' \to \infty} [-(\nabla_1 A(x_{j'}, u_{j'}))^{-1} \nabla_2 A(x_{j'}, u_{j'})] =$$
$$= -(\lim_{j' \to \infty} \nabla_1 A(x_{j'}, u_{j'}))^{-1} \lim_{j' \to \infty} \nabla_2 A(x_{j'}, u_{j'}) \in \partial \mu(u_0).$$

$\square$

The above statement (together with a suitable chain rule) can be used to compute generalized gradients of θ for many optimal control problems of type (P).

Proposition 2.3. Let $X = \mathbb{R}^n$, $U = \mathbb{R}^m$, $A[X \times U \to X]$ be locally Lipschitz over $X \times U$, $\overline{u} \in \omega$, $\overline{x} = \mu(\overline{u})$ and let the condition (2.1) be satisfied at $(\overline{x}, \overline{u})$. Assume that $(\overline{x}, \overline{u}) \in \Gamma_A$ with Γ_A like in Prop. 2.2, and let $\{(x_j, u_j)\}$ be a sequence converging to $(\overline{x}, \overline{u})$ and satisfying the inclusion (2.3). Further let $\{(x_{j'}, u_{j'})\}$ be a subsequence of $\{(x_j, u_j)\}$ such that $\lim_{j' \to \infty} \nabla A(x_{j'}, u_{j'})$ exists. Finally, let J be continuously differentiable on $X \times U$ and λ^* be the solution of the adjoint equation

$$[\lim_{j' \to \infty} \nabla_1 A(x_{j'}, u_{j'})]^* \lambda^* + \nabla_1 J(\overline{x}, \overline{u}) = 0. \tag{2.5}$$

Then

$$[\lim_{j' \to \infty} \nabla_2 A(x_{j'}, u_{j'})]^* \lambda^* + \nabla_2 J(\overline{x}, \overline{u}) \in \partial \theta(\overline{u}). \tag{2.6}$$

Proof. By applying of the Jacobian chain rule cf. [2] to the map $J \circ \left[\begin{smallmatrix} \mu(u) \\ u \end{smallmatrix} \right]$ one has

$$\partial \theta(\overline{u}) = (\partial \mu(\overline{u}))^* \nabla_1 J(\overline{x}, \overline{u}) + \nabla_2 J(\overline{x}, \overline{u})$$

and hence for any matrix $R^* \in (\partial \mu(\overline{u}))^*$

$$R^* \nabla_1 J(\overline{x}, \overline{u}) + \nabla_2 J(\overline{x}, \overline{u}) \in \partial \theta(\overline{u}).$$

Clearly, for $h \in \mathbb{R}^m$ and a matrix R specified by $\{(x_{j'}, u_{j'})\}$ in the sense of Prop. 2.2

$$\theta^0(\overline{u}; h) \ge <\nabla_1 J(\overline{x}, \overline{u}), Rh> + <\nabla_2 J(\overline{x}, \overline{u}), h> =$$
$$= - <\nabla_1 J(\overline{x}, \overline{u}), (\lim_{j' \to \infty} \nabla_1 A(x_{j'}, u_{j'}))^{-1} (\lim_{j' \to \infty} \nabla_2 A(x_{j'}, u_{j'}))h> +$$
$$+ <\nabla_2 J(\overline{x}, \overline{u}), h> =$$
$$= <[\lim_{j' \to \infty} \nabla_2 A(x_{j'}, u_{j'})]^* \lambda^* + \nabla_2 J(\overline{x}, \overline{u}), h>.$$

$\square$

Undoubtedly, the most complicated part when using Prop. 2.3 is the construction of a sequence $\{(x_{j'}, u_{j'})\}$ possessing the above mentioned properties. Fortunately, if we confine ourselves to systems described by ordinary differential equations discretized by the Euler method, then the previous assertion may be substantially simplified. First observe that in such a case we do not need to take care about condition (2.1).

Lemma 2.4. Let $x = (x_1, x_2, \cdots, x_k) \in (\mathbb{R}^n)^k$, $u = (u_0, u_1, \cdots, u_{k-1}) \in (\mathbb{R}^m)^k$ and functions $f_i[\mathbb{R}^n \times \mathbb{R}^m \to \mathbb{R}^n]$ be locally Lipschitz over $\mathbb{R}^n \times \mathbb{R}^m$ for $i = 0, 1, \cdots, k-1$. Then for $A[\mathbb{R}^{nk} \times \mathbb{R}^{mk} \to \mathbb{R}^{nk}]$ given by

$$A(x, u) = \begin{bmatrix} x_1 - a - f_0(a, u_0) \\ x_2 - x_1 - f_1(x_1, u_1) \\ \cdots \\ x_k - x_{k-1} - f_{k-1}(x_{k-1}, u_{k-1}) \end{bmatrix} \quad (a \in \mathbb{R}^n \text{ is given}) \quad (2.7)$$

all matrices of $P_x \partial A(x, u)$ are nonsingular.

Proof. For any sequence $\{(x_j, u_j)\}$ converging to (x, u) and such that the functions f_i are differentiable at $((x_i)_j, (u_i)_j)$ for $i = 1, 2, \cdots, k-1$, our f_0 is differentiable at $(a, (u_0)_j)$ and $\lim_{j \to \infty} \nabla_1 A(x_j, u_j)$ exists. This limit is a lower triangular matrix with elements 1 in the diagonal. $\square$

In Props. 2.5, 2.6 below it is assumed that A is given by (2.7), that, for the notational simplicity, $f_i = f$ for all i (i.e. the original system is autonomous) and $f[\mathbb{R}^n \times \mathbb{R}^m \to \mathbb{R}^n]$ is locally Lipschitz. Suppose that $u = (u_0, u_1, \cdots, u_{k-1}) \in (\mathbb{R}^m)^k$, $x = (x_1, x_2, \cdots, x_k) \in (\mathbb{R}^n)^k$ is the corresponding trajectory with respect to $A(x, u) = 0$ and for $i \in I(u) \subset \{0, 1, \cdots, k-1\}$ f is not differentiable at (x_i, u_i), $(x_0 = a)$. Finally, we assume that the (discretized) objective has the standard form

$$J(x, u) = \varphi(x_k) + \sum_{i=0}^{k-1} \psi(x_i, u_i), \quad (2.8)$$

where functions $\varphi[\mathbb{R}^n \to \mathbb{R}]$, $\psi[\mathbb{R}^n \times \mathbb{R}^m \to \mathbb{R}]$ are continuously differentiable.

Proposition 2.5. Let us have a discrete-time optimal control problem of the above specified form. Suppose that at a process (x, u) for all $i \in I(u) \setminus \{0\}$ there exist open sets $\mathcal{A}(x_i, u_i) \in \mathbb{R}^n \times \mathbb{R}^m$ such that

for any couple $(b, d) \in \mathcal{A}(x_i, u_i)$ f is continuously differentiable on a neighbourhood $\mathcal{O} \in \mathcal{U}_{n \times m}(b, d)$;

If $0 \in I(u)$, let there exist an open set $\mathcal{A}(u_0) \in \mathbb{R}^m$, such that

for any $d \in \mathcal{A}(u_0)$ $f(a, \cdot)$ is continuously differentiable on a neighbourhood $\mathcal{N} \in \mathcal{U}_m(d)$.

Finally we assume that there exist sequences of controls $\{u_j\} = \{(u_{0j}, u_{1j}, \cdots, u_{k-1,j})\}$, $u_{ij} \to u_i$, $i = 0, 1, \cdots, k-1$ which, together with their corresponding trajectories $\{x_j\} = \{(x_{1j}, x_{2j}, \cdots, x_{kj})\}$, satisfy the inclusions

$(x_{ij}, u_{ij}) \in \mathcal{A}(x_i, u_i)$ for $i \in I(u) \setminus \{0\}$ and all j,
$(a, u_{0j}) \in \mathcal{A}(u_0)$ for all j provided $0 \in I(u)$.

Then, (if necessary, by taking suitable subsequences denoted in the same way) we assert that the vector

$$- ([\lim_{j \to \infty} \nabla_2 f(a, u_{0j})]^* p_1, [\lim_{j \to \infty} \nabla_2 f(x_{1j}, u_{ij})]^* p_2, \cdots ,$$

$$[\lim_{j \to \infty} \nabla_2 f(x_{k-1,j}, u_{k-1,j})]^* p_k) + (\nabla_2 \psi(a, u_0), \nabla_2 \psi(x_1, u_1), \cdots , \nabla_2 \psi(x_{k-1}, u_{k-1}))$$

belongs to the generalized gradient of the corresponding function θ, provided $(p_1, p_2, \cdots , p_k) \in (\mathbb{R}^n)^k$ is the solution of the adjoint equation

$$p_i = [\lim_{j \to \infty} \nabla_1 f(x_{ij}, u_{ij})]^* p_{i+1} - \nabla_1 \psi(x_i, u_i), \; i = 1, 2, \cdots , k-1 \qquad (2.9)$$

with the terminal condition

$$p_k = - \nabla \varphi(x_k). \qquad (2.10)$$

The proof is evident and consists in a mere combination of the assertion of Prop. 2.3 and Lemma 2.4 if we take into account the form of A and J given by (2.7), (2.8), respectively.

Sometimes the situation is even more simple.

Proposition 2.6. Let us have a discrete-time optimal control problem of the above specified form. Suppose that at a process (x, u)

(i) for all $i \in I(u)$ there exist open sets $A(u_i) \subset \mathbb{R}^m$ such that for any $d \in A(u_i)$ function $f(x_i, \cdot)$ is continuously differentiable on a neighbourhood $M \in \mathcal{U}_m(d)$ and for any sequence $\{d_j\} \subset A(u_i)$, $d_j \to u_i$, $\lim_{j \to \infty} \nabla f(x_i, d_j)$ exists;

(ii) for all $i \in I(u)$ there exist sequences $u_{ij} \to u_i$ such that $u_{ij} \in A(u_i)$ and $x_{i+1}^\ell = f^\ell(x_i, u_{ij})$ for all j, whenever x_{i+1}^ℓ might influence some nondifferentiable terms in the future process ($\ell \in \{1, 2, \cdots , n\}$).

Then the vector $-([\lim_{j \to \infty} \nabla_2 f(a, u_{0j})]^* p_1, [\lim_{j \to \infty} \nabla_2 f(x_1, u_{1j})]^* p_2, \cdots , [\lim_{j \to \infty} \nabla_2 f(x_{k-1}, u_{k-1,j})]^* p_k) + (\nabla_2 \psi(a, u_0), \nabla_2 \psi(x_1, u_1), \cdots , \nabla_2 \psi(x_{k-1}, u_{k-1}))$ belongs to the generalized gradient of the appropriate function θ if $(p_1, p_2, \cdots , p_k) \in (\mathbb{R}^n)^k$ is the solution of the adjoint equation

$$p_i = [\lim_{j \to \infty} \nabla_1 f(x_i, u_{ij})]^* p_{i+1} - \nabla_1 \psi(x_i, u_i), \; i = 1, 2, \cdots , k-1 \qquad (2.11)$$

with the terminal condition (2.10).

This evident assertion can be applied e.g. to the following economic problem, where already the original problem formulation is finite-dimensional (but the controlled system is not autonomous).

Example 2.1. Let us consider the discrete-time optimal control problem

$$\sum_{i=0}^{k-1} e^{-\vartheta i} [-c_i \min\{z_i + u_i, v_i\} + g(u_i) + d(v_i - z_i - u_i)^+ + h z_i] \to \min$$

subj. to

$$z_{i+1} = z_i + u_i - \min\{z_i + u_i, v_i\}, z_0 = a$$
$$0 \le u_i \le b_i, i = 0, 1, \cdots, k-1, \tag{2.12}$$

where k is a given finite horizon,

z_i is the i-th coordinate of the state variable $z = (z_1, z_2, \cdots, z_k) \in \mathbb{R}^k$ which means the number of products in the stock at the time i,

u_i is the i-th coordinate of the control vector $u = (u_0, u_1, \cdots, u_{k-1}) \in \mathbb{R}^k$ which means the production in the time interval $[i, i+1)$,

v_i is the planned output (supply) at the time i,

c_i is the unit selling price at the time i,

$g[\mathbb{R} \to \mathbb{R}_+]$ is the production function, assumed to be continously differentiable,

d is the unit penalization for the case that $v_i > z_i + u_i$,

h is the unit inventory cost,

ϑ is the interest rate,

b_i is the upper bound for the production at the time i and

a is the initial number of products in the stock.

The aim of the optimization is to find such an admissible sequence of productions $u_0, u_1, \cdots, u_{k-1}$ which maximizes the total profit of the factory with respect to given sequences of outputs $(v_0, v_1, \cdots, v_{k-1})$ and prices $(c_0, c_1, \cdots, c_{k-1})$.

To be able to apply Prop. 2.6., we have to remove the nonsmooth terms from the objective by introducing a new-state variable. We obtain the recast problem.

$$y_k \to \min$$

subj. to

$$z_{i+1} = z_i + u_i - \min\{z_i + u_i, v_i\}, \quad z_0 = a$$
$$y_{i+1} = y_i + e^{-\vartheta i} s_i, \quad y_0 = 0 \tag{2.13}$$
$$0 \le u_i \le b_i, \quad i = 0, 1, \cdots, k-1,$$

where

$$s_i = \begin{cases} -c_i v_i + g(u_i) + h z_i & \text{if } z_i + u_i > v_i \\ -c_i(z_i + u_i) + g(u_i) + d(v_i - z_i - u_i) + h z_i & \text{if } z_i + u_i \le v_i, \end{cases}$$
$$i = 0, 1, \cdots, k-1.$$

For the appropriate functions $\theta : (u_0, u_1, \cdots, u_{k-1}) \mapsto y_k$ the following assertion holds:

Proposition 2.7. Let $u = (u_0, u_1, \cdots, u_{k-1}) \in \mathbb{R}^k$ and $z = (z_1, z_2, \cdots, z_k) \in \mathbb{R}^k$, $y = (y_1, y_2, \cdots, y_k) \in \mathbb{R}^k$ be the trajectories corresponding to u with respect to the system equations in (2.13). Then the function θ is locally Lipschitz. Suppose that $[2 \times 2]$ matrices C_i and vectors $B_i \in \mathbb{R}^2$, $i = 0, 1, \cdots, k-1$ are given by

$$C_i = \begin{bmatrix} 1 & 0 \\ e^{-\vartheta_i} h & 1 \end{bmatrix}, \quad B_i = \begin{bmatrix} 1 \\ e^{-\vartheta_i} \nabla g(u_i) \end{bmatrix}, \quad \text{if } z_i + u_i > v_i,$$

and

$$C_i = \begin{bmatrix} 0 & 0 \\ e^{-\vartheta_i}(-c_i - d + h) & 1 \end{bmatrix}, \quad B_i = \begin{bmatrix} 0 \\ e^{-\vartheta_i}(-c_i + \nabla g(u_i) - d) \end{bmatrix}, \quad \text{otherwise.}$$

Finally, let $(p_1, p_2, \cdots, p_k) \in (\mathbb{R}^2)^k$ be the solution of the adjoint equation

$$p_i = C_i^* p_{i+1}, \ i = 1, 2, \cdots, k-1 \tag{2.14}$$

with the terminal condition $p_k = -(0, 1)$. Then one has

$$-(B_0^* p_1, B_1^* p_2, \cdots, B_{k-1}^* p_k) \in \partial\theta(u). \tag{2.15}$$

Proof. The local Lipschitz continuity of θ is evident. To prove the inclusion (2.15) it suffices to note that the sets

$$\mathcal{A}(u_i) = \{d \in \mathbb{R} \mid d \leq u_i\}, \ i \in I(u) = \{i \mid z_i + u_i = v_i\}$$

satisfy the assumptions of Prop. 2.6. $\qquad\square$

This problem has been numerically solved for various sets of artificial data by using the codes BOREPS and M2FC1 of Cl. Lemarechal. Vectors from $\partial\theta$ were computed according to Prop. 2.7. For $k = 48$ we needed from 30 to 50 iterations to get the results within a sufficient accuracy. In case, state space constraints are present in (2.13), which we would add to the objective in an exact penalty approach, then Prop. 2.6 cannot be applied; however, we may proceed according to Prop. 2.5 as shown in [8].

3. Systems nonsmooth only in the control variable

Throughout this short section it will be assumed that U is a separable Banach space and X is a reflexive separable Banach space so that the extension of generalized Jacobians for locally Lipschitz maps according to [4], [12] can be used.

Proposition 3.1. Let J be continuously differentiable on $X \times U$. Let Z be a reflexive separable Banach space and

$$A(x, u) = A_1(x, B(u)),$$

where the map $B[U \to Z]$ is locally Lipschitz on U and Gâteaux differentiable on a set $H \subset U$ with $U \setminus H$ being of Haar measure zero and $A_1[X \times Z \to X]$ is continuously differentiable on $X \times Z$. Assume that $\overline{u} \in \omega$, $\overline{x} = \mu(\overline{u})$ and the partial derivative $\nabla_1 A(\overline{x}, \overline{u})$ is a linear homeomorphism of X onto X. Finally, let λ^* be the solution of the adjoint equation

$$[\nabla_1 A_1(\overline{x}, \overline{v})]^* \lambda^* + \nabla_1 J(\overline{x}, \overline{u}) = 0, \tag{3.1}$$

where $\overline{v} = B(\overline{u})(v = B(u))$. Then

$$M^*[\nabla_2 A_1(\overline{x}, \overline{v})]^* \lambda^* + \nabla_2 J(\overline{x}, \overline{u}) \in \partial \theta(\overline{u}) \tag{3.2}$$

for any $M \in \mathrm{plen}\{\partial_H B(\overline{u})\}$.

Proof. According to the classical implicit function theorem there exists a neighbourhood $\mathcal{O} \in \mathcal{U}_Z(\overline{v})$ and a unique map $\kappa[\mathcal{O} \to X]$ such that $\kappa(\overline{v}) = \overline{x}$, $A_1(\kappa(v), v) = 0$ on $\mathcal{O}$ and

$$\nabla \kappa(\overline{v}) = -(\nabla_1 A_1(\overline{x}, \overline{v}))^{-1} \nabla_2 A_1(\overline{x}, \overline{v}).$$

Using the generalized derivative chain rule (Prop. 2.4 of [12]), we obtain that

$$\partial_H \mu(\overline{u}) = \nabla \kappa(\overline{v}) \circ \partial_H B(\overline{u}).$$

By Props. 2.2 and 2.4 of [12] for $h \in U$

$$\theta^0(\overline{u}; h) = \max_{R \in \partial_H \mu(\overline{u})} < \nabla_1 J(\overline{x}, \overline{u}), Rh > + < \nabla_2 J(\overline{x}, \overline{u}), h > =$$

$$= \max_{S \in \partial_H B(\overline{u})} < -[\nabla_2 A_1(\overline{x}, \overline{v})]^*([\nabla_1 A_1(\overline{x}, \overline{v})]^*)^{-1} \nabla_1 J(\overline{x}, \overline{u}), Sh > +$$

$$+ < \nabla_2 J(\overline{x}, \overline{u}), h > =$$

$$= \max_{S \in \partial_H B(\overline{u})} < [\nabla_2 A_1(\overline{x}, \overline{v})]^* \lambda^*, Sh > + < \nabla_2 J(\overline{x}, \overline{u}), h > \geq$$

$$\geq < M^*[\nabla_2 A_1(\overline{x}, \overline{v})]^* \lambda^* + \nabla_2 J(\overline{x}, \overline{u}), h >$$

for any $M \in \mathrm{plen}\{\partial_H B(\overline{u})\}$ by definition. $\qquad\square$

An easy application of Prop. 3.1 is provided by a minimum-energy control of a linear plant with a dead band. Numerical experiments with this example and the code BOREPS are reported in [10].

4. Elliptic variational inequalities

In this section we will direct our attention to a special class of nondifferential systems - elliptic variational inequalities in $\mathbb{R}^n$. Such systems arise e.g. due to a finite element approximation of a unilateral boundary-value problem with a linear elliptic partial differential equation. The original continuous case was investigated in [6] using the conical derivatives and in [5] by means of the subdifferential of a convex mapping. Here, we assume that the controlled system attains the form

$$u \in Fx + N_k(x), \tag{4.1}$$

where $u, x \in \mathbb{R}^n$, F is a positively definite symmetric $[n \times n]$ matrix, $N_k(x)$ is the normal cone to a convex set K at x and $K = x_0 + \mathbb{R}_+^n$, $x_0 \in \mathbb{R}^n$ given. Note that this system is not of the form discussed in the previous sections.

The map $\mu : u \mapsto x$ given by (4.1) is Lipschitz (x is the projection of $F^{-1}u$ onto K in the F-metric). Incl. (4.1) may be easily rewritten as

$$
\begin{aligned}
& x^i \geq x_0 \\
& < F_i, x > -u^i \geq 0 \\
& (x^i - x_0^i)(< F_i, x > -u^i) = 0, \quad i = 1, 2, \cdots, n,
\end{aligned}
\tag{4.2}
$$

where F_i denotes the i-th row of F. We introduce now the index sets

$$
\begin{aligned}
& I_1(u) = \{i \in \{1, 2, \cdots, n\} \mid x^i = x_0^i, < F_i, x > -u^i > 0\} \\
& I_2(u) = \{i \in \{1, 2, \cdots, n\} \mid x^i = x_0^i, < F_i, x > -u^i = 0\} \\
& I_3(u) = \{i \in \{1, 2, \cdots, n\} \mid x^i > x_0^i\}
\end{aligned}
\tag{4.3}
$$

and recall the following well-known assertion:

Proposition 4.1. The map μ is directionally derivable at any $u \in \mathbb{R}^n$ for all directions $h \in \mathbb{R}^n$ and

$$
\begin{aligned}
& \mu^{i'}(u; h) = 0 && \text{for } i \in I_1(u) \\
& \mu^{i'}(u; h) \geq 0, \ < F_i, \mu'(u; h) >\geq h^i && \text{for } i \in I_2(u) \\
& < F_i, \mu'(u; h) >= h^i && \text{for } i \in I_3(u) \\
& \mu^{i'}(u; h)(< F_i, \mu'(u; h) > -h^i) = 0 && \text{for all } i,
\end{aligned}
\tag{4.4}
$$

where $\mu' = (\mu^{1'}, \mu^{2'}, \cdots, \mu^{n'})$.

The map μ is differentiable at u whenever $I_2(u) = \emptyset$. If we denote by $\tilde{F}$ the submatrix of F, composed from elements f_{ij}, $i, j \in I_3(u)$ and by C (with elements c_{ij}) the inverse of F, then one has

$$
(\nabla \mu(u))_{ij} = \begin{cases} c_{ij} & \text{for } i, j \in I_3(u) \\ 0 & \text{otherwise.} \end{cases}
\tag{4.5}
$$

The equations and inequalities (4.4) may be derived directly from the definition, using the relations (4.2). The differentiable case can be investigated e.g. by means of the classical implicit function theorem.

Proposition 4.2. Let $u \in \mathbb{R}^n$, $x = \mu(u)$ and $M \subset I_2(u)$. Suppose that $\tilde{F}^M$ is the submatrix of F, composed from elements f_{ij}, $i, j \in I_3(u) \cup M$ and C^M (with elements c_{ij}^M) is the inverse of $\tilde{F}^M$. Then

$$
\partial \mu(u) \supset \text{co } \{B^M \mid M \subset I_2(u)\},
\tag{4.6}
$$

where the elements b_{ij}^M of B^M are given by

$$
b_{ij}^M = \begin{cases} c_{ij}^M & \text{for } i, j \in I_3(u) \cup M \\ 0 & \text{otherwise.} \end{cases}
$$

Proof. According to the definition of the generalized Jacobian and with respect to the assertion of Prop. 4.1, it suffices to show that for any subset M of $I_2(u)$ there exists a direction $k_M \in \mathbb{R}^n$ such that $I_2(u + \lambda k_M) = \emptyset$ and $I_3(u + \lambda k_M) = I_3(u) \cup M$ for all $\lambda > 0$ sufficiently small. Let a vector k and the corresponding change of trajectory h $(x + h = \mu(u + k))$ satisfy the relations

$$x^i + h^i = x_0^i, \ < F_i, x + h > -u^i - k^i > 0 \text{ for } i \in I_1(u) \cup I_2(u) \setminus M.$$
$$x^i + h^i > x_0^i, \ < F_i, x + h > -u^i - k^i = 0 \text{ for } i \in I_3(u) \cup M.$$

With respect to (4.2) and the continuity of μ the above relations imply that

$$\begin{aligned}
h^i = 0 &\qquad \text{for } i \in I_1(u) \\
h^i = 0, &< F_i, h > -k^i > 0 \text{ for } i \in I_2(u) \setminus M \\
h^i > 0, &< F_i, h > -k^i = 0 \text{ for } i \in M \\
&< F_i, h > -k^i = 0 \text{ for } i \in I_3(u),
\end{aligned} \qquad (4.7)$$

provided $\|k\|$ is sufficiently small so that $< F_i, x > -u^i > - < F_i, h > +k^i$ for $i \in I_1(u)$ and $x^i + h^i > x_0^i$ for $i \in I_3(u)$. From (4.7) we obtain that

$$\sum_{j \in I_3(u) \cup M} f_{ij} h^j - k^i > 0 \text{ for } i \in I_2(u) \setminus M$$

$$\sum_{j \in I_3(u) \cup M} f_{ij} h^j - k^i = 0 \text{ for } i \in I_3(u) \cup M$$

$$h^i > 0 \text{ for } i \in M.$$

Thus, we may choose e.g. a vector $\bar{h}$ with $\bar{h}^i = 0$ for $i \in I_1(u) \cup I_2(u) \setminus M$, $\bar{h}^i > 0$ for $i \in M$ and, let us say, $\bar{h}^i = 0$ for $i \in I_3(u)$. Then we find a vector $\bar{k}$ satisfying the relations

$$\bar{k}^i < \sum_{j \in M} f_{ij} \bar{h}^j \text{ for } i \in I_2(u) \setminus M$$

$$\bar{k}^i = \sum_{j \in M} f_{ij} \bar{h}^j \text{ for } i \in I_3(u) \cup M$$

and, let us say,

$$\bar{k}^i = \sum_{j \in M} f_{ij} \bar{h}^j \text{ for } i \in I_2(u).$$

By (4.2) it can easily be seen that for all $\lambda > 0$ $\quad x + \lambda \bar{h} = \mu(u + \lambda \bar{k})$; thus $\bar{k}$ has the desired property, we may set $k_M = \bar{k}$ and the assertion has been proved. $\qquad \square$

Remark. Prop. 4.2 has been obtained in a different way in [3].

Of course, if we want to solve an optimal control problem of the form

$$J(x, u) \to \inf$$

subj. to

$$u \in Fx + N_k(x)$$

$$u \in \omega \subset \mathbb{R}^n, \tag{4.8}$$

with continuously differentiable cost $J[\mathbb{R}^n \times \mathbb{R}^n \to \mathbb{R}]$ by means of a bundle algorithm, then we perform the computation of some vector from the generalized gradient of corresponding function θ with the help of the appropriate adjoint equation.

Proposition 4.3. Let $u \in \omega$, $x = \mu(u)$ and $\hat{p}$ be the solution of the adjoint equation

$$(\tilde{F})^* \hat{p} + d = 0,$$

where d is the subvector of $\nabla_1 J(x, u)$ consisting from the partial derivatives $\frac{\partial J(x,u)}{\partial x^i}$; $i \in I_3(u)$. Then

$$-p + \nabla_2 J(x, u) \in \partial\theta(u) \tag{4.8}$$

provided

$$p^i = \begin{cases} \hat{p}^i & \text{for } i \in I_3(u) \\ 0 & \text{otherwise.} \end{cases}$$

In the proof we just combine Prop. 4.2 with the standard way of forming the adjoint equations.

Remark. Optimal control problems (4.8) are more deeply investigated in [11]; there also the system description is more general. Instead of (4.1) the variational inequality is of the form

$$g(u) \in F(u)x + N_k(x),$$

$u \in \mathbb{R}^m$, $g[\mathbb{R}^m \to \mathbb{R}^n]$. In this case, however, a straightforward generalization of formula (4.6) is not available.

References.

[1] Clarke, F. H.: *Generalized gradients and applications.* Trans. of the Amer. Math. Soc. 205 (1975), 247 – 262.

[2] Clarke, F. H.: *Optimization and nonsmooth analysis.* Wiley, New York (1983).

[3] Haslinger, J. and Roubiček, T.: *Optimal control of variational inequalities.* (in print in Appl. Math. Optim.).

[4] Hiriart-Urruty, J.-B. and Thibault, L.: *Existence et caractérisation de differentielles généralisées d'applications localement lipschitziennes d'un espace de Banach*

séparable dans un espace de Banach réflexif séparable. C.R. Acad. Sc. Paris 290 - A (1980), 1091 – 1094.

[5] Lemaire, B.: *Application of a subdifferential of a convex composite functional to optimal control in variational inequalities.* In: Nondifferentiable Optimization: Motivations and Applications (Demyanov, Pallaschke eds.), Lecture Notes 255, Springer Verlag (1984), 103 – 117.

[6] Mignot, F.: *Controle dans les inéquations variationelles eliptiques.* Journal of functional analysis 22 (1976), 130 – 185.

[7] Outrata, J. V.: *On a class of nonsmooth optimal control problems.* Appl. Math. and Optimization 10 (1983), 287 – 306.

[8] Outrata, J. V.: *Minimization of nonsmooth nonregular functions: Application to discrete-time optimal control problems.* Problems of Control and Information Theory 13 (1984), 413 – 414.

[9] Outrata, J. V.: *On numerical solution of optimal control problems with nonsmooth objectives: Applications to economic models.* Kybernetica 22, No. 6 (1986).

[10] Outrata, J. V.: *Dual methods in optimal control.* (in czech.), Academia, Prague (to appear).

[11] Roubiček, T.: *Evaluation of Clarkes generalized gradient in optimization of variational inequalities.* (to appear).

[12] Thibault, L.: *Sur les fonctions compactement lipschitziennes et leurs applications: Programmation mathematique, controle optimal, esperance conditionelle.* Theses at Université des Sciences et Techniques du Languedoc (1980).

[13] Zowe, J.: *Nondifferentiable optimization - a motivation and a short introduction into the subgradient and the bundle concept.* ASI Proceedings on Computational Mathematical Programming, Series F, Vol. 15 (1985), Springer-Verlag, 323 – 356.

International Series of
Numerical Mathematics, Vol. 84

On Extensions of the Second-Order Derivative.

D. Pallaschke and P. Recht

Universität Karlsruhe

Postfach 63 80

7500 Karlsruhe 1, West Germany

Summary. In this paper we will define a second-order derivative for non-smooth functions. The definition of this derivative is based on the characterization of the derivative for locally-lipschitz quasi-differentiable functions (see [2], [4]).

1. Introduction.

Let $(X, \|.\|)$ be a normed vector space over the field of real numbers and let X' denote its topological dual. To avoid confusion the norm of X is sometimes also denoted by $\| \cdot \|_X$.

The dual pairing then can be written as

$$< ., . > : X' \times X \to \mathbb{R}$$
$$(\varphi, x) \mapsto < \varphi, x > := \varphi(x).$$

Now, let $U \subseteq X$ be an open set, $x_0 \in U$ and let $f : U \to \mathbb{R}$ be a real-valued continuous function.

In the sense of *V. F. Demyanov* ([1], [2]) f is said to be *quasi-differentiable in x_0* if and only if the following two conditions are satisfied:

i.) For every $g \in X \setminus \{0\}$ the directional derivative

$$\frac{df}{dg}\Big|_{x_0} = \lim_{\substack{t>0 \\ t \to 0}} \frac{f(x_0 + tg) - f(x_0)}{t}$$

exists.

ii.) There exist two norm-bounded, weak-*-compact, convex subsets

$$\partial f|_{x_0} \subseteq X' \quad \text{and} \quad \overline{\partial} f|_{x_0} \subseteq X'$$

such that for all $g \in X \ \{0\}$

$$\frac{df}{dg}\Big|_{x_0} = \sup_{\varphi \in \partial f|_{x_0}} < \varphi, x > + \inf_{\psi \in \overline{\partial} f|_{x_0}} < \psi, x > .$$

To formulate condition ii) in a slightly different way, let us denote by

$$P(X) := \{p : X \to \mathbb{R} | p \text{ is sublinear and lipschitz-continuous}\}$$

the cone of all sublinear lipschitz-continuous functions defined on X. Moreover let

$$D(X) := P(X) - P(X).$$

Then the second condition in the definition of quasi-differentiability states, that the function

$$g : X \setminus \{0\} \to \mathbb{R}$$

given by

$$g \mapsto \frac{df}{dg}\big|_{x_0}$$

is an element of $D(X)$.

If X is finite-dimensional, then every continuous sublinear function is, of course, lipschitz-continuous.

In the following we will write P and D instead of $P(X)$ and $D(X)$, respectively, if no confusion is possible.

In [4] the following result was proved:

Theorem 1.1. Let $U \subseteq \mathbb{R}^n$ be an open subset, $x_0 \in U$ and

$$f : U \to \mathbb{R}$$

a locally-lipschitz function.

Then the following conditions are equivalent:
 i.) f is quasi-differentiable in x_0
 ii.) there exists an uniquely determined element

$$df|_{x_0} \in P(X)$$

such that for every $\varepsilon > 0$ there exists a $\delta > 0$, such that for all $h \in \mathbb{R}^n$ with $\|h\| \leq \delta$ and $x_0 + h \in U$ the inequality

$$|f(x_0 + h) - f(x_0) - df|_{x_0}(h)| \leq \varepsilon \cdot \|h\|$$

holds.

Let us remark, that from the proof of this theorem it follows, that for $h \neq 0$

$$df|_{x_0}(h) = \frac{df}{dh}\big|_{x_0}.$$

Starting point for a possible definition of a second-order derivative for non-smooth functions is the condition ii.) of the theorem above.

2. Convex cones of sublinear and bi-sublinear functions

For our further investigations let $(X, \|\cdot\|)$ be a normed vector space over the reals. Let $B \subseteq X$ denote the closed unit ball of this norm. Furthermore let

$$\text{Lip}_0(B) := \{f : B \to \mathbb{R} \,|\, f \text{ is lipschitz-continuous and } f(0) = 0\}$$

endowed with the norm

$$\|\cdot\|_0 : \text{Lip}_0 \to \mathbb{R}_+$$
$$\|f\|_0 := \sup_{\substack{x,y \in B \\ x \neq y}} \frac{|f(x) - f(y)|}{\|x - y\|}$$

denote the real Banach-space of all lipschitz-continuous functions which vanish at 0. (See e.g. [5], exercise 4.4.7 G).

Since every element of P is uniquely determined on the unit ball $B \subseteq X$, we will consider P as a cone of $\text{Lip}_0(B)$.

Obviously, for $p \in P$ with $p \geq 0$, we have

$$\|p\|_0 = \sup_{x \neq 0} \frac{p(x)}{\|x\|}$$

and, if $p, q \in P$, with $0 \leq p \leq q$, then we have

$$\|p\|_0 \leq \|q\|_0.$$

Let us remark that P is a closed subset of $\text{Lip}_0(B)$. This follows from the fact, that for every $z \in B$ the evaluation functional

$$\delta_z : \text{Lip}_0(B) \to \mathbb{R}$$
$$\delta_z(f) := f(z)$$

is continuous. Hence the sets

$$M_1 := \bigcap_{\substack{x,y \in B \\ x+y \in B}} (\delta_{x+y} - \delta_x - \delta_y)^{-1}([0, \infty[)$$

and

$$M_2 := \bigcap_{t \in \mathbb{R}_+} \sqcap_{x \in B} (\delta_{t \cdot x} - t \cdot \delta_x)^{-1}(\{0\})$$

are closed and since

$$P(X) = M_1 \cap M_2,$$

it follows, that $P(X)$ is a closed subset of $\text{Lip}_0(B)$.

In [1] it is shown that $D(X)$ is a vector-lattice with respect to the pointwise order. Thus the induced norm on $P(X)$ can be extended to the space $D(X)$ in the following way:

$$\|\cdot\| : D(X) \rightarrow \mathbb{R}$$

$$\|l\| := \|l^+\|_0 + \|l^-\|_0,$$

where

$$l^+ := \max(l, 0) \quad \text{and} \quad l^- := \min(l, 0).$$

For a second-order derivative, we have to consider D-valued, sublinear, lipschitz-continuous functions on X.
I.e. let

$$P_2 := P(X) := \{P : X \rightarrow D(X) | P \text{ sublinear and continuous}\}$$

denote the convex cone of all sublinear, continuous, $P(X)$-valued functions, and let

$$D_2 := D_2(X) := P_2(X) - P_2(X).$$

3. Second-order derivatives

In this section we will discuss types of second-order derivatives. Starting point is condition ii.) of Theorem 1.1., which can be considered as an analogon to the classical FRECHET-derivative.

Definition 3.1 Let $U \subseteq X$ be an open set of a normed vector-space X and let $x_0 \in U$. A function $f : U \rightarrow \mathbb{R}$ is said to be *strongly twice D_2-differentiable in x_0* if and only if there exists an element

$$d^2 f|_{x_0} \in D_2(X)$$

such that for every $\varepsilon > 0$ there is a $\delta > 0$ such that for all $k \in \mathbb{R}^n$ with $\|k\| < \delta$ and $x_0 + k \in U$ the following inequality holds:

$$\|df|_{x_0+k} - df|_{x_0} - d^2 f|_{x_0}(k)\|_D \leq \varepsilon \cdot \|k\|.$$

From standard arguments it follows, that $d^2 f|_{x_0} \in D_2(X)$ is uniquely determined.
Let us observe, that $d^2 f|_{x_0} \in D_2(X)$ is *not* symmetric, as the following examples shows:
Take

$$f : \mathbb{R} \rightarrow \mathbb{R}$$

$$f(x) := \frac{1}{2} \cdot \text{sign}(x) \cdot x^2$$

Then

$$df|_{x_0}(h) = |x| \cdot h$$

and

$$d^2 f|_{x_0}(k, h) = |k| \cdot h.$$

Moreover observe, that this definition is very restrictive, since for instance the Euclidean norm is *not strongly* twice differentiable in $x_0 = 0 \in \mathbb{R}^n$.

For this purpose, we will introduce two further definitions of second-order directional derivatives, which are less restrictive.

The first one is an immediate extension of the definition of quasi-differentiability of **DEMYANOV** ([1], [2]), given for the first-order derivative.

For this purpose, let us first define a notation of *the second-order directional derivative* for a quasi-differentiable function.

Definition 3.2 Let $(X, \| \cdot \|)$ be a normed vector space over the reals, $g \in X \setminus \{0\}$, $U \subseteq X$ an open set and $x_0 \in U$. Assume that

$$f : U \to \mathbb{R}$$

is quasi-differentiable in U. Then the mapping

$$df : U \to \mathcal{D}$$
$$x \mapsto df|_x$$

is said to be *directionally differentiable in $x_0 \in U$ with respect to g* if and only if there exist weak-*-compact, convex *sub*-sets

$$\underline{\partial}_g f|_{x_0} \subseteq \underline{\partial} f|_{x_0} \quad \text{and} \quad \overline{\partial}_g f|_{x_0} \subseteq \overline{\partial} f|_{x_0}$$

such that for the function

$$d_g f|_{x_0} : X \mapsto \mathbb{R}$$

given by

$$d_g f|_{x_0}(h) := \sup_{v \in \underline{\partial}_g |_{x_0}} < v, h > + \inf_{w \in \overline{\partial}_g |_{x_0}} < w, h > .$$

the limit

$$\frac{d}{dg}|_{x_0}(df) := \lim_{\substack{\alpha > 0 \\ \alpha \to 0}} \frac{df|_{x_0 + \alpha \cdot g} - d_g f|_{x_0}}{\alpha} \quad \text{exists in } \mathcal{D}.$$

The limit

$$\frac{d}{dg}|_{x_0}(df)$$

is called the *directional derivative of df in x_0 with respect to g*.

Let us remark that the function $d_g f|_{x_0} \in \mathcal{D}$ constructed in the definition above is uniquely determined, if it exists, and independent from the choice of the subsets

$$\underline{\partial}_g f|_{x_0} \quad \text{and} \quad \overline{\partial}_g f|_{x_0}.$$

For this let us assume, that there exist sets $\underline{\tilde{\partial}}_g f|_{x_0} \subseteq \underline{\partial} f|_{x_0}$ and $\overline{\tilde{\partial}}_g f|_{x_0} \subseteq \overline{\partial} f|_{x_0}$ and define $\tilde{d}_g f|_{x_0} \in D$ by:

$$\tilde{d}_g f|_{x_0}(h) := \sup_{v \in \underline{\tilde{\partial}} f|_{x_0}} <v, h> + \inf_{w \in \overline{\tilde{\partial}} f|_{x_0}} <w, h>.$$

Since both limits

$$\eta = \lim_{\substack{\alpha \to 0 \\ \alpha > 0}} \frac{df|_{x_0 + \alpha \cdot g} - df|_{x_0}}{\alpha} \text{ and}$$

$$\tilde{\eta} = \lim_{\substack{\alpha \to 0 \\ \alpha > 0}} \frac{df|_{x_0 + \alpha \cdot g} - \tilde{d} f|_{x_0}}{\alpha}$$

exist, we can estimate the norm of $\eta - \tilde{\eta}$ in D as follows:
Let $\varepsilon > 0$ be given. Then there exists a $\delta > 0$, such that for all $0 < \alpha < \delta$:

$$\||df|_{x_0 + \alpha \cdot g} - d_g f|_{x_0}\|_D - \alpha \cdot \|\eta\|_D \le \|df|_{x_0 + \alpha \cdot g} - d_g f|_{x_0} - \alpha \cdot \eta\|_D \le \varepsilon \cdot \alpha$$

and

$$\||df|_{x_0 + \alpha \cdot g} - \tilde{d}_g f|_{x_0}\|_D - \alpha \cdot \|\tilde{\eta}\|_D \le \|df|_{x_0 + \alpha \cdot g} - \tilde{d}_g f|_{x_0} - \alpha \cdot \tilde{\eta}\|_D \le \varepsilon \cdot \alpha.$$

Hence

$$\|d_g|_{x_0} - \tilde{d}_g|_{x_0}\| \le \|df|_{x_0 + \alpha \cdot g} - \tilde{d}_g f|_{x_0} + d_g f|_{x_0} - df|_{x_0 + \alpha \cdot g}\|$$
$$\le 2 \cdot \varepsilon \cdot \alpha + \alpha \cdot \max\{\|\eta\|_D, \|\tilde{\eta}\|_D,$$

which leads to a contradiction.
As in the definition of the quasi-differentiability we now state conditions on the function

$$X \setminus \{0\} \to D$$
$$g \mapsto \frac{d}{dg}|_{x_0}(df).$$

A possible condition is formulated in the following:

Definition 3.3 Let $U \subseteq X$ be an open set, $x_0 \in U$ and $f : U \to R$ a quasi-differentiable function.

We say that f is *quasi-differentiable of order two in* x_0 if and only if the function

$$df : U \to D(X)$$
$$x \mapsto df|_x$$

satisfies the following two conditions:
i.) $\frac{d}{dg}|_{x_0}(df)$ exists for all $g \in X \setminus \{0\}$.
ii.) the function $d^2 f|_{x_0} : X \mapsto D(X)$ with

$$d^2 f|_{x_0}(g) := \begin{cases} \frac{d}{dg}|_{x_0}(df) & \text{if } g \neq 0 \\ 0 & \text{if } g = 0 \end{cases}$$

is an element of $\mathcal{D}_2(X)$.

We will call $d^2 f|_{x_0} \in \mathcal{D}_2(X)$ *the second-order derivative of f in x_0.*

Proposition 3.4 Let $(X, \| \cdot \|)$ be a normed vector-space over the reals, $U \subseteq X$ an open subset, $\alpha \in \mathbb{R}$ and $x_0 \in U$.

Let $f, g : U \to \mathbb{R}$ be quasi-differentiable functions, such that $d^2 f|_{x_0}$ and $d^2 g|_{x_0} \in \mathcal{D}_2(X)$ exist.

Then

   i.) $d^2(\alpha \cdot f)|_{x_0} = \alpha \cdot d^2 f|_{x_0}$

   ii.) $d^2(f + g)|_{x_0} = d^2 f|_{x_0} + d^2 g|_{x_0}$.

Proof.

   i.) is obvious, since the subsets for the directional derivative, given in Definition 3.1, can be choosen as follows:

     let $v \in X \setminus \{0\}$, then

$$\underline{\partial}_v (\alpha \cdot f)|_{x_0} = \underline{\partial}_v f|_{x_0}$$

and

$$\overline{\partial}_v (\alpha \cdot f)|_{x_0} = \overline{\partial}_v f|_{x_0}.$$

   ii.) Let $v \in X \setminus \{0\}$ and let

$$\underline{\partial}_v f|_{x_0} \subseteq \underline{\partial} f|_{x_0}, \ \overline{\partial}_v f|_{x_0} \subseteq \overline{\partial} f|_{x_0}$$

and

$$\underline{\partial}_v g|_{x_0} \subseteq \underline{\partial} g|_{x_0}, \ \overline{\partial}_v g|_{x_0} \subseteq \overline{\partial} g|_{x_0}$$

be the corresponding subsets for the definition of the directional derivatives of f and g, respectively. Then the sets

$$\underline{\partial}_v (f + g)|_{x_0} := \underline{\partial}_v f|_{x_0} + \underline{\partial}_v g|_{x_0}$$

and

$$\overline{\partial}_v (f + g)|_{x_0} := \overline{\partial}_v f|_{x_0} + \overline{\partial}_v g|_{x_0}$$

are the corresponding sets for the definition of the second-order directional derivative of the function $f + g$ in x_0 and we have:

$$\frac{d}{dv}|_{x_0}(df|_x + dg|_x) = \frac{d}{dv}|_{x_0}(df|_x) + \frac{d}{dv}|_{x_0}(dg|_x).$$

The remainder of the proof follows from the rules of the quasi-differentiable calculus.

Q.E.D.

At this point let us remark, that for the definition of a second-order directional derivative, given above, the classical product-rule does not hold in general.
Take, for instance,

$$p : \mathbb{R}^2 \to \mathbb{R}$$

$$p(x_1, x_2) := |x_1| + |x_2|.$$

Then, for every $g \in \mathbb{R}^2 \setminus \{0\}$ the second-order directional derivative exists in $0 \in \mathbb{R}^2$, i.e.

$$\frac{d}{dg}|_0(dp) = 0 \in \mathcal{D}_2,$$

but for $g_0 := (-1, 1)$ the second-order directional derivative

$$\frac{d}{dg_0}|_0(dp^2)$$

does not exist.
If the second-order derivative exists for a function $f : U \to \mathbb{R}$ in $x_0 \in U$, then there exists a function

$$\varphi : (X \setminus \{0\}) \times X \to \mathbb{R}$$

$$(k, h) \mapsto \varphi(k, h)$$

which is positively homogenious of degree 0 in the first argument k, and is an element of $\mathcal{D}(X)$ in the second argument h, such that for every $h \in X$ the function

$$F_h : U \to \mathbb{R}$$
$$F_h(x_0 + k) := df|_{x_0+k}(h) - \varphi(k, h)$$

is quasi-differentiable in x_0.
Moreover

$$dF_h|_{x_0}(k) = d^2 f|_{x_0}(k, h).$$

The function φ is called a *regularization* and is given by the defect, i.e.

$$\varphi(k, h) := df|_{x_0}(h) - d_k f|_{x_0}(h).$$

If for all $h \in X$ the regularized function F_h is a locally-lipschitz function then the second-order derivative is characterized by:
for all $\varepsilon > 0$ there exist $\delta > 0$ such that for all $k \in X$ with $\|k\| < \delta$ and for all $h \in X$

$$|df|_{x_0+k}(h) - df|_{x_0}(h) - d^2 f|_{x_0}(k, h) - \varphi(k, h)| < \varepsilon \cdot \|k\| \cdot \|h\|$$

holds.

A further weaker notation of a second-order derivative is obtained if the bi-sublinear functions in P_2 are only evaluated on the diagonal. This leads to similar definitions of second-order derivatives as e.g. can be found by *Hiriart-Urruty* for convex functions ([3]).

To be more precise, let $(X, \|\cdot\|)$ be a normed vector space over $\mathbb{R}$ and

$$\gamma : X \to X \times X$$
$$x \mapsto (x, x)$$

denote the diagonal mapping.

Then define

$$Q_2 := \{P\gamma \mid P \in P_2\}$$

and

$$DQ_2 := Q_2 - Q_2.$$

Definition 3.5 Let $U \subseteq X$ be an open set and $x_0 \in U$. A function $f : U \to \mathbb{R}$ is said to have a *second-order subquadratic derivative in* x_0 if and only if there exists an element

$$d^2 f|_{x_0} \gamma \in D_2 Q(X)$$

such that for every $\varepsilon > 0$ there exists a $\delta > 0$ such that for all $h \in X$ with $\|h\| < \delta$ and $x_0 + h \in U$ the inequality

$$|df|_{x_0+h}(h) - df|_{x_0}(h) - d^2 f|_{x_0}(h, h)| < \varepsilon \cdot \|h\|^2$$

holds.

Obviously, the function $d^2 f|_{x_0} \gamma$ is uniquely determined in $D_2 Q(X)$.

In the following section examples for the different notations of a second-order derivative are given.

4. Examples

I. Let X be a normed vector space over the reals and $U \subseteq X$ an open subset. Moreover, let $x_0 \in U$ and let $f : U \to \mathbb{R}$ be a C^2-function. If $D^2 f|_{x_0}$ denotes the Hessian of f at x_0 then

$$D^2 f|_{x_0} \in L(X, X')) \subseteq D_2(X).$$

i.e.

$$d^2 f|_{x_0}(u, v) = <u, D^2 f|_{x_0}(v)> .$$

II. Let $(X, \|\cdot\|)$ be a normed vector space over the reals and $p : \mathbb{R}^n \to \mathbb{R}$ be a sublinear mapping. Then

$$d^2 p|_{x_0=0} = 0.$$

To show this, let us formulate the following three facts, namely:

i.) $\underline{\partial}p|_{\alpha\cdot v} = \underline{\partial}p|_v$ for all $v \in X \setminus \{0\}$ and for all $\alpha > 0$.

Observe that

$$\underline{\partial}p|_{\alpha\cdot v} = \{u \in X| < u, (x-v) > \leq p(x) - p(\alpha \cdot v) \text{ for all } x \in X\}$$
$$= \{u \in X| < u, (\alpha \cdot x - \alpha \cdot v) > \leq p(\alpha \cdot x) - p(\alpha \cdot v) \text{ for all } x \in X\}$$
$$= \{u \in X| < u, (x-v) > \leq p(x) - p(v) \text{ for all } x \in X\}$$
$$= \underline{\partial}p|_v.$$

ii.) $\underline{\partial}p|_v \subseteq \underline{\partial}p|_0$ for all $v \in X \setminus \{0\}$.

This follows from the subadditivity, since

$$\underline{\partial}p|_v = \{u \in X| < u, (x-v) > \leq p(x) - p(v) \text{ for all } x \in X\}$$
$$\subseteq \{u \in X| < u, (x-v) > \leq p(x-v) \text{ for all } x \in X\} = \underline{\partial}p|_0.$$

iii.) Moreover we have for $x \neq 0$:
$$dp|_x(x) = p(x).$$

From i.) it follows, that $dp|_{\alpha\cdot x}(h) = dp|_x(h)$, since

$$dp|_{\alpha\cdot x}(h) = \sup_{w \in \underline{\partial}p|_{\alpha\cdot x}} < w, h > = \sup_{w \in \underline{\partial}p|_x} < w, h > = dp|_x(h).$$

Now take

$$\underline{\partial}_v p|_{\alpha\cdot x} = \underline{\partial}p|_x \subseteq \underline{\partial}p|_0,$$

then

$$\frac{d}{dv}|_0(dp) = 0.$$

III. Let $\varphi_i : \mathbb{R} \to \mathbb{R}$, $i \in \{1,2\}$ be two C^2-functions and define

$$f : \mathbb{R} \to \mathbb{R}$$

by

$$f(x) := \max\{\varphi_1(x), \varphi_2(x)\}.$$

Furthermore, let us assume that $x_0 \in \mathbb{R}$ is such a point that $\varphi_1(x_0) = \varphi_2(x_0)$ and that for $x \leq x_0 : f(x) = \varphi_1(x)$ and for $x \geq x_0 : f(x) = \varphi_2(x)$, respectively. Then

$$df|_x(h) = \begin{cases} \varphi_1'(x) \cdot h & \text{if } x < x_0 \\ \max\{\varphi_1'(x) \cdot h, \varphi_2'(x) \cdot h\} & \text{if } x = x_0 \\ \varphi_2'(x) \cdot h & \text{if } x > x_0 \end{cases}$$

Hence

$$d^2 f|_{x_0}(k, h) = (\max\{\varphi_1''(x_0) \cdot k, \varphi_2''(x_0) \cdot k\}) \cdot h.$$

IV. Let us consider the function

$$f : \mathbb{R}^2 \to \mathbb{R},$$

given by

$$f(x, y) := |x^2 + y^2 - 8|.$$

Then

$$df|_{(x,y)}(h, k) = \begin{cases} 2 \cdot x \cdot h + 2 \cdot y \cdot k & \text{if } x^2 + y^2 > 8 \\ |2 \cdot x \cdot h + 2 \cdot y \cdot k| & \text{if } x^2 + y^2 = 8 \\ -2 \cdot x \cdot h - 2 \cdot y \cdot k & \text{if } x^2 + y^2 < 8 \end{cases}.$$

Hence, in the point (2,2), we have for the second-order derivative:

$$d^2 f|_{(2,2)}((u, v), (h, k)) = 2 \cdot |u \cdot h + v \cdot k|.$$

V. Let $(X, \| \cdot \|)$ be a normed vector space over the reals and let

$$p, q : X \to \mathbb{R}$$

be two sublinear functions. Now, define

$$f : X \to \mathbb{R}$$
$$\text{by}$$
$$f := \max\{p^2, q^2\}.$$

Then

$$df|_x(h) = \begin{cases} 2 \cdot p(x) \cdot dp|_x(h) & \text{if } p^2(x) > q^2(x) \\ 2 \cdot \max\{p(x) \cdot dp|_x(h), q(x) \cdot dq|_x(h)\} & \text{if } p^2(x) = q^2(x) \\ 2 \cdot q(x) \cdot dq|_x(h) & \text{if } p^2(x) < q^2(x) \end{cases}.$$

Since

$$dp|_x(x) = p(x)$$
$$\text{and}$$
$$df|_0(h) = 0,$$

we have:

$$d^2 f|_0(h, h) = \begin{cases} 2 \cdot p^2(h) & \text{if } p^2(h) > q^2(h) \\ 2 \cdot \max\{p^2(h), q^2(h)\} & \text{if } p^2(h) = q^2(h) \\ 2 \cdot q^2(h) & \text{if } p^2(h) < q^2(h) \end{cases}.$$

Hence f has a second-order subquadratic derivative in $0 \in X$, namely:

$$d^2 f|_0(h, h) = 2 \cdot \max\{p^2(h), q^2(h)\}.$$

VI. Let $(X, \|\cdot\|)$ be a normed vector space over $\mathbb{R}$ and

$$p, q : X \to \mathbb{R}$$

be two sublinear mappings.
Now define

$$f : X \to \mathbb{R}$$

by

$$f(x) := p(x) \cdot q(x).$$

Then

$$df|_x(h) = p(x) \cdot dq|_x(h) + q(x) \cdot dp|_x(h).$$

Hence

$$df|_0 = 0$$

and

$$df|_k(k) = 2 \cdot p(k) \cdot q(k).$$

Thus, f has a second-order subquadratic derivative in $0 \in X$, namely:

$$d^2 f|_0(k, k) = 2 \cdot p(k) \cdot q(k)$$

has a second-order subquadratic derivative in $0 \in \mathbb{R}^2$.

References.

[1] Demyanov, V. F.; Rubinov, A. M.: *Quasidifferential Calculus.* Preprint at the International Institute for Applied Systems Analysis, Laxenburg 1985.

[2] Demyanov, V. F. and Vasilev, L. V.: *Nondifferentiable Optimization.* Moscow Nauka 1981, Engl. Translation Berlin - Heidelberg - New York 1985.

[3] Hiriart-Urruty, J.-B.: *A New Set-valued Second Order Derivative for Convex Functions.* To appear in the proceedings of the FERMAT Days 1985 "Mathematics for Optimization".

[4] Pallaschke, D. ; Recht, P. and Urbanski, R.: *On Locally-Lipschitz Quasi-Differentiable Functions in Banach-Spaces.* Optimization 17 (1986) 3.

[5] Semadeni, Z.: *Banach Spaces of Continuous Functions.* (Vol. 1), Monografie Matematyczne Tom 55, Warszawa 1971.

Resume.

Dans ce travail nous presentons une definition de la 2^{ieme} derivation d'une fonction quasi-differentiable.
Cette definition est derive de la characterisation (c. f. [4]) des fonctions quasi-differentiable, qui sont localement Lipschitzienne.

International Series of
Numerical Mathematics, Vol. 84
(c) 1988 Birkhäuser Verlag Basel

Another duality scheme for Quasiconvex Problems

Jean Paul Penot
Faculté des Sciences
Avenue de l'Université
64000 Pau
France

Michel Volle
U.F.R. des Sciences, Université de Limoges
123 avenue Albert Thomas
87060 Limoges Cedex
France

Abstract. We introduce a new way of getting duality theories for quasiconvex problems. As in [13] it strongly relies on the use of a class K of nondecreasing functions. However the regularization process yielding the duality is taken with respect to a class of shifted K-linear functionals rather than with respect to a class of K-affine functionals as in [13]. A concept of subdifferential can be associated with the conjugation defined here; it can be used in connection with a notion of dual problem naturally associated with a primal problem or rather a perturbation of the primal problem.

A.M.S.-M.O.S. subject index: primary

Key words: Conjugation, duality, perturbation, polarity, quasiconvexity subdifferential.

Introduction.

In [13], [14], [16] we introduced a general and simple way of getting duality theories for quasiconvex functions by replacing the use of continuous affine functions in convex duality by the use of a class of quasi-affine functions. This enables one to keep the general framework of the Fenchel-Moreau-Rockafellar conjugation. Up to now the many attempts for devicing a duality theory for quasiconvex problems were unrelated to this general scheme and unrelated to other approaches; moreover these devices suffered from a lack of symmetry.

Here we present a new process which differs from the approach of [16] by important features. In particular it is not a conjugation of the Fenchel-Moreau-Rockafellar type. However it enters into the general framework of polarities [5], [20], [21] and it strongly relies on the use of quasi-affine functions. It can be specialized to several concrete instances of interest; moreover it is closely linked with a notion of subdifferential, a particular case of which is the one introduced by Plastria [18]. Finally it can be compared with the proposal made in [16]. We would like to point out that the present approach is closely related to the work of Martinez-Legaz presented in this Symposium [9] although both lectures were prepared independently.

1. From convex duality to quasiconvex duality.

Let us recall the general framework of the Fenchel-Moreau-Rockafellar duality scheme. Given two sets W, Z and a coupling functional $c : W \times Z \to \overline{\mathbb{R}}$ the c-conjugate of $f \in \overline{\mathbb{R}}^Z$ is given by

$$(1) \qquad f^c(w) = - \inf_{z \in Z} [c(w, z) \dot{+} (-f(z))].$$

The c-conjugate g^c of $g \in \overline{\mathbb{R}}^W$ is defined analoguously, the roles of W and Z being interchanged. This symmetric process leads to the biconjugate $f^{cc} = (f^c)^c$ of f which always satisfies $f^{cc} \leq f$ (weak duality results). The interest of this duality theory is enhanced by the fact that one is often able to present conditions in order to get the equality $f^{cc}(z_0) = f(z_0)$ at a given point z_0 (strong duality results).

In the sequel Y and Z are locally convex topological vector spaces put in duality by a non degenerate pairing $< ., . >$ and K is a class of non decreasing mappings from $\mathbb{R}$ into $\overline{\mathbb{R}}$. Let $W = K \circ Y = \{k \circ y : k \in K, y \in Y\}$ be the family of so-called K-linear functionals on Z. Using the evaluation mapping $c : (k \circ y, z) \mapsto k(< y, z >)$ as a coupling functional between W and Z we obtained in [16] a simple duality theory for quasiconvex problems. There, as in this paper, two choices of K are of fundamental importance: the set G of nondecreasing mappings from $\mathbb{R}$ into $\overline{\mathbb{R}}$ and the set Q of l.s.c. nondecreasing mappings from $\mathbb{R}$ into $\overline{\mathbb{R}}$. The first choice corresponds to the pioneering work of Greenberg and Pierskalla [6]; the second one recovers the fundamental work of Crouzeix [3]. Our approach in [16] relies on the fact that any l.s.c. quasiconvex function $f : Z \to \overline{\mathbb{R}}$ can be written as a supremum of a family of Q-affine functions, i.e. functions of the form $z \mapsto k \circ y(z) - r$ with $k \in Q$, $y \in Y$, $r \in \mathbb{R}$. Then for $k \circ y$ given in W, $f^c(k \circ y)$ is nothing but the best constant $r \in \mathbb{R}$ one can find in order to satisfy the following inequality:

$$(2) \qquad k \circ y - r \leq f.$$

Here by a slight change in the preceding inequality we obtain a quite different approach to quasiconvex duality. Namely, given a class K of nondecreasing l.s.c. extended real-valued functions on $\mathbb{R}$ ($K \subset Q$) we consider the best constant $r \in \mathbb{R}$ such that the following inequality

$$(3) \qquad k \circ (y - r) \leq f$$

is satisfied for a given pair $(y, k) \in Y \times K$. Let us call a function on Z of the form $k \circ (y - r) : z \mapsto k(< y, z > -r)$ a *shifted K-linear functional* on Z; we denote by $K \circ (Y - C)$ the set of such functionals, C standing for the set of constant functions on Z.

As k is taken in a subset K of the set Q of nondecreasing l.s.c. extended functions on $\mathbb{R}$ the following lemma enables us to solve inequation (3). In the sequel it will be convenient to extend any element k of Q by setting

$$k(-\infty) = -\infty, \; k(+\infty) = \sup k(\mathbb{R}).$$

In this way, k becomes nondecreasing and l. s. c. on $\overline{\mathbb{R}}$, hence satisfies the relation

$$(4) \qquad\qquad \sup_{i \in I} k(r_i) = k(\sup_{i \in I} r_i)$$

for any family $(r_i)_{i \in I}$ of extended real numbers (with $\sup \phi = -\infty$, as usual). On the other hand, the natural extension of a nondecreasing u.s.c. function $j : \mathbb{R} \to \overline{\mathbb{R}}$ is given by

$$j(-\infty) = \inf j(\mathbb{R}), \; j(+\infty) = +\infty,$$

so that the extended mapping j satisfies

$$(5) \qquad\qquad \inf_{i \in I} j(s_i) = j(\inf_{i \in I} s_i)$$

for any family $(s_i)_{i \in I}$ of extended real numbers.

1.1 - Lemma (see also [15]).
Given $k : \overline{\mathbb{R}} \to \overline{\mathbb{R}}$ nondecreasing, l.s.c. with $k(-\infty) = -\infty$ let $k^h : \overline{\mathbb{R}} \to \overline{\mathbb{R}}$ be given by

$$k^h(s) = \sup\{r \in \overline{\mathbb{R}} : k(r) \leq s\} \; \text{ for } \; s \in \mathbb{R} \cup \{+\infty\}, \; k^h(-\infty) = \inf k^h(\mathbb{R}).$$

Then k^h is nondecreasing, u.s.c., $k^h(+\infty) = +\infty$ and for any r, s in $\overline{\mathbb{R}}$

$$(6) \qquad\qquad r \leq k^h(k(r)), \; k(k^h(s)) \leq s$$
$$(7) \qquad\qquad (k(r) \leq s) \leftrightarrow (r \leq k^h(s)).$$

The last equivalence implies that the hypograph of k^h is the inverse of the epigraph of k (considered as relations from $\mathbb{R}$ to $\mathbb{R}$). For this reason k^h is called the *hypo-epi-inverse* of k [15].

Proof. The facts that k^h is nondecreasing and $k^h(+\infty) = +\infty$ are obvious. In as much as $k^h(-\infty) = \inf k^h(\mathbb{R}) = \liminf_{s \to -\infty} k^h(s)$ and the hypograph of k^h is closed if assertion (7) is true, k^h is u.s.c. Now if (6) holds true, for any r, s in $\overline{\mathbb{R}}$, with $k(r) \leq s$ we get $r \leq k^h(k(r)) \leq k^h(s)$; conversely if $r \leq k^h(s)$ holds true, by the second inequality of (6) we get

$$k(r) \leq k(k^h(s)) \leq s.$$

Thus it remains to prove (6). For $r \in \overline{\mathbb{R}}$ with $s := k(r) \neq -\infty$ the relation $r \leq k^h(k(r))$ is obvious from the definition. When $r \in \overline{\mathbb{R}}$ is such that $k(r) = -\infty$ we observe that as

$$k^h(-\infty) = \inf_{t \in \mathbb{R}} k^h(t) = \inf_{t \in \mathbb{R}} \inf k^{-1}(]t, +\infty]) \; \text{ the inequality } \; r > k^h(-\infty)$$

would imply the existence of some $t \in \mathbb{R}$, $q \in k^{-1}(]t, +\infty])$ with $r > q$, a contradiction, as k is nondecreasing and $-\infty = k(r) \geq k(q) > t$.

Now let us prove the second half of (6). Let $s \in \mathbb{R} \cup \{+\infty\}$ and let $(r_n) \subset \mathbb{R}$ be such that $\lim r_n = r := k^h(s)$ with $r_n \in k^{-1}([-\infty, s])$; then $k(r) = \lim k(r_n) \leq s$ as k is left continuous: this shows that $k(k^h(s)) \leq s$. This also entails the inequality $k(k^h(s)) \leq s$ for $s = -\infty$ since for each $t \in \mathbb{R}$ we have $k(k^h(-\infty)) \leq k(k^h(t)) \leq t$, hence $k(k^h(-\infty)) = -\infty$. $\quad\Box$

Remark. It follows from (6) that for k as above one has

$$(8) \qquad k = k \circ k^h \circ k, \quad k^h = k^h \circ k \circ k^h.$$

The preceding lemma shows that (3) is equivalent to

$$(9) \qquad y - r \leq k^h \circ f.$$

The choice of the best possible r verifying this inequality leads to the following definition.

1.2 - Definition. The conjugate of $f \in \overline{\mathbb{R}}^Z$ with respect to K is the mapping $f^\kappa \in \overline{\mathbb{R}}^{K \times Y}$ given by

$$(10) \qquad f^\kappa(k, y) = (k^h \circ f)^*(y) = \sup[<y, z> -k^h(f(z))]$$

for $(k, y) \in K \times Y$.

The main property of the conjugation operator defined above is given in the following statement:

1.3 - Proposition. For any family $(f_i)_{i \in I}$ of extended real-valued functions on Z one has

$$(11) \qquad (\inf_{i \in I} f_i)^\kappa = \sup_{i \in I} f_i^\kappa$$

Proof. For each $(k, y) \in K \times Y$, by definition 1.2 we have, with $f = \inf_{i \in I} f_i$,

$$(11) \qquad f^\kappa(k, y) = (k^h \circ f)^*(y) = (k^h \circ \inf_{i \in I} f_i)^*(y).$$

Using (5) and a well known property of the Fenchel transform we get

$$f^\kappa(k, y) = (\inf_{i \in I} k^h \circ f_i)^*(y) = \sup_{i \in I}(k^h \circ f_i)^*(y) = \sup_{i \in I} f_i^\kappa(y).$$

$\quad\Box$

Let us observe that although the conjugation $\kappa : f \mapsto f^\kappa$ is defined through the use of the Fenchel transform, it is not in general a conjugation of the Fenchel-Moreau-Rockafellar type ([11]) associated with some coupling functional. In fact it is easy to see that the relation

$$(f + c)^\kappa = f^\kappa - c$$

does not hold true for $f \in \overline{\mathbb{R}}^Z$, $c \in \mathbb{R}$ being considered as an element of C, the set of constant functions on Z, whereas this relation is always satisfied for any conjugation of Fenchel-Moreau-Rockafellar type ([20], Theorem 3.1).

However proposition 1.3 means that κ is a polarity between the complete lattices $\overline{\mathbb{R}}^Z$ and $\overline{\mathbb{R}}^{K \times Y}$. The concept of dual polarity ([5], [17], [21]) enables us, under appropriate assumptions, to reconstitute f from f^κ and to present a symmetric situation.

1.4 - Definition. The dual polarity Λ of κ is the mapping $\Lambda : \overline{\mathbb{R}}^{K \times Y} \to \overline{\mathbb{R}}^Z$ given by

$$\Lambda(g) := g^\Lambda := \inf\{f \in \overline{\mathbb{R}}^Z : f^\kappa \le g\}.$$

This general notion can be given here in a more tractable form.

1.5 - Proposition. For any $g \in \overline{\mathbb{R}}^{K \times Y}$ its conjugate g^Λ is given by

$$g^\Lambda = \sup_{k \in K} k \circ (g_k)^*$$

where $g_k(y) := g(k, y)$.

Proof. The relation $f^\kappa \le g$ which occurs in the definition of g^Λ is easily seen to be equivalent to each one of the following assertions:

$$\forall k \in K, \ \forall y \in Y \qquad (k^h \circ f)^*(y) \qquad \le g(k, y)$$

$$\forall k \in K, \ \forall y \in Y, \ \forall z \in Z < y, z > -k^h(f(z)) \le g_k(y)$$

$$\forall k \in K, \ \forall y \in Y, \ \forall z \in Z < y, z > -g_k(y) \qquad \le k^h(f(z))$$

$$\forall k \in K, \qquad (g_k)^* \qquad \le k^h \circ f$$

$$\forall k \in K, \qquad k \circ (g_k)^* \qquad \le f,$$

as shown by relation (7). Thus $g^\Lambda = \inf\{f \in \overline{\mathbb{R}}^Z : \sup_{k \in K} k \circ (g_k)^* \le f\} = \sup_{k \in K} k \circ (g_k)^*$. $\qquad \Box$

Taking for g the conjugate f^κ of some $f \in \overline{\mathbb{R}}^Z$ and observing that $g_k = (k^h \circ f)^*$ by definition 1.2, we get a convenient formula for the biconjugate $f^{\kappa \Lambda} = (f^\kappa)^\Lambda$ of f.

1.6 - Corollary. The biconjugate $f^{\kappa \Lambda}$ of $f \in \overline{\mathbb{R}}^Z$ is given by

$$f^{\kappa \Lambda} = \sup_{k \in K} k \circ (k^h \circ f)^{**}.$$

The general fact that the pair (κ, Λ) is a Galois correspondence ([2], [12], [21], ...) between the complete lattices $\overline{\mathbb{R}}^Z$ and $\overline{\mathbb{R}}^{K \times Y}$ yields several useful consequences:

(12) $$\forall f \in \overline{\mathbb{R}}^Z \quad f^{\kappa \Lambda \kappa} = f^\kappa$$

(13) $$\forall f \in \overline{\mathbb{R}}^Z, \forall g \in \overline{\mathbb{R}}^{K \times Y} \quad f^\kappa \leq g \Leftrightarrow g^\Lambda \leq f$$

(14) $$\forall f \in \overline{\mathbb{R}}^Z \quad f^{\kappa \Lambda} \leq f$$

(15) $$\forall f \in \overline{\mathbb{R}}^Z \quad f^{\kappa \Lambda} = f \Leftrightarrow \exists g \in \overline{\mathbb{R}}^{K \times Y} : f = g^\Lambda$$

(16) $$\Gamma_K := \{ f \in \overline{\mathbb{R}}^Z : f = f^{\kappa \Lambda} \} \text{ is stable under suprema.}$$

Let us say that $f \in \overline{\mathbb{R}}^Z$ is K-*convex-transformable* if there exist $k \in K$ and $\hat{f} : Z \rightarrow \mathbb{R}^\bullet = \mathbb{R} \cup \{+\infty\}$ proper convex l.s.c. such that $f = k \circ \hat{f}$. Such a function is characterized by its conjugate as shown by the following result.

1.7 - Proposition. Suppose $f \in \overline{\mathbb{R}}^Z$ is K-convex-transformable. Then $f = f^{\kappa \Lambda}$.

Proof. Let $k \in K$, $\hat{f}$ be proper convex l.s.c. such that $f = k \circ \hat{f}$. Using relation (6) we see that

$$f^{\kappa \Lambda} \geq k \circ (k^h \circ k \circ \hat{f})^{**} \geq k \circ (\hat{f})^{**} = k \circ \hat{f} = f$$

so that $f^{\kappa \Lambda} = f$. □

More generally we have the following characterization of the set of $f \in \overline{\mathbb{R}}^Z$ which can be reconstituted from their conjugate.

1.8 - Theorem. The following assertions about $f \in \overline{\mathbb{R}}^Z$ are equivalent:
(a) $f = f^{\kappa \Lambda}$;
(b) f is the supremum of a family of shifted K-linear functionals on Z: there exists a family $((k_i, y_i, r_i))_{i \in I}$ of elements of $K \times Y \times \mathbb{R}$ such that

$$f = \sup_{i \in I} k_i \circ (y_i - r_i).$$

Proof. (a) $\Rightarrow$ (b)   Using (5) and Proposition 1.5 we can find $g \in \overline{\mathbb{R}}^{K \times Y}$ such that $f = \sup_{k \in K} k \circ (g_k)^*$. Now for each $k \in K$ there exists a family $((y_j, r_j))_{j \in J_k}$ of elements of $Y \times \mathbb{R}$ such that $(g_k)^* = \sup_{j \in J_k} (y_j - r_j)$. Using relation (4) we get

$$f = \sup_{k \in K} \sup_{j \in J_k} k \circ (y_j - r_j)$$

and we can set $I = \cup_{k \in K} \{k\} \times J_k$, and for $i = (k, j) \in I$, $k_i = k$, $(y_i, r_i) = (y_j, r_j)$.

(b) $\Rightarrow$ (a)   Taking (16) into account, it suffices to prove that for each $(k, y, r) \in K \times Y \times \mathbb{R}$ one has

$$(k \circ (y - r))^{\kappa \Lambda} = k \circ (y - r).$$

But, by Corollary 1.6 and relation (6)

$$(k \circ (y - r))^{\kappa\Lambda} \geq k \circ (k^h \circ k \circ (y - r))^{**}$$
$$\geq k \circ (y - r)^{**} = k \circ (y - r).$$

As the opposite inequality always holds true by (14) equality ensues. □

Theorem 1.8 can be restated as follows: $f \in \overline{\mathbb{R}}^Z$ coincides with $f^{\kappa\Lambda}$ iff f is the supremum of the set of shifted K-linear functionals on Z bounded above by f. When K is reduced to I, the identity mapping of $\mathbb{R}$, or when $K = \{pI+q : p \in \mathbb{R}_+, q \in \mathbb{R}\}$ the set of shifted K-linear functionals on Z is simply the set of continuous affine functionals; then Theorem 1.8 reduces to the classical Fenchel-Moreau characterization of the set of proper convex l.s.c. functions (to which the constant functions with values $+\infty$ and $-\infty$ are adjoined). Taking for K the whole set Q of nondecreasing l.s.c. functions on $\mathbb{R}$ we get a newer result.

1.9 - Corollary. For $K = Q$ and $f \in \overline{\mathbb{R}}^Z$, $f^{\kappa\Lambda}$ is the l.s.c. quasiconvex regularized function f^q associated with f, i.e. the greatest l.s.c. quasiconvex function bounded above by f.

Proof. This follows from the fact that for $K = Q$ any shifted K-linear functional is a K-linear functional so that $f^{\kappa\Lambda}$ is the supremum of the family of K-linear functionals majorized by f, in other words the supremum of the family of l.s.c. quasi-affine functionals majorized by f, i.e. f^q ([8], [16]). □

In the following corollary we denote by $S(K)$ the set of functions $g : \mathbb{R} \to \overline{\mathbb{R}}$ which are suprema of a family of functions obtained by shifting elements of K:

$$g(r) = \sup_{i \in I} k_i(r - r_i) \quad \text{for } r \in \mathbb{R}$$

where $((k_i, r_i))_{i \in I}$ is a family of $K \times \mathbb{R}$.

1.10 - Corollary. Let K_1, K_2 be subfamilies of Q such that $S(K_1) = S(K_2)$. Then the biconjugate of $f \in \overline{\mathbb{R}}^Z$ with respect to K_1 and K_2 coincide. In particular if $S(K) = Q$, $f^{\kappa\Lambda} = f^q$, the l.s.c. quasiconvex hull of f.

Proof. The first assertion follows from the fact that for any $K \subset Q$ and any $f \in \overline{\mathbb{R}}^Z$ we have, with $k_r(t) = k(t - r)$

$$f^{\kappa\Lambda} = \sup\{k \circ (y - r) : k \in K, r \in \mathbb{R}, y \in Y, k \circ (y - r) \leq f\}$$
$$= \sup\{k_r \circ y : k \in K, r \in \mathbb{R}, y \in Y, k_r \circ y \leq f\}$$
$$= \sup\{g \circ y : g \in S(K), y \in Y, g \circ y \leq f\}.$$

The second assertion is a consequence of the first one and of corollary 1.9 as $S(Q) = Q$. □

2. Examples.

In this section we describe some more examples obtained by taking different choices of subclasses K of Q.

2.1 - Examples Let $K = \{k_q : q \in \mathbb{R}\}$ where k_q is the l.s.c. function on $\mathbb{R}$ given by $k_q(r) = -\infty$ for $r \leq 0$, $k_q(r) = q$ for $r > 0$. Then the shifted K-linear functional $k_q \circ (y - r)$ is bounded above by $f \in \overline{\mathbb{R}}^Z$ iff $f(z) \geq q$ for each z in the open half-space $\{z \in Z :< y, z >> r\}$. On the other hand the hypo-epi-inverse $(k_q)^h$ of k_q is given by

$$(k_q)^h(s) = 0 \text{ for } s < q, (k_q)^h(s) = +\infty \text{ for } s \geq q.$$

Therefore, denoting by ψ_A the indicator function of A ($\psi_A(z) = 0$ for $z \in A$, $\psi_A(z) = +\infty$ for $z \in Z \setminus A$) and denoting by $\{f < q\} = \{z \in Z : f(z) < q\}$ the strict slice of f of level r we get that $f^\kappa(k_q, .)$ is the support function of $\{f < q\}$:

$$(k_q)^h \circ f = \psi_{\{f<q\}},$$
$$f^\kappa(k_q, y) = (\psi_{\{f<q\}})^*(y) = \sup_{f(z)<q} < y, z > .$$

Moreover, denoting by $\overline{co}\, A$ the closed convex hull of a subset A of Z, Corollary 1.6 yields

$$f^{\kappa\Lambda} = \sup_{q \in \mathbb{R}} k_q \circ (\psi_{\{f<q\}})^{**} = \sup_{q \in \mathbb{R}} k_q \circ \psi_{\overline{co}\{f<q\}},$$

or, more explicitely, for $z \in Z$

$$f^{\kappa\Lambda}(z) = \sup_{q \in \mathbb{R}} \{q : z \notin \overline{co}\{f < q\}\}.$$

Using the fact that for any q_1, q_2 in $\mathbb{R}$ with $q_1 \leq q_2$ one has $\overline{co}\{f < q_1\} \subset \overline{co}\{f < q_2\}$ it is easy to see that one can also write

$$f^{\kappa\Lambda}(z) = \inf\{q \in \mathbb{R} : z \in \overline{co}\{f < q\}\}.$$

Moreover, as for $q_1 < q_2$

$$\overline{co}\{f < q_1\} \subset \overline{co}\{f \leq q_1\} \subset \overline{co}\{f < q_2\} \subset \overline{co}\{f \leq q_2\}$$

one also gets a known formula for the l.s.c. quasiconvex hull f^q of f ([3] chap. 1, prop. 5) using corollary 1.10 and the easily seen fact that $S(K) = Q$ with the present choice of K:

$$f^q(z) = \inf\{q \in \mathbb{R} : z \in \overline{co}\{f \leq q\}\}.$$

2.2 - Example. Now let $K = \{i_q : q \in \mathbb{R}\}$ where $i_q(r) := \min(q, r) = q \wedge r$, $r \in \mathbb{R}$. With this choice of K the set of shifted K-linear functionals is composed of concave and quasiconvex functions which are called *subaffine*. As the hypo-epi-inverse $(i_q)^h$ of i_q is given by

$$(i_q)^h(s) = s \ \text{ for } \ s \in [-\infty, q), (i_q)^h(s) = +\infty \ \text{ for } \ s \in [q, +\infty],$$

one obtains for each $f \in \overline{\mathbb{R}}^Z$, $y \in Y$, $q \in \mathbb{R}$

$$(i_q)^h \circ f = f \dotplus \psi_{\{f<q\}},$$
$$f^\kappa(i_q, y) = f \dotplus \psi_{\{f<q\}})^*(y).$$

Then Corollary 1.6 yields

$$f^{\kappa\Lambda} = \sup_{q\in\mathbb{R}} q \wedge (f \dotplus \psi_{\{f<q\}})^{**}.$$

When $Z = \mathbb{R}$ the class $\Gamma_K := \{f \in \overline{\mathbb{R}}^Z : f^{\kappa\Lambda} = f\}$ with K as above is easily seen to be the class of l.s.c. quasiconvex mappings bounded below by some subaffine function, augmented with the constant map with value $-\infty$. This is no more true for dim $Z > 1$ as shown by the following counterexample.

2.3 - Counterexample. Let $f : \mathbb{R}^2 \to \mathbb{R}$ be given by

$$f(x, y) = \begin{cases} y & \text{for } y \geq 0 \\ 0 & \text{for } y < 0, \, x \leq 0 \\ -x \exp(\frac{1}{y}) & \text{for } y < 0, \, x > 0 \end{cases}$$

Then f is easily seen to be a continuous quasiconvex function. It is bounded below by the subaffine function $(x, y) \mapsto (-x) \wedge 0$.
Let us show that f is not the supremum of its subaffine minorants. Let $z_0 = (x_0, y_0)$ with $y_0 > 0$ and let $c \in (0, y_0)$. Suppose there exist some $p, q \in \mathbb{R}$, $w = (a, b) \in (\mathbb{R}^2)^*$ with $f \geq p \wedge w + q$, $p \wedge w(z_0) + q > c$. As the inequality $p\wedge$ by $+q \leq -x \exp\frac{1}{y}$ for any $x > 0$, $y > 0$ is impossible, we have $a \neq 0$. But then there exists $z_1 = (x_1, y_1)$ in the line $\{z : w(z) = w(z_0)\}$ with $y_1 < 0$, so that $p \wedge w(z_1) + q \leq f(z_1) \leq 0$, a contradiction with $p \wedge w(z_1) + q = p \wedge w(z_0) + q \geq c > 0$. $\qquad\square$

Nevertheless, the following result points out an important class of functions f such that $f = f^{\kappa\Lambda}$.

2.4 - Theorem. Each l.s.c. quasiconvex function defined on a locally convex space and minorized by a continuous affine functional coincides with the supremum of its subaffine minorants.

The proof of this result relies on the following lemma as a sum of two affine functions is affine.

2.5 - Lemma. Let $f, g : Z \to \overline{\mathbb{R}}$ with $f \geq g$, f l.s.c. and quasiconvex. Then f is the supremum of the family

$$F = \{h = (g + y - p) \wedge m : m, p \in \mathbb{R}, y \in Y, h \leq f\}.$$

Proof. Given a $a \in Z$ and $\alpha \in \mathbb{R}$ with $\alpha < f(a)$ we have to find $h \in F$ with $h(a) > \alpha$. As f is l.s.c. and quasiconvex and

$$a \notin \{f \leq \alpha\} = \overline{co}\{f \leq \alpha\} = \cap_{\alpha < \beta < f(a)} \overline{co}\{f \leq \beta\}$$

we can find $\beta \in (\alpha, f(a))$ and $y \in Y$, $\gamma \in \mathbb{R}$ such that

(18) $$\gamma \geq \sup(<y, z> : z \in \{f < \beta\}),$$

(19) $$<y, a> > \gamma.$$

For $r \in \mathbb{R}_+$ let $h_r \in \overline{\mathbb{R}}^Z$ be given by

$$h_r = (g + r(y - \gamma)) \wedge \beta.$$

By (18) we have $h_r(z) \leq g(z) \wedge \beta \leq f(z)$ for each z in $\{f < \beta\}$ so that $h_r \leq f$ for any $r \in \mathbb{R}_+$. Now, using (19) we see that choosing r large enough we have

$$g(a) + r(<y, a> -\gamma) \geq \beta,$$

hence $h_r(a) = \beta > \alpha$ and $h_r \in F$. $\qquad\square$

2.6 - Corollary. For any l.s.c. quasiconvex function f on Z which is minorized by a continuous affine functional one has

$$f = \sup_{p \in \mathbb{R}} p \wedge (f + \psi_{\{f \leq p\}})^{**}.$$

Proof. This follows from Theorem 1.8 and 2.4 along with formula (16) and the following inclusions already used above, for $p_1 < p_2$ in $\mathbb{R}$:

$$\{f < p_1\} \subset \{f \leq p_1\} \subset \{f < p_2\} \subset \{f \leq p_2\}.$$

$\qquad\square$

2.7 - Example. Let us take $K = \{\frac{1}{R} ln\}$ where $R > 0$ and ln is the logarithmic function extended to $\overline{\mathbb{R}}$ by setting $ln(r) = -\infty$ for $r \leq 0$, $ln(+\infty) = +\infty$. Let us denote by exp the exponential function extended to $\overline{\mathbb{R}}$ by $\exp(-\infty) = 0$, $\exp(+\infty) = +\infty$. Then $(\frac{1}{R} ln)^h(s) = \exp(Rs)$, so that for each $y \in Y$

$$f^\kappa(\frac{1}{R} ln, y) = (\exp Rf)^*(y)$$

$$f^{\kappa\Lambda} = \frac{1}{R} ln(\exp Rf)^{**}$$

$$f = f^{\kappa\Lambda} \Leftrightarrow \exp Rf = (\exp Rf)^{**}.$$

Therefore $f^{\kappa\Delta}$ is nothing but the l.s.c. R-convex hull of f in the sense of [1].

3. A notion of K-subdifferential.

As in the convex case we can define the subdifferential of $f \in \overline{\mathbb{R}}^Z$ at some point $a \in Z$ by attainement in the supremum occuring in Theorem 1.8(b). We prefer to define as a subdifferential a subset of the usual space Y rather than a subset of $K \times Y$.

3.1 - Definition. The K-subdifferential of $f \in \overline{\mathbb{R}}^Z$ at $a \in f^{-1}(\mathbb{R})$ is the set $\partial^K f(a)$ of $y \in Y$ such that there exist $k \in K$, $r \in \mathbb{R}$ with $k \circ (y - r) \le f$, $k(<y, a> -r) = f(a)$.

Another natural choice stems from the formula giving $f^{\kappa\Delta}$ in Corollary 1.6: using relation (4) we have

$$f^{\kappa\Delta}(a) = \sup_{k \in K} k[\sup_{y \in Y}(<y, a> -(k^h \circ f)^*(y))]$$

$$= \sup_{y \in Y} \sup_{k \in K} k(<y, a> -(k^h \circ f)^*(y)).$$

3.2 - Definition. The reduced K-subdifferential of $f \in \overline{\mathbb{R}}^Z$ at $a \in f^{-1}(\mathbb{R})$ is the set $\partial_*^K f(a)$ of $y \in Y$ such that there exists $k \in K$ with $(k^h \circ f)^*(y)$ finite and $k(<y, a> -(k^h \circ f)^*(y)) = f(a)$.

Since for $r = (k^h \circ f)^*(y)$ we have $y - r \le k^h \circ f$, hence by (7), $k \circ (y - r) \le f$ we observe that $\partial_*^K f(a) \subset \partial^K f(a)$. The following result points out some other links and some connections with the familiar subdifferential operator ∂ of convex analysis.

3.3 - Proposition. Let $f \in \overline{\mathbb{R}}^Z$ be finite at $a \in Z$ and let $y \in Y$. Then the following assertions are equivalent and imply that $y \in \partial_*^K f(a) \subset \partial^K f(a)$:

(a) there exists $k \in K$ such that $y \in \partial(k^h \circ f)(a)$ and $(k \circ k^h)(f(a)) = f(a)$;

(b) there exists $k \in K$ such that $(k^h \circ f)^*(y) \in \mathbb{R}$, $k(<y, a> -(k^h \circ f)^*(y)) = f(a)$, $<y, a> -(k^h \circ f)^*(y) = k^h(f(a))$;

(c) there exist $k \in K$ and $r \in \mathbb{R}$ such that $k \circ (y - r) \le f$, $k(<y, a> -r) = f(a)$, $<y, a> -r = k^h(f(a))$.

Proof. (a) $\Rightarrow$ (b). Let $k \in K$ be as in assertion (a). Then, by the Young-Fenchel equality

$$(k^h \circ f)^*(y) = <y, a> -(k^h \circ f)(a) \in \mathbb{R}$$

as $(k^h \circ f)(a)$ is finite. Moreover, by our second assumption,

$$k(<y, a> -(k^h \circ f)^*(a)) = k((k^h \circ f)(a)) = f(a).$$

(b) $\Rightarrow$ (c). We already observed that for $r = (k^h \circ f)^*(y)$ the inequality $k \circ (y-r) \le f$ always holds true; with this choice of r we also have $k(<y, a> -r) = f(a)$, $<y, a> -r = k^h(f(a))$ by our assumptions.

(c) $\Rightarrow$ (a). As $k \circ (y - r) \leq f$ we have $y - r \leq k^h \circ f$. As $< y, a > -r = (k^h \circ f)(a)$ we get that $y \in \partial(k^h \circ f)(a)$. Finally, using the first equality in (8) we get, with $s =< y, a > -r$:

$$(k \circ k^h)(f(a)) = (k \circ k^h)(k(s)) = k(s) = f(a).$$

□

The following two properties are immediate consequences of Theorem 1.8:

$$\partial^K f(a) \neq \phi \Rightarrow f^{\kappa\Lambda}(a) = f(a)$$
$$f^{\kappa\Lambda}(a) = f(a) \Rightarrow \partial^K f^{\kappa\Lambda}(a) = \partial^K f(a)$$

Moreover $\partial^K f(a)$ can be used for optimality conditions as in the convex case.

3.4 - Proposition. For any $f \in \overline{\mathbb{R}}^Z$ and $a \in Z$ such that $f(a)$ is finite the following assertions are equivalent:
(a) $0 \in \partial^K f(a)$;
(b) a is a minimizer of f and there exists $k \in K$ such that $(k \circ k^h)(f(a)) = f(a)$.

Proof. Suppose $0 \in \partial^K f(a)$. Then there exist $k \in K$, $r \in \mathbb{R}$ with $k(-r) \leq f$, $k(-r) = f(a)$ so that a is a minimizer of f. Moreover $(k \circ k^h)(f(a)) = (k \circ k^h)(k(-r)) = k(-r) = f(a)$.

Conversely, if a is a minimizer of f and if there exists $k \in K$ with $(k \circ k^h)(f(a)) = f(a)$, setting $r = -k^h(f(a))$ we have $k(-r) = (k \circ k^h)(f(a)) = f(a) \leq f(z)$ for each $z \in Z$ so that $0 \in \partial^K f(a)$.

□

Let us now interpret the subdifferential in each of the examples presented above.
When $K = \{I\}$, $\partial^K f(a)$ obviously coincides with $\partial f(a)$ in the usual sense.

When $K = Q$, as any shifted K-linear functional is K-linear, we have that $y \in \partial^K f(a)$ iff there exists $k_1 \in K$ such that $k_1 \circ y \leq f$, $k_1(< y, a >) = f(a)$. This means that $\partial^K f(a)$ coincides with the *tangential* of f at a in the sense of J. P. Crouzeix ([3] p. 54).

When $K = \{k_q : q \in \mathbb{R}\}$ as in Example 2.1 we have that $y \in \partial^K f(a)$ if $f(a) \in \mathbb{R}$ and there exist $q, r \in \mathbb{R}$ with $k_q(< y, a > -r) = f(a)$, $f(z) \geq q$ for each $z \in Z(y, r) := \{z \in Z :< y, z >> r\}$. Therefore

$$\partial^K f(a) = \{y \in Y : \exists r \in \mathbb{R}, r << y, a >, \forall z \in Z(y, r)\ f(z) \geq f(a)\}$$
$$= \{y \in Y : \exists r \in \mathbb{R}, a \in Z(y, r), Z(y, r) \cap S_a = \phi\}$$

for $S_a = \{z \in Z : f(z) < f(a)\}$. We observe that if $\partial^K f(a)$ is nonempty then f attains at a a local minimum, conversely if f attains at a its minimum on some open half space containing a, then $\partial^K f(a)$ is nonempty. Moreover

$$\partial^K f(a) = \{y \in Y : \sup(< y, z >: z \in S_a) << y, a >\} = \partial_*^K f(a).$$

Let us consider with some attention the case $K = \{i_p : p \in \mathbb{R}\}$ as in Example 2.2, with $i_p(r) = p \wedge r$ for $r \in \mathbb{R}$ and compare in this case $\partial^K f(a)$, $\partial_*^K f(a)$ and the lower-subdifferential of f at a in the sense of Plastria [18]:

$$\partial^- f(a) = \{y \in Y : \forall z \in S_a \ <y, z-a> +f(a) \le f(z)\}.$$

3.5 - Proposition. For $K = \{i_p : p \in \mathbb{R}\}$, with $i_p(r) = p \wedge r$ for $r \in \mathbb{R}$ one has for any $f \in \overline{\mathbb{R}}^Z$ finite at a

$$\partial^K f(a) = \partial^- f(a) = \partial_*^K f(a).$$

Proof. Let $y \in \partial^K f(a)$: there exist $p \in \mathbb{R}$, $r \in \mathbb{R}$ such that

$$p \wedge (y - r) \le f, \quad p \wedge (<y, a> -r) = f(a).$$

Then $p \ge f(a)$, $<y, a> -r \ge f(a)$ so that for each $z \in S_a$ we have $f(z) < p$ hence $<y, z> -r \le f(z)$ by what precedes. It follows that

$$<y, z - a> +f(a) \le <y, z> -r \le f(z)$$

and $y \in \partial^- f(a)$.

Now let $y \in \partial^- f(a)$ so that

$$\inf\{f(z)- <y, z>: z \in S_a\} \ge f(a)- <y, a> .$$

Setting $p = f(a)$ and recalling that

$$-(i_p^h \circ f)^*(y) = -(f \underset{\bullet}{+} \psi_{S_a})^*(y) = \inf\{f(z)- <y, z >: z \in S_a\}$$

we see that

$$i_p(< y, a > -(i_p^h \circ f)^*(y)) \ge i_p(f(a)) = f(a)$$

hence $y \in \partial_*^K f(a) \subset \partial^K f(a)$. $\qquad\square$

3.6 - Corollary. If Z is a n.v.s. and $K = \{i_p : p \in \mathbb{R}\}$ with $i_p(r) = p \wedge r$ for $r \in \mathbb{R}$, any lipschitzian quasiconvex function f on Z is such that $f^{\kappa \Lambda} = f$, i.e. is the supremum of its subaffine minorants.

This result which completes Theorem 2.4 is an immediate consequence of (an easy adaptation of) [18] Theorem 2.3 and Theorem 1.8 above.

Finally let us consider the case $K = \{\frac{1}{R}ln\}$ where ln is defined as in Example 2.7. For $f \in \overline{\mathbb{R}}^Z$ with $f(a) \in \mathbb{R}$ we have $y \in \partial^K f(a)$ iff there exists $r \in \mathbb{R}$ with $\frac{1}{R}ln \circ (y - r) \le f$, $\frac{1}{R}ln(< y, a > -r) = f(a)$. This means that $< y, a > -r > 0$, $< y, a > -r = \exp Rf(a)$ and $y - r \le \exp Rf$, or, in other words, that $y \in \partial(\exp Rf)(a)$:

$$\partial^K f(a) = \partial(\exp Rf)(a).$$

4. Application to quasiconvex duality.

What precedes can be applied to the performance function (or marginal function) p of a parametrized minimization problem:

$$(P_z) \quad \text{minimize} \quad F_z(x) : x \in X$$

where X is an arbitrary set (decision space), Y is a locally convex topological vector space and $F_z : X \to \overline{\mathbb{R}}$ is deduced from some perturbation function $F : X \times Y \to \overline{\mathbb{R}}$ by $F_z(x) = F(x, z)$ for $x \in X$. Setting

$$p(z) := \inf\{F_z(x) : x \in X\}$$

the primal problem consists in solving $(P) := (P_0)$, in particular in finding $p(0)$. The fact that $p(0) \geq p^{\kappa\Delta}(0)$ suggests to introduce the following dual problem.

4.1 - Definition. Given a subclass K of Q, the K-dual problem of (P) is the problem:
(D_K) maximize on Y the function $y \mapsto \sup_{k \in K} k(-(k^h \circ p)^*(y))$.

As $p^{\kappa\Delta}(0) \leq p(0)$ we have

$$\sup(D_K) \leq \inf(P)$$

with equality iff $p^{\kappa\Delta}(0) = p(0)$. In particular this occurs if $\partial^K p(0)$ is nonempty. Moreover, when $\overline{y} \in \partial_*^K p(0)$ we can find $\overline{k} \in K$ with

$$\overline{k}(-(\overline{k}^h \circ p)^*(\overline{y})) = p(0) = p^{\kappa\Delta}(0) = \sup_{y \in Y} \sup_{k \in K} k(-(k^h \circ p)^*(y))$$

and $\overline{y}$ is a solution to (D_k) as well as a solution to

$$(D_{\overline{k}}) \quad \text{maximize on } Y \text{ the function} \quad \overline{k}(-(\overline{k}^h \circ p)^*(y)).$$

Conversely, when there exists some $\overline{k} \in K$ such that $\overline{y}$ is a solution to $(D_{\overline{k}})$ and $(\overline{k}^h \circ p)^*(\overline{y})$ is finite with $\sup(D_{\overline{k}}) = \inf(P)$ then $\overline{y} \in \partial_*^K p(0)$.

In several cases of interest, such as Examples 2.1 and 2.2, K is a family parametrized by $\mathbb{R}$. Then (D_K) consists in maximizing a function defined over $\mathbb{R} \times Y$, a vector space, instead of maximizing a function over $K \times Y$. This way of setting a dual problem appears to be more tractable and more closely connected with usual dual problems in which an extra parameter is frequently introduced.

For instance, taking $K = \{k_q : q \in \mathbb{R}\}$ as in Example 2.1 we get

$$\sup(D_K) = \sup_{y \in Y} \sup\{q \in \mathbb{R} : \sup(<z, y> : \exists x \in X, F(x, z) < q) < 0\}$$

$$= \sup_{y \in Y} \inf\{q \in \mathbb{R} : \sup(<z, y> : \exists x \in X, F(x, z) < q) \geq 0\}$$

Taking $K = \{i_q : q \in \mathbb{R}\}$ as in Example 2.2, formula (17) yields

$$\sup(D_K) = \sup_{y \in Y} \sup_{q \in \mathbb{R}} q \wedge \inf_{p(z) < q} [p(z) - < y, z >].$$

Now it is easy to see that for each $y \in Y$

$$\sup_{q \in \mathbb{R}} q \wedge \inf_{p(z) < q} [p(z) - < y, z >] = \inf_z [p(z) \vee (p(z) - < y, z >)]$$

so that writing $y_+ = \max(y, 0) = y \vee 0$, we get

$$\sup(D_K) = \sup_{y \in Y} \inf_z [p(z) + (-y)_+(z)].$$

We observe that (D_K) consists in maximizing on Y the opposite of the function

$$y \mapsto \sup_z [< y, z > \wedge 0 - p(z)]$$

which is a supremum of subaffine functions. Moreover, setting

$$L(x, y) = \inf_z [F(x, z) + (-y)_+(z)]$$

the definition of $p(z)$ yields

$$\sup(D_K) = \sup_{y \in Y} \inf_{x \in X} L(x, y).$$

The present Lagrangian is very similar to the ordinary Lagrangian of convex duality given by

$$L(x, y) = \inf_z [F(x, z) - < y, z >].$$

Conclusion.

For any family K of nondecreasing extended real-valued functions on $\mathbb{R}$ and any $f \in \overline{\mathbb{R}}^Z$, where Z is a topological vector space one can define a regularisation $\hat{f}$ of f by

$$\hat{f} = \sup\{k \circ (y - r) : k \in K, y \in Z^*, r \in \mathbb{R}, k \circ (y - r) \leq f\}.$$

When the elements of K are lower semicontinuous this regularization is obtained through the use of a biconjugation with respect to a polarity and its dual. When K is stable under shifting and addition of constants this conjugation coincides with the one introduced in [16]. This is the case for the important case $K = Q$, the set of all lower semicontinuous nondecreasing functions. In general the device described here differs from the duality scheme of [16] as it is not a conjugation of the Fenchel-Moreau type. New duality formulas can be derived from the present approach.

References.

[1] Avriel, M.: *r-convex functions.* Core discussion papers, 7106, 1971 Louvain.

[2] Birkhoff, G.: *Lattice theory.* Providence, A.M.S., 1966.

[3] Crouzeix, J. P.: *Contributions à l'étude des fonctions quasiconvexes.* Thèse, Université de Clermont-Ferrand II (1977).

[4] Ekeland, I. and Temam, R.: *Analyse convexe et problèmes variationnels.* Dunod, Paris 1974.

[5] Evers, J. J. M. and van Maaren, H.: *Duality principles in mathematics and their relations to conjugate functions.* Nieuw Arch. Wiskunde 3 (1985), 23 – 68.

[6] Greenberg, H. P. and Pierskalla, W. P.: *Quasiconjugate functions and surrogate duality.* Cahiers du Centre d'études de Rech. Oper. 15 (1973), 437 – 448.

[7] Laurent, P. J.: *Approximation et optimisation.* Hermann, Paris 1972.

[8] Martínez-Legaz, J. E.: *A generalized concept of conjugation.* In Optimisation théorie et algorithmes. Proc. Internat. Confer. Confolant, March 1981. Lecture Notes in pure and applied Math., Marcel Dekker, New York, 45 – 59.

[9] Martínez-Legaz, J. E.: *On lower subdifferentiable functions.* (These Proceedings.)

[10] Martos, B.: *Quasiconvexity and quasimonotonicity in nonlinear programming.* Studia Sci. Math. Hung. 2 (1967), 265 – 279.

[11] Moreau, J. J.: *Inf-convolution, sous-additivité, convexité des fonctions numériques.* J. Math. pures et appl. 49 (1970), 109 – 154.

[12] Ore, O.: *Galois connexions.* Trans. Amer. Math. Soc. 55 (1944), 493 – 513.

[13] Penot, J. P.: *Modified and augmented Lagrangian theory revisited and augmented.* Unpublished Lecture, Fermat Days: "Mathematics for optimization", Toulouse, May 1985.

[14] Penot, J. P. and Volle, M.: *Sur la dualité quasi-convexe.* Publications Mathématiques de Limoges (1986).

[15] Penot, J. P. and Volle, M.: *Inversion of real valued functions and applications.* (Submitted).

[16] Penot, J. P. and Volle, M.: *On quasiconvex duality.* (Submitted paper (1986)).

[17] Pickert, G.: *Bemerkungen über Galois-Verbindungen.* Arch. Math., Vol. 3 (1952), 285 – 289.

[18] Plastria, F.: *Lower subdifferentiable functions and their minimization by cutting planes.* J. Optim. Theory Appl. 46 (1985), 37 – 53.

[19] Rockafellar, R. T.: *Convex analysis.* Princeton University Press (1970).

[20] Singer, I.: *Conjugate operators.* In Proc. 8th Symposium on Operations Research, Karlsruhe, August 1983.

[21] Volle, M.: *Conjugaison par tranches.* Annali Mat. Pura Applicata 139 (1985), 279 – 311.

International Series of
Numerical Mathematics, Vol. 84
(c) 1988 Birkhäuser Verlag Basel

Duality in D.C. (Difference of Convex functions) Optimization. Subgradient Methods

Pham Dinh Tao & El Bernoussi Souad
Laboratoire TIM3
Institut IMAG
B. P. No. 68
38402 Saint Martin d'Hères cedex, France

1. Introduction.

In recent years, research is very active in nonconvex optimization. There are two principal reasons for this:

The first is the importance of its applications to concrete problems in practice.

The second is a natural way of leaving the convex optimization (which is sufficiently studied and can be considered as practically solved) and passing to the nonconvex optimization. More especially as the resolution of a nonconvex optimization problem requires in general, at each step, the resolution of a convex optimization problem; and then it is necessary to adapt and to make efficient the existent algorithms of convex optimization for solving the nonconvex optimization problems.

The following typical problems constitute a large class of nonconvex and non differentiable optimization problems which possesses many interesting properties (for its qualitative study as well as for its quantitative study) and is very important because of its applications:

1) $\sup\{f(x) : x \in C\}$
2) $\inf\{f(x) - g(x) : x \in C\}$
3) $\inf\{f(x) : x \in C, g(x) \geq 0\}$

where f and g are proper convex and lower semicontinuous on $X = \mathbb{R}^n$ and C a closed convex set in X.

These problems are equivalent in the sense that solving one of them implies the resolution of the others.

Historically, the studies of this class of nonconvex optimization problems can be summarized as follows:

- The first work, which concerns the problem 1) in the case where C is a polyedron is due to HOANG TUY (1964). He proposes an algorithm of combinatorial type for solving this problem.

We could say that TUY's quantitative study of the problem 1) (because his work does not go really to the analytical characterization of the optimal solution of this problem) belongs to the combinatorial optimization. Then this work is especially known by people of operations research.

In the period 1964 – 80 there were a large number of publications related to the development of TUY's algorithm and its variants. Most of the authors are specialists in operations research.

- In a completely different way, our works relative to the problem 1) begin with the elaboration of the algorithms for computing the bound-norms of matrices (1974). Our algorithms are based on the analytical characterization (of local type) of optimal solution to this problem.

They are at the cross-road of these (quantitative and qualitative) studies and constantly use the algorithms of convex optimizations.

- The duality theory in nonconvex optimization studied by J. F. TOLAND (1979) generalizes our previous results concerning the problem of convex maximization over compact convex set.

This duality is dealing with the d.c functions. The studies of the analytical characterizations of optimal solution (qualitative studies) are recent and are especially the works of PHAM DINH TAO, EL BERNOUSSI, J. B. HIRIART-URRUTY, R. ELLAIA and J. F. TOLAND among others.

- With the second paper on the resolution of the problem 1), (1980), HOANG TUY sets to work again in this domain.

During the last years, there are many papers on the quantitative studies of this class of nonconvex optimization problems. There are especially the works of HOANG TUY (and his students), J. B. ROSEN, MAJTHAY & WHINSTON, BALAS, BURDET, HILLESTAD, JACOBSEN, HORST, PHAM DINH TAO, BENACER, EL BERNOUSSI. Actually for solving this class of nonconvex optimization problems, we dispose two families of algorithms:

1) Family of algorithms of combinatorial optimization

It is composed from algorithms of "cutting plane" type (i.e. using hyperplane for localizing an optimal solution) [2-8, 13, 14, 16 – 20] which are introduced by HOANG TUY.

Theoretically these algorithms lead to an optimal solution; however they are applied only to problems of small size because of their complexity and their cumbersomeness concerning the effective programming. For a long time, people have been interested in these algorithms and have developed HOANG TUY's idea under different form. We must admit nevertheless, that in spite of a large number of publications on this subject, an efficient implementation of these algorithms for concrete problems of reasonable size does not yet exist.

2) Family of algorithms of convex and nonconvex optimization

There are subgradient-methods which are based on the duality in d. c. optimization. Being introduced by the author, [24 – 34], the subgradient algorithms are easy to program and are actually the only ones which enable to treat the practical problems of large size; their only drawback is that, in general, one cannot say if the local optimal solution furnished are effectively global optimal solution unless an initial vector x^0 is near enough to a global optimal solution. Such an x^0 can be obtained by algorithms of the first family.

Conversely the algorithms of the second family can furnish to the algorithms of the first family a "good" local optimal solution in order to accelerate their convergence.

This paper is devoted to the duality in d.c optimization (DCO) and to methods of subgradient for solving DCO problems.

2. Duality in DCO optimization.

Let X be the n-dimensional real space $\mathbb{R}^n$ and let $\Gamma_0(X)$ the set of proper convex, lower semicontinuous functions on X.

Let g, $h \in \Gamma_0(X)$ and consider the following DCO problem (P):

$$\lambda = \inf\{g(x) - h(x) : x \in X\}$$

whose set of solutions is denoted by P.

By introducing the conjugate functions g^* and h^*, we can write $(Y = \mathbb{R}^n)$:

$$\lambda = \inf\{g(x) - \sup\{<x, y> -h^*(y) : y \in Y\} : x \in X\}$$
$$= \inf\{g(x) + \inf\{h^*(y)- <x, y> : y \in Y\} : x \in X\}$$
$$= \inf_{x \in X} \inf_{y \in Y} \{h^*(y) + g(x)- <x, y>\}$$
$$= \inf_{y \in Y} \{h^*(y) + \inf_{x \in X} \{g(x)- <x, y>\}\}$$
$$= \inf\{h^*(y) - g^*(y) : y \in Y\}$$

The dual problem (Q) is then defined by:

$$\lambda = \inf\{h^*(y) - g^*(y) : y \in Y\} \qquad (Q)$$

We shall denote by Q the solution set of (Q).

2.1. Global Duality in DCO. Let us begin with the following principal result of global duality in DCO. Its proof is completely different from TOLAND's approach [45 – 47]. It is very close to the reasoning used in [24 – 34] and is based on the theory of the subdifferential and of the conjugate of convex functions.

This result completes preceding ones in a happy way.

Theorem 2.1. Let $f, g \in \Gamma_0(X)$, then we have:
(1) $\partial h(x^*) \subset \partial g(x^*), \quad \forall x^* \in P$;
(2) $\partial g^*(y^*) \subset \partial h^*(y^*), \quad \forall y^* \in Q$;
(3) $\cup_{y^* \in Q} \partial g^*(y^*) \subset P$ and the equality holds if h is subdifferentiable on P (for instance if $P \subset \mathrm{ri}\,(\mathrm{dom}\,h)$);
(4) $\cup_{x^* \in P} \partial h(x^*) \subset Q$ and the equality holds if g^* is subdifferentiable on Q (for instance if $Q \subset \mathrm{ri}\,(\mathrm{dom}\,g^*)$).

Proof. By duality, we only need to show properties (1) and (2). If $x^* \in P$, then for every y^* in $\partial h(x^*)$ we have

$$\lambda = g(x^*) - h(x^*) = g(x^*) - \langle x^*, y^* \rangle + h(y^*).$$

Because of the inequality $g(x^*) - \langle x^*, y^* \rangle \geq -g^*(y^*)$ and of the equality of infimums of the problems (P) and (Q), it follows that $h^*(y^*) - g^*(y^*) = \lambda$ and $y^* \in \partial g(x^*)$. Consequently $\partial h(x^*) \subset \partial g(x^*)$, $\forall x^* \in P$ and $\cup_{x^* \in P} \partial h(x^*) \subset Q$.

Thus we have proved (1) and the inclusion in (4).

Similarly we obtain

$$\bigcup_{x^* \in P} \partial h(x^*) \subset Q.$$

Let us consider now $x^* \in P$. As it has been verified above, if $y^* \in \partial h(x^*)$ then $y^* \in \partial g(x^*)$, i.e. $x^* \in \partial g^*(y^*)$.

It follows that if h is subdifferentiable on P (for instance if $P \subset \mathrm{ri}\,(\mathrm{dom}\,h)$), then

$$\bigcup_{y^* \in Q} \partial g^*(y^*) = P.$$

$\square$

2.2. Local duality in DCO. Let us consider now local solutions of problems (P) and (Q). We begin by defining the sets $P_|$ and $Q_|$ which represent necessary conditions of local solutions of (P) and (Q) respectively.

$$P_| = \{x^* \in X : \partial h(x^*) \subset \partial g(x^*)\}$$
$$Q_| = \{y^* \in Y : \partial g^*(y^*) \subset \partial h^*(y^*)\}.$$

It is worth noting that these conditions are not far from sufficiency. They are even effectively sufficient in many cases [24 – 34, 38].

In section 3, we shall see how our subgradient method can furnish some elements (in $P_|$ and $Q_|$) which are local solutions of (P) and (Q) respectively.

Theorem 2.2.

(1) $x^* \in P_|$ if and only if

$$g'(x^*; d) - h'(x^*; d) \geq 0, \quad \forall d \in X$$

This latter property is equivalent to

$$\min\{g'(x^*; d) - h'(x^*; d) : d \in X\} = 0$$

(2) $y^* \in D_|$ if and only if

$$(h^*)'(y^*; d) - (g^*)'(y^*; d) \geq 0, \quad \forall d \in Y.$$

Proof. It suffices to prove property (1). By definition of the subdifferential of g, $h \in \Gamma_0(X)$, we have $x^* \in P_1$ if and only if

$$g(x) - g(x^*) \geq <x - x^*, y>, \quad \forall x \in X, \forall y \in \partial h(x^*).$$

This is equivalent to

$$g(x) - g(x^*) \geq \sup_{y \in \partial h(x^*)} <x - x^*, y> = h'(x^*; x - x^*) \quad \forall x \in X.$$

Since $g'(x^*; .)$ is the most of the positively homogeneous functions k such that

$$g(x) - g(x^*) \geq k(x - x^*), \quad \forall x \in X$$

the proof is now achieved. $\quad\square$

The preceding results lead us to introduce the local duality in DCO in the following way:
For each $x^* \in X$, we denote by $S(x^*)$ the problem

$$\inf\{h^*(y) - g^*(y) : y \in \partial h(x^*)\} \qquad (S(x^*))$$

which is equivalent to

$$\inf\{<x^*, y> - g^*(y) : y \in \partial h(x^*)\}$$

because $h(x^*) + h^*(y) = <x^*, y>, \forall y \in \partial h(x^*)$.
Let $S(x^*)$ be the set of solutions of problem $S(x^*)$.
Similarly and dually, for each $y^* \in Y$, we define the problem $T(y^*)$ by

$$\inf\{g(x) - h(x) : x \in \partial g^*(y^*)\} \qquad (T(y^*))$$

which is equivalent to

$$\inf\{<x, y^*> - h(x) : x \in \partial g^*(y^*)\}$$

whose solution set is denoted by $T(y^*)$.

We shall now establish the main results of local duality in DCO. These results constitute the basis of our subgradient method for solving DCO problems.

Theorem 2.3.
(1) $x^* \in P_1$ if and only if there exists $y^* \in S(x^*)$ such that $x^* \in \partial g^*(y^*)$; in other words $x^* \in (\partial g^* \circ S)(x^*)$.
(2) $y^* \in Q_1$ if and only if there exists $x^* \in T(y^*)$ such that $y^* \in \partial h(x^*)$; in other words $y^* \in (\partial h \circ T)(y^*)$.

Proof. By duality we only need to show (1).

If $x^* \in P_|$ then $< x^*, y > -g^*(y) = g(x^*)$, $\forall y \in \partial h(x^*)$ because $\partial h(x^*) \subset \partial g(x^*)$. It follows that $S(x^*) = \partial h(x^*)$ and hence $x^* \in \partial g(y^*)$ for every $y^* \in S(x^*)$. Conversely let $x^* \in X$ such that $x^* \in \partial g^*(y^*)$ for some $y^* \in S(x^*)$. Because $y^* \in S(x^*)$, we have

$$-g^*(y) + g^*(y^*) - < x^*, y^* > \geq - < x^*, y >, \quad \forall x \in \partial h(x^*).$$

But $x^* \in \partial g^*(y^*)$, then $g(x^*) = < x^*, y^* > -g^*(y^*)$. It follows that

$$-g^*(y) - g(x^*) \geq - < x^*, y >, \quad \forall y \in \partial h(x^*).$$

By using the definition of g^*, we can now obtain the following inequality

$$g(x) - g(x^*) \geq < x - x^*, y >, \quad \forall x \in X \text{ and } \forall y \in \partial h(x^*).$$

So the proof is achieved. □

Corollary. If $x^* \in P_|$ then we have
(1) $S(x^*) = \partial h(x^*)$
(2) $h^*(y) - g^*(y) = g(x^*) - h(x^*)$, $\forall y \in \partial h(x^*)$.
Dually, if $y^* \in Q_|$ then we have
(3) $T(y^*) = \partial g^*(y^*)$
(4) $g(x) - h(x) = h^*(y^*) - g^*(y^*)$, $\forall x \in \partial g^*(y^*)$.

Proof. This is immediate from the proof of the previous theorem. □

Remarks.
(1) It is easily shown that $x^* \in P_|$ if and only if

$$< x^*, y > -g^*(y) = g(x^*), \quad \forall y \in \partial h(x^*).$$

(2) Dually, we can obtain the following property: $y^* \in Q_|$ if and only if

$$< x, y^* > -h(x) = h^*(y^*), \quad \text{for every } x \in \partial g^*(y^*).$$

(3) We shall see below, in the description of methods of subgradients, the roles of problems $S(x^*)$ and $T(y^*)$, and at the same time, a possible justification of the convergence of these methods towards a couple (x^*, y^*) of optimal solutions of (P) and (Q) respectively, when the initial vector x^0 is close enough to an element of P.

Lemma.
(1) The multivalued mapping S is upper semicontinuous on $P_|$.
(2) The multivalued mapping T is upper semicontinuous on $Q_|$.

Proof. By using related results in [1,21] and the preceding corollary, the lemma is easy to prove.

3. Subgradient methods for solving DCO problems.

We are now ready to describe our subgradient methods for solving DCO problems. These methods are based on the (global and local) duality in DCO. We construct two sequences x^k and y^k as follows:

$$
\begin{aligned}
x^0 &\qquad\qquad \mapsto y^0 \in S(x^0) \\
x^1 &\in T(y^0) \quad \mapsto y^1 \in S(x^1) \\
&\vdots \qquad\qquad\quad \vdots \\
x^{k+1} &\in T(y^k) \mapsto y^{k+1} \in S(x^{k+1})
\end{aligned}
$$

Theorem 3.
(1) $g(x^{k+1}) - h(x^{k+1}) \le h^*(y^k) - g^*(y^k) \le g(x^k) - h(x^k)$.
Equality $(g(x^{k+1}) - h(x^{k+1}) = g(x^k) - h(x^k))$ if and only if

$$
x^k \in \partial g^*(y^k) \text{ and } y^k \in \partial h(y^{k+1}).
$$

In this case we have $x^k \in P_1$, $y^k \in Q_1$.
(2) If λ is finite, then we have:

(2.1) $\qquad \lim_{k\to\infty} \{g(x^k) - h(x^k)\} = \lim_{k\to\infty} \{h^*(y^k) - g^*(y^k)\} = \mu \ge \lambda$.

(2.2) $\qquad \lim_{k\to\infty} \{g(x^k) + g^*(y^k) - <x^k, y^k>\} = 0$

(3) If λ is finite and if the sequences x^k and y^k are bounded, then for every cluster point x^* of x^k (respectively y^* of y^k), there exists a cluster point y^* of y^k (respectively x^* of x^k) such that:

(3.1) $\qquad x^* \in P_1$ and $g(x^*) - h(x^*) = \mu$.

(3.2) $\qquad y^* \in Q_1$ and $h^*(y^*) - g^*(y^*) = \mu$.

(3.3) $\qquad \lim_{k\to\infty} \{g(x^k) + g^*(y^k)\} = g(x^*) + g^*(y^*) = <x^*, y^*>$.

(3.4) $\qquad \lim_{k\to\infty} \{h(x^k) + h^*(y^k)\} = h(x^*) + h^*(y^*) = <x^*, y^*>$.

Proof. Because $y^k \in \partial h(x^k)$, we have

$$
h(x^{k+1}) \ge h(x^k) + <x^{k+1} - x^k, y^k>.
$$

It follows that

$$
g(x^{k+1}) - h(x^{k+1}) \le g(x^{k+1}) - <x^{k+1} - x^k, y^k> -h(x^k).
$$

But $x^{k+1} \in \partial g^*(y^k)$, then

$$g(x^k) \geq g(x^{k+1}) - <x^{k+1} - x^k, y^k> .$$

This latter inequality implies that

$$g(x^{k+1}) - <x^{k+1} - x^k, y^k> -h(x^k) \leq g(x^k) - h(x^k).$$

Parallely we have

$$g(x^{k+1}) - <x^{k+1} - x^k, y^k> -h(x^k) = h^*(y^k) - g^*(y^k)$$

because $x^{k+1} \in \partial g^*(y^k)$ and $y^k \in \partial h(x^k)$.
So we have proved the inequalities of (1).

Sufficiency
Suppose that $x^k \in \partial g^*(y^k)$ and $y^k \in \partial h(x^{k+1})$. Then we have

$$g(x^k) + g^*(x^k) = <x^k, y^k>$$

and

$$h(x^{k+1}) + h^*(y^k) = <x^{k+1}, y^k> .$$

But by the construction $x^{k+1} \in \partial g^*(y^k)$, then

$$g(x^{k+1}) + g^*(y^k) = <x^{k+1}, y^k> .$$

Moreover, the fact $y^k \in \partial h(x^k)$ is equivalent to

$$h(x^k) + h^*(y^k) = <x^k, y^k> .$$

From these relations, it is easily shown that

$$g(x^{k+1}) - h(x^{k+1}) = g(x^k) - h(x^k).$$

Necessity
We have

$$g(x^{k+1}) - h(x^{k+1}) - (g(x^k) - h(x^k)) \leq g(x^{k+1}) - g(x^k) - <x^{k+1} - x^k, y^k> \leq 0$$

because $y^k \in \partial h(x^k)$.
But $x^{k+1} \in \partial g^*(y^k)$ implies that

$$g(x^{k+1}) - g(x^k) - <x^{k+1} - x^k, y^k> \leq 0.$$

Hence, if $g(x^{k+1}) - h(x^{k+1}) = g(x^k) - h(x^k)$, then

$$g(x^{k+1}) - g(x^k) = < x^{k+1} - x^k, y^k > .$$

Taking once more into account $x^{k+1} \in \partial g^*(y^k)$, we obtain

$$g(x^k) + g^*(y^k) = < x^k, y^k > .$$

In other words $x^k \in \partial g^*(y^k)$. This implies, by virtue of Theorem 2.3, that $x^k \in P_|$ because $y^k \in S(x^k)$ by construction.

It remains to prove that $y^k \in Q_|$.

If $g(x^{k+1}) - h(x^{k+1}) = g(x^k) - h(x^k)$, then $x^k \in T(y^k)$. Theorem 2.3 gives now $y^k \in Q_|$ because $y^k \in \partial h(x^k)$ by construction.

(2) Because λ is finite, property (2.1) is simple consequence of property (1). It follows that:

$$\lim_{k \to \infty} \{g(x^{k+1}) - < x^{k+1} - x^k, y^k > -g(x^k)\} = 0,$$

in other words:

$$\lim_{k \to \infty} \{g(x^k) + g^*(y^k) - < x^k, y^k >\} = 0.$$

(3) Suppose now that λ is finite and that the sequences x^k and y^k are bounded. The sets of cluster points of x^k and of y^k are nonempty because x^k and y^k are supposed bounded.

Let x^* be a cluster point of x^k; for the sake of simplicity in notations we shall write:

$$\lim_{k \to \infty} x^k = x^*.$$

We can suppose (extracting subsequences if necessary) that the sequence y^k converges to a point $y^* \in \partial h(x^*)$. Property (2.2) gives now

$$\lim_{k \to \infty} \{g(x^k) + g^*(y^k)\} = \lim_{k \to \infty} < x^k, y^k > = < x^*, y^* > .$$

Set $\theta(x, y) = g(x) + g^*(y)$ for $(x, y) \in X \times Y$. It is clear that $\theta \in \Gamma_0(X \times Y)$. Then, because of the semicontinuity of θ, we obtain

$$\theta(x^*, y^*) \leq \liminf_{k \to \infty} \theta(x^k, y^k) = \lim_{k \to \infty} \theta(x^k, y^k) = < x^*, y^* > .$$

This is equivalent to $\theta(x^*, y^*) = g(x^*) + g^*(y^*) = < x^*, y^* >$, so property (3.3) is proved and $x^* \in \partial g^*(x^*)$.

Theorem 2.3, its Corollary and Lemma in §2 now allow us to affirm that $x^* \in P_|$. The lemma stated below gives:

$$\lim_{k \to \infty} g^*(y^k) = g^*(y^*).$$

$$\lim_{k \to \infty} h(x^k) = h(x^*).$$

It follows from property (3.3) that $\lim_{k\to\infty} g(x^k) = g(x^*)$. Thus we can write:

$$\mu = \lim_{k\to\infty} \{g(x^k) - h(x^k)\} = g(x^*) - h(x^*).$$

Dually and in the same way, it is easy to prove properties (3.2) and (3.4). The proof is then complete. □

Lemma. Let $h \in \Gamma_0(X)$ and let x^k be a sequence which possesses the following properties:

1) $x^k \to x^*$
2) There exists a bounded sequence $y^k \in \partial h(x^k)$
3) $\partial h(x^*)$ is nonempty.

Then $\lim_{k\to\infty} h(x^k) = h(x^*)$.

Proof. In fact let $y^* \in \partial h(x^*)$, we have

$$h(x^k) \geq h(x^*) + <x^k - x^*, y^*>.$$

But $y^k \in \partial h(x^k)$, then:

$$h(x^*) \geq h(x^k) + <x^* - x^k, y^k>.$$

This is equivalent to

$$h(x^k) \leq h(x^*) + <x^k - x^*, y^k>.$$

As $x^k \to x^*$, we have $\lim_{k\to\infty} <x^k - x^*, y^*> = 0$. Moreover $\lim_{k\to\infty} <x^k - x^*, y^k> = 0$ because the sequence y^k is bounded. It follows that $\lim_{k\to\infty} h(x^k) = h(x^*)$. □

Remarks.

1) If the sequences x^k and y^k are constructed in the more simpler following manner:

$$x^{k+1} \in \partial g^*(y^k); \quad y^k \in \partial h(x^k)$$

then in Theorem 3. we should replace in property (3.1) (respectively (3.2)) $x^* \in P_1$ (respectively $y^* \in Q_1$) by $\partial g(x^*) \cap \partial h(x^*) \neq \emptyset$ (respectively $\partial g^*(y^*) \cap \partial h^*(y^*) \neq \emptyset$).

2) This is the fact $y^k \in S(x^k)$ (respectively $x^{k+1} \in T(y^k)$) which allows to prove $x^* \in P_1$ (respectively $y^* \in Q_1$) in property (3.1) (respectively (3.2)).

3) If g is strongly convex (i.e. there exists $\rho_1 > 0$ such that

$$g(x_2) \geq g(x_1) + <x_2 - x_1, y_1> + \rho_1\|x_2 - x_1\|^2$$

for every x_1, x_2 in X and every $y_1 \in \partial g(x_1)$), then we have

$$g(x^{k+1}) - h(x^{k+1}) \leq g(x^k) - h(x^k) - \rho_1\|x^{k+1} - x^k\|^2$$

This result (which is also true for sequence x^k and y^k constructed as above in 1)) is immediate from the proof of Theorem 3.

In the same way if h is strongly convex with constant $\rho_2 > 0$, then

$$(*) \qquad g(x^{k+1}) - h(x^{k+1}) \le g(x^k) - h(x^k) - \rho_2 \|x^{k+1} - x^k\|^2.$$

Evidently if both the functions g and h are strongly convex then

$$(**) \qquad g(x^{k+1}) - h(x^{k+1}) \le g(x^k) - h(x^k) - (\rho_1 + \rho_2)\|x^{k+1} - x^k\|^2.$$

Equality $(g(x^{k+1}) - h(x^{k+1}) = g(x^k) - h(x^k))$ in $(*)$ and $(**)$ holds if and only if $x^{k+1} = x^k$.

4) If g or h is strongly convex then $\lim_{k \to \infty} \|x^{k+1} - x^k\| = 0$. Moreover if the set of cluster points of x^k is finite then the whole sequence x^k converges. (See [24 – 34])

5) Without loss of generality, we can suppose that f and g are strongly convex. In fact we can write:

$$g(x) - h(x) = (g + \varphi)(x) - (h + \varphi)(x) = g_1(x) - h_1(x)$$

and then it suffices to take φ strongly convex (e.g. $\varphi(x) = (1/2)\|x\|^2$). This procedure could render differentiable the functions g^* and h^* in the dual problem (Q).

Parallely we can apply to primal problem (P) the following regularization procedure: (See [11, 15])

$$\alpha = \inf\{(g_\nabla \theta)(x) - (h_\nabla \theta)(x) : x \in X\} \qquad (P')$$

(where $\theta \in \Gamma_0(X)$ and ∇ being the infimal convolution operator) whose dual problem is:

$$\alpha = \inf\{(h^* + \theta^*)(y) - (g^* + \theta^*)(y) : y \in Y\} \qquad (Q')$$

It is clear that problems (Q) and (Q') are equivalent. This is not the case for (P) and (P'). (See Theorem 2.1). However the regularization performed in (P') can simplify the programmation of our algorithm. (See Section 3).

6) Remark that we can regularize both the primal and dual problems: We denote by $P(\varphi)$ the following problem: $(\varphi \in \Gamma_0(X))$

$$\alpha = \inf\{(g + \varphi)(x) - (h + \varphi)(x) : x \in X\} \qquad P(\varphi)$$

which is equivalent to (P). By regularizing $P(\varphi)$ as above mentioned, we obtain:

$$\alpha = \inf\{((g + \varphi)_\nabla \theta)(x) - ((h + \varphi)_\nabla \theta(x) : x \in X\} \qquad P(\varphi)'$$

whose dual problem is:

$$\alpha = \inf\{((h + \varphi)^* + \theta^*)(y) - ((g + \varphi)^* + \theta^*)(y) : y \in Y\}.$$

The latter is equivalent to the dual problem $Q(\varphi)$ of $P(\varphi)$.

$$\alpha = \inf\{((h + \varphi)^*)(y) - ((g + \varphi)^*)(y) : y \in Y\} \qquad Q(\varphi)$$

which can take, under some well-known condition, the following form:

$$\alpha = \inf\{(h^*_\nabla \varphi^*)(y) - ((g^*_\nabla \varphi^*))(y) : y \in Y\}.$$

From a practical viewpoint, we should be prudent in evaluating the complexity and the performance of our algorithm with these regularizations. The interesting problem of finding a better (or optimal) decomposition of $f - g$ remains open. (See Section 4).

4. Applications.

In this section, we shall illustrate the preceding results by simple examples. Some well-known algorithms (of convex and nonconvex optimization) can then be rediscovered.

4.1. Maximization of convex function over convex set. We are concerned with the following problem:

$\lambda = \sup\{f(x) : x \in C\}$, where $f \in \Gamma_0(X)$ and C is a closed convex set in X.

This problem is clearly equivalent to

$-\lambda = \inf\{\chi_C(x) - f(x) : x \in X\}$ (χ_C being the indicator function of C)

The description of our algorithm for solving this problem, (see Section 3), is immediate. Remark that our algorithm is finite if f or C is polyedral (see further details in [24 - 34]).

Let us now consider the particular case where $f(x) = (1/2) < x, Ax >$, (A being a symmetric positive definite matrix) and $C = \{x \in X : \|x\| \le 1\}$, the euclidean unit ball, i.e. the problem of computing the largest eigenvalue λ_M of A, $((\lambda_M)^2 = 2\lambda)$. We have then:

$$- \lambda = \inf\{\chi_C(x) - (1/2) < x, Ax >: x \in X\} \qquad (P)$$
$$- \lambda = \inf\{(1/2) < y, A^{-1}y > -\|y\| : y \in Y\} \qquad (Q)$$

We note that $P = \{x^* \in X : \|x^*\| = 1, Ax^* = \lambda_M x^*\}$ and

$$Q = \{y^* \in Y : y^* = Ax^*, x^* \in P\} \quad \text{(Cf. Theorem 2.1)}$$

Our algorithm is described as follows:

x^0 arbitrarily chosen such that $\|x^0\| = 1$

$y^k = Ax^k \to x^{k+1} = Ax^k/(\|Ax^k\|)$.

We observe that the sequence x^k defines exactly the power method (see [12]) for computing λ_M.

It follows the convergence of our algorithm towards optimal solutions of (P) and (Q):

$$x^k \to x^* \in P, \quad y^k \to y^* \in Q.$$

4.2. Convex minimization. This is the following problem

$$\lambda = \inf\{f(x) : x \in X\} \qquad (P) \qquad (f \in \Gamma_0(X))$$

which is equivalent to

$$\lambda = \inf\{f(x) + h(x) - h(x) : x \in X\} \qquad (g(x) = f(x) + h(x), \text{ where } h \in \Gamma_0(X)).$$

We are then dealing with a DCO problem (which is in fact a convex minimization problem and can then be solved). Its dual problem is:

$$\lambda = \inf\{h^*(y) - (f + g)^*(y) : y \in Y\} \qquad (Q)$$

which is a true DCO problem. The remarkable fact here is that we can solve problem (Q) in virtue of Theorem 2.1. Moreover in this case, we have under slight conditions (for instance if h is continuous on $P_|$) the following equivalent properties:

1) $0 \in \partial f(x^*)$ (i.e. $x^* \in P$)
2) $\partial h(x^*) \subset \partial g(x^*) = \partial(f + h)(x^*)$ (i.e. $x^* \in P_|$).

By consequent our algorithm furnishes optimal solutions of problems (P) and (Q). (See Theorem 3).

Let us now apply the regularization procedure to dual problem (Q), i.e. by taking $h(x) = (1/2)\|x\|^2$. Then we have:

$$\lambda = \inf\{(1/2)\|y\|^2 - (f_\nabla^* h)(y) : y \in Y\} \qquad (Q).$$

It follows from Theorem 2.1 that $P = Q$. Now look at the description of our algorithm for this problem.

x^0 arbitrarily chosen

$y^k = x^k \to x^{k+1} = \nabla(f_\nabla^* h)(x^k) = (I + \partial f)^{-1}(x^k)$.

(We recognize here the proximal mapping $(I + \partial f)^{-1}$ of f [36, 37, 42, 43]. In other words x^{k+1} is the solution of

$$\inf\{f(x) + (1/2)\|x - x^k\|^2\}.$$

Therefore, our algorithm is exactly the proximal point algorithm for solving problem (P). It is worth noting the interesting effect of regularizing dual problem (Q) on our algorithm: it leads us to regularizing proximal algorithm for solving primal problem (P).

Finally we can conclude [36, 37, 42, 43] that our algorithm converges to an optimal solution of (P) and (Q):

$$x^k \to x^*, \quad y^k \to y^*, \quad x^* = y^* \in P = Q.$$

References.

[1] Auslender, A.: *Optimisation. Méthodes numériques.* Masson, Paris 1976.

[2] Balas, E.: *Intersection cuts. An new type of cutting plane for integer programming.* Oper. Res. 19 (1971), 19 – 39.

[3] Balas, E. and Burdet, C. A.: *Maximizing a convex quadratic function subject to linear constraints.* Management Science Report N. 299, GSIA Carnegie-Mellon University, Pittsburgh, PA (1973).

[4] Benacer, R. and Pham Dinh Tao: *Etude de certains algorithmes pour la résolution d'une classe de problèmes d'optimisation non convexe.* Journées de Fermat, Mathématiques pour l'optimisation, 6-10 (1985), Toulouse, Mai 1985.

[5] Benacer, R. and Pham Dinh Tao: *Linear programs with reverse convex constraints.* Submitted to Math. Programming (1985).

[6] Benacer, R. and Pham Dinh Tao: *Two general algorithms for solving linear programs with an additional reverse convex constraint.* Submitted to Math. Programming Study (devoted to analysis and optimization of d. c. functions) edited by J. B. Hiriart-Urruty and Hoang Tuy (1985).

[7] Benacer, R.: *Contribution à l'étude des algorithmes de l'optimisation non convexe et non différentiable.* Thèse de Doctorat de Mathématiques. Université de Grenoble 1986.

[8] Benacer, R. and Pham Dinh Tao: *Global optimization of a nondefinite quadratic function over a convex polyedron.* Fermat Days 85: Mathematics for Optimization. J. B. Hiriart-Urruty (ed.) Elsevier Science Publishers B.V. (North Holland) 1986.

[9] Ellaia, R.: *Contribution à l'analyse et l'optimisation de différences de fonctions convexes.* Thèse de 3ème cycle de l'Université Paul Sabatier, 1984.

[10] Ellaia, R. and Hiriart-Urruty, J. B.: *The conjugate of the difference of convex function.* To appear in J. of Optim. Theory and Applications.

[11] Gabay, D.: *Minimizing the difference of two convex functions. Part I: Algorithms based on exact regularization.* Working paper, INRIA 1982.

[12] Gastinel, N.: *Analyse numérique linéaire.* Hermann, Paris 1966.

[13] Hillestad, R. J. and Jacobsen, S. E.: *Reverse convex programming.* Appl. Math. Optim. 6 (1980), 63 – 78.

[14] Hillestad, R. J. and Jacobsen, S. E.: *Linear programs with an additional reverse convex constraint.* Appl. Math. Optim. 6 (1980), 257 – 269.

[15] Hiriart Urruty, J. B.: *Generalized differentiability, duality and optimization for problems dealing with differences of convex functions.* Lecture Notes in Economics and Math. Systems 256 (1985), 37 – 70.

[16] Hoang Tuy: *Concave programming under linear constraints.* Dokl. Akad. Nauk SSSR 159 (1964), 32 – 35; translated Soviet Math. 5 (1964), 1437 – 1440.

[17] Hoang Tuy and Nguyen van Thoai: *Convergent algorithms for minimizing a concave function.* Oper. Res. 5, No. 4 (1980).

[18] Hoang Tuy: *Global optimization of a difference of two convex functions.* Submitted to Math. Programming Study (1985).

[19] Hoang Tuy and Ng. Q. Thai: *A conical algorithm for globally minimizing a concave function over a closed convex set.* To appear in Math. Oper. Res.

[20] Hoang Tuy: *Convex programs with an additional reverse convex constraint.* (Preprint)

[21] Hogan, W. W.: *Point-to-set maps in mathematical programming.* Working paper No. 170, Western Management Sciences Institute, University of California, Los Angeles 1981.

[22] Kelley, J. E.: *The cutting plane method for solving convex programs.* SIAM 8 (1960), 703 – 712.

[23] Majthay, A. and Whinston, A.: *Quasiconcave minimization subject to linear constraints.* Discrete Math. 9 (1974), 35 – 59.

[24] Pham Dinh Tao: *Elements homoduaux d'une matrice relatifs à un couple de normes (φ, ς). Applications au calcul de $S_{\varphi,\varsigma}(A)$.* Séminaire d'Analyse Numérique, USMG Labo IMAG, Grenoble 1975.

[25] Pham Dinh Tao: *Calcul du maximum d'une forme quadratique définie positive sur la boule unité de la norme du maximum.* Séminaire d'Analyse Numérique, USMG, Labo IMAG, Grenoble 1976.

[26] Pham Dinh Tao: *Méthodes directes et indirectes pour le calcul du maximum d'une forme quadratique définie positive sur la boule unité de la norme du maximum.* Colloque national d'Analyse Numérique (Port Bail), 1976.

[27] Pham Dinh Tao: *Contribution à la théorie de normes et ses applications à l'analyse numérique.* Thèse de Doctorat d'Etat dès Sciences, USMG, Grenoble 1981.

[28] Pham Dinh Tao: *Algorithmes de calcul du maximum d'une forme quadratique sur la boule unité de la norme du maximum.* Numer. Math. 45 (1984), 377– 440.

[30] Pham Dinh Tao: *Convergence of subgradient method for computing the bound-norm of matrices.* Linear Alg. and its Appl. 62 (1984), 163 – 182.

[31] Pham Dinh Tao: *Méthodes itératives pour le calcul des normes d'opérateurs de matrices.* A paraître dans Linear Alg. and its Appl.

[32] Pham Dinh Tao: *Subgradient methods for convex minimization over compact convex sets.* Submitted to JOTA.

[33] Pham Dinh Tao: *Algorithmes pour la résolution d'une classe de problèmes d'optimisation non convexe. Méthodes de sous-gradients.* Journées de Fermat. Mathématiques pour l'optimisation, Toulouse, 6 – 10 Mai 1985.

[34] Pham Dinh Tao and El Bernoussi Souad (1986): *Algorithms for solving a class of nonconvex optimization problems. Methods of subgradients.* Fermat Days 85: Mathematics for Optimization, J. B. Hiriart Urruty (ed.), Elsevier Science Publishers B.V. (North Holland), 1986.

[35] Rockafellar, R. T.: *Convex analysis.* Princeton University Press 1970.

[36] Rockafellar, R. T:. *Monotone operators and the proximal point algorithm.* SIAM J. Control Optim. 14 (1976), 877 – 898.

[37] Rockafellar, R. T.: *Augmented Lagrangians and the proximal point algorithm in convex programming.* Math. OR 1 (1976), 97 – 116.

[38] Selim, S. Z. and Shetty, C. M.: *Optimization of linear-convex programs.* Math. Programming 1985.

[39] Singer, I.: *A Fenchel-Rockafellar type duality theorem for maximization.* Bull. of the Austral. Math. Soc. 20 (1979), 193 – 198.

[40] Singer, I.: *Maximization of lower semi-continuous convex functionals on bounded subsets of locally convex spaces. II: Quasi-Lagrangian duality theorems.* Result. Math. 3 (1980), 235 – 248.

[41] Singer, I.: *Optimization by level set methods: Duality formulae. Optimization theory and algorithms.* Lecture notes in pure and applied mathematics 86 (1983), J. B. Hiriart Urruty, Oettli, W., Stoer, J. (eds.).

[42] Spingarn, J. E.: *Partial inverse of a monotone operator.* Appl. Math. Optim. 10 (1983), 247 – 265.

[43] Spingarn, J. E.: *Applications of the method of partial inverses to convex programming.* To appear.

[44] Topkis, D. M.: *Cutting plane methods without nested constraints sets.* Oper. Res. 18 (1970), 404 – 413.

[45] Toland, J. F.: *Duality in nonconvex optimization.* J. Math. Anal. App. 66 (1978), 399 – 415.

[46] Toland, J. F.: *On subdifferential calculus and duality in nonconvex optimization.* Bull. Soc. Math. France, Mémoire 60 (1979), 173 – 180.

[47] Toland, J. F.: *A duality principle for nonconvex optimization and the calculus of variations.* Arch. Rational Mech. Anal. 71 (1979), 41 – 61.

International Series of
Numerical Mathematics, Vol. 84
(c) 1988 Birkhäuser Verlag Basel

Solving Constrained Nonlinear Least Squares Problems by a General Purpose SQP-Method

K. Schittkowski

Mathematisches Institut

Universität Bayreuth

Universitätsstraße 30

8580 Bayreuth, West Germany

Abstract. Nonlinear least squares problems are extremely important in many domains of mathematical programming applications, e.g. maximum likelihood estimations, nonlinear data fitting or parameter estimation, respectively. A large number of
special purpose algorithms is available in the unconstrained case, but only very few
methods were developed for the nonlinearly constrained case. The paper shows that
a simple transformation of the original problem and its subsequent solution by a general purpose sequential quadratic programming algorithm retains typical features of
special purpose methods, i.e. a combination of a Gauß-Newton and a quasi-Newton
search direction. Moreover the numerical investigations indicate that the algorithm
can be implemented very easily if a suitable sequential quadratic programming code is
available, and that the numerical test results are comparable to that of special purpose
programs.

1. Introduction.

The idea to consider specific solution methods for constrained nonlinear least squares problems, was born when designing an interactive software system for mathematical programming, see Schittkowski (1985). Any programming system of this type with emphasis on nonlinear models, should contain an option for solving nonlinear least squares problems because of their practical importance. Typical applications are maximum likelihood estimation and nonlinear data fitting or parameter estimation, respectively.

The mathematical problem we want to solve is described as follows:

$$\min \frac{1}{2} F(x)^T F(x)$$

$$g_j(x) = 0, \quad j = 1, \cdots, m_e,$$

(1) $\quad x \in \mathbb{R}^n:$

$$g_j(x) \geq 0, \quad j = m_e + 1, \cdots, m,$$

$$x_l \leq x \leq x_u.$$

The function $F(x)$ is composed of l real-valued functions, i.e.

$$F(x) = (f_1(x), \cdots, f_l(x))^T,$$

and it is assumed that $f_1, \cdots, f_l$ and $g_1, \cdots, g_m$ are continuously differentiable. For practical reasons any implementation of a method solving (1), should be capable to treat simple upper and lower bounds on the variables separately.

Although many nonlinear least squares programs were developed in the past, see Hiebert (1979), for an overview and numerical comparison, the author knows of only very few programs that were written for the nonlinearly constrained case, e.g. the code NLSNIP of Lindström (1983). However, the implementation of one of these or any similar special purpose code is an additional burden, not only for the mentioned software system with respect to storage requirements and organizational reasons, but also for any other application as well, in particular if a general nonlinear programming code is available. In this paper we consider the question, how an existing nonlinear programming code of a special algorithmic class can be used to solve constrained nonlinear least squares problems in an efficient and robust way. We will see that a simple transformation of the model under consideration and solution by a sequential quadratic programming (SQP-)algorithm retains typical features of special purpose methods, i.e. the combination of a Gauß-Newton search direction with a quasi-Newton correction. Numerical test results indicate that the proposed approach is at least as efficient as the usage of special purpose methods, although the required programming effort is negligible, provided that an SQP-code is available.

The following section describes some basic features of sequential quadratic programming methods, which belong to the most efficient and reliable nonlinear programming methods we know at present for smooth and small scale problems. To understand the motivation, Section 3 summarizes basic characteristics of "typical" nonlinear least squares methods and indicates numerical difficulties we have to be aware of. The transformation of a least squares into a special nonlinear programming problem is described in Section 4. We will see how some basic features of special purpose algorithms are retained. Finally Section 5 displays numerical test results and compares them with others found in the literature.

2. Sequential quadratic programming methods.

First we introduce the abbreviation 'SQP' for sequential quadratic programming and assume that we want to solve a general nonlinear programming problem of the type

$$
\begin{aligned}
& \min f(x) \\
& x \in \mathbb{R}^n : \quad g_j(x) = 0, \quad j = 1, \cdots, m_e, \\
& \qquad\qquad g_j(x) \geq 0, \quad j = m_e + 1, \cdots, m
\end{aligned}
$$

(2)

with continuously differentiable real-valued functions f and $g_1, \cdots, g_m$. Simple upper and lower bounds on the variables are omitted now to facilitate the mathematical description.

Sequential quadratic programming methods belong to the most active research topics in nonlinear programming since a couple of years, see e.g. Stoer (1985) for a review on the theoretical background. Their excellent numerical performance was tested and compared with other methods in Schittkowski (1980), and since then they were frequently used to solve practical optimization problems particularly arising in mechanical engineering. The basic idea is to formulate and solve a quadratic programming subproblem in each iteration which is obtained by linearizing the constraints and approximating the Lagrange function

$$(3) \qquad L(x, u) := f(x) - \sum_{j=1}^{m} u_j g_j(x)$$

quadratically, where $x \in \mathbb{R}^n$, $u = (u_1, \cdots, u_m)^T \in \mathbb{R}^m$.

To formulate the quadratic programming subproblem, we proceed from given iterates $x_k \in \mathbb{R}^n$ (approximation of solution), $v_k \in \mathbb{R}^m$ (approximation of multipliers) and $B_k \in \mathbb{R}^{n \times n}$ (approximation of Hessian of Lagrange function). Then one has to solve the following quadratic programming subproblem:

$$(4) \qquad d \in \mathbb{R}^n : \begin{aligned} &\min \frac{1}{2} d^T B_k d + \nabla f(x_k)^T d \\ &\nabla g_j(x_k)^T d + g_j(x_k) = 0, \quad j = 1, \cdots, m_e, \\ &\nabla g_j(x_k)^T d + g_j(x_k) \geq 0, \quad j = m_e + 1, \cdots, m. \end{aligned}$$

Let d_k be the optimal solution and u_k the corresponding multiplier. A new iterate is obtained by

$$(5) \qquad \begin{pmatrix} x_{k+1} \\ v_{k+1} \end{pmatrix} = \begin{pmatrix} x_k \\ v_k \end{pmatrix} + \alpha_k \begin{pmatrix} d_k \\ u_k - v_k \end{pmatrix},$$

where $\alpha_k \in (0, 1]$ is a suitable steplength parameter. Although we are able to guarantee that the matrix B_k is positive definite, it is possible that (4) is not solvable due to inconsistent constraints. One possible remedy is to introduce an additional variable $\delta \in \mathbb{R}$, leading to the modified problem

$$(6) \qquad \begin{aligned} &\min \frac{1}{2} d^T B_k d + \nabla f(x_k)^T d + \rho_k \delta^2 \\ d \in \mathbb{R}^n, \quad &\nabla g_j(x_k)^T d + (1 - \delta) g_j(x_k) \begin{Bmatrix} = \\ \geq \end{Bmatrix} 0, \quad j \in J_k, \\ \delta \in \mathbb{R} : \quad &\nabla g_j(x_{k(j)})^T d + g_j(x_k) \geq 0, \quad j \in K_k, \\ &0 \leq \delta \leq 1. \end{aligned}$$

The active set J_k is given by

$$(7) \qquad J_k := \{1, \cdots, m_e\} \cup \{j : m_e < j \leq m, g_j(x_k) < \varepsilon \text{ or } u_j^{(k)} > 0\}$$

and K_k is the complement, i.e. $K_k := \{1, \cdots, m\} \setminus J_k$.

In (7), ε is any small tolerance to define the active constraints and $u_j^{(k)}$ denotes the j-th coefficient of u_k. Obviously, the point $d_0 := 0$, $\delta_0 := 1$ satisfies the linear constraints of (6) which is then always solvable. Moreover it is possible to avoid unnecessary gradient evaluations by recalculating only those gradients of restriction functions, that belong to the active set, as indicated by the index '$k(j)$'. ρ_k is a suitable penalty parameter to be chosen in dependence upon the used merit function, cf. Schittkowski (1983) for details.

The steplength parameter α_k is required in (5) to enforce global convergence of the SQP-method, i.e. the approximation of a point satisfying the necessary Kuhn-Tucker optimality conditions when starting from arbitrary initial values, e.g. a user-provided $x_0 \in R^n$ and $v_0 := 0$, $B_0 := I$. α_k should satisfy at least a sufficient decrease of a merit function $\phi_r(\alpha)$ given by

$$(8) \qquad \phi_r(\alpha) := \psi_r\left(\begin{pmatrix} x \\ v \end{pmatrix} + \alpha \begin{pmatrix} d \\ u - v \end{pmatrix}\right)$$

with a suitable penalty function $\psi_r(x, v)$. Possible choices of ψ_r are the L_1-penalty function, cf. Han (1977) and Powell (1978a), or the augmented Lagrangian function, cf. Schittkowski (1983).

Finally one has to approximate the Hessian matrix of the Lagrange function in a suitable way. To avoid calculation of second derivatives and to obtain a final superlinear convergence rate, the standard approach is to update B_k by the BFGS-quasi-Newton formula, cf. Powell (1978b) or Stoer (1985). The calculation of any new matrix B_{k+1} depends only on B_k and two vectors

$$(9) \qquad \begin{aligned} q_k &:= \nabla_x L(x_{k+1}, u_k) - \nabla_x L(x_k, u_k), \\ p_k &:= x_{k+1} - x_k, \end{aligned}$$

i.e.

$$(10) \qquad B_{k+1} := \Pi(B_k, q_k, p_k),$$

where

$$(11) \qquad \Pi(B, q, p) := B + \frac{qq^T}{q^T p} - \frac{Bpp^T B}{p^T Bp}.$$

The above formula yields a positive definite matrix B_{k+1} provided that B_k is positive definite and $q_k^T p_k > 0$. A simple modification of Powell (1978a) gives positive definite matrices even if the latter condition is violated.

We will see in the subsequent sections how one could use the SQP-method to solve constrained nonlinear least squares problems efficiently by transforming them into a general nonlinear programming problem and by exploiting their special structure.

3. Nonlinear least squares problems.

Solution methods for solving unconstrained nonlinear least squares problems

$$(12) \qquad \min \frac{1}{2} F(x)^T F(x)$$
$$x \in \mathbb{R}^n$$

with $F(x) = (f_1(x), \cdots, f_l(x))^T$ possess a long history in nonlinear programming, since these problems are extremely important in practice, e.g. in nonlinear data fitting or maximum likelihood estimation. Consequently a large number of mathematical algorithms is available for solving (12). To understand their basic features, we need the notation

$$(13) \qquad f(x) := \frac{1}{2} F(x)^T F(x)$$

for the objective function, also called the residual. Then

$$(14) \qquad \nabla f(x) = \nabla F(x) F(x)$$

defines Jacobian of the objective function with

$$\nabla F(x) := (\nabla f_1(x), \cdots, \nabla f_l(x)).$$

If we assume now that the problem functions $f_1, \cdots, f_l$ are twice continuously differentiable, we get the Hessian matrix of f by

$$(15) \qquad \nabla^2 f(x) = \nabla F(x) \nabla F(x)^T + B(x),$$

where

$$(16) \qquad B(x) := \sum_{i=1}^{l} f_i(x) \nabla^2 f_i(x).$$

Proceedings from a given iterative x_k, Newton's method can be applied to (12) to get a search direction $d_k \in \mathbb{R}^n$ by solving the linear system

$$\nabla^2 f(x_k) d + \nabla f(x_k) = 0$$

or alternatively,

$$(17) \qquad \nabla F(x_k) \nabla F(x_k)^T d + B(x_k) d + \nabla F(x_k) F(x_k) = 0.$$

By assuming now that

(18) $$F(x^*) = (f_1(x^*), \cdots, f_l(x^*))^T = 0$$

at an optimal solution x^*, i.e. that the residual $F(x)^T F(x)$ vanishes at x^*, one could neglect the matrix $B(x_k)$ in (17), cf. (16). Then (17) defines the normal equations of the linear least squares problem

(19) $$\min \| \bigtriangledown F(x_k)^T d + F(x_k) \|,$$
$$d \in \mathbb{R}^n$$

and a new iterate is obtained by $x_{k+1} := x_k + \alpha_k d_k$, where d_k is a solution of (19) and where α_k denotes a suitable steplength parameter. It is obvious that a quadratic convergence rate is achieved when starting sufficiently close to an optimal solution. The above calculation of a search direction is known as the Gauß-Newton method and represents the traditional way to solve nonlinear least squares problems.

However, difficulties arise when we want to solve problems with a large residual, i.e. if $F(x^*)^T F(x^*)$ is not sufficiently small relative e.g. to $\| \bigtriangledown F(x^*) \|$. Numerous proposals have been made in the past to deal with this situation, and it is outside the scope of this paper to give a review on all possible attempts developed in the last 20 years. Only a few remarks are presented to illustrate basic features of the main approaches, for further review see Gill, Murray and Wright (1981), Ramsin and Wedin (1977) or Dennis (1977).

A straight-forward idea is to replace $B(x_k)$ in (17) by any quasi-Newton-matrix B_k, cf. e.g. Dennis (1973). But some additional safeguards are necessary to deal with indefinite matrices $\bigtriangledown F(x_k) \bigtriangledown F(x_k)^T + B_k$ in order to get a descent direction. A modified algorithm was proposed by Gill and Murray (1978), where B_k is either equal to $B(x_k)$, a second order approximation of $B(x_k)$, or a quasi-Newton-matrix. In this case a diagonal matrix is added to $\bigtriangledown F(x_k) \bigtriangledown F(x_k)^T + B_k$ to obtain a positive definite matrix. Lindström (1982) proposed a combination of a Gauß-Newton and a Newton method by using a certain subspace minimization. If however, the residual is too large then there is no possibility to exploit the special structure, and a general unconstrained minimization algorithm, e.g. a quasi-Newton method, can be applied.

4. Solving constrained nonlinear least squares problems by a general purpose SQP-method.

Despite of the difficulties outlined in the previous section, a lot of efficient special purpose computer programs are available to solve unconstrained nonlinear least squares problems, and there is no specific need to add another implementation. However, the situation changes if we want to solve a constrained nonlinear least squares problem of the type (1). A combination of an SQP-method with an approach discussed in the previous section was proposed by Mahdavi-Amiri (1981) in his dissertation, which contains also numerical test results. Lindström (1983) developed a similar method based on an active set idea leading to equality constrained linear least squares problems. Numerical results are presented and the corresponding computer program is distributed on request. But any other algorithms are not known to the author.

On the other hand, a couple of codes were developed and distributed in the last years which are based on the SQP-method described in Section 2, or any similar variant, see VFO2AD (Powell, 1978a), NLPQL (Schittkowski, 1984), NPSOL (Gill, Murray, Saunders, Wright, 1983) for instance. Since most nonlinear least squares problems are ill-conditioned, it is less senseful to solve (1) directly by a general nonlinear programming method. But we will see in this section that a simple transformation of the original problem and its subsequent solution by an SQP-method retains typical features of a special purpose code and prevents the need to take care of any negative eigenvalues of an approximated Hessian matrix. The corresponding computer program can be implemented in a few lines provided that an SQP-algorithm is available.

The transformation is performed by introducing l additional variables $y = (y_1, \cdots, y_l)^T$ and l additional equality constraints of the form

$$(20) \qquad f_i(x) - y_i = 0, \quad i = 1, \cdots, l.$$

First we consider only the unconstrained least squares problem (12). Taking nonlinear constraints and bounds on the variables into account is straightforward and will be discussed subsequently. Then the equivalent transformed problem is

$$(21) \qquad \binom{x}{y} \in \mathbb{R}^{n+l} : \quad \begin{array}{c} \min \dfrac{1}{2} y^T y \\[2ex] F(x) - y = 0. \end{array}$$

We consider now (21) as a general nonlinear programming problem of the form

$$(22) \qquad \overline{x} \in \mathbb{R}^{\overline{n}} \quad \begin{array}{c} \min \overline{f}(\overline{x}) \\[2ex] \overline{g}(\overline{x}) = 0 \end{array}$$

with $\overline{n} := n + l$, $\overline{x} := \binom{x}{y}$, $\overline{f}(\overline{x}) := \frac{1}{2} y^T y$, $\overline{g}(\overline{x}) := F(x) - y$, and apply the SQP-method derived in Section 2. The quadratic programming subproblem is

$$(23) \qquad \overline{d} \in \mathbb{R}^{\overline{n}} : \quad \begin{array}{c} \min \dfrac{1}{2} \overline{d}^T \overline{B}_k \overline{d} + \nabla \overline{f}(\overline{x}_k)^T \overline{d} \\[2ex] \nabla \overline{g}(\overline{x}_k)^T \overline{d} + \overline{g}(\overline{x}_k) = 0 \end{array}$$

where a bar is used to avoid confusion with the notation of Section 2. In (23) $\overline{x}_k = \begin{pmatrix} x_k \\ y_k \end{pmatrix}$ is a given iterate and

$$(24) \qquad \overline{B}_k = \begin{pmatrix} B_k : C_k \\ C_k^T : D_k \end{pmatrix}$$

a given approximation of the Hessian of the Lagrange function $L(\overline{x}, u)$ of (22) defined by

$$(25) \qquad \begin{aligned} L(\overline{x}, u) &= \overline{f}(\overline{x}) - u^T \, \overline{g}(\overline{x}) \\ &= \frac{1}{2} y^T y - u^T (F(x) - y). \end{aligned}$$

Since

$$(26) \qquad \nabla L(\overline{x}, u) = \begin{pmatrix} - \nabla F(x) u \\ y + u \end{pmatrix}$$

and

$$(27) \qquad \nabla_{\overline{x}}^2 L(\overline{x}, u) = \begin{pmatrix} B(x) & : & 0 \\ 0 & : & I \end{pmatrix}$$

with

$$(28) \qquad B(x) := - \sum_{i=1}^{l} u_i \, \nabla^2 \, f_i(x),$$

it seems to be reasonable to proceed now from a quasi-Newton matrix given by

$$(29) \qquad \overline{B}_k := \begin{pmatrix} B_k & : & 0 \\ 0 & : & I \end{pmatrix}$$

where $B_k \in \mathbb{R}^{n \times n}$ denotes a suitable positive definite approximation of $B(x)$. Inserting this $\overline{B}_k$ into (23) gives the equivalent quadratic programming subproblem

$$(30) \qquad \begin{pmatrix} d \\ e \end{pmatrix} \in \mathbb{R}^{n+1} \qquad \begin{aligned} &\min \frac{1}{2} d^T B_k d + \frac{1}{2} e^T e + y_k^T e \\[2mm] &\nabla F(x_k)^T d - e + F(x_k) - y_k = 0 \end{aligned}$$

where we replaced $\overline{d}$ by $\begin{pmatrix} d \\ e \end{pmatrix}$. Some simple calculations show that (30) is equivalent to the linear system

$$(31) \qquad \nabla F(x_k) \nabla F(x_k)^T d + B_k d + \nabla F(x_k) F(x_k) = 0.$$

This equation is identical with (17), if $B_k = B(x_k)$, and we obtain the following lemma.

(4.1) Lemma: Assume that for a given iterate $x_k \in \mathbb{R}^n$, an SQP-iteration is performed with $B_k = B(x_k)$, $B(x)$ defined by (16) and $\overline{B}_k$ decomposed in the form (29). Then we obtain a Newton-step for solving the least squares problem (12).

Note that $B(x)$ defined by (16) and $B(x)$ defined by (28) coincide at an optimal solution of (12), since $F(x_k) = y_k = -u_k$, cf. (26). Moreover the SQP-method can be applied to (22) in a way that the used quasi-Newton-matrices $\overline{B}_k$ are always positive definite, and consequently also the matrix B_k defined by (24). Therefore we omit numerical difficulties imposed by negative eigenvalues as found in the usual approaches for solving (12).

When starting the SQP-method one could proceed from a user-provided initial guess x_0 for the variables and define

(32)
$$y_0 := F(x_0),$$
$$B_0 := \begin{pmatrix} \mu I & : & 0 \\ 0 & : & I \end{pmatrix} \begin{matrix} \}n \\ \}l \end{matrix} \,,$$

so that the initial point $\overline{x}_0$ is feasible. The choice of B_0 satisfies condition (29) and allows a user to provide some information on the estimated size of the residual, if available. If he knew that the residual $F(x^*)^T F(x^*)$ is close to zero at the optimal solution x^*, he could choose a small μ in (32). At least in the first iterates, the search directions calculated by (31) are very similar to the traditional Gauß-Newton direction obtained by (17). Otherwise a user could define $\mu := 1$, if a large residual is expected.

There remains the question, whether the assumption that $\overline{B}_k$ is decomposed in the form (29), can be satisfied at least approximately in the neighbourhood of a solution.

(4.2) Lemma: Assume that an iterate $x_k \in \mathbb{R}^n$, and a positive definite matrix $B_k \in \mathbb{R}^{n \times n}$ are given. Let an SQP-iteration be performed with steplength $\alpha_k = 1$, $\overline{B}_k$ be defined by (29) and $\overline{B}_k$ be updated by the BFGS-formula (11). If $(d_k, e_k) \neq 0$ and

(33)
$$\nabla F(x_{k+1})(\nabla F(x_k)^T d_k + F(x_k)) = 0,$$

then $\overline{B}_{k+1}$ is well-defined, i.e. $\overline{p}_k^T \overline{q}_k > 0$, and $\overline{B}_{k+1}$ is of the form (29).

The proof follows directly from the quasi-Newton-formula and the optimality conditions of the quadratic programming subproblem (30), in our case

$$B_k d_k - \nabla F(x_k) u_k = 0,$$
$$e_k + y_k + u_k = 0,$$
$$\nabla F(x_k)^T d_k + F(x_k) = e_k + y_k(= -u_k).$$

Assumption (33) of Lemma (4.2) is never satisfied in practice, but seems to be reasonable, since the intention is to find an $x^* \in \mathbb{R}^n$ with

$$\nabla F(x^*)F(x^*) = 0,$$

and $\nabla F(x_k)^T d_k + F(x_k)$ is a Taylor approximation of $F(x_{k+1})$. Note also that the usual way to derive Newton's method is to assume that the optimality condition is satisfied for a certain linearization of a given iterate x_k, and to use this linearized system for obtaining a new iterate.

It is now very easy to take nonlinear constraints into account. Then the following transformed problem is to be solved by an SQP-method:

(34) $\qquad \begin{pmatrix} x \\ y \end{pmatrix} \in \mathbb{R}^{n+1} :$
$$\min \frac{1}{2} y^T y$$
$$f_i(x) - y_i = 0, \ i = 1, \cdots, l,$$
$$g_j(x) = 0, \ j = 1, \cdots, m_e,$$
$$g_j(x) \geq 0, \ j = m_e + 1, \cdots, m,$$
$$x_l \leq x \leq x_u,$$

where $y = (y_1, \cdots, y_l)^T$. In this case the quadratic programming subproblem is of the kind

(35) $\qquad \begin{pmatrix} d \\ e \end{pmatrix} \in \mathbb{R}^{n+1} :$
$$\min \frac{1}{2}(d^T : e^T) \quad \overline{B}_k \begin{pmatrix} d \\ e \end{pmatrix} + y_k^T e$$
$$\nabla f_i(x_k)^T d - e_i \ + f_i(x_k) - y_i^{(k)} = 0, \ i = 1, \cdots, l,$$
$$\nabla g_j(x_k)^T d \quad + g_j(x_k) \qquad = 0, \ j = 1, \cdots, m_e,$$
$$\nabla g_j(x_k)^T d \quad + g_j(x_k) \qquad \geq 0, \ j = m_e + 1, \cdots, m,$$
$$x_l - x_k \leq d \leq x_u - x_k.$$

(35) is identical with (4) besides of the additionally introduced bounds for the variables. It is however possible to simplify (35) by substituting

$$e = \nabla F(x_k)^T d + F(x_k) - y_k,$$

so that the quadratic programming subproblem depends on only n variables and m constraints. This is an important observation from the numerical point of view, since the computational effort to solve (35), reduces from the order of $(n + 1)^3$ to n^3, and the remaining computations in the outer SQP-frame are in the order of $(n + 1)^2$. Therefore the computational work envolved in the proposed least squares algorithm, is very roughly comparable with that required by special purpose methods mentioned in the beginning of this section.

When performing the above substitution one has to be aware that the quadratic programming subproblem might be expanded by an additional variable δ, cf. (6), so that some safeguards are required. Besides of this limitation, the proposed transformation (34) is independent from the used variant of the SQP-method, so that any available code could be used in form of a 'black box'.

In principle, one could use the starting points proposed in (32). Numerical experience suggests, however, to use the initial point $y_0 := F(x_0)$ only if the constraints are satisfied in x_0, i.e. if

$$g_j(x_0) = 0, \quad j = 1, \cdots, m_e,$$
$$g_j(x_0) \geq 0, \quad j = m_e + 1, \cdots, m.$$

In all other cases it is proposed to proceed from $y_0 := 0$.

A final remark concerns the theoretical convergence of the algorithm. Since the original problem is transformed into a general nonlinear programming problem, we can apply all convergence results known for SQP-methods. If an augmented Lagrange function is prefered for formulating the merit function, a global convergence theorem is found in Schittkowski (1983), which states that starting from an arbitrary initial value, a Kuhn-Tucker-point is approximated, i.e. a point satisfying the necessary optimality conditions. If, on the other hand, an iterate is sufficiently close to an optimal solution and if the steplength is one, then the convergence speed of the algorithm is superlinear, cf. Powell (1978b). This theorem explains the fast final convergence rate one observes in practice. The assumptions on the problem functions are standard and are also required by any special purpose algorithm in the one or other form. But in our case we do not need any regularity condition for the functions $f_1, \cdots, f_l$, i.e. the assumption that the matrix $\bigtriangledown F(x_k)$ is of full rank, to adapt the mentioned convergence results to the least squares case. The reason is found in the special form of the quadratic programming subproblem (35), since the first l constraints are linearly independent and are also independent from the remaining restrictions.

5. Numerical test results.

The proposed nonlinear least squares algorithm was implemented and tested on a VAX 11/780 in double precision FORTRAN. The corresponding nonlinear programming problem was solved by subroutine NLPQL of Schittkowski (1984). Two sets of unconstrained and constrained test problems were defined. The problems were found in Gill, Murray (1978) and Lindström (1983), respectively. The software system EMP of Schittkowski (1985) was used to write the source programs, to execute the codes and to process the results. Gradients were determined either analytically (for 'simple' functions) or numerically (for 'difficult' functions) for simplicity.

Table 1 contains some characteristic data of the unconstrained test problems of Gill and Murray (1978), i.e. the number of variables n, the number of experiments l and the residual $f(x^*)$ at the optimal solutions. Moreover the table contains the number of iterations nit and the number of function evaluations nf for the proposed transformation method and the quasi-Newton variant of the least squares algorithm investigated by Gill and Murray (1978).

In a similar way the numerical results for the constrained least squares test problem set are displayed. In addition, Table 2 contains the number m_e of equality constraints and the total number m of all constraints. A function call nf means execution of all l objective function terms $f_1, \cdots, f_l$ and of all m constraints $g_1, \cdots, g_m$. The gradient evaluation ndf stands for calculation of l objective fucntion gradients $\nabla f_1, \cdots, \nabla f_l$ and at least a subset of the constraint gradients $\nabla g_1, \cdots, \nabla g_m$, since an active set strategy is performed in NLPQL. The test results presented by Lindström (1983) were interpreted in a similar way and are also shown in Table 2. His algorithm, however, requires the calculation of Hessian matrices in certain situations either analytically or by numerical approximation. Thus an additional column headed by nhf is included in Table 2 that shows the corresponding figures. Problem numbers with '*' indicate a feasible starting point.

A reader should interpret the presented numerical test results very carefully. They were obtained on different hardware and software environments, i.e. on different machines and with different test programs. Moreover, a direct comparison of an algorithm using second derivatives with another one using only first derivatives, is nearly impossible. These tests were not intended to show the superiority of one algorithm over some others, since we have seen that there are some common mathematical ideas behind all three approaches. The main purpose of this paper is to show that a simple and easily implemented transformation of a least squares problem into a general nonlinear programming problem and its solution by an SQP-method leads to an algorithm, which is at least as efficient and reliable as some known special purpose codes. If a SQP-based subroutine is available, the required programming effort is negligible compared with the work to be done otherwise.

Test problem	n	l	$f(z^*)$	Gill, Murray (1978) nf	nit	Transformation method nf	nit
Rosenbrock	2	2	.0	31	12	3	3
Helix	3	3	.0	14	11	2	1
Singular	4	4	.0	14	13	9	9
Woods	9	7	.0	73	54	18	18
Zangwill	3	3	.0	2	1	5	5
Engvall	3	5	.0	15	9	29	20
Branin	2	2	.0	2	1	2	2
Beale	2	3	.0	14	7	12	11
Cragg, Levy	4	5	.0	15	13	11	11
Box	3	10	.0	5	4	5	5
Freudenstein, Roth	2	2	.0	27	18	14	9
Watson	6	31	$.26 \cdot 10^{-2}$	23	20	7	6
Watson	9	31	$.14 \cdot 10^{-5}$	6	5	6	6
Watson	20	31	$.24 \cdot 10^{-10}$	5	4	5	5
Davidson	4	20	$.86 \cdot 10^{+5}$	57	35	44	27
Bard	3	15	$.82 \cdot 10^{-2}$	9	8	6	6
Jennich, Sampson	2	10	$.12 \cdot 10^{+3}$	45	22	26	19
Kowalik, Osborne	4	11	$.31 \cdot 10^{-3}$	21	18	11	8
Osborne 1	5	33	$.55 \cdot 10^{-4}$	23	11	17	11
Osborne 2	11	65	$.40 \cdot 10^{-1}$	32	23	32	23
Madsen	2	3	.77	24	22	11	11
Total				457	311	275	216

Table 1: Numerical test results for unconstrained problems

Test problem	n	l	m_e	m	$f(z^*)$	Lindström (1983) nf	ndf	nhf	Transformation method nf	ndf
1	4	9	2	2	$.21 \cdot 10^{-3}$	8	7	2	8	7
3*	5	4	3	3	.0	10	9	0	13	12
3	5	4	3	3	.0	9	9	0	12	12
4*	5	4	2	2	.0	13	13	0	14	12
5*	2	2	1	1	$.45 \cdot 10^{+2}$	5	5	3	12	10
6	3	5	2	2	$.48 \cdot 10^{+3}$	27	3	0	30	19
7*	4	4	0	3	$.18 \cdot 10^{+2}$	28	15	1	11	9
8	7	9	0	4	$.38 \cdot 10^{+3}$	55	25	1	15	12
Total						155	86	7	115	93

Table 2: Numerical test results for constrained problems

References.

Dennis, J. E., Jr. (1973): *Some computational technique for the nonlinear least squares problem*. In: Numerical solution of systems of nonlinear algebraic equations, G. D. Byrne, C. A. Hall (eds.), Academic Press, London, New York.

Dennis, J. E., Jr. (1977): *Nonlinear least squares*. In: The state of the art in numerical analysis, D. Jacobs (ed.), Academic Press, London, New York.

Gill, P. E. and Murray, W. (1978): *Algorithms for the solution of the nonlinear least-squares problem*. SIAM Journal on Numerical Analysis 15 (1978), 977 – 992.

Gill, P. E., Murray, W. and Wright, M. H. (1981): *Practical optimization*. Academic Press, London, New York, Toronto, Sydney, San Francisco.

Gill, P. E., Murray, W., Saunders, M. and Wright, M. H. (1983): *User's Guide for SQL/NPSOL: A Fortran package for nonlinear programming*. Report SOL 83-12, Dept. of Operations Research, Stanford University, California.

Han, S.-P. (1976): *Superlinearly convergent variable metric algorithms for general nonlinear programming problems*. Mathematical Programming 11 (1976), 263 – 282.

Han, S.-P. (1977): *A globally convergent method for nonlinear programming*. Journal of Optimization Theory and Applications 22 (1977), 297 – 309.

Hiebert, K. (1979): *A comparison of nonlinear least squares software*. Sandia Technical Report SAND 79-0483, Sandia National Laboratories, Albuquerque, New Mexico.

Lindström, P. (1982): *A stabilized Gauß-Newton algorithm for unconstrained nonlinear least squares problems*. Report UMINF-102.82, Institute of Information Processing, University of Umea, Umea, Schweden.

Lindström, P. (1983): *A general purpose algorithm for nonlinear least squares problems with nonlinear constraints*. Report UMINF-103.83, Institute of Information Processing, University of Umea, Umea, Schweden.

Mahdavi-Amiri, N. (1981): *Generalized constrained nonlinear least squares and generating nonlinear programming test problems: Algorithm approach*. Dissertation, The John Hopkins University, Baltimore, Maryland/USA.

Powell, M. J. D. (1978a): *A fast algorithm for nonlinearly constrained optimization calculations*. In: Numerical Analysis, G. A. Watson (ed.), Lecture Notes in Mathematics 630 (1978), Springer, Berlin, Heidelberg, New York.

Powell, M. J. D. (1978b): *The convergence of variable metric methods for nonlinearly constrained optimization calculations*. In: Nonlinear Programming 3, O. L. Mangasarian, R. R. Meyer, S. M. Robinson (eds.), Academic Press, New York, San Francisco, London.

Ramsin, H. and Wedin, P. A. (1977): *A comparison of some algorithms for the nonlinear least-squares problems.* Nordisk Tidstr. Informationsbehandlung (BIT) 17 (1977), 72 – 90.

Schittkowski, K. (1980): *Nonlinear programming codes.* Lecture Notes in Economics and Mathematical Systems 183 (1980), Springer, Berlin, Heidelberg, New York.

Schittkowski, K. (1983): *On the convergence of a sequential quadratic programming method with an augmented Lagrangian search direction.* Mathematische Operationsforschung und Statistik, Ser. Optimization 14 (1983), 197 – 216.

Schittkowski, K. (1984): *NLPQL: A FORTRAN subroutine solving constrained nonlinear programming problems.* Submitted for publication.

Schittkowski, K. (1985): *EMP: A software system supporting the numerical solution of mathematical programming problems.* Report, Mathematisches Institut, Universität Bayreuth, Bayreuth, Germany, F. R.

Stoer, J. (1985): *Foundations of recursive quadratic programming methods for solving nonlinear programs.* In: Computational Mathematical Programming (K. Schittkowski, ed.), NATO ASI Series, Series F: Computer and Systems Sciences 15 (1985), Springer, Berlin, Heidelberg, New York, Tokyo.

International Series of
Numerical Mathematics, Vol. 84
(c) 1988 Birkhäuser Verlag Basel

New Algorithms in Convex Programming Based on a Notion of "Centre" (for Systems of Analytic Inequalities) and on Rational Extrapolation

Gy. Sonnevend
Dept. of Numerical Analysis, Inst. of Math.
Eötvös University
Muzeum krt. 6-8
10.88. Budapest, Hungaria

Abstract. With the aim of providing new algorithmic tools for assuring good, global convergence properties for methods solving convex programming problems, we present some results and proposals concerning: 1.) a new, homotopy method for solving linear (convex, analytic) programming problems; 2.) global rational extrapolation (approximation) as a tool (combined with suitable analytic homotopies) for path following (e.g. solving analytic systems equations for saddle points). While introducing these tools we emphasize the importance of the use of "global" and "analytic" tools (in contrast to the use of "local" notions and "nondifferentiable" objects): from this (rather general) perspective a linear (convex, analytic) programming problem should be regarded as a "nondifferentiable" one only if the number of constraints is much higher than the number of variables.

Key words: Convex programming, linear programming, ellipsoidal approximations, an analytic centre for linear inequalities, rational (global) extrapolation for path following, globalization of Newton's method.

Abbreviated title: (for running heads): New methods in convex programming.

Introduction

Increasing importance has been given to the algorithmic aspects of convex analysis with the advance of fast (efficient) computers and, of course, with the increasing demand for the more accurate, fast and stable solution of large scale (high dimensional) optimization problems. The most difficult problems (of efficiency) of the existing general purpose algorithms are surely those concerning *global* "behaviour" (i.e. global convergence speed from arbitrary initial "approximations") and *stability* with respect to errors in the data and rounding errors during the computation. Here we have to specify: in concrete cases the main problem might well consist in exploiting the special structure of the problem (which allows a reduction of dimension, memory size or provides good initial guess for the solution); in this paper we are interested in problems for constructing general purpose algorithms (tools for them) even if we believe that further progress will mainly consist in finding – for new *subclasses* of problems – new "optimal" (for these subclasses) algorithms.

In fact one of the outcome of our study is already a new "classification" of linear (or more generally of convex, analytic) programming problems. In order to outline this we note first that the *"local"* aspects of algorithms – concerning various types of superlinear, n-step quadratic etc. convergence of quasi-Newton or sequential quadratic programming methods in the "smooth" case, or finite termination for cutting plane or bundle methods in the "nonsmooth", say, "piecewise linear" case – have been studied and understood fairly well. On the other hand the problems of global behaviour (convergence rate) of the proposed methods are less well understood, in fact the need for new "globalization" methods – which would assure better global convergence – has been felt for quite a long time. The reason for the better understanding of the local convergence problem is simple: there is a sufficiently well developed theory of *local* notions and models like (sub)gradient, normal cone, Hessian, quadratic and piecewise linear models, ... The aspects of global behaviour, obviously, require the use of results of global (convex) analysis, for which a "theory" does not exist, even if many, already known material in books like [2] will be useful for such a theory. The ellipsoid method was the first method where the existence of a *global* bound on the convergence rate is proved by using a theorem from the real m of global convex analysis (concerning the minimal volume of ellipsoids containing one half of a given ellipsoid). The earlier method of centers of gravity (see [10] for a accelerated version of it) could not be regarded as an acceptable method (algorithm) because of the lack of simple (arithmetically low cost) implementation. It should be noted however that the latter method is near to "optimal" (somewhat loosely speaking) under the conditions that the unknown function to be minimized is just convex and the computation of one of its value and subgradient – at an arbitrary point – is very expensive. There are rather nontrivial payoff relations between arithmetical complexity, stability and speed of convergence of a method, these will be dealt with (only partially) below.

When we treat the minimization problem (say for a single analytic, convex function) as an "approximation" problem, then the "nonexistence" of a global theory is apparent from the fact that the currently available "fast" methods are using, in general, no more than a *local* quadratic model for the function; in other words these methods are not able to exploit that the function to be minimized is analytic (i.e. not only C^3 smooth). Now in classical analysis the most strong results of global approximation have been attained in the theory of analytic functions. Analytic continuation and extrapolation (by *rational functions*) will be the tools we are going to "introduce" to numerical convex analysis. The notion of a *suitably* constructed *homotopy* will be also an important ingredient of the proposed methods.

With these aims in mind we can think about the linear programming problem

$$(1.1) \qquad \min\{<c,x> \mid <a_i,x> \leq b_i, \ i=1,\cdots,m, \ x \in R^n\},$$

as a convex, analytic problem (when m is not too large), expressing the fact that an analytic, convex function is to be minimized on a set described by a finite set of analytic, convex inequalities:

$$(1.2) \qquad \min\{f_0(x) \mid f_i(x) \leq 0, \ i=1,\cdots,m, \ x \in R^n\}.$$

Of course, the linearity of the functions $f_0, f_1, \cdots, f_m$ makes (1.1) very much different from (i.e. more easy than) (1.2), the two classes of problems (1.1) and (1.2) have been put in the same class ("category") because – at first approximation in (1.2) – our aim might be only to exploit analyticity and convexity.

The problem, where $f_0(x) = \max\{f_{0,j}(x) \mid j=1,\cdots,r\}$, $r \geq 1$, where the functions $f_{0,j}$, $j=1,\cdots,r$ are convex and analytic should not be dealt with as if we had a non-differentiable cost function f_0, but by introducing the convex constraints $f_{0,j}(x) \leq \lambda$, $j=1,\cdots,r$ and the cost function $\lambda \equiv f_0^{new}(x,\lambda)$, so that a convex, analytic problem is obtained.

We shall deal in Section 2, mainly with the basic problem (1.1), in fact with the more fundamental problem of "solving" and "approximating" a given system of linear inequalities: for given $a_1,\cdots,a_m \in R^n$ and $b_1,\cdots,b_m \in R^1$, find a solution

$$(1.3) \qquad x(a^m,b^m) \in P(a^m,b^m) = \{z \mid <a_i,z> \leq b_i, \ i=1,\cdots,m, \ z \in \mathbb{R}^n\}$$

and an ellipsoid $E(a^m,b^m) = \{z \mid <Bz,z> \leq 1\}$, $B \in R^{n \times n}$ such that

$$x(a^m,b^m) + E(a^m,b^m) \subseteq P(a^m,b^m) \subseteq x(a^m,b^m) + \rho E(a^m,b^m),$$

holds, where ρ is a possibly small and independent of (a^m,b^m) number, while $x(a^m,b^m)$ and $E(a^m,b^m)$ (that is the parameters of B) are easily computable and stable functions of the data (a^m,b^m). Here a^m stands for $(a_1,a_2,\cdots,a_m)$ and b^m for $(b_1,\cdots,b_m)$. Note that the "dual" problem to (1.3) is to construct – if it exists – a hyperplane which separates a given point from the convex hull of a finite number of given points, this finds application e.g. in bundle (ε-subgradient) methods, see below.

We said that the above is the fundamental problem, because the optimization problem (1.2) can be reduced to the feasibility problem (i.e. the problem (1.1) to (1.3)) by considering the one-parameter family of feasibility problems:

$$(1.5) \qquad f_0^* = \min\{\lambda \mid \exists x \in R^n, f_0(x) \leq \lambda, \ f_i(x) \leq 0, \ i=1,\cdots,m\}.$$

In order that this reduction be implementable – at least for the case of linear functions $f_1,\cdots,f_m$ – we need such solution $x(a^m,b^m)$ which can be easily updated when we add or change (by changing λ) one of the constraints: here the inequality $\lambda \geq < c, x >$. This means – in other words – that the homotopy path $x(\lambda) := x(a^m, c, b^m, \lambda)$, $\lambda \geq f_0^*$, leading to a solution of (1.2) should be easy to follow numerically.

While piecewise linear homotopies for the solution of linear programming (and some "complementarity") problems have been proposed long ago, see e.g. Lemke's algorithm, we emphasize that here we propose an analytic, very smooth homotopy. In fact our method for solving (1.1) is related to the interior point methods proposed in [5], [6] and to the "classical" method of logarithmic penalty (barrier) functions; a very important point is that $x(a^m, b^m)$, being an interior, "central" point of $P(a^m, b^m)$ depends not on the polyhedron $P(a^m, b^m)$ – like the center of gravity of $P(a^m, b^m)$ – but on the parameters (a^m, b^m) being an affine invariant analytic function of the latter; notice that the center of gravity of $P(a^m, b^m)$ is only piecewise smooth in (a^m, b^m) but allows to obtain a more tight ellipsoidal approximation $\rho \leq n$, while for our "analytic" ellipsoid $E(a^m, b^m)$ only $\rho \leq m - 1$ is guaranteed.

The requirement of the existence of an easily computable and possibly tight ellipsoidal approximation – while natural in itself say for solving – approximately – some control problems for linear dynamical systems with bounded controls and disturbances, under linear inequality state constraints – will be further motivated in Section 3 where we show that for the general nonsmooth convex programming problem – when reduced to the minimization of an arbitrary convex function – such ellipsoidal approximations allow to construct nice algorithms, which can be regarded as improved versions of the graph ellipsoid method proposed in [10].

One way to explain this briefly is to note that for a linear programming problem with many constraints $m >> n$ it is better not to "generate" all constraints – as in the above continuation algorithm or in Karmarkar's method – but to consider them in some order, say, always including the one mostly violated and drop any of them if an ellipsoidal approximation of the "current feasible set" shows, i.e. guarantees, that it will not be active at the optimum.

Since we are interested in large scale problems, it is instructive to look to infinite dimensional analogons of the above problems. For the feasibility problem (1.3), the proposed "analytic centre" solution $x(a^m, b^m)$ corresponds to the following solution $\overline{\mu}$ of a generalized moment problem

$$(1.6) \quad \sup\{\int_S \log \mu'(s)ds \,|\, c_i = \int_S K(t_i, s)\mu'(s)ds, \, i = 1, \cdots, p, \, \mu'(s) \geq 0, \text{ a.e. on } S\}$$

here $K(.,.)$ is a given kernel function, c_i are fixed results of measurements, they are the "generalized moments" of an unknown positive mass distribution and by the above extremum problem a special solution (mass distribution) is selected. What is rather reassuring is that, for the important case of Nevanlinna-Pick type interpolation (moment) problems, including the classical polynomial and trigonometric moment problems, the solution of (1.6) $\overline{\mu}'$ – for arbitrarily given nodes t^p and c^p – can be exactly computed by solving a linear equation with a $(p \times p)$ Toeplitz matrix, i.e. in $0(p^2)$ arithmetical operations, see [9].

Moreover the solution density function, $\bar{\mu}'$, is here a *rational* function of the "variables" c^n. This is interesting for us since it supports our belief that the analytic centre $x(a^m, b^m)$ is one of the most smooth solution – i.e. the most simply updatable one – of the inequality system (a^m, b^m) and in this context it is interesting to note that the minimal support, atomic solutions of the Nevanlinna-Pick type moment problems (analogons of the gaussian quadrature formula) and geometrically: special extreme points of the polyhedron, $P(t^p, c^p)$, corresponding to the data, cannot be computed so simply: in order to compute them we have to solve – at best – an eigenvalue problem for a $(k \times k)$ symmetric matrix when $p = 2k$, see [9]. Of course, with the last remark we argued in favour of our method for solving the linear programming problem as constrasted to simplex-type methods which work with extreme points of $P(a^m, b^m)$. A further point in favour of working with the analytic centre is that being an interior point – in fact a "central" solution – which is a smooth function of the data, it is more *stable* with respect to perturbations of the data (a^m, b^m), than any of the conceivable extreme point solutions. Our "conjecture" is that the function $x(\lambda) := x(a^m, c, b^m, \lambda)$ – for arbitrary a^m, b^m and c – can be well approximated by rational functions.

In section 4 we present a new method for solving an equation for saddle points

$$(1.7) \qquad\qquad g(x, y) = 0,$$

where g is an analytic vector function $R^{q \times r} \to R^{q \times r}$, being the gradient of a function F, which is convex in x and concave in y. By a suitable homotopy and increasing order rational extrapolation we obtain a new method of globalization for Newton's method which more fully exploits the smoothness (analyticity) of g than the other known methods (based on line search or on trust regions, see [1]).

It will be shown that a particular case of the proposed method – for the case of a linear function g – has deep connection (is identical) with the method of conjugate gradients.

2. A method for linear programming using continuation rational extrapolation along analytic centres

In [8] we introduced a special solution, the "analytic centre" $x(a^m, b^m)$ of a system of linear inequalities $\{a^m, b^m\}$, see (1.3) and studied some of the properties of this solution and of an associated ellipsoidal approximation for $P(a^m, b^m)$. We summarize the main points as follows.

Given (a^m, b^m) – for which $P(a^m, b^m)$ is bounded and has a nonempty interior in $R^n - x(a^m, b^m)$ is defined as the solution of the following "convex, analytic" problem

$$(2.1) \qquad\qquad \max\{\prod_{i=1}^{m} |b_i - \,<a_i, x>\,|\,x \in P(a^m, b^m)\}.$$

(2.1) has a unique solution which solves the equation

$$(2.2) \qquad \frac{\partial}{\partial x} \log \psi(x) = \sum_{i=1}^{m} \frac{a_i}{b_i - \langle a_i, x \rangle} = 0,$$

the concave – on $P(a^m, b^m)$ – function to be maximized, $\log \psi$, has an algebraically simple Hessian

$$(2.3) \qquad D^2 \log \psi(z) = \sum_{i=1}^{m} a_i a_i^* (b_i - \langle a_i, z \rangle)^{-2}.$$

Defining the linear map $L : R^m \to R^n$ by $Le_i = a_i(b_i - \langle a_i, \bar{x} \rangle)^{-1}$, where $\bar{x} = x(a^m, b^m)$ and an ellipsoid

$$(2.4) \qquad E(a^m, b^m) := (m-1)\{z | \langle Bz, z \rangle \leq 1\}, \; B := ((m-1)m)^{-1} LL^*,$$

the relations in (1.4) hold with $\rho = m - 1$. Both $x(a^m, b^m)$ and $E(a^m, b^m)$ are invariant under affine transformations of the data, i.e. of R^n. For $m = n + 1$, i.e. for simplices $P(a^{n+1}, b^{n+1})$, $x(a^{n+1}, b^{n+1})$ is the centre of gravity of $P(a^{n+1}, b^{n+1})$, thus can be computed on $0(n^3)$ arithmetical operations. Introducing the variables $\mu_i = (b_i - \langle a_i, z \rangle)$, $i = 1, \cdots, m$, the polyhedron $P(a^m, b^m)$ can be represented in the form

$$P(k^p, c^p) = \{\mu | \langle k_j, \mu \rangle = c_j, \; j = 1, \cdots, p, \; \mu_i \geq 0, \; i = 1, \cdots, m\},$$

where $p = m - n$, the point $\bar{\mu} = \mu(k^p, c^p)$ corresponding to $\bar{x} = x(a^m, b^m)$ solves the problem

$$(2.5) \qquad \max\{\sum_{i=1}^{m} \log \mu_i | \mu \in P(k^p, c^p)\},$$

which is the finite dimensional analogon of the problem (1.6). Moreover $\mu(k^p, c^p)$ is the center of gravity of an $(m-1)$ dimensional simplex $[M_1, \cdots, M_m]$ which is cut away from R_+^m by the (i.e. on the) hyperplane tangential to the surface $\mu_1 \cdots \mu_m \equiv$ const., going through $\mu(k^p, c^p)$. Thus $P(a^m, b^m)$ is obtained as the intersection of an $(m-1)$ dimensional simplex $S = S(a^m, b^m)$ with an n dimensional linear manifold $\ell(a^m, b^m)$ going through the centre of S, the inner and outer ellipsoids in (1.4) are the intersection of $\ell(a^m, b^m)$ with the largest resp. smallest volume ellipsoids contained in, resp. containing S.

Using the existence and uniqueness of this canonical, "central" imbedding of $P(a^m, b^m)$ into a simplex one can prove that the above notion of centre – over the "category" of systems of linear inequalities is the only one which associates to simplexes $P(a^{n+1}, b^{n+1})$ in R^n their centres of gravity and is closed under the operation of linear restriction: the "centre" of an arbitrary system of $(n-1)$ dimensional inequalities arising by adding, to an arbitrary n-dimensional system $\{a^m, b^m\}$ a constraint $< a, x >= b$, which is satisfied by $x(a^m, b^m)$ must remain $x(a^m, b^m)$.

Remark. The generalization of the solution concept (2.1) to the nonlinear feasibility problem is straightforward:

$$(2.6) \qquad \max\{\prod(-f_i(x))|f_i(x) \le 0, \; i = 1, \cdots, m, \; x \in R^n\}.$$

In view of the importance of ellipsoidal approximations – due to their good invariance and hereditary properties – the following observation (giving an application for (2.6)) might provide a useful tool for constructing inner and outer ellipsoidal approximations for the intersection of two or more ellipsoids:

$$E_1 \cap E_2 = \{z | 1 \ge< A_1^{-1}z, z >, \; 1 \ge< A_2^{-1}(z - x_0), z - x_0 >, \; z \in R^n\},$$

where A_1 and A_2 are symmetric, positive definite matrices.

Let $f(x) = -1 + < A_1^{-1}x, x >$, and $f_2(x) = -1 + A_2^{-1}(x - x_0), x - x_0 >$ and let x^* be the unique maximumpoint of the strongly concave function $\psi = 2^{-1} \log f_1 f_2$.

For the case $x_0 = 0$, it is not difficult to prove that

$$x^* + E \subset E_1 \cap E_2 \subset x^* + 2E,$$

and it can be conjectured that the same inclusion holds also in the general case (notice the analogy with the constructions for the case of linear $f_i - s$).

In order to describe the proposed algorithm for linear programming, we note first that there are many ways to reduce a linear programming (through homotopies) to solution of linear inequalities; in fact, considering the primal-dual system there is an equivalence between the two problems (without any homotopy), however to solve that primal-dual system numerically – using the analytic centre solution for inequalities – we should use homotopies, e.g. by enlarging all right hand sides with an additive positive constant λ (to obtain polyhedrons with nonempty interior) and then tending λ to zero.

It seems to be more natural (computationally simple) to follow an other way. If c^*, the optimum value of (1.1) is finite, then $x(\lambda) = x(a^m, c; b^m, \lambda)$ is well defined (exists) for all $\lambda \ge c^*$ and is an analytic function of the open interval (c, ∞) by the implicit function theorem, in fact from the equation (2.2) we see that x is an *algebraic* function of λ. The equation for $x(\lambda)$ can be written in the following form

$$(2.7) \quad 0 = E(\lambda, x) = g_0(x) + \lambda g(x) = c - \sum_{i=1}^{m} \frac{< c, x > a_i}{b_i- < a_i, x >} + \lambda \sum_{i=1}^{m} \frac{a_i}{b_i- < a_i, x >},$$

where $g(x)$ is the gradient of a convex function. For $\lambda \to \infty$, $x(\lambda)$ tends to $x(a^m, b^m)$ or if the latter does not exist, i.e. $P(a^m, b^m)$ is unbounded, then it tends to infinity as a linear function of λ. The idea of using (in view of the above limit behaviour) diagonal or superdiagonal Padé approximants for extrapolating "following" the curve $x(\lambda)$, $\lambda \geq c^*$, is natural since for analytic (algebraic) functions rational approximation is well known to be superior, in general, to polynomial extrapolations, on this see e.g. [3], [4], [11], [12] and the references there. It is interesting that in some modern works on continuation (homotopy) methods in convex programming – see e.g. the survey paper by Allgover and Georg in [1] – the use of rational predictors is not proposed, while – even for a large class of analytic (mildly stiff) ordinary differential equations – rational extrapolation techniques, see e.g. [11], have been proved to be rather effective, of course the context is somewhat different: there is a difference in following a curve defined like in (2.7) or the trajectory of a differential equation, in the latter case the values $x(\lambda_i)$, $i \leq k$ used for extrapolating $x(\lambda_{k+1})$ are itself not accurate. For the special case of our curve $x(\lambda)$, $\lambda \geq c^*$ the efficiency of these extrapolations (in addition to their arithmetical low complexity) is indicated by more deep relations as mentioned in connection with the Nevanlinna-Pick moment problems (note that varying c^P for fixed t^p corresponds to varying b^m for fixed a^m) and the properties of equation (2.7), see section 4.

Algorithm 1. In order to describe the proposed, "conceptual" algorithm we use induction with respect to the step number k. Suppose that $x(\lambda_0), \cdots, x(\lambda_k)$ has been already computed within prescribed residual (say, machine) accuracy $\|E(\lambda_j, \tilde{x}(\lambda_j))\| \leq \varepsilon_0$, $j = 0, \cdots, k$. Let $\lambda_{k+1} := \lambda_k + 2(\lambda_k - \lambda_{k-1})$ and compute, by rational diagonal, multipoint Padé extrapolation (see below) an approximation $\hat{x}(\lambda_{k+1})$ for $x(\lambda_{k+1})$, from the multipoint data $\{(\lambda_j, \tilde{x}(\lambda_j)), j = 0, \cdots, k\}$. Starting from $\hat{x}(\lambda_{k+1})$ perform (a fixed number n_0 of) Newton steps for the equation $E(\lambda_{k+1}, z) = 0$. If during these steps the residual condition $\|E(\lambda_{k+1}, z_{k+1}^i)\| \leq \varepsilon_0$ is satisfied for some $i = i_0 \leq n_0$, and if all the values of $b_j - < a_j, z_{k+1}^{i_0} >$ are positive, then set $\tilde{x}_{k+1} := z_{k+1}^{i_0}$ if not, let $\lambda_{k+1}^{new} := \lambda_k + \frac{1}{2}(\lambda_{k+1} - \lambda_k)$.

By definition, the diagonal, multipoint Padé approximation for the analytic vector functions $x : R^1 \to R^n$, based on the nodes $\lambda_0, \cdots, \lambda_k$ is a rational vector function $\tilde{x}^i(\lambda) = p^i(\lambda)/q(\lambda)$, $i = 1, \cdots, n$ such that $\deg p \leq \deg q \leq d$,

$$p^i(\lambda) - q(\lambda)\tilde{x}^i(\lambda) = \psi^i(\lambda) \prod_{j=0}^{k}(\lambda - \lambda_j), \ i = 1, \cdots, n,$$

holds for some vector function ψ which is analytic and d is the smallest number for which $(n+1)d+n \geq (k+1)n$. Concerning the existence and the methods for computing such a function, see e.g. the papers of Draux and Graves-Morris, Jenkins in [12]. In the onedimensional case, $n = 1$, the corresponding approximants are exactly the well known Thiele fractions, see [11]. In the multidimensional case we should not compute n independent one dimensional approximations, i.e. separate ones for each of the coordinates, since then the denominators would be, in general, different for different coordinates and the whole procedure would not be affine invariant.

Of course many details of implementation remain to be worked out. When performing the Newton steps for the solution of $E(\lambda, x)$ with a fixed λ, the simple form of the Hessian matrix: $D^2\psi(x) = AD(x)A^*$, where A is a fixed matrix, D is a diagonal matrix simply depending on x, allows for special update methods, e.g. the updates of Karmarkar, see [6], are directly applicable. A further possibility is to extrapolate not only the vector function $x(.)$ but also the inverses of the Hessians (along the trajectory $x(.)$). In order to solve the first phase problem: that of the computation of the analytic centre $x(a^m, b^m)$, or more generally to find out whether $P(a^m, b^m)$ is empty or not, we can again use special homotopies, see e.g. the methods given in sections 3 and 4. Eventual inconsistencies can be detected e.g. by adding a large number λ to the right hand sides of the inequalities, and diminishing λ till the solution set is nonvoid. By considering the primal and dual systems together we could assume $c^* = 0$, or alternatively that (1.1) is reduced to solve a set of linear inequalities (and equalities), whose solutions are just the optimal solutions of the primal and dual problems. The right choice of a homotopy should depend, of course, also on the inner (e.g. block) structure of the problem. Due to stability problems, the highest allowed degree of the rational extrapolation should be regulated by suitable automatic, adaptive restart procedures, we emphasize that this degree is raised without any a priori bounds, for a partial justification for this see section 4. At the end of the trajectory, i.e. when at $\lambda = c^*$, a singularity occurs; however, going over to an extended system –

$$c + \sum_{i=1}^{m} \mu_i a_i = 0, \ \mu_i(b_i - < a_i, x >) = \lambda - < c, x >, \ i = 1, \cdots, m,$$

i.e. to the homotopy curve $(x(\lambda), \mu(\lambda)) \in R^{n+m}$, there will be no singularity at the optimum, i.e. at $\lambda = c^*$, if and only if both the primal and the dual problems have a unique solution. The critical value $\lambda = c^*$ can be "recognized" form the "vanishing" of $b_i - < a_i, x >$, for at least one index i.

If there is a primal degeneracy at the optimum, the solution $x(\lambda)$, for $\lambda \searrow c^*$, tends to the analytic centre of the set of optimal primal solutions. Since the latter set is not a continuous function of the parameters (a^m, b^m, c), it is reasonable to provide – as the "solution" of the linear programming problem (1.1) – the ellipsoidal approximation for the set $P(a^m, b^m) \cap \{x | < c, x > \leq c^* + \varepsilon\}$ for an $\varepsilon > 0$; this will be a more "stable" solution concept. Methods could be given for "maintaining" a "basic" solution i.e. combine the above method with cutting plane or simplex type methods, see e.g. [10].

3. Algorithms for minimization of general, convex functions

The algorithm for linear programming we described in the previous section, in general, cannot be regarded as competitive – even when compared with the ellipsoid method – when $m >> n$, (# independent variables $= n$). The existence of ellipsoidal approximation for the sets $P(a^m, c, b^m, \lambda)$ allows to delete some of the constraints – at specific $\lambda = \lambda_{k_i}$, $i = 1, 2, \cdots$, i.e. those which contain the ellipsoid

$$x(a^m, c, b^m, \lambda) + mE(a^m, c, b^m, \lambda)$$

in their interior. The latter is a condition very easy to check: the necessary and sufficient condition for an ellipsoid $E = \{z| < A^{-1}(z - x_0), z - x_0 > \leq 1\}$ to be contained in the halfspace $b \geq < a, z >$, is given by the inequality

$$b - < a, x_0 > \|a\|^{-1} \geq \|a\|^{-1} < Aa, a >^{1/2} .$$

It is, however, nontrivial how to select the "moments" k_i, $i = 1, \cdots$ since by deleting some of the constraints we "destroy" the smoothness of the continuation curve $x(\lambda) = x(a^m, c, b^m, \lambda)$, so that a new rational approximation should be built up again during the period (k_i, k_{i+1}). In any case it should be noted that the above ellipsoidal approximations – in which the updating of $E(a^m, c, b^m, \lambda)$ is equally simple as that of $x(a^m, c, b^m, \lambda)$ – allow to detect all the constraints active at the minimum and delete those which are inactive.

Now we describe an algorithm in which the constraints will be "generated" successively, i.e. will not be considered simultaneously from the beginning. For greater generality we present the corresponding conceptual algorithm for the problem of minimizing an arbitrary convex function defined on R^n, when at each step of the algorithm we can measure – at a specified point $x \in R^n$ – the values of $f(x)$ and $g(x)$: one of the subgradients of f at x.

This algorithm can be viewed as an "approximate" implementation of the method of graph centers of gravity, proposed in [10].

Algorithm 2. Suppose that the values of $f(x_j)$, $g(x_j)$, $j = 0, 1, \cdots, k$ have already been computed and let $c(k) := (\varphi(k), z(k))$, be the analytic centre of the current set of localization, L_k, for the possible "minimumpairs"

$$(3.1) \quad L_k := \{(\varphi, z)| \varphi \leq \min_{j \leq k} f(x_j); \varphi \geq f(x_j) + < g(x_j), z - x_j >, j = 0, \cdots, k\}.$$

Let $x_{k+1} := z(k)$ and compute the values of $f(x_{k+1})$ and $g(x_{k+1})$ and the analytic centre for L_{k+1}.

Note that L_{k+1} arises from L_k by introducing at most two new constraints:

$$(3.2) \quad \varphi \leq \min_{j \leq k+1} f(x_j), \ \varphi \geq f(x_{k+1}) + < g(x_{k+1}), z - x_{k+1} >,$$

therefore the following continuation (homotopy) can be used to compute $c(k+1)$ from $c(k)$.

Let β be a sufficiently large number and let for $0 \le \lambda \le 1$, $y(\lambda)$ the analytic centre of the inequality system

(3.3)
$$L_k(\lambda) := L_k \cap \{(\psi, x) | \lambda \psi_0 + (1-\lambda)\psi_1 \ge \psi, \psi + \beta\lambda \ge f(x_{k+1}) + <g(x_{k+1}), x - x_{k+1}>\}$$

where

$$\psi_0 := \min_{j \le k} f(x_j), \quad \psi_1 := \min\{\psi_0, f(x_{k+1})\}.$$

Since β is large, $L_k(\lambda)$ for $\lambda = 1$ is close to (i.e. almost identical with) the system L_k while for $\lambda = 0$, it is identical to L_{k+1}. Thus, in order to obtain x_{k+1}, we have to follow the curve $y(\lambda)$. Again at some steps $k = k_i$, $i = 1, 2, \cdots$ some of the constraints $\varphi \ge f(x_j) + <g(x_j), x - x_j>$, $j \le k$ can be deleted from (3.1).

Based on the ellipsoidal bounds (1.4), where $\rho \le k + 1$, can be chosen depending on the number of constraints not yet deleted from (3.1) – it is easy to prove the convergence (in fact to give a guaranteed speed of convergence) as, for the ellipsoid method: using the fact that the volume of the localization set L_{k+1} is smaller than the volume of L_k by a factor whose worst case value (less than one) depends only on n and k. Since this worst case value depends also on k, we have to make "restarts" after each $u(n)$ steps, where $u(n)$ is a low order polynomial function of n, in order to obtain a method with a reasonable, guaranteed speed in convergence. In fact, it seems to be true that – while the guaranteed global convergence speed of such methods will be not better than of the ellipsoid method – in an "average sense" these methods will be quite good, see (3.4).

In the restart steps, i, the current set of localization L_{k_i} is included into a simplex of small volume, e.g. the one of smallest volume containing the outer ellipsoid, see (1.4), obtained for L_{k_i}. Concerning details of such simple restart techniques and the corresponding estimations we refer to a preprint of the author available from the Dept. of Numerical Analysis, Eötvös University, where they are used to construct implementations of the method of centers of gravity (requiring less arithmetical operations as the original version to attain the same speed of convergence) and a stabilization of the ellipsoid method. In the same preprint it is proved that for the onedimensional case, $n = 1$, algorithm 2 implemented so, that only the three "active" constraints are considered for computing the centre of L_k, assures that

(3.4)
$$\min_{j \le N} f(x_j) - f^* \le \quad \text{const.} \, 9^{-N/3}, \quad \text{for all} \quad N,$$

i.e. the (worst case) convergence rate – for the uncertainty in the minimal value of f after N-steps – of algorithm 2 is less than $1/2$.

In order to obtain a method for which the guaranteed rate of decrease of volume of the current graph sets of localizations L_k is better, we can make the following modification: use the inner ellipsoids, constructed for L_k, see (1.4), as starting "points" for computing the center, $\gamma(L_k)$, of the largest in volume ellipsoid contained in L_k and select x_{k+1} as the projection of $\gamma(L_k)$ to R^n. The computation of that ellipsoid (its centre and quadratic form) is a "convex" analytic programming problem since $\det^{1/n}(A)$, is a concave function over the set of positive definite symmetric matrices $A \in R^{n \times n}$, while the constraint set is also convex. Of course, it is not necessary to compute that ellipsoid, or its centre with great precision and – since we can regard this problem as an example of (1.2) – we propose to apply again analytic continuation along solutions of the corresponding equations

$$(3.5) \qquad \frac{\partial f_0(x)}{\lambda - f_0(x)} + \sum_{i=1}^{m} \frac{\partial f_i(x)}{-f_i(x)} = 0,$$

in order to approach to the optimal solution. Thus for updating the maximal volume ellipsoids corresponding to the sets of localizations L_k, we propose to proceed through updating the "analytic" ellipsoids and continuation along the curve (3.5). We could go further in this direction trying to characterize the center of gravity of L_k as the solution of a simple convex analytic programming problem (at present we do not know how to do this) to be solved at each step. Of course such method should be used only if the computation of $f(x)$ and $g(x)$ at points $x \in R^n$ is much more expensive as machine time.

In order to outline an other application of the notion of analytic centre to general convex nondifferentiable minimization theory we note first that the problem "dual" to the feasibility problem (for a finite set of linear inequalities) is the problem to find out whether a given point, – say, the origin – belongs to the convex hull of a finite number of given points $[w_1, \cdots, w_m]$ in R^n, and if it does not, to find a separating hyperplane. By routine duality transformations we easily obtain an algorithm for solving the latter problem (of finding a "central" separating hyperplane). The latter problem arises – as a subproblem, to be solved at each step, i.e. "recursively" as far as possible, in bundle (or ε-subgradient) methods, see [7], [13].

There it is usually replaced by a quadratic programming problem to find that element of the convex hull which is nearest to the origin; a closer look shows that in order to find a good "descent direction", i.e. to "update" the bundle, it is again adviseable to find a "central" one among the separating hyperplanes, especially if the latter can be done more quickly than the solution of the quadratic programming problems, allowing also simple updating, i.e. recursive methods of solutions.

4. Globalization of Newton's method via rational extrapolation of a homotopy path

Suppose that we have to solve an equation

$$(4.1) \qquad g(x) = 0, \; g : R^n \mapsto R^n, \; g = \operatorname{grad} F,$$

where g is the gradient of a convex analytic function $F : R^n \to R$. The more general case where $x = (y, z)$ and F is convex in y and concave in z, can be treated in essentially the same way, therefore we restrict us to the above case.

As noted in the introduction, the majority of algorithms known today (especially the computer codes written for the solution of (4.1)) use variants of the classical Newton's method, i.e. are based on local quadratic models of F and doing so they do not exploit the analyticity (high order smoothness) of F but only that F is C^3 smooth. This "weakness" is apparent in the poor performance of these methods in regard of global convergence speed; the latter is usually enforced via "line search" or "trust region" methods, not exploiting higher order smoothness.

A classical method to solve (4.1) is via introducing a suitable homotopy and following the homotopy path. The simplest general way to do this is choosing an exactly solvable equation $g_0(x) = 0$, such that g_0 is in some sense near to g and consider

$$(4.2) \qquad E(\lambda, x) := (1 - \lambda)g_0(x) + \lambda g(x) = 0.$$

Now if g_0 is analytic in x and also the derivative of a convex function, then such is $E(\lambda, \cdot)$ and the curve $x(\lambda)$ over $0 \le \lambda \le 1$, note that in general $F_1(y, z) + F_2(y, z)$ is also convex in y and concave in z, if F_i, $i = 1, 2$, are such and has a unique saddle point if at least one of them is strongly convex, resp. concave in y, resp. in z. In order to solve (4.1), we shall "follow" the curve defined by (4.2) in the same way as described in section 3, i.e. using rational, diagonal Padé extrapolations and Newton corrections. Here we would like to further justify this method and relate it – among others – to the method of conjugate gradients and to the theory of Padé approximants for Stieltjes functions. For brevity we present only the main relations, the aim being to connect classical research areas (which seemed unrelated) to numerical convex analysis.

For simplicity let us choose first

$$(4.3) \qquad g_0(x) := x \text{ and } g(x) := Ax - b$$

where A is a symmetric, positive definite matrix, $b \in R^n$.

The solution curve is a rational vector function

$$(4.4) \qquad x(\lambda) = ((1 - \lambda)I + \lambda A)^{-1}b = p(\lambda)/q(\lambda),$$

such that the degree (in λ) of the numerator is less than the degree of the denominator, the latter being equal to the rank of the matrix $(b, Ab, \ldots, A^{n-1}b)$, as we shall see below from the relation of function in (4.4) to symmetric transfer functions – by referring to the well known computation of their Smith, MacMillan degree.

In order to analyse the function $x(\lambda)$ it is convenient to introduce the variable transformation $z = (\lambda - 1)\lambda^{-1}$, then

$$(4.5) \qquad x(z) = -\lambda - 1(zI - A)^{-1}b,$$

we notice that the function $(zI - A)^{-1}b$, is the well known resolvent function associated to A and b. Moreover

$$(4.6) \qquad f(z) := <(zI - A)^{-1}b, b> = \int_S \frac{1}{z - s}\mu(ds) = \sum_{k=0}^{\infty} <A^k b, b> z^{-k-1},$$

is a "Stieltjes function" (or a "symmetric transfer function"), defined also whenever a self adjoint operator A and a vector b is given in a Hilbert space H. The measure $d\mu$ in (4.6) is concentrated on the spectrum of A, it corresponds to the spectral resolution of A via the formula

$$\mu(\lambda_2) - \mu(\lambda_1) = <(E^A(\lambda_2) - E^A(\lambda_1))b, b>, A = \int_S \lambda dE_\lambda^A.$$

Now computing the function $x(\lambda)$ for $\lambda = \lambda_0, \cdots, \lambda_k$ which all tend to $\lambda = 0$, corresponds computing the derivatives of $x(\lambda)$ at $\lambda = 0$, up to order k. This is the same as computing the derivatives of $f(z)$ at infinity, $z = \infty$. The latter are just constant multiples of $A^j b$, $j = 0, \cdots, k$. The derivatives of $x(\lambda)$ at $\lambda = 0$ are constant multiples of $A^j b$, $j = 0, \cdots, k$. Now the Padé extrapolation problem amounts to approximate $x(1)$, resp. $f(0)$ from derivatives of x at zero, resp. of f at ∞, by rational functions of specified degree. Thus from the values of b, Ab, $\cdots$, $A^{k-1}b$ we have to approximate $A^{-1}b$ in the vector case, and from the values of $<b, b>$, $\cdots$, $<A^{2k-1}b, b>$ we have to approximate $<A^{-1}b, b>$ in the scalar case, in both cases by proper rational vector functions with denominator degree at most k, (by definition, p/q is proper if $\deg p < \deg q$). Looking to the scalar case, we see that in the method of conjugate gradients the same problem is solved

$$(4.7) \qquad \min\{\|b - Az\| \mid z = \alpha_0 b + \cdots + \alpha_{k-1}A^{k-1}b\}$$

since the subdiagonal Padé approximation $f_{k-1,k}$ to f is identical with the Stieltjes function defined as f in (4.6), but A replaced by its restriction $A_k : R^k \to R^k$ to the Krylov subspace $\{b, \cdots, A^{k-1}b\}$.

This is nothing else than the well known relation existing between orthogonal polynomials, restrictions of symmetric operators to Krylov subspaces and Padé approximations to Stieltjes functions, see e.g. [3], [4], [11]. Specially we see that the $(k - 1, k)$ type Padé approximation to $f(0)$, i.e. to $<A^{-1}b, b>$ based on the values of $f^j(\infty)$, $j = 0, \cdots, 2k - 1$, i.e. on $<b, b>$, $\cdots$, $<A^{2k-1}b, b>$, allows to compute the solution of (4.7). Moreover even for the general multipoint case when $x(1)$ or $x(\lambda_{k+1})$ is approximated from $x(\lambda_0), \cdots, x(\lambda_k)$, we have nice expressions for the extrapolation error, see [4], which show fast geometric convergence, i.e. of the type α^k, $\alpha < 1$ for an infinite dimensional A, already for the case $0 = \lambda_0 = \cdots = \lambda_k$ (as we know also from the theory of conjugate gradient methods).

Note that a nice property of the subdiagonal multipoint Padé approximants to a Stieltjes function is that their poles lie always on the convex hull the support of the corresponding measure (: spectrum of A), i.e. *outside* the interval of extrapolation.

In order to assess the quality of the proposed methods let us mention, that – using the fact that $\log(-y)$ is a Stieltjes function – one can prove that the analogous method of inverse interpolation, with increasing order, diagonal Padé approximants for solving $e^x = -y$, $y < 0$, gives a globally convergent method of "infinite" order, thus a method surely superior to Newton's method (for the same problem).

References.

[1] Bachem, A., Grötschel, M. and Korte, B. (eds.): *Mathematical Programming, The State of Art.* Springer Verlag, Berlin, 1983.

[2] Bonnesen, T. and Fenchel, W.: *Theorie der konvexen Körper.* Springer Verlag, Berlin, 1934.

[3] Goncar, A. A.: *On the rate of convergence of rational approximations to analytic functions.* Trudi Inst. Matem. V. A. Steklowa, Vol. 166 (1984), Nauka, Moscow.

[4] Goncar, A. A. and Lopez, G.: *On Markov's theorem for multipoint Padé approximations.* URSS Math. Sbornik 105 (147), No. 4, 511 - 524.

[5] Iri, M., Imai, H.: *A multiplicative penalty function method for linear programming.* Proc. of the 6th Math. Progr. Symp., Japan (1985), to appear in Algorithmica, 1986.

[6] Karmarkar, N.: *A new polynomial-time algorithm for linear programming.* Combinatorica 4 (4), 373 - 395.

[7] Lemarechal, C.: *Basic theory in nondifferentiable optimization.* Preprint, INRIA, 1986.

[8] Sonnevend, Gy.: *An analytic centre for polyhedrons and new classes of global algorithms for linear (smooth, convex) programming.* Proc. of the 12th IFIP Conference. (1985), in Lect. Notes in Control and Inf. Sci., Vol. 84, A. Prékopa et al.(eds), 866 - 876.

[9] Sonnevend, Gy.: *Sequential, stable and low complexity methods for the solution of moment (mass recovery) problems.* Proc. Seminar on Approximation Theory at the Int. Banach Center, 22 pages, Z. Ciesielski (ed.), 1986, to appear.

[10] Sonnevend, Gy.: *A modified ellipsoid method ...* In: Lect. Notes in Economics and Math. Systems 255 (1984), 264 - 278, Demyanov, V. F. and Pallaschke, D. (eds.), Springer Verlag, Berlin.

[11] Stoer, J.: *Introduction to Numerical Analysis.* Springer Verlag, Berlin 1981.

[12] Werner, H. and Bünger, H. J. (eds.): *Padé approximation and its applications, Bad Honnef, 1983*. Lect. Notes in Math. 1071 (1984), Springer Verlag, Berlin.

[13] Zowe, J.: *Nondifferentiable optimization*. In: Computational Mathematical Programming, K. Schittkowski (ed.), **NATO ASI Series F**, Vol. 15 (1985), Springer Verlag.

International Series of
Numerical Mathematics, Vol. 84
(c) 1988 Birkhäuser Verlag Basel

A Few Examples of Least Squares Optimization in Physical Chemistry and Astronomy.

Edgar Soulie

IRDI-DESICP-DPC-SCM et U.A.331 du C.N.R.S.

Centre d'Etudes Nucléaires de Saclay

91191 Gif-sur-Yvette Cedex, France

Abstract. Four examples are presented on the applications of least squares optimization to real problems. The first three deal with physical chemistry and are: 1. the determination of the molecular force constants of a molecular species from the observed vibrational frequencies of that species; 2. the determination of the parameters describing the interaction of a neptunium 237 nucleus with its environment from the recoilless absorption spectrum of gamma rays, or Mössbauer spectrum, by a neptunium containing substance. 3. the determination of the electronic hamiltonian parameters describing the unfilled f-shell of a paramagnetic ion from the electronic absorption spectrum and/or the paramagnetic susceptibility.

In each of these examples, the model may have to be simplified or enriched in order to properly account for the observed spectrum or curve.

Conversely, the orbit determination of double stars, which pertains to celestial mechanics, relies on an invariable model of ephemeris calculation. The analytical partial derivatives are therefore used in the optimization, contrary to the three other examples.

1. Introduction.

Many data interpretation problems encountered in the physical sciences imply the minimization of a function of residuals, or differences between observed and calculated quantities. This function is almost always the sum of squares, not only because this criterion is theoretically adequate for a gaussian distribution of errors [1], but also because it is the simplest positive functional with continuous first derivatives of those residuals.

In each case, physical ideas lead to a *mathematical model* which enables to *predict* the values of the dependent observables, knowing the parameters of the model, and possibly independent variables (times, temperatures, etc.). Models are generally *approximations*, and if final values of residuals appear too large, this may be ascribed either to an insufficient adjustment, or to errors on measurements, or to the approximations involved in the model.

In most problems, a major difficulty stems from the fact that the sum of squares of residuals has *several* minima, whereas only one is physically meaningful; and nothing proves that the required minimum coincides with the deepest or "global" minimum, although it seems likely.

Prior to optimization, an approximate set of parameters therefore has to be determined, that will serve as a starting point to optimization.

In each of the four examples given below, we describe the model and comment on the minimization algorithm applied, and the encountered problems.

2. Molecular force constants.

2.1 The model

A recalling force $f = -k(d - d_0)$ tends to maintain the distance d between the atoms of a diatomic molecule close to the equilibrium distance d_0; k is the force constant. This molecule may vibrate at frequency

$$(1) \qquad \nu = \frac{1}{2\pi}\sqrt{\frac{k}{\mu}}$$

where μ is the "reduced mass" such that $\frac{1}{\mu} = \frac{1}{m_A} + \frac{1}{m_B}$, and absorb the electromagnetic radiation having the frequency ν, or an integer multiple of it, called "harmonic".

In the general case of a polyatomic molecule, several fundamental frequencies (as well as harmonics and "combination bands") may be measured by infrared absorption spectroscopy or Raman scattering spectroscopy. The determination of the force constants implies the assignment of observed frequencies and an optimization.

For a molecule of n atoms and $N = 3n - 6$ degrees of freedom, the potential energy in the harmonic approximation is expressed as a quadratic function of the internal coordinates q, namely the displacements from equilibrium values of bond distances, bond angles, torsion angles:

$$(2) \qquad V = \frac{1}{2}\sum_{i,j}^{N} f_{ij} q_i q_j$$

where f_{ij} is a force constant.
The kinetic energy

$$(3) \qquad T = \frac{1}{2}\sum_{i}^{n} m_i(\dot{x}_i^2 + \dot{y}_i^2 + \dot{z}_i^2)$$

where $m_i, \dot{x}_i, \dot{y}_i, \dot{z}_i$ are the mass and time derivatives of the cartesian coordinates of i-atom is transformed by Wilson's method [2] into:

$$(4) \qquad T = \frac{1}{2}\sum_{i,j}^{N} (g^{-1})_{ij} \dot{q}_i \dot{q}_j$$

where $\dot{q}_i$ stands for the time derivative of the i-th internal coordinate, and g^{-1} is a matrix calculated as a function of equilibrium molecular geometry and molecular masses. A unitary transformation between internal coordinates q and *symmetry* internal coordinates Q enables the simultaneous block factorization of the matrices G^{-1} and F replacing g^{-1} and f. Each block corresponds to an irreducible representation of the group of symmetry elements of the molecule.

The Lagrange equations:

(5)
$$\frac{d}{dt}\left(\frac{\partial T}{\partial \dot{Q}_i}\right) = \frac{\partial V}{\partial Q_i}$$

lead to the following matrix equation:

(6)
$$\ddot{Q} = GFQ.$$

Solutions are linear combinations of sinusoidal functions of time. The frequencies ν_k of these functions are linked to the eigenvalues λ_k of matrix GF by:

(7)
$$\nu_k = \frac{\sqrt{\lambda_k}}{2\pi}.$$

With no symmetry element, and $N = 3n-6$ internal degrees of freedom, the symmetric matrix F depends on $N(N+1)/2$ force constants, whereas at most N frequencies are observable. The problem would be undetermined if a large number of force constants could not be neglected, so as to keep the number of adjustable parameters equal to at most the number of observed frequencies.

2.2 Optimization of force constants

In order to reduce the calculations involved at each iteration, ROUSSON et al. [3] suggested that minimization be applied to the objective function:

(8)
$$\mathcal{F} = \sum_k p_k (\det |G.F - \lambda_k^{obs} I_d|)^2$$

where $\lambda_k^{obs} = (2\pi\nu_k^{obs})^2$ and p_k is the weight of the k-th observed frequency; I_d stands for the identity matrix.

This functional involves lesser calculation than the usual sum:

(9)
$$\sum_k p_k (\nu_k^{obs} - \nu_k^{calc})^2.$$

To perform the minimization, the simplex algorithm as embodied in the "STEPIT" subroutine was first used [4]. This algorithm enabled determination of force constants of ClO_2F [5], UF_6^- [6] and UOF_5 [7]. Even for a small and highly summetrical species such as UF_6^-, many iterations were necessary. A faster subroutine taking advantage of the specific form of the objective function (sum of squares) was desirable to expedite future calculations. The subroutine "VAO5A" written by M. J. D. Powell, and appearing in the Harwell library of subroutines [8] was selected because it makes use of the famed Marquardt algorithm [9] and resorts to numerical approximations of partial derivatives of the residuals with respect to the adjustable parameters. The newer program much faster led to the same results.

Future work will rely on measurements made on isotopically "tagged" molecules, such as $.^{35}Cl^{16}OF_3$ and $.^{35}Cl^{18}OF_3$. These have slightly different g or G matrices, as a result of mass differences, but the same force constants and F matrices. The experimental frequencies of both species may be used simultaneously to obtain a better, more accurate determination of force constants.

3. Recoilless absorption spectrum of gamma rays. (Mössbauer spectrum)

3.1 The model

For a series of atomic nuclei, such as iron 57, tin 119, and, in our case, neptunium 237, recoilless absorption of gamma radiation of the appropriate energy, or Mössbauer effect, may occur. The absorption level is generally quite small compared to the transmission, and sharply varies with the wavelenght of the incoming gamma radiation. The wavelength is varied by moving the gamma source with respect to the sample, as a result of the Doppler-Fizeau effect.

The observed spectrum (adsorption versus source speed) results from the splitting of both the ground and excited nuclear manifolds (Fig. 1). In the case of neptunium 237, both have six states corresponding to nuclear spin $I = 5/2$.

Interactions which split the manifolds are described by an Hamiltonian operator, one for each manifold; in the basis of nuclear states, these are expressed as hermitian matrices. They account for the dipolar interaction of the nuclear spin with the effective magnetic field, and the quadrupolar interaction with the electric field gradient.

Resonant absorption occurs when the energy of the gamma photon matches the difference between two energy levels belonging to the nuclear excited and ground manifolds, respectively. This difference is:

$$(10) \qquad E_{ij} = \Delta E + \lambda_i^{exc} - \lambda_j^{gnd}$$

where ΔE is the energy difference of the barycenters, λ_i^{exc} and λ_j^{gnd} are the i-th and j-th eigenvalues of the hamiltonians pertaining to excited and ground manifolds. The corresponding adsorption intensity is:

$$(11) \qquad P_{ij} = (\tilde{\psi}_i^{exc} \cdot C \cdot \psi_j^{gnd})^2$$

where ψ_i^{exc} and ψ_j^{gnd} are the corresponding eigenvectors, and C is a matrix of Clebsch-Gordan coefficients. Each absorption has a lineshape given by the Breit-Wigner formula:

$$(12) \qquad f(E) = \frac{\Gamma^2}{\Gamma^2 + 4(E - E_{ij})^2}$$

where Γ is the linewidth.

Assuming that all transitions have the same linewidth, the transmitted intensity (count of gamma photons) is:

$$(13) \qquad T(E) = T_0 - F \cdot \sum_{i,j} \frac{\Gamma^2 \cdot P_{ij}}{\Gamma^2 + 4(E - E_{ij})^2}$$

where T_0 is the transmitted intensity outside absorption region and F the scale factor of absorption. In this model, the adjustable parameters are T_0, F, Γ, the difference between the values of ΔE for the studied species and a reference species, or *isomeric shift*, and the parameters entering both Hamiltonians [10]: the intensity and spherical coordinates of the magnetic field, the quadrupolar coupling constant, and an anisotropy parameter (which is a pure number).

3.2 Parameter determination and optimisation.

Because adsorption is so small, and because the count of transmitted gamma rays fluctuates, data accumulation must last long enough so that the level of absorption peaks is well above the level of fluctuations. Estimates of the parameters T_0, F, Γ and the isomeric shift may be deduced from the observed spectrum. The visual inspection of a series of calculated spectra for various values of the magnetic field and quadrupole coupling constant enables to make a rough estimate of these two important parameters.

It is essential that approximate values of the parameters having a major effect on the spectrum be known before any optimization is undertaken, all the more as the optimizer cannot perform the pattern recognition than the human eye does in order to make these estimations.

The least squares criterion was selected to estimate the goodness of fit:

$$(14) \qquad \mathcal{F} = \sum_k (T_k^{obs} - T(E_k))^2$$

where energy E_k corresponds to the k-th sampled speed. For the same reason than in the force constant problem, the algorithm embodied in subroutine "VAO5A" by M. J. D. Powell [8] was selected. In this case, however, the parameters have very different orders of magnitude: T_0 has the order of millions, F the orders of tens of thousands, whereas other parameters, expressed in the usual speed unit of a mm/s., have the order of unity. The parameters were therefore scaled so that *internal* parameters were equal to unity before optimization took place. Thus, a common increment could be selected for the estimation of first derivatives of the residuals with respect to parameters by finite differences. The asymmetry parameter, by definition, is comprised between 0 and 1; now, during optimization, values outside these boundaries were encountered. Accordingly, the following change of parameter was made to avoid resorting to an algorithm with constraints:

$$(15) \qquad \eta = \frac{s^2}{1 + s^2} \quad \text{or} \quad s = \sqrt{\frac{\eta}{1 - \eta}}.$$

Parameter optimization was done for a series of spectra of neptunium compounds, and in most instances, a fairly good fit resulted. It however turned out that, probably on account of a large correlation between F and Γ, the value of Γ under the control of the optimizer systematically increased beyond the most likely value, which the linewidth of an isolated line in the observed spectrum. This event prompted a change of status of Γ from *adjustable* to blocked parameter. As no provision is made for blocking parameters in "VAO5A", the status change implied an alteration of the program, rather than of the data, and the need to maintain several versions of the program. Another subroutine displaying the flexibility that "VAO5A" lacks was searched for. The subroutine "BSOLVE", a variant of Marquardt's algorithm implemented by BALL [11], provided with a blocking option and boundary constraints for each parameter, but proved far less efficient than "VAO5A".

After completion of optimization, the goodness of fit is measured by the criterion MISFIT introduced by RUBY [12] for the case of photon counting where the uncertainty on each count is the square root of the count number. Whereas MISFIT may range between 0 and 1, its value lies in the range 6 - 10 % for good fits.

4. Paramagnetic ions.

4.1 Absorption spectroscopy.

4.1.1. The model

Paramagnetic ions are characterized by an outer electronic shell which is *partly filled* with electrons. The number of unpaired electrons on this shell defines a *configuration*, or set of electronic states. For an f-shell with N electrons, configuration f^N has $K = \frac{14!}{N!(14-N)!}$ states. The main interactions lifting its degeneracy are [13]:
 - the Coulombic repulsion between electrons
 - the interaction between the angular momentum and the spin for each electron, or "spin-orbit coupling"
 - the crystal field interaction between the unpaired electrons and the electric charges surrounding the ion.

These interactions add in the Hamiltonian operator $\mathcal{H}$ which is represented by an hermitian matrix of dimension K for a given set of basic states. This matrix is expressed as a sum of terms:

$$(16) \qquad H = \sum_k \partial_k \cdot A_k$$

where the A_k are matrices of pure numbers, and the ∂_k adjustable parameters having the dimension of an energy. The Coulomb repulsion contributes three terms, and the spin-orbit coupling one term. The number of crystal-field terms depend on the symmetry of the environment of the paramagnetic ion: two parameters in the case of a cubic or tetrahedral symmetry, but nine for the symmetry of the water molecule, labelled C_{20}. When symmetry elements are present, the Hamiltonian matrix H factorizes into smaller blocks, each of which corresponds to an irreducible representation of the point group.

The energy levels of the configuration are the eigenvalues of the operator $\mathcal{H}$ and its matrix H. The energies of transitions appearing as lines in an electronic absorption spectrum are differences the various energy levels and the *lowest* energy level.

4.1.2. First estimation of the Hamiltonian parameters

Whereas an estimation of Coulomb repulsion and spin-orbit parameters may be derived from atomic spectroscopy results, crystal field parameters significantly vary with the chemical environment of the paramagnetic ion. Electrostatic calculations provide with starting values that may, or not, be adequate. Once estimations are available, the difficult problem of *identification* arises: which of the calculated transition corresponds to a given observed transition?

In some instances, a number of experimental energy levels may be labelled by the appropriate irreducible representations on the basis of selection rules [13]. Although this narrows the set of possible "line assignments", identification of spectral lines often stands as a stumbling block, and it would be hopeless to start an optimization based on erroneous assignments. In order to escape the identification bottleneck, use is made of the magnetic susceptibility, as described below in 4.2.

4.1.3. Parameter optimization

No good theory accounts for line shapes, so that the objective function relies on transition energies, not intensities:

$$(17) \qquad \mathcal{F} = \sum_j \left(\frac{E_j^{obs} - E_j^{calc}}{\Delta E_j} \right)^2$$

where E_j^{obs} and E_j^{calc} match, as discussed previously. The number of terms may be smaller than that of observed transitions, because certain transitions may be entangled or because line assignment could be done for certain transitions only, at the outset. More assignments may be suggested by the result of optimization.

The first derivative of energy E_j with respect to parameter ∂_k is:

(18)
$$\frac{\partial E_j}{\partial \partial_k} = \tilde{\psi}_j \cdot \frac{\partial H}{\partial \partial_k} \cdot \psi_j = \tilde{\psi} \cdot A_k \cdot \psi_j$$

where ψ_j is the eigenvector corresponding to eigenvalue E_j. This formula applies if eigenvalue E_j is single, and not otherwise. The standard Marquardt algorithm [9] is applicable thank to formula (18), and has been used by other groups involved in spectroscopy. In our own programs, however, spectroscopic data are combined with magnetic susceptibility data to be described below.

4.2 Paramagnetic susceptibility.

4.2.1. Van Vleck's formula and the susceptibility curve

Within the model described in 3.1.1., the molar paramagnetic susceptibility depends on temperature according to the Van Vleck's formula:

(19)
$$\chi(T) = \frac{N\beta^2}{k} \cdot \frac{\sum_i (\frac{\varepsilon_i^{(1)}}{T} - \varepsilon_i^{(2)}) \exp(-E_i/T)}{\sum_i \exp(-E_i/T)}$$

where N is Avogadro's number, β the Bohr magneton, k the Boltzmann constant, and:

(20)
$$\varepsilon_i^{(1)} = \tilde{\psi}_i \cdot Z \cdot \psi_i$$
$$\varepsilon_i^{(2)} = 2 \sum_{j \neq i} \frac{(\tilde{\psi}_j \cdot Z \cdot \psi_i)^2}{E_i - E_j}$$

where Z is the matrix of the Zeeman operator $\vec{u}.\ (\vec{L} + 2.\vec{S})\ \vec{u}$ is the unit vector in the direction of the magnetic field. In formula (19), energies are expressed in temperature units. In the case of cubic or tetrahedral symmetry, the three principal values of the susceptibility tensor are equal. For lower symmetries, the susceptibility tensor has two or three different principal values. Experimentally, in the case of a single crystal, two or three sets of measurements corresponding to the principal orientations of the crystal in the magnetic field are made. For each orientation, the susceptibility is measured at sampled temperatures, usually between 4,2 and 300 Kelvins. Although one of the principal susceptibilities may first increase with temperature, the paramagnetic susceptibilities usually decrease as temperature rises.

At the lowest energy states dominate in Van Vleck's formula on account of the Boltzmann factor $\exp(-E_i/T)$ the magnetic susceptibility is quite insensitive to those parameters which essentially determine the highly excited levels. For this reason, it may be relevant to restrict the set of basis states to those spanning the lowest spectroscopic term, or even the lowest spectroscopic multiplet. In the latter case, the crystal field parameters alone determine the energy levels within the multiplet, and the magnetic susceptibility curves.

4.2.2. Optimization

The objective function depends on the number of different principal magnetic susceptibilities. In the case of an axial susceptibility tensor, the objective function is:

$$(21) \qquad \mathcal{F} = \sum_i (\frac{\chi_{//i}^{exp} - \chi_{//}^{calc}(T_i)}{\Delta\chi_{//i}})^2 + \sum_j (\frac{\chi_{\perp j}^{exp} - \chi_{\perp}^{calc}(T_j)}{\Delta\chi_{\perp j}})^2$$

$\Delta\chi_{//i}$ and $\Delta\chi_{\perp j}$ stand for the uncertainties on the measurements of the i-th parallel
and j-th perpendicular susceptibilities. Energy levels may be taken in account by
adding the right hand side of eq.(17). Increasing the uncertainties on transition energies
will put more weight on the susceptibilities.

The nonlinear regression program of M. Borne, F. Bibian and M. Tournarie (see
Tournarie [14]) was used to interpret the powder susceptibility curve of $U(NCS)_8$
$[N(C_2H_5)_4]_4$ [15]. For this species with cubic symmetry, the whole f^2 configuration
was treated, whereas the susceptibility curve of $U(acac)_4$ was interpreted under the
simplifying assumption of a pure, isolated $^3H_4$ multiplet [16].

For another coordination compound of the same family, a single crystal was available, so that the objective function of eq.(21) could be used, under the same assumption
[17]. For the latter work, the program of Borne et al. was again replaced by the subroutine "VAO5A".

5. Orbit of a visual double star.

5.1 Introduction.

At epoch t, the observer measures the angle between the direction of the north and
the vector joining the two stars of a *physical* couple; this is the position angle θ. The
observer also measures the angular distance ρ between these two stars. Given a set of
observations extending over a sufficient time interval, often more than hundred years,
and made by several astronomers, the problem consists in the evaluation of the seven
parameters which determine the relative orbit of the "companion star" around the
main star [18, 19]. From Newton's law of graviation this orbit is an ellipse, a focus of
which is occupied by the main star, and the law of areas applies to the motion. The
ephemeris formulae result from the solution of the "two body problem" and from a
projection of the orbit plane on the celestial sphere [18, 19]. Contrary to the three
previous applications, the *model* need not be altered from one case to the next.

5.2 First orbit determination.

If no orbit is known, the starting values of the orbit parameters may not be chosen at
random. A *first orbit* determination is therefore based on a method different from that
of orbit improvement. Disregarding the law of areas, the parameters of the cartesian
equation of the apparent orbit are adjusted by the minimization of a *quadratic* function
of them, which implies only the solution of a linear system [20].

5.3 Orbit optimization.

Because an important feature of the motion is missing in the process used to obtain estimates of the parameters, these are only approximate. The orbit improvement then proceeds by the minimization of an adequate objective function [21]:

$$(22) \qquad \mathcal{F} = \sum_i \left(\frac{\theta_i^{obs} - \theta^{calc}(t_i)}{\Delta \theta_i} \right)^2 + \left(\frac{\rho_i^{obs} - \rho_i^{calc}(t_i)}{\Delta \rho_i} \right)^2$$

analogous to that of eq.(21). Before the differences in position angles are introduced into formula (22), however, they must first be translated *modulo* 360 degrees within the interval $[-180; +180[$. Estimations of uncertainties $\Delta\theta$ and $\Delta\rho$ are more difficult than for the other examples given above, because measurements do not constitute an homogeneous series, made under comparable conditions, as noted before.

The seven so-called Campbell parameters which define an orbit are: the period P in years, the epoch of passage at periastron T in years, the eccentricity e, the semimajor axis a in arc-seconds, the inclination of the orbit plane i, the position angle of periastron ω, the position angle of the line of nodes Ω. As the eccentricity of an ellipse satisfies the inequalities:

$$(23) \qquad 0 \leq e < 1$$

an algorithm with constraints would be required in principle. As before, the change of parameter:

$$(24) \qquad e = \frac{s^2}{1 + s^2} \quad \text{or} \quad s = \sqrt{\frac{e}{1 - e}}$$

removed the need for constraints on the eccentricity.

Besides, the analytical expressions of the partial derivatives of θ and ρ with respect to the Campbell and s parameters are easily derived from the ephemeris formulae. The standard Marquardt algorithm [9] was therefore applied, and in the many cases tested provided with an improved orbit after only a few iterations, so that after twenty iterations, are parameters were well stabilized.

Once the orbit parameters have been adjusted, they can be controlled by minimization of the sum of absolute values:

$$(25) \qquad \mathcal{F} = \sum_i \left| \frac{\theta_i^{obs} - \theta^{calc}(t_i)}{\Delta \theta_i} \right|^2 + \left| \frac{\rho_i^{obs} - \rho^{calc}(t_i)}{\Delta \rho_i} \right|^2$$

thank to the algorithm and program of Claude Lemaréchal [22]. Whereas the uncertainties on P and a may be fairly large, the ratio a^3/P^2 is much better known, as remarked by BAIZE from published orbits [23]. The reason is that for elongated orbits, both P and a are correlated with $1 - e$, whereas a^3/P^2 is not. This is fortunate as this ratio, combined with the parallax, determines the sum of the masses of the two stars.

6. Conclusion.

As more elaborate theories and models appear in the physical sciences in order to account for more numerous and accurate experimental (or observational) results, the applications of nonlinear least squares optimization will continue to expand. The combination in the objective function of several sums of squares of residuals, corresponding to different types of experiments or observations, will become standard practice.

For example, in order to unravel the electronic structure of paramagnetic ions, one can also resort to other experimental techniques, such as neutron inelastic scattering, electron paramagnetic resonance, and specific heat measurements, which imply other simulators.

New algorithms and programs appear [24], but an efficient optimizer combining the flexibility of BSOLVE [11] and the efficiency of VAO5A is still needed.

Changing the optimizer for comparison or other purpose ought to be straightforward. A prerequisite is a *complete separation* of functions between the optimizer and the simulator. Therefore, when the meaningful range for a physical variable is limited, contrary to the choice of Morbey [1], the simulator should *never* alter the value of this variable; either internal, or "slack" variables should be introduced, as we have done, or an algorithm with boundary constraints should replace the algorithm without constraints.

The ease with which we have been able to change from one optimizer to another has critically depended on the choice of FORTRAN as a programming language. In its current standard [25], this very widely used language however has limitations. For an efficient execution, communication between the main program and the simulator through COMMON instructions is advisable. But dimensions of arrays shared must be fixed, and identical in the main program and simulator. To avoid this lack of flexibility, one can pass the arrays as arguments *through* the optimizer, where they logically ought not to appear, and a lesser execution speed results.

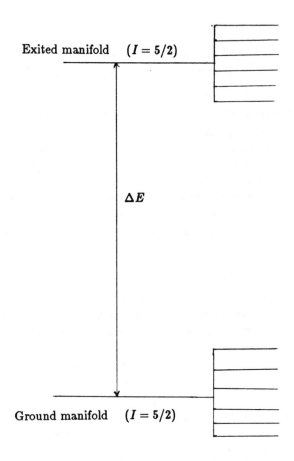

Exited manifold $(I = 5/2)$

ΔE

Ground manifold $(I = 5/2)$

Fig. 1 –   The level scheme of the nuclear states of Neptunium 237, relevant to Mössbauer spectroscopy.
Each manifold is split by hyperfine interactions involving the nuclear spin.

References.

[1] Morbey, C. L.: *A synthesis of the solutions of spectroscopic and visual binary orbits.* Publications of the Astronomical Society of the Pacific 87 (1975), 689 – 693.

[2] Wilson, E. Bright, Jr.; Decius, J. C. and Cross, Paul C.: *Molecular vibrations; the theory of infrared and Raman spectra.* McGraw-Hill Book Cy, New York (1955).

[3] Rousson, Roger; Tantot, Georges and Tournarie, Max: *Numerical determination of vibrational force constants by means of a simplex minimizing method.* Journal of Molecular Spectroscopy 59 (1976), 1 – 7.

[4] Chandler, J. P.: *STEPIT – Minimum of a function of several (N) variables.* QCPE No. 66.1, Quantum Chemistry Program Exchange, Bloomington, Indiana, USA.

[5] Tantot, Georges: *Etude structurale de quelques dérivés oxyfluorés des halogènes.* Thèse de doctorat d'état, Université de Paris-6 (1976).

[6] Soulie, Edgar: *Etude de quelques composes à électrons f non appariés.* Rapport CEA-R-4849 (1977).

[7] Joubert, Philippe: *Synthèses, études dynamiques et structurales de quelques dérivés d'addition de l'oxytétrafluorure d'uranium et de fluorures monovalents.* Thèse de doctorat d'état, Université de Limoges (1979).

[8] Powell, M. J. D.: *VA05A, a subroutine to minimize a sum of squares of m functions in n variables (m × n), without analytical derivatives.* In: "Harwell subroutine library, a catalogue of subroutines" complied by M. J. Hopper, AERE-R-9185, fourth edition, November 1981, p. 51, last subroutine revision on 10/09/1974.

[9] Marquardt, Donald W.: *An algorithm for least squares estimation of nonlinear parameters.* J. Soc. Indust. Appl. Math. 11 (2) (1963), 431 – 441; Jorge J. Moré: "The Levenberg-Marquardt algorithm: implementation and theory" in: Numerical Analysis; G. A. Watson (ed.), Lecture Notes in Mathematics 630 (1977), 105 – 116, Springer Verlag, Berlin.

[10] Pillinger, W. L. and Stone, J. A.: *Methodology of the ^{237}Np Mössbauer effect.* In: Mössbauer effect methodology 4 (1968), 217 – 236, Irwin J. Gruverman (ed.), Plenum Press, New York.

[11] Ball, W. E.: *BSOLVE: Solution to a set of nonlinear equations by Marquardt's method.* In: Material and energy balance computations by Ernest J. Henley and Edward M. Rosen, John Wiley & Sons, Inc., New York (1969), Appendix E 560 – 566.

[12] Ruby, Stanley L.: *Why MISFIT when you already have χ^2?* In: Mössbauer effect methodology 8 (1973), 263 – 276, Irwin J. Gruverman and Carl W. Seidel (eds.), Plenum Press, New York.

[13] Caro, Paul: *Structure électronique des éléments de transition; l'atome dans le cristal.* Presses Universitaires de France, Paris (1976).

[14] Tournarie, Max: *Evaluations optimales des inconnues d'un système statistique non linéaire I. Principe et théorie.* Journal de Physique 30 (10) (1969), 737 – 751.

[15] Soulie, Edgar and Goodman, Gordon: *Niveaux d'énergie électronique et susceptibilité magnetique des ions de configuration f^2 en champ cristallin cubique.* Theoret. Chim. Acta (Berl.) 41 (1976), 17 – 36; Erratum, Theoret. Chim. Acta (Berl.) 51 (1979), 259 – 260.

[16] Soulie, Edgar: *Champ de coordinats, anisotropie de susceptibilité magnétique et deplacement chimique dans le tetrakis-(acetylacetonato) uranium (IV).* Inst. Phys. Conf. Ser. No. 37 (1978), 166 – 172.

[17] Blaise, Alain; Genet, Michel; Song, Chong-Li and Soulie, Edgar: *Structure électronique du tetrakis-(1,1,1-trifluoro-4-phénylbutane -2,4-dionato) uranium (IV): étude magnétochimique.* Journal of the Less Common Metals (sous presse).

[18] Couteau, Paul: *L'observation des étoiles doubles visuelles.* Flammarion, Paris (1978).

[19] Heintz, Wulff Dieter: *Doppelsterne.* Wilhelm Goldmann Verlag, München (1971).

[20] Yvon Villarceau, Antoine: *Méthode pour calculer les orbites des étoiles doubles, déduite de considerations géométriques.* In: Additions à la Connaissance des Temps, Gauthier Villars (ed.), Paris (1877).

[21] Soulie, Edgar: *L'amélioration de l'orbite d'une étoile double visuelle.* Astron. Astrophys. 164 (1986), 408 – 414.

[22] Lemarechal, Claude: *Nonsmooth optimization: use of the code DYNEPS.* Communication No. WP-80-36 to the International Institute for Applied Systems Analysis, Laxenburg, Austria (1980).

[23] Baize, Paul: *Les masses des étoiles variables à longue Période.* L'Astronomie 94 (1980), 71 – 84. note en bas de page 72.

[24] Dennis, Jr. John E.; Gay, David, M. and Welsch, Roy E.: *An adaptive nonlinear least squares algorithm.* ACM Transactions on Mathematical Software 7 (3) (1981), 348 – 368; Algorithm 573 NL2SOL – An adaptive nonlinear least squares algorithm, ACM Transactions on Mathematical Software 7(3) (1981), 369 – 383.

[25] *Traitement de l'information: Langage de programmation FORTRAN.* Norme AFNOR NF-Z 65-110, Paris La Defense (juin 1983).

International Series of
Numerical Mathematics, Vol. 84
(c) 1988 Birkhäuser Verlag Basel

Duality in Generalized Fractional Programming

Jochen Werner

Institut für Numerische und Angewandte Mathematik
Universität Göttingen
3400 Göttingen, West Germany

We consider generalized fractional programs where the ratio of finitely many functionals is to be minimized under convex explicit and implicit constraints. We give a geometric motivation for a dual program and prove a strong duality theorem which contains the classical Lagrange-duality theorem as a special case. Finally applications to discrete rational Chebyshev-approximation problems and to first order necessary optimality conditions for nonlinearly constrained min-max programs are presented.

Key words: Fractional Programming, Duality, Necessary Optimality Conditions.

1. Introduction.

We consider an optimization problem of the following form

$$(P) \qquad \text{Minimize } F(x) := \max_{i=1,\cdots,l} \frac{f_i(x)}{g_i(x)} \text{ on } M := \{x \in X : x \in C, h(x) \in -K\}.$$

which is called a generalized fractional program. A survey of fractional programming (here $l = 1$ in the formulation of (P)) is given by Schaible [12, 13].

In order to obtain duality results we make the following assumptions:

A)i) X is a linear space, $C \subset X$ nonempty and convex. Y is a normed linear space, $K \subset Y$ a nonempty, convex cone.

ii) $f_i, g_i : C \to \mathbb{R}$, $g_i(x) > 0$ for all $x \in M$ $(i = 1, \cdots, l)$.

iii) (P) feasible (i.e. $M \neq \emptyset$), $\inf(P) := \inf\{F(x) : x \in M\} > -\infty$ and $f_i - \inf(P)g_i : C \to \mathbb{R}$ convex $(i = 1, \cdots, l)$.

iv) $h : C \to Y$ is K-convex (i.e. convex with respect to the cone K).

In the finite dimensional case (i.e. $X = \mathbb{R}^n$, $Y = \mathbb{R}^m$) several duality results for generalized fractional programs have been proven e.g. by Crouzeix [1, 2], Gol'stein [5], Flachs [4], Jagannathan and Schaible [6] and Crouzeix, Ferland and Schaible [3] (there many problems leading to generalized fractional programs are mentioned) under less general conditions. For instance (A) iii) holds if (P) is feasible, f_i, $-g_i$ are convex functions and $f_i(x) \geq 0$ for all $x \in M$ and $i = 1, \cdots, l$. Furthermore usually K is supposed to be the nonnegative orthant in $\mathbb{R}^m$. Since we do not assume K to have a nonempty interior affine linear equality constraints are not excluded.

It is the aim of this paper to present a simple selfcontained approach to duality theory for generalized fractional programs, to apply these results to discrete rational

Chebyshev-approximation problems and to establish a maximum-principle resp. a Lagrange-multiplier theorem of Kuhn-Tucker type for nonlinearly constrained min-max problems by using a strong duality theorem applied to a linearized min-max problem.

In section 2 we give a geometric motivation for a program dual to (P). This program turns out to be in complete analogy with that given by Jagannathan and Schaible [6]. Under a certain constraint qualification which for Y finite dimensional is shown to be equivalent to a generalized Karlin's constraint qualification (see e.g. Mangasarian [8]) a strong duality theorem is proven. In the finite dimensional case (i.e. $X = \mathbb{R}^n$, $Y = \mathbb{R}^m$) this constraint qualification is shown to be obsolete if the implicit constraint $h(x) \in -K$ is polyhedral and $M \cap ri(C) \neq \emptyset$ which generalizes a result given by Flachs [4]. Finally we consider similar to Crouzeix, Ferland and Schaible [3] generalized linear fractional programs where f_i, g_i and h are affine linear and C, K are polyhedral cones.

In section 3 we apply the results of section 2 to discrete rational Chebyshev-approximation problems and get all the duality results given by Krabs [7]. Finally nonlinearly constrained min-max problems are considered. Under a constraint qualification first given by Robinson [10] and Zowe and Kurzyusz [15] a Lagrange-multiplier theorem of Kuhn-Tucker type is proven. As in the differentiable case (see e.g. Werner [14]) the Lagrange multipliers are shown to be a solution of a program dual to a linearized min-max problem.

2. Duality in generalized fractional programming.

In this section we suppose that the generalized fractional Program (P) is given and the assumptions (A)i) – iv) of section 1 hold.

The starting point for obtaining a program dual to (P) is the observation that (P) is equivalent to:

Minimize μ subject to

$$(\theta, \theta) \in \Lambda_\mu := \{(f(x) - \mu g(x) + y, h(x) + z) \in \mathbb{R}^l \times Y : x \in C, y \geq \theta, z \in K\}.$$

Here and in the following θ means the nullelement of the corresponding linear space, for $y \in \mathbb{R}^l$ the inequality $y \geq \theta$ is to be understood componentwise and $f, g : C \to \mathbb{R}^l$ are defined by

$$f(x) := (f_1(x), \cdots, f_l(x)), \quad g(x) := (g_1(x), \cdots, g_l(x)).$$

A program (D) dual to (P) is given in geometric terms by:

(D) $\qquad\qquad$ Maximize λ subject to $\Lambda_\lambda \subset H^+(u, v)$

where

$$H(u, v) := \{(y, z) \in \mathbb{R}^l \times Y : u^T y + < v, z >= 0\}$$

is a closed hyperplane in $\mathbb{R}^l \times Y$ through (θ, θ) not parallel to $\mathbb{R}^l$ and $H^+(u, v)$ is the corresponding nonnegative halfspace. More precisely (D) is given by

$$(D) \quad \begin{cases} \text{Maximize } \lambda \text{ on} \\ N := \{(u, v, \lambda) \in \mathbb{R}^l \times Y^* \times \mathbb{R} : u \geq \theta, u \neq \theta, v \in K^+, \\ u^T(f(x) - \lambda g(x)) + < v, h(x) >\geq 0 \text{ for all } x \in C\} \end{cases}$$

Here Y^* is the dual space to Y and

$$K^+ := \{v \in Y^* :< v, z >\geq 0 \text{ for all } z \in K\}$$

is the cone dual to K.

It is evident from the geometric motivation of the program (D) dual to (P) that a weak duality result holds, i.e.

$$x \in M \,(x \text{ feasible for (P)}), (u, v, \lambda) \in N((u, v, \lambda) \text{ feasible for (D)}) \Rightarrow \lambda \leq F(x).$$

Furthermore:

$$(u, v, \inf(P)) \in N \Rightarrow (u, v, \inf(P)) \text{ is a solution of (D) and } \max(D) = \inf(P).$$

A strong duality result is given in

Theorem 2.1. *Let the generalized fractional program (P) be given. Suppose the assumptions (A)i) – iv) are fulfilled. With*

$$\Lambda_{\inf(P)} := \{(f(x) - \inf(P)g(x) + y, h(x) + z) : x \in C, y \geq \theta, z \in K\}$$

let

$$(CQ) \qquad\qquad\qquad \text{int}\Lambda_{\inf(P)} \cap \mathbb{R}^l \times \{\theta\} \neq \emptyset.$$

Then the program (D) dual to (P) has a solution and there is no duality gap: $\max(D) = \inf(P)$.

Proof. We obtain the desired result in three steps.

   i) $(\theta, \theta) \notin \text{int}\Lambda_{\inf(P)}$ by the definition of $\inf(P)$.

   ii) (θ, θ) and the nonempty convex set $\Lambda_{\inf(P)}$ can be separated by a closed hyperplane in $\mathbb{R}^l \times Y$ such that $\text{int}\Lambda_{\inf(P)}$ lies in the corresponding open positive halfspace. Thus there exist

$$(u, v) \in \mathbb{R}^l \times Y^* \setminus \{(\theta, \theta)\}$$

such that

$$0 \leq u^T(f(x) - \inf(P)g(x) + y) + < v, h(x) + z >$$
$$\text{for all } x \in C, \, y \geq \theta, \, z \in K$$

and

$$0 < u^T q + < v, r > \quad \text{for all } (q, r) \in \text{int}\Lambda_{\inf(P)}.$$

Obviously

$$u \geq \theta, \, v \in K^+$$

and

$$0 \leq u^T(f(x) - \inf(P)g(x)) + < v, h(x) > \quad \text{for all } x \in C.$$

We get $u \neq \theta$ since by (CQ) there exists $(q, \theta) \in \text{int}\Lambda_{\inf(P)}$. Thus $(u, v, \inf(P)) \in N$ is feasible for the program (D) dual to (P).

iii) An application of weak duality gives the desired result.

In certain cases we can give simple equivalent formulations for the constraint qualification (CQ) in theorem 2.1. In the following cone (A) always means the convex conical hull of A, i.e. the smallest convex cone containing A.

Theorem 2.2. Let the assumptions (A)i) – iv) be fulfilled. Then we have:
  i) If Y is finite dimensional the following statements are equivalent:
    a) $\text{int}\Lambda_{\inf(P)} \cap \mathbb{R}^l \times \{\theta\} \neq \emptyset$.
    b) $(h(C) + K)^+ = \{\theta\}$ (Karlin constraint qualification)
    c) cone $(h(C) + K) = Y$.
  ii) If $\text{int}K \neq \emptyset$ then a), b), c) in i) are equivalent to
    d) There exists $\hat{x} \in C$ with $h(\hat{x}) \in \text{int}K$ (Slater constraint qualification).

Proof. i) Let Y be finite dimensional.
a) $\Rightarrow$ b) Suppose $(q, \theta) \in \text{int}\Lambda_{\inf(P)}$, let $p \in (h(C) + K)^+ \setminus \{\theta\}$. Then (θ, p) determines a hyperplane in $\mathbb{R}^l \times Y$ through (θ, θ) separating $(q, \theta) \in \text{int}\Lambda_{\inf(P)}$ from $\Lambda_{\inf(P)}$, a contradiction. Thus $(h(C) + K)^+ = \{\theta\}$.
b) $\Rightarrow$ c) Suppose $(h(C) + K)^+ = \{\theta\}$. If $cone(h(C) + K) \not\subseteq Y$ an element $y \in Y \setminus cone(h(C) + K)$ can be separated from $cone(h(C) + K)$. Thus there exists $p \in Y^* \setminus \{\theta\}$ with

$$< p, y > \leq < p, \lambda(h(x) + z) > \quad \text{for all } \lambda \geq 0, x \in C, z \in K$$

and consequently $p \in (h(C) + K)^+$ contradicting $p \neq \theta$. Thus $cone(h(C) + K) = Y$.
c) $\Rightarrow$ a) Suppose $cone(h(C) + K) = Y$. We have

$$M := \{x \in X : x \in C, h(x) \in -K\} \neq \emptyset$$

since otherwise $\theta \notin h(C)) + K$ and a separation argument again leads to a contradiction. Then we have

$$(f(\hat{x}) - \inf(P)g(\hat{x}) + \hat{y}, \theta) \in \text{int}\Lambda_{\inf(P)} \cap \mathbb{R}^l \times \{\theta\} \quad \text{for all } \hat{x} \in M, \hat{y} > \theta.$$

This can be seen by noting that $\mathbb{R}^l \times Y$ is finite dimensional and that $(f(\hat{x}) - \inf(P)g(\hat{x}) + \hat{y}, \theta)$ belongs to the algebraic interior of $\Lambda_{\inf(P)}$ and thus to $\text{int}\Lambda_{\inf(P)}$.

ii) Suppose $\text{int}K \neq \emptyset$ (possibly Y infinite dimensional).

a) $\Rightarrow$ b) See i).

b) $\Rightarrow$ c) Suppose $(h(C) + K)^+ = \{\theta\}$. The observation

$$h(C) + \text{int}K \subset \text{int cone}(\text{h(C)} + \text{K})$$

leads to $cone(h(C) + K) = Y$ just as in i).

c) $\Rightarrow$ d) Suppose $cone(h(C) + K) = Y$. The assumption

$$(h(C) + K) \cap -\text{int}K = \emptyset$$

leads via a separation argument to a contradiction. Thus there exists an element $\hat{x} \in C$ with

$$h(\hat{x}) \in -(K + \text{int}K) \subset -\text{int}K.$$

d) $\Rightarrow$ a) Suppose there exists $\hat{x} \in C$ with $h(\hat{x}) \in -\text{int}K$. Then

$$(f(\hat{x}) - \inf(P)g(\hat{x}) + \hat{y}, \theta) \in \text{int}\Lambda_{\inf(P)} \cap \mathbb{R}^l \times \{\theta\} \quad \text{for all } \hat{y} > \theta.$$

For the rest of this section we consider generalized fractional programs with affine linear implicit constraints and show that in the finite dimensional case a strong duality result holds without the constraint qualification (CQ) in Theorem 2.1.

In the following theorem which is essentially only a slight modification of a theorem in Rockafellar [11, p. 187], $ri(C)$ means the relative interior of a set $C \subset \mathbb{R}^n$, i.e. the interior of C relative to $aff(C)$, the affine hull of C.

Theorem 2.3. *Let the generalized fractional program (P) be given and the assumptions (A)i) – iv) be fulfilled. Furthermore assume:*

$$X = \mathbb{R}^n, \ Y = \mathbb{R}^m, \ h : \mathbb{R}^n \to \mathbb{R}^m \ \text{affine linear},$$

$$K \subset \mathbb{R}^m \ \text{polyhedral cone}$$

$$M \cap ri(C) \neq \emptyset.$$

Then the program (D) dual to (P) has a solution and there is no duality gap: $\max(D) = \inf(P)$.

Proof. We sketch the proof. As an abbreviation we define $\psi := f - \inf(P)g$. Let

$$C_1 := \{(\psi(x) + y, h(x)) : x \in C, y > \theta\}, \ C_2 := -\mathbb{R}^l_+ \times K$$

where R^l_+ denotes the nonnegative orthant in R^l. C_1 and C_2 are nonempty disjoint convex sets in $\mathrm{R}^l \times \mathrm{R}^m$, C_2 is a polyhedral cone. Then there exists a hyperplane in $\mathrm{R}^l \times \mathrm{R}^m$ separating C_1 and C_2 and not containing C_1 (Rockafellar [11, p. 181]). Then we easily get the existence of

$$(u, v) \in \mathrm{R}^l \times \mathrm{R}^m \setminus \{(\theta, \theta)\}, \ u \geq \theta, \ v \in K^+$$

with

$$0 \leq u^T \psi(x) + v^T h(x) \ \text{ for all } \ x \in C$$

and

$$0 < u^T (\psi(x_0) + y_0) + v^T h(x_0)$$

for at least one pair (x_0, y_0) with $x_0 \in C$, $y_0 > \theta$.

If $u = \theta$ we have $0 \leq v^T h(x)$ for all $x \in C$, $0 < v^T h(x_0)$ for at least one $x_0 \in C$. By assumption there exists an $\hat{x} \in M \cap ri(C)$, since $v \in K^+$ we necessarily have $0 = v^T h(\hat{x})$. For a given $x \in C$ there exists an $\mu > 1$ with $\mu \hat{x} + (1 - \mu)x \in C$ (Rockafellar [11, p. 47]) and thus

$$\begin{aligned} 0 \leq v^T h(\mu \hat{x} + (1 - \mu)x) &= \mu v^T h(\hat{x}) + (1 - \mu)v^T h(x) \ (h \ \text{affine linear}) \\ &= (1 - \mu)v^T h(x) && (v^T h(\hat{x}) = 0) \\ &\leq 0 && (1 - \mu < 0, v^T h(x) \geq 0) \end{aligned}$$

which implies $v^T h(x) = 0$, contradicting $0 < v^T h(x_0)$ for at least one $x_0 \in C$. Thus $(u, v, \inf(P))$ is feasible for the program (D) dual to (P) and by weak duality we get the desired result.

If in Theorem 2.3 the set C of explicit constraints is a polyhedral cone the feasible set

$$M := \{x \in \mathrm{R}^n : x \in C, h(x) \in -K\}$$

can be written as

$$M := \{x \in \mathrm{R}^n : (-x, h(x)) \in C \times -K\}$$

with the polyhedral cone $C \times K$ in $\mathrm{R}^n \times \mathrm{R}^m$. A direct application of Theorem 2.3 leads to

Theorem 2.4. *Let the generalized fractional program (P) be given and the assumptions (A)i) – iv) be fulfilled. Furthermore assume:*

$$X = \mathrm{R}^n, Y = \mathrm{R}^m, C \subset \mathrm{R}^m \ \text{ and } \ K \subset \mathrm{R}^m \ \text{ polyhedral cones,}$$

$$h : \mathrm{R}^n \to \mathrm{R}^m \ \text{ affine linear } \ f - \inf(P)g : \mathrm{R}^n \to \mathrm{R}^l \ \text{ convex .}$$

Then the program (D) dual to (P) has a solution and there is no duality gap: $\max(D) = \inf(P)$.

For the special case that f_i, g_i are affine linear for $i = 1, \cdots, l$ and C, K are the nonnegative orthants in R^n resp. R^m Theorem 2.4 reduces to one of the main results in Crouzeix, Ferland and Schaible [3, Theorem 4.1]. Furthermore the solvability of (P) can be characterized as we will show in the following theorem (for an alternative proof see Theorem 4.2 in Crouzeix, Ferland and Schaible [3]).

Theorem 2.5. *Let the generalized fractional program (P) be given and the assumptions (A)i) – iv) be fulfilled. Furthermore assume:*

$$X = \mathbb{R}^n, Y = \mathbb{R}^m, C \subset \mathbb{R}^m \text{ and } K \subset \mathbb{R}^m \text{ polyhedral cones,}$$

$$h : \mathbb{R}^n \to \mathbb{R}^m; f, g : \mathbb{R}^n \to \mathbb{R}^l \text{ affine linear :}$$

$$h(x) = Hx + \eta, f(x) = Ax + \alpha, g(x) = Bx + \beta.$$

Then (P) has a solution if and only if for all solutions $(u, v, \inf(P))$ of (D) one has

$$\inf(P)u^T \beta = u^T \alpha + v^T \eta.$$

Proof. If $(u, v, \inf(P))$ is a solution of (D) one has

$$0 \leq u^T(Ax + \alpha - \inf(P)(Bx + \beta)) + v^T(Hx + \eta) \text{ for all } x \in C.$$

With $x = \theta$ we get

$$\inf(P)u^T \beta \leq u^T \alpha + v^T \eta \text{ for all solutions } (u, v, \inf(P)) \text{ of } (D).$$

Now (P) has no solution if and only if

$$(\theta, \theta) \notin \Lambda_{\inf(P)} := \{(f(x) - \inf(P)g(x) + y, h(x) + z) : x \in C, y \geq \theta, z \in K\}.$$

Since f, g, h are affine linear and C, K are polyhedral cones the nonempty set $\Lambda_{\inf(P)}$ is convex and closed. Thus (P) has no solution if and only if $\{(\theta, \theta)\}$ and $\Lambda_{\inf(P)}$ can be strictly separated by a hyperplane. But this is equivalent to the existence of a solution $(u, v, \inf(P))$ of (D) with

$$\inf(P)u^T \beta < u^T \alpha + v^T \eta,$$

the theorem is proven.

3. Applications.

In the first part of this section we show that one of the earliest applications of duality in generalized fractional programming was given by Krabs [7] in the study of duality in discrete rational Chebyshev-approximation problems.

Consider the problem

$$(P) \quad \begin{cases} \text{Minimize } F(a, b) := \max_{i=1,\cdots,l} |f_i - \frac{(Ua)_i}{(Vb)_i}| \\ \text{on } M := \{(a, b) \in \mathbb{R}^r \times \mathbb{R}^s : Vb \geq e\} \end{cases}$$

where $f = (f_i) \in \mathbb{R}^m$, $U = (u_{ij}) \in \mathbb{R}^{m \times r}$, $V = (v_{ik}) \in \mathbb{R}^{m \times s}$ are given and $e := (1, \cdots, 1)^T \in \mathbb{R}^m$.

With $V_f := \mathrm{diag}(f_1, \cdots, f_m)V = (f_i v_{ik}) \in \mathbb{R}^{m \times s}$ the program (P) is obviously equivalent to the generalized fractional program

$$\text{Minimize } \mu \text{ subject to}$$

$$\begin{pmatrix} -U & V_f \\ U & -V_f \end{pmatrix} \begin{pmatrix} a \\ b \end{pmatrix} \leq \mu \begin{pmatrix} \theta & V \\ \theta & V \end{pmatrix} \begin{pmatrix} a \\ b \end{pmatrix}$$

$$(\theta - V)\begin{pmatrix} a \\ b \end{pmatrix} + e \leq \theta.$$

Thus as the program dual to (P) we get

$$(D) \qquad \begin{cases} \text{Maximize } \lambda \text{ subject to } u = \begin{pmatrix} u_1 \\ u_2 \end{pmatrix} \geq \theta, u \neq \theta, v \geq \theta \\ U^T(u_1 - u_2) = \theta, V_f^T(u_1 - u_2) = \lambda V^T(u_1 + u_2) + V^T v \end{cases}$$

resp.

$$(D) \qquad \begin{cases} \text{Maximize } \lambda \text{ subject to } c \neq \theta, v \geq \theta \\ U^T c = \theta, V_f^T c = V^T(\lambda|c| + v) \end{cases}$$

This agrees (at least if $\inf(P) > 0$) exactly with the formulation of the program dual to (P) given by Krabs [7]. From Theorem 2.4 resp. Theorem 2.5 we immediately get the result:

Let (P) be feasible. Then we have
 a) (D) has a solution and $\max(D) = \inf(P)$.
 b) (P) has a solution if and only if $v = \theta$ for all solutions $(c, v, \inf(P))$ of (D).
Obviously more general constraints in (P) can be handled in a similar way.
As a further application of the duality results in section 2 we show that Theorem 2.1 can be applied to obtain necessary optimality conditions for nonlinearly constrained min-max programs.

Theorem 3.1. *Let the nonlinearly constrained min-max program*

$$(P) \qquad \begin{cases} \text{Minimize } F(x) := \max_{i=1,\cdots,l} f_i(x) \\ \text{on } M := \{x \in X : x \in C, h(x) \in -K\} \end{cases}$$

be given. Suppose
A)i) X, Y are Banach spaces, $C \subset X$ is nonempty, closed and convex, $K \subset Y$ is a nonempty closed convex cone.
ii) $f = (f_1, \cdots, f_l) : X \to \mathbb{R}^l$ is Fréchet-differentiable, $h : X \to Y$ is continuously Fréchet-differentiable at a local solution $\overline{x} \in M$ of (P).
Furthermore assume

$$(CQ) \qquad h'(\overline{x})\mathrm{cone}(C - x) + \mathrm{cone}(K + h(\overline{x})) = Y.$$

Then there exists $(\overline{u}, \overline{v}) \in V^* \times \mathbb{R}^*$ with

a) $\overline{u} \geq \theta$, $\overline{u} \neq \theta$, $\overline{u}_i = 0$ for all $i \notin I(\overline{x}) := \{i : f_i(\overline{x}) = F(\overline{x})\}, \overline{v} \in K^+$.

b) $(\overline{u}^T f'(\overline{x}) + \overline{v} \cdot h'(\overline{x}))(x - \overline{x}) \geq 0$ for all $x \in C$.

c) $< \overline{v}, h(\overline{x}) > = 0$.

Proof. The proof proceeds along the same lines as the corresponding one for smooth optimization problems (see for instance Werner [14, p. 166]). We therefore leave out some details in the proof.

i) First one observes that F has a convex Hadamard-Variation at $\overline{x}$ given by

$$F'(\overline{x}; p) := \max_{i \in I(\overline{x})} f_i'(\overline{x}) p$$

This means:

For given $\{t_k\} \subset \mathbb{R}_+$, $\{r_k\} \subset X$ with $t_k \to 0$, $r_k / t_k \to \theta$

$$\lim_{k \to \infty} (F(\overline{x} + t_k p + r_k) - F(\overline{x})) / t_k = \max_{i \in I(\overline{x})} f_i'(\overline{x}) p.$$

ii) Since $\overline{x} \in M$ is a local solution of (P) we have

$$F'(\overline{x}; p) \geq 0 \quad \text{for all } p \in T(M; \overline{x})$$

where $T(M; \overline{x}) := \{p \in X : \text{There exist } \{t_k\} \subset \mathbb{R}_+, \{r_k\} \subset X \text{ with}$

i) $\overline{x} + t_k p + r_k \in M$

ii) $t_k \to 0, r_k / t_k \to \theta\}$

denotes the tangent cone to M at $\overline{x}$. A result first proven by Robinson [10] shows that

$$L(M; \overline{x}) := \{p \in X : p \in cone(C - \overline{x}), h'(\overline{x}) p \in -cone(K + h(\overline{x}))\} \subset T(M; \overline{x})$$

(for an alternative proof see Werner [14, p. 157]). Thus $\overline{p} = \theta$ is a solution of the linearized program

(PL)   Minimize $F'(\overline{x}; p)$ on $L(M; \overline{x})$

and $\min(PL) = 0$.

iii) Now we want to apply Theorem 2.1. Therefore we have to show that the constraint qualification in Theorem 2.1 holds, i.e. that

$$\text{int} \Lambda_0 \cap \mathbb{R}^{|I(\overline{x})|} \times \{\theta\} \neq \emptyset$$

with

$$\Lambda_0 := \{((f_i'(\overline{x}) p + y_i)_{i \in I(\overline{x})}, h'(\overline{x}) p + z) : p \in cone(C - \overline{x}),$$
$$y_i \geq 0 (i \in I(\overline{x})), z \in cone(K + h(\overline{x}))\}.$$

In view of Theorem 2.2 and

$$(CQ) \qquad h'(\overline{x})cone(C - \overline{x}) + cone(K + h(\overline{x})) = Y$$

this is evident if Y is finite dimensional or $\text{int}K \neq \emptyset$. Otherwise a generalized open mapping theorem of Zowe and Kurzyusz [15, Theorem 2.1] shows the existence of a $\rho > 0$ such that

$$B[\theta; \rho] \subset h'(\overline{x})((C - \overline{x}) \cap B[\theta; 1]) + (K + h(\overline{x})) \cap B[\theta, 1]$$

where $B[\theta, \rho]$ denotes the closed ball with center θ and radius ρ. But then it is easily verified that

$$((\hat{y}_i)_{i \in I(\overline{x})}, \theta) \in \text{int}\Lambda_0 \cap \mathbb{R}^{|I(\overline{x})|} \times \{\theta\}$$
$$\text{for all } (\hat{y}_i)_{i \in I(\overline{x})} \text{ with } \hat{y}_i > 0 \ (i \in I(\overline{x}))$$

Theorem 2.1 tells us that the program (DL) dual to (PL) has a solution and that $\max(DL) = \min(PL) = 0$. Thus there exist

$$(\overline{u}_i)_{i \in I(\overline{x})} \text{ with } \overline{u}_i \geq 0 \ (i \in I(\overline{x})), \overline{v} \in cone(K + h(\overline{x}))^+$$

with

$$0 \leq \Big(\sum_{i \in I(\overline{x})} \overline{u}_i \, f_i'(\overline{x}) + \overline{v} \cdot h'(\overline{x}) \Big)p \text{ for all } p \in cone(C - \overline{x}).$$

Defining $\overline{u}_i = 0$ for $i \notin I(\overline{x})$ and observing that $\overline{v} \in cone(K + h(\overline{x}))^+$ is equivalent to $\overline{v} \in K^+$, $< \overline{v}, h(\overline{x}) >= 0$, we get the desired result.

As a final remark we note that a similar approach in obtaining necessary optimality conditions is possible for other nonsmooth objective functions. For instance Parida and Sen [9] studied objective functions $F : \mathbb{R}^n \to \mathbb{R}$ of the form

$$F(x) := f(x) + \max_{s \in S} s^T x$$

where $f : \mathbb{R}^n \to \mathbb{R}$ is supposed to be smooth and $S \subset \mathbb{R}^n$ compact. Then it is an easy exercise to derive necessary optimality conditions for a local solution $\overline{x}$ of

$$\text{Minimize } F(x) \text{ on } M := \{x \in \mathbb{R}^n : x \in C, h(x) \in -K\}$$

under the same assumptions (A)i), ii) (but with $X = \mathbb{R}^n$, $Y = \mathbb{R}^m$) and (CQ) as in Theorem 3.1.

References.

[1] Crouzeix, J. P.: *Contributions à l'étude des fonctions quasiconvexes*. Doctoral Thesis, Université de Clermont (Clermont, France, 1977).

[2] Crouzeix, J. P.: *A duality framework in quasiconvex programming*. In: S. Schaible and W. T. Ziemba (eds.), Generalized Concavity in Optimization and Economics (Academic Press, New York (1981), 207 – 225.)

[3] Crouzeix, J. P; Ferland, J. A. and Schaible, S.: *Duality in generalized linear fractional programming*. Mathematical Programming 27 (1983), 342 – 354.

[4] Flachs, J.: *Global saddle-point duality for quasi-concave programs, II*. Mathematical Programming 24 (1982), 326 – 345.

[5] Gol'stein E.G.: *Theory of convex programming*. Translations of mathematical monographs 36 (American Mathematical Society, Providence, Rhode Island, 1972).

[6] Jagannathan, R. and Schaible, S.: *Duality in generalized linear fractional programming via Farkas Lemma*. Journal of Optimization Theory and Applications 41 (1983), 417 – 424.

[7] Krabs, W.: *Dualität bei diskreter rationaler Approximation*. ISNM 7 (1967), 33 – 41.

[8] Mangasarian, O.L.: *Nonlinear programming*. Mc Graw, New York, 1969.

[9] Parida, J. and Sen, A.: *Duality and existence theory for nondifferentiable programming*. Journal of Optimization Theory and Applications 48 (1986), 451 – 458.

[10] Robinson, S. M.: *Stability theory for systems of inequalities, Part II: Differentiable nonlinear systems*. SIAM J. Numer. Anal. 13 (1976), 497 – 513.

[11] Rockafellar, R.T.: *Convex Analysis*. Princeton University Press, Princeton, NJ, 1970.

[12] Schaible, S.: *A survey of fractional programming*. In: S. Schaible and W. T. Ziemba (eds.), Generalized Concavity in Optimization and Economics (Academic Press, New York (1981), 417 – 440.)

[13] Schaible, S.: *Fractional programming*. Zeitschrift für Operations Research 27 (1983), 39 – 54.

[14] Werner, J.: *Optimization. Theory and Applications*. Vieweg, Braunschweig-Wiesbaden, 1984.

[15] Zowe, J. and Kurzyusz, S.: *Regularity and stability for the mathematical programming problem in Banach spaces*. Appl. Math. Optim. 5 (1979), 49 – 62.

International Series of
Numerical Mathematics, Vol. 84
(c) 1988 Birkhäuser Verlag Basel

On Recent Developments in Linear Programming

Uwe Zimmermann
Abteilung für Mathematische Optimierung
Universität Braunschweig
3300 Braunschweig, West Germany

Introduction.

Linear programming remains a central subject of Mathematical Programming although already in 1947, Dantzig developed the Simplex method for solving Linear Programming problems. That method has been implemented in quite powerful codes which are very efficient for solving real world problems. With the growing interest in the complexity of algorithms, however, it turned out that the Simplex method is exponential in the worst case (Klee-Minty [1972]). Until now the existence of pivoting rules resulting in a polynomial variant of the Simplex Method is an open question. For most known rules conterexamples to polynomiality have been constructed. The worst case approach itself is due to much criticizm. The analysis of the average case is usually much harder, but seems to explain the typically efficient performance of the Simplex method much better. For a broad discussion of average case analysis of the Simplex method we refer the reader to Borgwardt [1984].

The exponential performance of the Simplex method raised the question whether linear programming problems can be solved in polynomial time by some other algorithm. The positive answer is due to Khachian ([1979], [1980]) who succeeded in proving a polynomial time bound for the ellipsoid method. On the other hand, all attempts to implement an efficient version of the ellipsoid method more or less failed in comparison to the Simplex method. In 1984, Karmarkar proposed another polynomial algorithm for solving linear programming problems. Under suitable assumptions his algorithm has better worst case complexity than the ellipsoid method. His claim that his method outperforms the Simplex method, gave reason to much controverse in the mathematical programming community. On the other hand that claim stimulated much recent research in the field of linear programming. The purpose of this expository paper is to introduce to the different developments influenced by Karmarkar's findings and to provide a list of related papers. It goes without saying that for such a fast developing area references must be incomplete.

In chapter I, we consider extensions and improvements of the original approach proposed in Karmarkar [1984]. In particular, these methods use explicitly or implicitly projective transformations for the formulation of an iterative step. This fact should not be confused with the use of projections occuring in all methods referenced in this survey. The use of projective transformations allows a control of the decrease of certain potential functions per iteration which leads to polynomial time bounds. All methods in chapter II are not known to be polynomial.

We begin with a detailed development of the basic projective method for solving a feasibility problem in section 1. Its application to linear programming problems is discussed in section 2. In section 3 we describe a variant of de Ghellinck and Vial [1986]. The final section 4 of chapter I tries to gather information on approaches for an actual implementation of the method. All the many differing proposals in the literature are made with more or less preliminary computational experience. Anybody interested in the development of an LP-code will find a vast field for further experiments. Most of the important addressed difficulties are shared by the other interior point methods in chapter II.

After the broad discussion of the projective method in order to keep the survey short, we decided to give only rather brief descriptions of related interior point methods in chapter II. However, we should stress the fact that at the time being nobody can tell which approach will turn out to be more or less successful for solving LP in the future.

In section 5, projective transformations are replaced by affine transformations which are conceptually simpler. On the other hand, convergence of the resulting "scaling methods" can only be proved under more or less technical assumptions.

In section 6, certain barrier function methods are related to Karmarkar's approach in order to make use of well developed techniques from nonlinear programming.

Last but not least, a related penalty approach with globally linear and locally superlinear convergence under suitable assumptions is described in section 7.

I. The Projective Algorithm.

1. The Basic Method

In 1984, Karmarkar proposed a new polynomial method for solving the linear programming problem (LP) which we call the projective method. That algorithm directly applies only to LPs in a special form but Karmarkar shows that any LP can be transformed to the special form without destroying the complexity bound. In this section, we discuss the basic projective method which constructs a feasible rational solution x of the linear system

$$(1.1) \qquad Ax = 0, \ \mathbf{1}^T x = n, \ x \geq 0, \ c^T x \leq 0,$$

for rational $m \cdot n$-matrix A, n-vector c, with $A\mathbf{1} = 0$. Starting from the initial solution $\mathbf{1}$ a sequence of solutions $x \in P \cap S$ is generated where

$$P := \{x | Ax = 0\}, \quad S := \{x | \mathbf{1}^T x = n, x \geq 0\}.$$

In order to drive $c^T x$ to 0, $c^T x$ is locally minimized in a ball of feasible points around the current solution. We consider balls $B(\underline{x}, r)$ centered at $\underline{x}$ of radius r in the affine hull of the simplex S, i.e.

$$B(\underline{x}, r) := \{x | \mathbf{1}^T x = n, (x - \underline{x})^T (x - \underline{x}) \leq r^2\}.$$

In fact, we solve

$$\min\{c^T x | x \in P \cap B(1, \tfrac{1}{2}r)\}$$

where $r := [n/(n-1)]^{1/2}$. $B(1, r)$ is the largest sphere centered at 1 inside the simplex S. Let p denote the projection of c to $U := \{x | Ax = 0, 1^T x = 0\}$ (cf. figure 1).

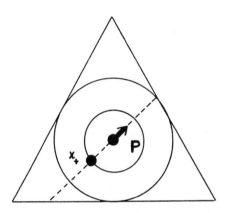

Figure 1: Initial Step.

Minimization on $P \cap B(1, \tfrac{1}{2}r)$ is much easier than minimization on $P \cap S$ (in figure 1 $P \cap S$ is indicated by a dashed line). In fact, moving from 1 opposite to the direction p as far as possible leads to the desired minimum, i.e.

$$x_+ := 1 - \frac{1}{2}r\frac{p}{\|p\|}.$$

Here, $\| \cdot \|$ denotes the Euclidean norm. x_+ defines the first iterate. The following iterations need some preparation in order to center the current solution x_+ in a suitable simplex. For that purpose Karmarkar uses a projective map $T : S \rightarrow S$ defined by

$$T(x) := \frac{n}{1^T D^{-1}x}D^{-1}x$$

where D is a diagonal matrix with diagonal $(x_+)_i$, $1 \le i \le n$. In short notation, we write $D := \text{diag}(x_+)$. The invers of T is given by

$$T^{-1}(y) := \frac{n}{1^T Dy}Dy.$$

Obviously, T maps x_+ to $\mathbf{1}$ (cf. figure 2).

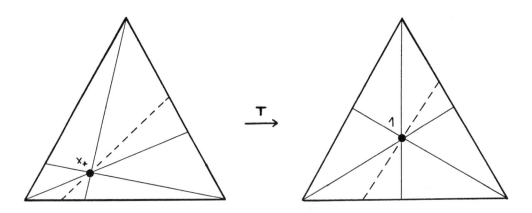

Figure 2: The Projective Mapping.

Cancelling some irrelevant positive factors $n/(\mathbf{1}^T Dy)$, the original problem (1.1) is transformed to the equivalent problem

$$(1.2) \qquad ADy = 0, \ \mathbf{1}^T y = n, \ y \geq 0, \ c^T Dy \leq 0$$

which has the same structure as the original problem. We can now repeat the initial step for the transformed problem and, successively transform its solution y_+ back to the original space. The complete iteration is given below.

The iterative step 1.1
1. $x := x_+$; $D := \mathrm{diag}(x)$
2. $p := [I - (AD)^T (AD^2 A^T)^{-1} (AD) - \frac{1}{n} \mathbf{1}\mathbf{1}^T] Dc$
3. $y_+ := \mathbf{1} - \frac{1}{2} r \frac{p}{\|p\|}$
4. $x_+ := \frac{n}{\mathbf{1}^T Dy_+} Dy_+$

We observe that one iterative step consists of $O(m^2 n)$ arithmetic operations (cf. section 4). The greatest part of the computational effort is necessary for the computation of the projection of the transformed cost vector Dc to the transformed subspace $\{y \mid ADy = 0, \mathbf{1}^T = 0\}$. The formula given above follows from elementary linear algebra using the fact $AD\mathbf{1} = 0$ and is valid only if A is of full row rank. In general, the projection p may be defined in terms of pseudoinverses (cf. Gay [1985]).

In order to derive a polynomial time bound on the number of the iterations, some descent function monitoring the success of the iterations must be known. As the objective function does not necessarily decrease in each iteration, Karmarkar suggests the use of $(c^T x)^n / \Pi x$, where $\Pi x := x_1 \cdots x_n$. The key to the polynomial behaviour of the algorithm is given in the following theorem.

Convergence Theorem 1.2. If (1.1) admits a feasibel solution then

$$\frac{(c^T x_+)^n}{\Pi x_+} < \frac{2}{e} \cdot \frac{(c^T x)^n}{\Pi x}.$$

The theorem shows the sucessful balance which the algorithm keeps between the objective function $c^T x$ and the barrier term $1/\Pi x$. We will describe a proof of theorem 1.2 based on the following lemma 1.3 which was independently observed by many researchers (e.g. cf. Blair [1985], Schrijver [1985], Padberg [1986]).

Lemma 1.3. Let $y \in B(1, \frac{1}{2}r)$. Then

$$\Pi y \geq \frac{1}{2}(1 + \frac{1/2}{n-1})^{n-1}.$$

Let $\hat{y}$ denote the optimal solution of

$$\min\{c^T D y \mid A D y = 0, y \in B(1, R)\}$$

where $R := [n(n-1)]^{1/2}$, i.e.

$$\hat{y} = 1 - R \cdot \frac{p}{\|p\|}.$$

Existence of a feasible solution to (1.2) implies $c^T D \hat{y} \leq 0$, as $B(1, R)$ contains the simplex S. In fact, $B(1, R)$ is the smallest sphere centered at 1 containing S (cf. figure 3).

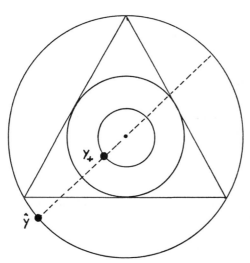

Figure 3: Proof of Convergence.

As $y_+ = (1 - \frac{1}{2}/(n-1))\mathbf{1} + \frac{1}{2}/(n-1)\hat{y}$, we find

$$c^T D y_+ \le (1 - \frac{1/2}{n-1})c^T D\mathbf{1} = (1 - \frac{1/2}{n-1})c^T x$$

where x denotes the current solution at the beginning of the iteration. Using lemma 1.3 and some elementary analytical inequalities, we derive

$$[\frac{c^T D y_+}{c^T x}]^n \cdot \frac{1}{\Pi y} \le (1 - \frac{1/2}{n-1})^n \cdot \frac{1}{\frac{1}{2}(1 + \frac{1}{2}/(n-1))^{n-1}} < \frac{2}{e}.$$

By $\Pi(Dy_+) = (\Pi y_+) \cdot (\Pi x)$ and by $x_+ = \beta \cdot Dy_+$ for some positive constant β, we find that the left hand side equals

$$= [\frac{c^T D y_+}{c^T x}]^n \cdot \frac{\Pi x}{\Pi(Dy_+)} = (\frac{c^T x_+}{c^T x})^n \frac{\Pi x}{\Pi x_+}$$

which yields theorem 1.2.

From theorem 1.2, we conclude that after k iterations with positive objective value

$$\frac{c^T x_+}{(\Pi x_+)^{1/n}} < (\frac{2}{e})^{k/n} \cdot \frac{c^T \mathbf{1}}{(\Pi x)^{1/n}} = (\frac{2}{e})^{k/n} \cdot \Sigma_j c_j.$$

As $x_+ \in S$, the arithmetic-geometric mean inequality bounds the denominator of the left-hand-side by 1 which implies

(1.3) $$c^T x_+ < (\frac{2}{e})^{k/n} \cdot \Sigma_j c_j.$$

(1.3) shows that in the worst case the algorithm converges linearly. In fact, Charnes, Song, and Wolfe [1984] provide examples for which the algorithm converges linearly. Although in linear programming such a convergence is not considered to be very fast it suffices to derive a polynomial bound on the number of the iterations of the projective method.

W.l.o.g. we assume that A and c are integral. Following Schrijver [1985] we use $T := \max\{|a_{ij}|, |c_j| \mid 1 \le i \le m, 1 \le j \le n\}$ as a measure of the input size of the problem (1.1). Obviously,

$$c^T x_+ < (\frac{2}{e})^{k/n} \cdot nT.$$

Therefore, after at most $K := \lceil (2/(1 - ln2))n^2 ln(nT) \rceil$ iterations we find a solution x_+ satisfying

(1.4) $$c^T x_+ < n^{-n} T^{-n}.$$

As $x_+ \in P \cap S$, some elementary linear algebra steps transform x_+ into a vertex x_0 of $P \cap S$ with $c^T x_0 \leq c^T x_+$. Let a_j/b_j be the j-th component of x_0 for appropriate nonnegative integers a_j, b_j, $1 \leq j \leq n$. Then, by Cramer's rule $1 \leq \Pi b \leq n^n T^n$. Thus $(c^T a) \cdot \Pi b < 1$. As c is integral, $c^T x_0 \leq 0$.

If (1.1) is infeasible Karmarkar's method stops after K iterations. Therefore, (1.1) is solved in $O(n^2 \log(nT))$ iterations, each of which needs $O(m^2 n)$ arithmetic operations. For a polynomial complexity bound, the necessary precision in the arithmetic operations must be shown to be polynomially bounded, too. Due to Schrijver [1985], $O(n^2 \log T)$ digits are sufficient. For a detailed discussion we refer to Grötschel, Lovasz, and Schrijver [1986].

The chosen fixed stepsize $(\frac{1}{2}r)$ of the basic method has raised several discussions. Better local improvement (c.f. e.g. Blair [1986]) is discussed as well as better asymptotic behaviour (c.f. e.g. Blum [1985]). Theoretically, one has to take into account the necessary precision in the arithmetic operations which bounds the steplenght in order to avoid infeasibility. On the other side for a practical implementation, much larger flexible stepsizes are known to reduce the total number of iterations considerably (cf. section 4).

On the theoretical side, for fixed stepsize Karmarkar [1984] devised an intricate modification of his basic projective method which reduces the complexity of the method by a factor $n^{1/2}$. In the basic projective method y_+ solves

$$\min\{c^T Dy | ADy = 0, y \in B(1, \frac{1}{2}r)\}.$$

Karmarkar observed that the ball may be replaced by an ellipsoid

$$E(1, r/4) := \{y | 1^T y = n, (y-1)^T E^{-2}(y-1) \leq (r/4)^2\}$$

provided that $E = \text{diag}(e)$ with $1/2 \leq (e_j)^2$. Then

$$B(1, r/8) \subseteq E(1, r/4) \subseteq B(1, \frac{1}{2}r)$$

implies that the complexity analysis is not essentially changed. The new optimal solution is $y' = 1 - (r/4) \cdot p'/\|p'\|$ where p' solves

$$\max\{c^T Dp' | Bp' = 0, p'^T E^{-2} p' \leq 1\}$$

where $B^T := (DA^T | 1^T)$. For $Eq := p'$ that problem transforms to

$$\max\{c^T DEq | BEq = 0, q^T q \leq 1\}$$

which is solved by the normalized projection of $c^T DE$ to the subspace defined by $BEq = 0$. Transforming back yields

$$p' = \alpha[I - E^2 B^T (BE^2 B^T)^{-1} B]E^2 Dc$$

for some $\alpha > 0$. Let $BE^2 B^T u := BE^2 Dc$. Then $p' = \alpha E^2 [Dc - B^T u]$. Shanno [1986] proposes the following approach for determining $u^T =: (\underline{u}^T, u_n)$. Let $(BE^2 Dc)^T =: (\underline{h}^T, h_n)$. If L is the Cholesky factor of $ADE^2 DA^T$, i.e. $LL^T = ADE^2 DA^T$, then

$$[LL^T - (1/\beta)ww^T]\underline{u} := g - (h_n/\beta)w,$$
$$u_n := (1/\beta)(h_n - w^T \underline{u}),$$

where $\beta := \mathbf{1}^T E^2 \mathbf{1}$, $w := ADE^2 \mathbf{1}$. As the first system is a rank one correction of LL^T, the formula of Shermann-Morrison-Woodbury can be used to calculate u in $O(m^2)$.

Now, the key to the theoretical improvement is Karmarkar's observation that updating $ADE^2 DA^T$ is easier than updating $AD^2 A^T$ as in the basic method. Instead of the changes in D only the changes in the matrix $\underline{D} = DE = \mathrm{diag}(d)$ with

(1.5) $$1/2 \leq (d_j/x_j)^2 \leq 2$$

are important. For some suitable $\underline{D}$ he proposes to define $\underline{D}_+ = \mathrm{diag}(d_+)$ by

$$(d)_{+j} := \begin{cases} \sigma \cdot d_j & 1/2 \leq [\sigma \cdot d_j/(x_+)_j]^2 \leq 2 \\ (x_+)_j & \text{otherwise} \end{cases}$$

where $\sigma := [\Sigma_j(x_+)_j/x_j]/n$ is some scaling factor. Then (1.5) remains true for $d := d_+$ and $x := x_+$ and

$$A(\underline{D}_+)^2 A^T = A\underline{D}^2 A^T + \Sigma_j[(d_+)_j^2 - d_j^2]A_j A_j^T,$$

where A_j denotes the j-th column of A. If k is the number of the indices violating

(1.6) $$1/2 \leq [\sigma \cdot d_j/(x_+)_j]^2 \leq 2$$

then k rank-one corrections lead from $A\underline{D}^2 A^T$ to $A(\underline{D}_+)^2 A^T$. Shanno [1985] proposes the use of an algorithm of Fletcher and Powell [1974] which constructs the new Cholesky factor in $O(k \cdot m^2)$ operations. Karmarkar shows that in m steps the number of rank-one updates is $O(m \cdot n^{1/2})$. Therefore, on the average each iteration needs only $O(m^2 n^{1/2})$ arithmetic operations compared to $O(m^2 n)$ in the original approach.

2. Application to linear programming

Standard formulations of linear programming problems are quite different from (1.1). Here, we consider

(2.1) $$z_* := \min\{c^T x | Ax = b, x \geq 0\}$$

for rational data c, A, and b. Karmarkar's projective method directly solves (2.1) only under the quite restrictive assumptions

(A) initial interior point known,

(B) homogeneous constraints, boundedness of the feasible set,

(C) optimal objective value known.

Karmarkar [1984] shows that at least in theory (A) – (C) can be achieved by suitable transformations of the given LP. Various approaches are proposed in the references.

For theoretical purposes we sketch the following reduction of (2.1) to (1.1) (similar to Schrijver [1985]). By the duality theorem of linear programming a feasible solution x, y to

$$Ax = b, \ y^T A \leq c^T, \ c^T x \leq y^T b, \ x \geq 0,$$

satisfies $z_* = c^T x$, i.e. x solves (2.1). Splitting y into the difference of two nonnegative vectors and adding some slack variables, the feasibility problem attains the form

(2.2)
$$Ax = b, \ x \geq 0,$$

with suitably modified A and b. Let T denote the maximum absolute value of the entries in A and b. If (2.2) is feasible than a feasible vertex x_0 exists. By Cramer's rule, its components are bounded by $n^n T^n$ where n is the current dimension of x. Therefore, it suffices to consider

$$Ax = b, \ x \geq 0, \ 1^T x + \alpha = n^{n+1} T^n, \ \alpha \geq 0.$$

Subtracting multiples of the new equation from the equations in $Ax = b$ leads to equivalent homogeneous equations. Subsequent scaling of the variables changes the right-hand-side of the new equation to n, and the feasibility problem translates to

$$Ax = 0, \ 1^T x = n, \ x \geq 0,$$

for suitably modified matrix A. If $A1 = 0$, then 1 solves the feasibility problem. Otherwise, by an obvious scaling of the rows and, in case of rows with zero right-hand-sides, by some additions of rows we can assume w.l.o.g. $A1 = 1$. Then,

(2.3)
$$Ax - 1z = 0, \ 1^T x + z = n, \ x \geq 0, \ z \geq 0, \ z \leq 0,$$

is an equivalent feasibility problem of the form (1.1) with $c^T := (0^T 1)$. As the size of this system is polynomially bounded in the size of the original LP, the basic method applied to (2.3) solves the LP in polynomial time.

For practical purposes the above approach is less helpful. The dimension of the resulting feasibility problem has $m + n + 2$ rows and $2(m + n) + 3$ columns where m and n denote the number of the rows and columns of the original LP. The used row combinations will destroy any nice structure (e.g. sparsity) of the original problem, and the theoretical bound drawn from Cramer's rule is much too large for practical implementations.

Cum grano salis, the assumptions (A) – (C) can be avoided by suitable modifications of the basic projective method.

(A) can be handled by some phase I approach. For example, solving

(2.4)
$$\min\{\alpha | Ax + (b - A\mathbf{1})\alpha = b, \; x \geq 0, \alpha \geq 0\}$$

leads to a suitable initial interior solution provided that no zero variables occur in the problem, i.e. if the LP is feasible then it has feasible solutions with $x_j > 0$ for arbitrary j, $1 \leq j \leq n$.

For (B), an approach of the following form is discussed by several authors (cf. Lustig [1985], and Gay [1985]). In a preliminary draft of his paper Karmarkar considers a projective mapping $T : \mathbb{R}^n \to \mathbb{R}^{n+1}$ defined by

$$y := T(x) := \frac{n+1}{\mathbf{1}^T D^{-1} x + 1} \begin{bmatrix} D^{-1}x \\ 1 \end{bmatrix},$$

$$x := T^{-1}(y) := \frac{1}{y_{n+1}} \cdot D \begin{bmatrix} y_1 \\ \vdots \\ y_n \end{bmatrix},$$

where $D := \mathrm{diag}(x_0)$ for some interior feasible point. T maps the nonnegative orthant into the simplex $S := \{y \in \mathbb{R}^{n+1} | \mathbf{1}^T y = n + 1, y \geq 0\}$. In particular, x_0 is mapped to $\mathbf{1}$. For bounded LP, y_{n+1} remains bounded from zero for all feasible solutions. The constraints of the LP transform into

$$[AD| - b]y = 0, \mathbf{1}^T y = n + 1, \; y \geq 0.$$

Any bounded optimal solution of (2.1) transform into an optimal solution of the LP (cf. Lustig [1985])

$$\min\{[c^T D - z_*]y | [AD| - b]y = 0, \mathbf{1}^T y = n + 1, \; y \geq 0\}.$$

A different preprocessing of the LP is proposed in Todd and Burrell [1985] who explicitly add a constraint bounding the sum of the variables after some equilibration of the problem. In fact, they assume that for $n := n + 3$ after equilibration and subsequent scaling the inequality $\mathbf{1}^T x \leq n - 2$ is either strictly satisfied by some optimal solution or that an optimal solution with equality in that inequality implies unboundedness of the LP. Then the original LP may be replaced by

$$\min\{c^T x | Ax - b\beta = 0, \beta = 1, \mathbf{1}^T x + \alpha = n - 1, \; x \geq 0, \; \alpha \geq 0, \; \beta \geq 0\}.$$

Adding one more column with artificial high cost M also covers (A):

$$\min\{[c^T x + M\delta | Ax - b\beta + (b - A\mathbf{1})\delta = 0, \beta = 1, \mathbf{1}^T x + \alpha + \beta + \delta = n,$$
$$x \geq 0, \ \alpha \geq 0, \ \beta \geq 0, \ \delta \geq 0\}.$$

Finally, $\beta = 1$ is homogenized by subtracting a multiple of the last constraint which results in the new equation $-\mathbf{1}^T x - \alpha + (n-1)\beta - \delta = 0$. For suitably modified A, the final transformed LP is of the form

$$(2.5) \qquad \min\{[c^T x | Ax = 0, \mathbf{1}^T x = n, x \geq 0\}$$

with $A\mathbf{1} = 0$. Boundedness remains a serious problem in both approaches.

To motivate the following *discussion of (C)*, let z_* be known. Then

$$(2.6) \qquad 0 = \min\{d^T x | Ax = 0, \mathbf{1}^T x = n, x \geq 0\}$$

for $d_j := c_j - z_*/n$, $1 \leq j \leq n$, since $d^T x = c^T x - z_*(\mathbf{1}^T x)/n = c^T x - z_*$ for all feasible solutions. Therefore, the basic method can be applied for solving (2.6). Now, the main result in Todd and Burrell [1985] is a version of the projective method for solving (2.5) without explicit knowledge of z_*. Gay [1985] shows that their ideas can also be combined with the above described projective transformation. The key idea is to use lower bounds from the dual of (2.5), i.e. of

$$\max\{n \cdot \tau | u^T A + \tau \mathbf{1}^T \leq c^T\},$$

in order to modify the coefficients of the primal problem. Let u be arbitrary. Then, (u, τ) with $\tau := \min\{(c - u^T A)_j | 1 \leq j \leq n\}$ is dually feasible and, therefore, $n \cdot \tau$ is a lower bound on $z*$.

Accordingly, the cost coefficients $c^T D$ in the transformed problem (1.2) are replaced by $(c - \tau \mathbf{1})^T D$. We denote the linear map projecting to a subspace U by P_U. Then the projection of the changed cost vector to the subspace $Y := \{y | ADy = 0\}$ is

$$P_Y D(c - \tau \mathbf{1}) =: v - \tau \cdot w.$$

A tentative new dual solution u is defined by the orthogonal complement, i.e.

$$v - \tau \cdot w + DA^T u := D(c - \tau \mathbf{1}).$$

Now, (u, τ) is dually feasible if $v - \tau \cdot w = D(c - \tau \cdot \mathbf{1} - A^T u) \geq 0$. Therefore, if $v - \tau \cdot w > 0$ then the lower bound can be improved by replacing τ by

$$\tau := \max\{\alpha | v - \alpha \cdot w \geq 0\}.$$

Otherwise, τ is not changed in the current iteration. After the possible update of τ the iterative step 1.1 is applied with the accordingly modified cost vector. The complete iterative step is given below.

The modified iterative step 2.1

1. $x := x_+$. $D := \text{diag}(x)$.
M1. For $Y := \{y | ADy = 0\}$ calculate $v := P_Y Dc$, $w := P_Y D1$.
M2. If $v - \tau \cdot w > 0$ then $\tau := \min\{v_j/w_j | w_j > 0\}$.
2. $p := [I - (1/n) \cdot \mathbf{1}\mathbf{1}^T](v - \tau \cdot w)$.
3. $y_+ := \mathbf{1} - (1/3)p/\|p\|$.
4. $x_+ := (n/\mathbf{1}^T Dy_+)Dy_+$.

We observe that the only modifications are in steps M1 and M2. In step 2, p can be derived from v and w by a simpler formula as $P_U = P_Q \cdot P_Y$ for the subspaces $Q := \{y | \mathbf{1}^T y = 0\}$ and $U := \{y | ADy = 0, \mathbf{1}^T y = 0\}$. At any stage of the method dual solutions are available. Todd and Burrel [1985] provide the following convergence result. After k iterations (starting from an interior initial solution x_0) the current primal solution x and the current lower bound $z := n \cdot \tau$ satisfy

$$\frac{c^T x - z_*}{c^T x_0 - z_*} \le \exp(-k/5n), \quad \frac{z_* - z}{c^T x_0 - z_*} \le \frac{\exp(-k/5n)}{1 - \exp(-k/5n)}.$$

Again, the worst case linear convergence assured by these formulas is sufficient to prove a polynomial bound on the number of the iterations of the method.

Using results from fractional programming, Anstreicher [1985] develops a similar method. A direct transformation of (2.5) as in the basic method results in the fractional program

$$\min\{(n \cdot c^T Dy)/(\mathbf{1}^T Dy) | ADy = 0, \mathbf{1}^T y = n, y \ge 0\}.$$

The fractional objective may be replaced by the linear objective $(n \cdot c - z \cdot \mathbf{1})^T Dy$ with parameter z. If z coincides with the optimal value z_* of the fractional program then the corresponding LP is equivalent to the fractional program. Anstreicher generates a sequence of lower bounds on z_* which are sufficient to show linear convergence. A similar approach is discussed in Nickels et al. [1985]. Goldfarb and Mehrotra [1986] remark that Anstreicher's lower bounds are locally inferior to those of Todd and Burrell.

Gonzaga [1986] discusses the importance of the simplex constraints in projective methods. He considers LP of the form

$$\min\{c^T x | Ax = 0, a^T x = n, x \ge 0\}$$

for $a \ge 0$, $a \ne 0$. Replacing w in step M2 by $w := P_Y Da$ and x_+ in step 4 by $x_+ := [n/a^T Dy_+)] \cdot Dy_+$ linear convergence is assured. Gonzaga proposes to replace steps 2 and 3 by some subiterations in Y starting from $\mathbf{1}$ which decrease the function

$$g(y) := \log \frac{[(v - \tau \cdot w)^T y]^n}{\Pi y}$$

with

$$\text{grad } g(y)^T := \frac{n}{(v - \tau \cdot w)^T y} \cdot (v - \tau \cdot w)^T - (1/y_1, \cdots, 1/y_n).$$

As can be seen from the proof of linear convergence in section 1, a sufficient decrease in $g(y)$ is the key to linear convergence. Now, the gradient of g at $\mathbf{1}$ parallels the projection p in method 2.1. Therefore, if the first subiteration is a gradient step linear convergence is implied. Further subiterations can be performed applying well known techniques from nonlinear optimization. In particular, further subiterations involve no recalculation of the projections v and w. Therefore, Gonzaga expects a reduction in the necessary computational effort.

Gay [1985] develops his version of the method directly in terms of the LP (2.1) under the assumption that the set of feasible solutions is bounded and contains an interior point.

Gale's iterative step 2.2

1. $x := x_+$; $D := \text{diag}(x)$.
M1. For $Y := \{y | ADy - b\alpha = 0\}$ calculate $v := P_Y \begin{bmatrix} Dc \\ 0 \end{bmatrix}$, $w := P_Y \begin{bmatrix} 0 \\ n+1 \end{bmatrix}$.
M2. If $v - \tau \cdot w > 0$ then $\tau := \min\{v_j/w_j | w_j > 0\}$.
2. $p := [I - \frac{1}{n+1} \cdot \mathbf{11}^T](v - \tau \cdot w)$.
3. $y_+ := \mathbf{1} - (1/3)p/\|p\|$.
4. $x_+ := \frac{1}{(y_+)_{n+1}} D \begin{bmatrix} (y_+)_1 \\ \vdots \\ (y_+)_n \end{bmatrix}$.

We observe that the transformed space has dimension $n + 1$. In step M1 the subspace Y is chosen with respect to the transformed linear system. Then, in the transformed space all steps coincide with the modified iterative step. In step 4 the constructed new solution y_+ is mapped back to the original space. Gay proves that after k iterations the current solution x and the current lower bound $z := (n+1) \cdot \tau$ satisfy the inequality

$$\frac{(c^T x - z)^{n+1}}{\Pi x} \leq \exp(-k/5) \cdot \frac{(c^T x_0 - z_0)^{n+1}}{\Pi x_0}$$

which due to boundedness enforces linear convergence (x_0 is an initial interior solution, and $z_0 = (n + 1) \cdot \tau_0$ is an initial lower bound on z_*). If $c \geq 0$, an initial lower bound for z_* is $z_0 = 0$. Otherwise, let $\mathbf{1}^T x \leq M$ for all feasible solutions of (2.1). Then $z_0 := M \cdot \min\{c_j | 1 \leq j \leq n\}$ is a suitable bound.

Goldfarb and Mehrotra [1986] develop variants of the method of Todd and Burrell with linear convergence when only certain approximations of the necessary projections are available. However, suitable approximations must lie in $Y := \{y | ADy = 0\}$. The convergence analysis in section 1 is based on the fact that the objective value of the current transformed objective is nonpositive at the point

$$\hat{y} := \mathbf{1} - R \cdot \frac{p}{\|p\|}.$$

For exact projections this can always be achieved by a suitable increase of the current lower bound z, e.g. as in the above methods. The projection of a vector a to the subspace Y may be calculated from either of the following formulas

$$(2.7) \qquad P_Y a = a - DA^T u, \; P_Y a = Zw$$

where u and w are least-squares-solutions to

$$(2.8) \qquad DA^T u := a, \; Zw := a,$$

and where the columns of Z span Y. When AD is of full rank, say $AD = (B|N)$ with regular matrix B, then

$$Z := \begin{bmatrix} -B^{-1}N \\ I \end{bmatrix}$$

spans Y. From the above formulas we derive

$$(2.9) \qquad u = B^{-T}(a_B - (Zw)_B), \; w = a_B - N^T u.$$

Therefore, an approximation of u or w easily yields a corresponding approximation of w or u. Let $a := (c - \tau \mathbf{1})^T D$.

In a null space method w is approximated and provides an approximate projection Zw in Y. Then a tentative dual solution u is calculated from (2.9). u leads to an approximate projection $r := a - DA^T u$. If r is not positive, then Zw is accepted. Otherwise, an approximate w' is calculated for $a' := D\mathbf{1}$. An according u' from (2.9) leads to $r' := a' - DA^T u'$. Now, τ must be increased by

$$(2.10) \qquad \beta := \min\{r_j/r'_j | r'_j > 0\}.$$

Therefore, $Z(w - \beta \cdot w')$ is used as projection and $\tau := \tau + \beta$. If

$$(2.11) \qquad (c - \tau \cdot \mathbf{1})^T D\hat{y} \le 0,$$

then the iteration will be accepted, too. Otherwise, the generated approximations are not accurate enough.

In a range space method u is approximated. If $r := a - DA^T u$ is not positive, then Zr_N is accepted as approximate projection. Otherwise, an approximate u' to the least squares problem $DA^T u' = D\mathbf{1}$ leads to $r' := D\mathbf{1} - DA^T u'$. Then, $Z(r_N - \beta \cdot r'_N)$ is used as an approximate projection where β is drawn from (2.10). Let $\tau := \tau + \beta$. If the test (2.11) fails more accurate approximations are necessary. Otherwise, the iteration will be accepted.

Goldfarb and Mehrotra mention further possible approaches generating suitable directions in Y. In order to achieve (2.11) feasible solutions (u, β) with $\beta > 0$ of the current dual

$$\max\{n \cdot \beta | u^T AD + \beta \cdot \mathbf{1}^T \le (c - \tau \cdot \mathbf{1})^T\}$$

are helpful. Any such solution can be used to increase τ by some obvious $\underline{\beta} \geq \beta$ since $(u, 0)$ is still dual feasible for $\tau := \tau + \underline{\beta}$ and $n \cdot (\tau + \underline{\beta}) \leq z_*$. For any method using a search direction in Y satisfying (2.11) linear convergence can be proved as in section 1.

An initial lower bound $z_0 = n \cdot \tau_0$ may be calculated from

$$0 = \min\{(c - \tau_0 \cdot \mathbf{1})^T Dy | \mathbf{1}^T y = n, y \geq 0\}.$$

Obviously, $\tau_0 = \min\{c_j | 1 \leq j \leq n\}$.

For the case that search directions stay only approximately in Y some sufficient conditions for linear convergence can be found in Mehrotra [1986].

Different lower bounds preserving polynomiality are discussed in Ye [1985b]. Ye [1985a] also proposes the use of upper bounds instead of lower bounds for modifying the objective function. That approach is implemented in Lustig [1985]. As mentioned in section 2, in transformed space Lustig considers the LP

$$\min\{[c^T D - z_*]y \mid [AD - b]y = 0, \mathbf{1}^T y = n + 1, y \geq 0\}.$$

Using the upper bound $c^T x$ with the current best solution x, he actually works on

$$\min\{[c^T D - c^T x]y \mid [AD - b]y = 0, \mathbf{1}^T y = n + 1, y \geq 0\}.$$

In combination with a "sliding objective technique" also used in Karmarkar [1984], the upper bound approach guarantees polynomial complexity (cf. Ye [1985a]).

3. Exterior Projective Method
De Ghellinck and Vial [1986] extend an approach of the same authors [1985] from homogeneous equation solving to LP in standard form. At first, we consider

$$Ax = b, \ x \geq 0$$

with $b \neq 0$. As in previous sections boundedness has to be assumed in some form. Here, a suitable assumption is that $Ax = 0$, $x \geq 0$ implies $x = 0$. Then, $b = 0$ implies that $x = 0$ is the only feasible solution. Introducing a further variable x_0, that problem is equivalent to

$$(3.1) \qquad\qquad Ax = 0, \ x_0 = 1, \ x \geq 0,$$

where $A := (-b|A)$. The basic algorithm in de Ghellinck and Vial [1986] constructs approximate solutions $x \in R^{n+1}$ to (3.1). Starting from $x := \mathbf{1} \in R^{n+1}$, the algorithm generates a sequence of positive vectors x with $x_0 = 1$. Unlike the algorithms in the previous sections the generated vectors do not satisfy the homogeneous constraints. If (3.1) is feasible the algorithm stops when

$$\|Ax\|_\infty \leq \varepsilon \cdot (\Pi x)^{1/(n+1)}$$

where $\varepsilon > 0$ is a given prescribed tolerance.

Iterative step for homogeneous system 3.1

1. $x := x_+$; $D := \text{diag}(\mathbf{x})$.
G1. If $\|Ax\|_\infty \leq \varepsilon \cdot (\Pi x)^{1/(n+1)}$ then stop [comment: x approx. feasible].
2. For $Y := \{y | ADy = 0\}$ calculate $p := P_Y \mathbf{1}$.
G2. If $p_{\max} < 1$ then stop [comment: (3.1) infeasible]; if $p \geq 0$ then stop [comment: $(1/p_0) \cdot Dp$ is feasible].
3. $y_+ := \mathbf{1} + \alpha \cdot p$.
4. $x_+ := 1/(y_+)_0 \cdot Dy_+$.

If in step G2 the algorithm stops with $p \geq 0$ then $p_0 > 0$. Otherwise, Dp would solve $ADp = 0$, $Dp \geq 0$, $(Dp) \neq 0$ contrary to the made assumption on the boundedness of the system.

The main computational effort lies again in the calculation of a certain projection. In order to reduce all residuals the constant vector $\mathbf{1}$ is projected to Y in each iteration. Then y_+ solves the auxiliary problem

$$(3.2) \qquad \max\{\mathbf{1}^T y | ADy = 0, y \in B(\mathbf{1}, \alpha \cdot \|p\|)\}$$

for some suitably chosen steplength α. The effect of that approach is easily seen from

$$Ax_+ = A[1/(y_+)_0 \cdot D(\mathbf{1} + \alpha p)] = 1/(y_+)_0 \cdot Ax$$
$$\Pi x_+ = \Pi x \cdot \Pi y_+/(y_+)_0^{n+1}$$

implying

$$(3.3) \qquad \frac{Ax_+}{(\Pi x_+)^{1/(n+1)}} \leq \frac{Ax}{(\Pi x)^{1/(n+1)}} \frac{1}{(\Pi y_+)^{1/(n+1)}}$$

Now, $\mathbf{1} = p + DA^T u$ (cf. 2.7). Therefore, $p < 1$ implies $A^T u > 0$. Then $u^T Ax > 0$ for all $x \geq 0$ with $x_0 = 1$, i.e. (3.1) is infeasible. Otherwise, $p_{\max} \geq 1$. Let $\alpha := 1/(1 + p_{\max})$. Then $y_+ \geq 0$ and $\Pi y_+ \geq e/2$ which shows a sufficient decrease in (3.3). In particular, if $\varepsilon := 2^{-dL}$ for some positive integer d, then the algorithm stops after at most $O(nL)$ iterations. As each iteration needs $O(n \cdot m^2)$ operations, that assures the polynomial bound $O(n^2 m^2 L)$. For integral data, $d = 10$ and problem size

$$L := m \cdot n + [\log(\prod_{b_i \neq 0} b_i \cdot \prod_{a_{ij} \neq 0} a_{ij})] + 1$$

de Ghellinck and Vial prove that the successful determination of an approximate solution implies feasibility. Some postprocessing is necessary to generate an actual feasible solution in $O(n^3 m^2 L)$ operations.

The basic method can be used to solve LP in standard form

(3.4) $$z_* := \max\{c^T x + c_0 | Ax = b, x \geq 0\}.$$

An equivalent formulation is

$$\max\{z | (z - c_0) \cdot x_0 - c^T x = 0, -b \cdot x_0 + Ax = 0, x \geq 0, x_0 = 1\}.$$

The latter problem is viewed as a parametric feasibility problem with unknown parameter z. Starting from $x := \mathbf{1} \in R^{n+1}$ with some upper bound $z \geq z_*$, the algorithm generates a sequence of positive vectors x with $x_0 = 1$ and a decreasing sequence of upper bounds z. If the LP is feasible the algorithm stops when

$$\|Bx\|_\infty \leq \varepsilon \cdot (\Pi x)^{1/(n+1)}$$

where B is the matrix of the homogeneous constraints and where $\varepsilon > 0$ is a given prescribed tolerance. Infeasibility of the LP is detected by $z \to -\infty$. In the algorithm the vectors

$$\mathbf{1}, D \cdot \begin{bmatrix} c_0 \\ c \end{bmatrix}, \begin{bmatrix} 1 \\ 0 \end{bmatrix}$$

are projected to the subspace $Y := \{y | (-b | A) D y = 0\}$ in each iteration. The corresponding projections will be denoted by q, r, and s. The complete iteration is described in the following.

De Ghellinck and Vial: The iterative step 3.2
1. $D := \operatorname{diag}(x_+)$.
G1. Compute the projections q, r, and s.
G2. If $r = \beta \cdot s$ for some β then stop [comment: $\beta = z_* = c^T x + c_0$ for all x feasible for the original LP (3.4)].
G3. $p(z) := q - q^T (z \cdot s - r) \cdot \frac{z \cdot s - r}{\|z \cdot s - r\|^2}$, if $p(z) \geq 0$ then stop [comment: $(1/p_0) \cdot Dp$ is optimal].
G4. Compute a better upper bound $z_+ := \max\{z' | z' \leq z, p_{\max}(z') \geq 1\}$; if $z_+ = -\infty$ then stop [comment: LP is infeasible]; $z := z_+$.
G5. If $\|Bx\|_\infty \leq \varepsilon \cdot (\Pi x)^{1/(n+1)}$ then stop [comment: x approx. optimal].
2. $p := p(z)$.
3. $y_+ := \mathbf{1} + \alpha \cdot p$.
4. $x_+ := 1/(y_+)_0 \cdot D y_+$.

In step 2. the search direction p is calculated. It can be seen that

$$p(z) = p_U \mathbf{1}$$

for the subspace $U(z) := \{y \in Y | (z - c_0 | - c^T) D y = 0\}$. From a computational point of view calculation of p via r, s, and q is hardly more laborious than direct calculation of p as all projections are to the same subspace. The main advantage lies in the easy handling of a necessary change in the upper bound. The new bound follows from the fact that $p_{max}(z) < 1$ implies infeasibility of the constraints for the current parameter z. Calculation of the new bound needs evaluation of the zeroes of $n+1$ quadratic equations. If the constraints are satisfied up to some tolerance (step G5.) the algorithm stops. Otherwise, the problem

$$(3.5) \qquad \max\{\mathbf{1}^T y | BDy = 0, y \in B(\mathbf{1}, \alpha \cdot \|p\|)\}$$

is solved by y_+. Its solution is mapped back to the subspace $x_0 = 1$ by a projective map in step 4.

For a suitable choice of the stepsize α (as above), de Ghellinck and Vial [1986] prove that the algorithm stops after at most $2K$ iterations where

$$K := \big[(n+1)\log(2/e)\log(\sigma/\varepsilon)\big] + 1$$

with $\sigma := \max\{z_0 - \mathbf{1}^T c, \max_i |\Sigma_j a_{ij}|\}$. For integral data and $\varepsilon := 2^{-20L}$ with problem size

$$L := m \cdot n + \big[\log(\prod_{b_i \neq 0} b_i \cdot \prod_{a_{ij} \neq 0} a_{ij} \cdot \prod_{c_j \neq 0} c_j)\big] + 1$$

either the infeasibility of the original LP or its optimal value can be determined in at most $O(nL)$ iterations and $O(n^2 m^2 L)$ operations. Then an optimal solution can be constructed from some postprocessing in $O(n^3 m^2 L)$ operations.

De Ghellinck and Vial [1986] propose several procedures for improving the generation of upper bounds during the algorithm.

4. Towards an Implementation of the Projective Method

From the very first presentation of his approach at the 16th Annual ACM Symposium on Theory of Computing in April 1984, Narendra Karmarkar of AT & T Bell Laboratories claimed that his algorithm was fast in practice, in particular, faster than Dantzig's Simplex method which has shown to be very efficient in practice for nearly 40 years. Much criticizm commented such a statement which was not supported by published computational results. Charnes, Song and Wolfe [1984] provided examples showing that for fixed step length the method is of linear convergence. Quick implementations of the basic projective method using ad hoc transformations of LPs to the necessary form (1.1) were outperformed by the available well-established LP-software. As the issue of propriatory interests remains unsettled early attempts to establish some cooperative test effort with AT & T in order to provide a sound basis for the evaluation of the approach fail.

At the time being the best results seem to be due to a group around Ilan Adler at Berkely (cf. Kozlov and Black [1986]) who in cooperation with Karmarkar implemented a version which is mentioned to be about two times faster than MINOS 4.0 (cf.

Murtagh and Saunders [1983]), a quite sophisticated implementation of Dantzig's simplex method from the Systems Optimization Laboratory at Stanford University. That factor averages the behaviour of the code for a set of 30 LP test problems gathered by Gay [1985].

In fact, the implementation of the projective method raises many questions. All proposals made for implementation purposes need further extensive experimentation. Here, we can only outline some of the occuring difficulties.

In section 2, we already discussed several reformulations of a standard LP formulation which are necessary in order to enable the application of differing versions of the projective method. The necessary assumption of boundedness or even of the knowledge of explicit bounds may lead to some difficulties. For example, the assumed scaling in the approach of Todd and Burrell [1985] may lead to underestimated lower bounds as noted in Chiu and Ye [1985] (cf. section 5).

The chosen steplength in step 3. is of major influence on the number of iterations. Many researchers (cf. e.g. Tomlin [1985], Nickels et al. [1985], Roos [1985], Karmarkar in Lustig [1985]) observe that larger steps within the interior of the feasible region are recommendable. Line searches (e.g. Todd and Burrell [1985]) as well as heuristics (e.g. cf. Roos [1985]) depending on differing descent functions have been proposed and tested. The easiest implementable successful rule is to use 99 % of the step leading to the boundary which can be evaluated by some ratio test. Common experience in all implementations using such rules seems to be the small number of iterations which grows encouragingly slow. Empirically, Karmarkar claims a growth of $O(\log n)$.

Convergence criteria may be based on the fact that the values of the modified objective functions converge to zero. A serious problem is the presence of null variables. Then the problem has no interior points. Therefore such variables must be detected in phase I before the interior point methods can be applied. Even for the exterior projective method where no phase I is necessary difficulties will occur because any basic feasible solution is degenerate in the presence of null variables. For phase I Lustig proposes to test

$$y_j/(p_j/y_j) < \varepsilon$$

for some $\varepsilon > 0$ when y_j is a blocking variable in the ratio test. Then y_j is assumed to be a null variable and is eliminated with a step to the boundary. A similar problem arises when the algorithm converges to a basic feasible solution which is degenerate. Then AD converges to a rank-deficient matrix resulting at least in slow convergence (cf. e.g. Shanno [1985]). Identifying basic variables which are zero in the optimal solution seems to be necessary to eliminate the resulting severe numerical difficulties. Thresholds for dropping variables approaching zero are used in Shanno and Marsten [1985]. Several researchers suppose effective rules for dynamically dropping and resurrecting such variables to be of key importance for the algorithm's performance.

When a constructed solution x passes the convergence criteria then some postprocessing is necessary. As $x > 0$, it has to be converted into a point in the optimal face of the polyhedron, preferably into an optimal basic solution. Procedures for converting a nonbasic solution into a basic solution whose objective value is at least as good are available in many LP codes. For a general description we refer to Benichou et al. [1977] or Kortanek and Shi [1985]. The general idea of using the projective method to "front-end" the simplex method is pursued by several researchers (cf. Tomlin [1985]).

However, the major effort in applying projective methods (as well as the related methods in the following sections) appears in the calculation of the used projections. Let a denote a vector to be projected to the subspace $Y := \{y | ADy = 0\}$ where A is an $m \cdot n$ matrix and D is a positive $n \cdot n$ diagonal matrix. As remarked above, AD converges to a rank-deficient matrix when the generated solutions approach a degenerate solution. Consequently, methods proposed for projecting have to be prepared to cope with severe ill-conditioning.

If AD is of full rank then the projection $P_Y a$ of a can be calculated from the normal equations

$$(4.1) \qquad AD^2 A^T u := ADa, \quad P_Y a := a - DA^T u$$

which is used in step 2 of the basic projective method. Todd and Burrell [1985] discuss QR factorization of DA^T where Q is orthogonal and where the first m rows of R build an upper triangular matrix R_m while the remaining rows contain only zero entries. QR factorization can be obtained in $O(m^2 n)$ floating point operations if DA^T is dense (cf. Golub and van Loan [1983]). Then u is recursively calculated from

$$R_m^T R_m u := ADa$$

in $O(m^2)$ floating point operations. As the projection is the residual of the least squares problem (cf. 2.8)

$$\min \|a - DA^T u\|$$

many fast and numerically stable least squares techniques have been discussed: Cholesky factorization (Nickels et al. [1985], Shanno [1985]), Householder- (cf. Tomlin [1985]) or Gram-Schmidt orthogonalization techniques (cf. Roos [1985]), conjugate gradient techniques (Shanno and Marsten [1985]), in particular, the LSQR and CGLS algorithms of Paige and Saunders [1982] (Lustig [1985] and Goldfarb and Mehrotra [1985]).

In the case of sparse original constraints the matrix A is sparse with the exception of the last one or two dense columns (introduced via the necessary LP-reformulation). The above approaches have to be adapted in order to exploit sparsity. For example, QR factorization using Givens Rotations as developed in George and Heath [1980] is discussed by Tomlin [1985] and Todd and Burrell [1985]. For a barrier method related to the projective method (cf. section 6), Gill et al. [1985] use a hybrid version of LSQR with a sophisticated triangular preconditioner C where $C^T C = \underline{A} D^2 \underline{A}^T \approx AD^2 A^T$, i.e. C is the Cholesky factor of a sparse matrix approximating AD^2A^T. Then LSQR is applied to solving

$$\min \|a - DA^T C^{-1} s\|,$$

implying $Ru := s$. Moreover, LSQR is accelerated by using an incremental scheme as in Lustig [1985] proposed by Saunders. In fact, LSQR is applied to

$$\min \|\delta a - DA^T C^{-1} \delta s\| \text{ with } \delta a := a - DA^T u,$$

where only the correction term δu of the previous solution u is calculated from $R\delta u := \delta s$. Gay [1985] reports on successful experiments with preconditioning when solving the normal equations with a conjugate gradient technique. Gill et al. [1986] discuss LU preconditioning. Although an expensive feature preconditioning is considered to be crucial in order to achieve the required high accuracy fast enough.

As already remarked in section 2 (cf. 2.7-2.9), the projection may also be calculated via solving the least squares problem

$$\min \|a - Zw\|$$

when the columns of Z span Y. Then $P_Y a := Zw$. A conjugate gradient algorithm (without preconditioning) solving that "null space"-least squares problem is implemented in Shanno and Marsten [1985]. Goldfarb and Mehrotra [1986] give a much more detailed discussion of such a "null space method" including update formulas for Z. The theoretically necessary accuracy of the generated solution w given by (2.11) is reported to be quickly achieved by the used CGLS algorithm in Paige and Saunders [1983]. However, for more rapid convergence some additional ad hoc rules are implemented. Relaxing the expensive requirement of high accuracy of the solution of the solved least squares problem is an obvious advantage. With the development of more sophisticated rules for choosing basic variables, Goldfarb and Mehrotra [1986] expect about m updates of Z on the average.

Karmarkar's modification of the basic projective method which reduces the complexity by a factor of $n^{1/2}$ has been implemented by Schreck [1985] and by Shanno [1985]. Shanno [1985] implemented a stable version using Cholesky factorization with a rank one correction procedure of Fletcher and Powell [1974]. He reports on computational experiments using

$$1/\mu \leq [\sigma \cdot d_i/(x_+)_i]^2 \leq \mu$$

instead of (1.6) for $\mu \in \{2, 5, 10, 15\}$ demonstrating the complexity tradeoff between the number of iterations and the number of rank one updates per iteration. For $\mu = 2$ (the choice made in the theoretical development in section 1) the average number of rank one updates is remarkably close to the theoretical estimate $n^{1/2}$ (per iteration).

II. Related Interior Point Methods.

5. Scaling Methods

While the simplex method for solving the LP

(5.1) $$\min\{c^T x | Ax = b, x \geq 0\}$$

geometrically moves from vertex to vertex on the boundary of the set of feasible solutions, interior point methods generate a sequence of feasible solutions in the relative interior $\{x | Ax = b, x > 0\}$. Obviously, projective methods as in chapter I are interior point methods.

Starting from some interior point one may move in the opposite direction of the gradient projected to the affine hull of the polyhedron in order to improve the objective function value. A substantial decrease is possible only if the current solution is sufficiently distant from the boundary of the polyhedron. Therefore, the current solution has to be centered in the polyhedron in some way. Inspired by the projective method Cavalier and Soyster [1985] as well as Vanderbei, Meketon, and Freedman [1985] proposed to map the current feasible solution x_+ to $\mathbf{1}$ using the linear mapping $T : R^n \to R^n$, defined by

$$y := T(x) := D^{-1}x$$

where $D = \text{diag}(x_+)$. Then, a projected gradient step is performed in the transformed space and its solution y_+ is transformed back to the original space. The complete iterative step is given below.

The iterative step 5.1

1. $x := x_+$; $D := \text{diag}(x)$.
2. $p := [I - (AD)^T (AD^2 A^T)^{-1}(AD)]Dc$.
3. $y_+ := \mathbf{1} - \alpha \frac{p}{p_{\max}}$ with $p_{\max} := \max\{p_j | 1 \leq j \leq n\}$ and $\alpha \in (0, 1)$.
4. $x_+ := Dy_+$.

Conceptually, the scaling approach is much simpler and works directly with the LP in standard form. As in the projective method the main computational effort lies in the determination of p. Let u denote the solution of the normal equations, i.e. $AD^2 A^T u := AD^2 c$. Then

$$p = D[c - A^T u]$$

and the new iterate satisfies

$$x_+ = \phi(x) := x - (\alpha/p_{\max})D^2[c - A^T u],$$
$$c^T x_+ = c^T x - (\alpha/p_{\max})\|p\|^2.$$

Clearly, the reduced costs $r := [c - A^T u]$ depend on x. Vanderbei et al. prove convergence of the algorithm to an optimal solution under the assumptions

$$A \cdot \text{diag}(x) \text{ is of full rank for every feasible } x,$$

(5.2)   the LP is bounded and feasible,

$$c - A^T u \text{ contains at most } m \text{ zeroes for every } u \in R^m.$$

The first assumption implies that the iteration function ϕ is continuous and that the primal LP is nondegenerate. If x is not a vertex then D contains at most $n - m - 1$ zeroes and, by the third assumption, $Dp \neq 0$. On the other hand, if x is a vertex then $c - A^T u$ concides with the usual reduced cost vector from linear programming theory which implies $Dp = 0$. Obviously, $p = 0$ iff $Dp = 0$. If $0 \neq p \leq 0$ for some feasible x then $x - \alpha Dp$ is feasible for all $\alpha > 0$ contrary to boundedness. Therefore, if a feasible x is not a vertex then $p_{max} > 0$. Thus, the objective value is monotonically decreasing. In particular, the LP has a unique optimal vertex. Boundedness implies that the sequence of objective values converges. Hence its differences $(\alpha/p_{max}) \cdot \|p\|^2$ converge to 0, i.e. p converges to 0. Thus, any limit point $\underline{x}$ of the sequence of generated solutions is a vertex. Boundedness assures the existence of limit points.

Convergence Lemma 5.2. Under the assumptions (5.2) the sequence of generated feasible solutions converges to an optimal vertex.

Proof. Let $\underline{x}$ be a limit point. By the first and the third assumption,

$$\frac{1}{2} \cdot \min\{|r_j(\underline{x})| \mid \underline{x}_j = 0\} =: \varepsilon > 0.$$

Let $N := \{j | \underline{x}_j = 0\}$ (the nonbasic variables in LP theory). Let $W(\delta)$ denote the set of all feasible points with $x_j < \delta$ for all $j \in N$. We choose $\delta > 0$ small enough to imply that $\underline{x}$ is the unique vertex contained in $W(2\delta)$ and that $|r_j(x)| > \varepsilon$ in $W(\delta)$ for all $j \in N$. As $(\alpha/p_{max}) \cdot \|Dr\|^2$ converges to 0, $(\alpha/p_{max}) \cdot (x_j)^2 \cdot (r_j)^2$ converges to 0 for all $j \in N$. Therefore,

$$C(\delta, \varepsilon) := \{x \in W(\delta) | (\alpha/p_{max})(x_j)^2(r_j)^2 < \varepsilon \cdot \delta \text{ for all } j \in N\}$$

is a neighbourhood of $\underline{x}$ intersected with the set of feasible points. Since $C(\delta, \varepsilon) \subseteq W(\delta)$, $\phi[C(\delta, \varepsilon)] \subseteq W(2\delta)$. If the sequence of generated solutions admits another limit point, then it leaves $C(\delta, \varepsilon)$ infinitely often passing through $W(2\delta)/W(\delta)$. In particular, a subsequence must converge to another limit point in the closure of $W(2\delta) \setminus W(\delta)$ contrary to the fact that no vertex is contained in that closure. Thus the sequence converges to $\underline{x}$.

If the reduced cost vector $r(\underline{x})$ is nonnegative, then the usual optimality criterion of LP theory is satisfied, i.e. $\underline{x}$ is optimal. Otherwise, by continuity of $r(x)$ there exists a neighbourhood Q of $\underline{x}$ with $r_j(x) < r_j(\underline{x})/2 < 0$ in Q for some fixed j. As $\underline{x}$ is a vertex $\underline{x}_j \cdot r_j(\underline{x}) = 0$, implying $\underline{x}_j = 0$. Now, an iteration within Q increases the value of the j-th component since $(x_+)_j = x_j - \alpha \cdot (x_j)^2 \cdot r_j(x)$ contrary to $x_j \rightarrow \underline{x}_j = 0$. Thus $\underline{x}$ is an optimal vertex. $\square$

Vanderbei et al. give some stopping rules and remark that for practical purposes the difference $c^T x - u^T b$ may be monitored. As in the projective approach the final interior point generated has to be converted to a vertex without increasing the objective function (cf. section 4). Computational experiments are reported in Cavalier and Soyster [1985], Vanderbei et al. [1985], Kortanek and Shi [1985], Chandru and Khochar ([1985] and [1986]). Similar to the projective method primal degeneracy may lead to severe numerical difficulties.

By now, several authors (Kortanek and Shi [1985], Sherali [1985], and Chandru and Khochar [1985]) have developed somewhat better convergence results. In the following we suppose that an infinite sequence of feasible solutions is generated by the algorithms.

For bounded polyhedra and A of full rank, Kortanek and Shi [1985] prove two optimality criteria for a limit point $\underline{x}$:

(1) $\{A_j| \liminf_k(x_j)^k > 0\}$ spans R^m

(2) for all j with $\underline{x}_j = 0$ there exists K_j with $(x_j)^k \to \underline{x}_j$ non-increasing for all $k \geq K_j$.

In this case one also obtains dual convergence. Chandru and Khochar [1985] perturb D to D' in the algorithm by

$$D'_{jj} := \begin{cases} D_{jj} & \text{if } D_{jj} \geq \varepsilon \text{ or } r_j > -2\delta \\ \varepsilon & \text{otherwise.} \end{cases}$$

Mainly dropping the third assumption in (5.2) they prove that sufficiently small $\delta > 0$ and $\varepsilon(\delta) > 0$ can be chosen to imply convergence of the objective value to the optimal value. If all reduced costs satisfy $r_j > -2\delta$ (i.e. if the solution is quite close to being optimal), then the gap to the optimal value drops by a factor $1 - 1/n^{1/2}$. As they expect that case to happen permanently at the tail end of the generated sequence they conjecture polynomial time bounds for the method or some minor variant. They mention a similar result with a factor $1 - 1/(n - m)^{1/2}$ in Barnes [1985].

Sherali [1985] discusses a different perturbation technique. Under the assumptions:

A is of full rank
$X := \{x|Ax = b\} \subseteq \{x|\mathbf{1}^T x = 1\}$,
X contains an interior point,
the optimal value of the LP is 0,

he proposes to choose a termination tolerance $\varepsilon > 0$ on the objective function value and to replace the transformed cost vector Dc by

$$Dc - \mu \cdot \mathbf{1}$$

with some (infinitesimally) small constant $\mu > 0$, in particular $\varepsilon/n > \mu$. As long as the objective function value is larger than $\bar{\varepsilon}$, the iterative step 5.1 is performed with steplength α defined by

$$\alpha := \min\{.99/p_{\max}, 1.99 \cdot (f(x) - \varepsilon/2)/\|Dc - \mu \cdot \mathbf{1}\|\}$$

where $f(x) := c^T x - \underline{\mu} \cdot ln \Pi x$ with $\Pi x := x_1 \cdots x_n$. As $\Pi x < 1$, $f(x) > c^T x > \varepsilon$, and, due to $c^T x > \varepsilon$, $\|Dc\|^2 \geq (\varepsilon/n)^2$.

Sherali relates his modification to the work on subgradient methods (cf. Poljak [1967]) and space dilation techniques (cf. Shor [1983]). He chooses $\underline{\mu}$ sufficiently small such that an optimal solution x_* of the nonlinear problem

$$(5.3) \qquad\qquad \min\{f(x)|x \in X\}$$

satisfies $f(x_*) \leq \varepsilon/2$. Using T, (5.3) transforms to

$$-\underline{\mu} \cdot ln \Pi x + \min\{c^T Dy - \underline{\mu} \cdot ln \Pi y | ADy = b\}.$$

At the current iterate $\mathbf{1}$ in y-space the gradient is $Dc - \underline{\mu} \cdot \mathbf{1}$. Projecting to the feasible set in y-space results in a step exactly in the direction proposed by his variant of the scaling method when the above steplength is chosen.

Sherali proves convergence to an ε-optimal solution in a finite number of steps under two additional assumptions on the existence of a subsequence x^k, $k \in K$ of the sequence of feasible solutions:

(1S) $f(x^k)$ and $(p_{\max})^k$ are bounded from above for all $k \geq k_*$,

(2S) $x^k \to \underline{x}$, $x^{k+1} \to \underline{x}$, and for $k \geq k_*$, $x_i^k \geq x_i^{k+1} > 0$ for each i with $\underline{x}_i = 0$

where k_* is sufficiently large. (2S) corresponds to (2) in Kortanek and Shi [1985].

If the optimal value of the LP is not zero, then essentially the same result can be proved. At first the termination criterion $(c^T x \leq \varepsilon)$ is cancelled. Secondly, the steplength is replaced by

$$\alpha := \min\{.99/p_{\max}, (1.99 \cdot \varepsilon/2)/\|Dc - \underline{\mu} \cdot \mathbf{1}\|\}.$$

$0 < \underline{\mu} < 1/n$ is assumed to be sufficiently small such that (5.3) has an optimal solution $x_* > 0$ with $0 \leq f(x_*) - z_* \leq \varepsilon/2$. W. l.o.g. let $c \geq \mathbf{1}$. Then, under all previous assumptions, the algorithm generates in a finite number of iterations an ε-optimal solution.

Scaling methods allow a quite flexible handling of special constraints. Upper bound constraints (Vanderbei et al. [1985]), generalized upper bounds and variable upper bounds (Chandru and Khochar [1986]) may be incorporated in the method. For that purpose it is helpful to remind the complementary slackness condition of LP-theory for (5.1), i.e.

$$0 = x^T(c - A^T u) = \Sigma_j x_j \cdot (c_j - A_j^T u),$$

where x is feasible for (5.1) and u is feasible for the dual LP max $\{u^T b | A^T u \leq c\}$. In the scaling method the generated solutions u are not dually feasible. Therefore, the error terms in the complementary slackness conditions are not necessarily nonnegative. In order to drive the error to zero, one minimizes the quadratic objective

$$(c - A^T u)^T D^2 (c - A^T u) = \Sigma_j [x_j \cdot (c_j - A_j^T u)]^2.$$

For the LP $\min\{c^T x | Ax = b, f \leq x \leq g\}$ the error in complementary slackness may be minimized by choosing a different matrix D with

(5.4) $\qquad D_{jj} := [(g_j - x_j) \cdot (x_j - f_j)/(g_j - f_j)]^t$ for some $t > 0$.

Chandru and Khochar [1986] propose a further modification of (5.4) in order to exploit knowledge on the search direction

$$D_{jj} := \begin{cases} x_j - f_j & \text{if } r_j \geq \varepsilon \\ g_j - x_j & \text{if } r_j \leq -\varepsilon \end{cases}$$

where $\varepsilon > 0$ is suitably small. More general, D^2 may be replaced by some positive (semi-)definite matrix describing reasonable weights for the respective problem (cf. Chandru and Khochar [1986]).
Computational results for assignment problems

$$\min\{\Sigma_{ij} c_{ij} \cdot x_{ij} | \Sigma_i x_{ij} = 1, 1 \leq j \leq n; \Sigma_j x_{ij} = 1, 1 \leq i \leq n, x \geq 0\}$$

are reported by Aronson et al. [1985] and Chandru and Khochar [1986]). Both implementations were compared to implementations of NETFLO from Kennington and Helgason [1980]. Aronson et al. report a factor of more than 200 in favour of NETFLO while Chandru and Khochar report a factor of less then 4 when CPU-time is compared. The numbers of iterations are quite the same ranging from 9 to 11 for n from 40 to 80. As far as can be jugded by the respective descriptions the made implementations seem to be quite different.

Some explanation of the discrepancy in the numerical experiences may be due to the fact that Aronson et al. directly apply LSQR (cf. section 4) to the full size $(n^2 \cdot (2n - 1))$ least squares problem whereas Chandru and Khochar use the IMSL routine leqt2f for inverting the $n \cdot n$ matrix

$$M := [D_I - D_2 \, D_J^{-1} D_2^T]$$

where $(D_I)_{ii} := \Sigma_j (x_{ij})^2$, $1 \leq i \leq n$, and $(D_J)_{jj} := \Sigma_i (x_{ij})^2$, $1 \leq j \leq n$, are diagonal matrices and where $D_2 := [(x_{ij})^2]$. Then, r is calculated from

$$Mu := c_I - D_2 \, D_J^{-1} c_J,$$
$$v := D_J^{-1}(c_J - D_2^T u),$$
$$r := [c_{ij} - u_i - v_j].$$

where $(c_I)_i := \Sigma_j(x_{ij})^2 \cdot c_{ij}, 1 \le i \le n$, and $(c_J)_j := \Sigma_i(x_{ij})^2 \cdot c_{ij}, 1 \le j \le n$. Aronson et al. use a different weight matrix $D = \mathrm{diag}(d)$ with

$$d_{ij} := \min(1 - x_{ij}, x_{ij})$$

for $1 \le i \le n, 1 \le j \le n$. Further they report on disappointing experiences with an implementation of a corresponding null space method.

Megiddo [1985] proposes a nice variant of the usual scaling method. In transformed space the iterative step 5.1 may be interpreted as solving

$$\min\{c^T Dy | ADy = b, (y-1)^T(y-1) \le 1\}$$

up to the stepsize α. Thus, the scaling method centers the current solution in the positive orthant at 1 and constructs an optimal solution of the transformed problem in a ball of radius 1 around 1. Meggiddo replaces this problem by

(5.5) $$\min\{c^T Dy | ADy = b, y^T[I - 11^T/(n-1)]y \le 0\}$$

up to some stepsize. His method also centers the current transformed solution in the positive orthant at 1 but constructs an optimal solution in a cone C with vertex 0 generated from the ball $B(1, r)$ inscribed in the Simplex $S = \{y | 1^T y = n, y \ge 0\}$, i.e.

$$C := cone(S \cap B(1, r)).$$

C defines clearly a better nonlinear approximation of the nonnegative orthant than the unit ball around 1. Transforming back to original space, (5.5) turns into

$$\min\{c^T x | Ax = b, x^T D^{-1} G D^{-1} x \le 0\}.$$

where $G := I - 11^T/(n-1)$. Its solution can be found from solving the system

$$Ax = b,$$
$$A^T u + \beta \cdot D^{-1} G D^{-1} x = c,$$
$$x^T D^{-1} G D^{-1} x = 0.$$

Meggiddo [1985] also discusses how to incorporate explicit bounds in his approach and mentions promising preliminary computational experience.

6. The barrier function approach

Barrier function methods provide an approach to optimization problems with inequality constraints. That inequalities are replaced by adding terms to the original objective function which tend to infinity when the boundary is approached. Many different functions have been designed for that purpose. Gill et al. [1985] relate the logarithmic barrier function of Frisch [1955] to the projective method of Karmarkar. For the dual of the LP (5.1)

$$(6.1) \qquad \max\{b^T u | A^T u \le c\}$$

the standard barrier function approach consists in solving problems of the form

$$(6.2) \qquad \max\{F(u, \mu) | u \in R^m\}$$

for a sequence of "barrier parameters" $\mu > 0$ with $\mu \to 0$, where

$$F(u, \mu) := b^T u + \mu \cdot ln\Pi(c - A^T u)$$

with $\Pi(d) := d_1 \cdots d_n$. If the generated sequence $u(\mu)$ of solutions converges to some $\underline{u}$ then $\underline{u}$ maximizes (6.1). Convergence will be assumed throughout the section. Moreover,

$$(6.3) \qquad x'_j(\mu) := \mu/(c - A^T u(\mu))_j \to \underline{x}_j$$

where $\underline{x}_j$ is a Kuhn-Tucker multiplier of the j-th constraint (cf. Fiacco and McCormick [1968]). Many properties of the sequence can be found in the literature (cf. Mifflin [1972], Jittorntrum [1978], Jittorntrum and Osborne [1980], and Osborne [1986]), in particular, the rate of convergence is $O(\mu)$ even in the case of nonunique optima. For the LP (5.1) an analogue barrier function approach considers problems of the form

$$(6.4) \qquad \min\{f(x, \mu) | Ax = b\}$$

for barrier parameters $\mu > 0$ with $\mu \to 0$, where

$$f(x, \mu) := c^T x - \mu \cdot ln\Pi(x).$$

As F is strictly concave and f is strictly convex the necessary optimality conditions show that $x'(\mu)$ defined by (6.3) for (6.2) solves (6.4) and, vice versa, if $r'(\mu)$ is defined by $r'_j(\mu) := \mu/x_j(\mu)$ for the solution $x(\mu)$ minimizing (6.4) then $r'(\mu) = c - A^T u(\mu)$ (cf. Osborne [1986]).

For solving (6.4), Gill et al. [1985] propose a Newton method. The search direction s at the current solution x is found from solving the quadratic program

$$\min\{g^T s + \frac{1}{2}s^T Hs | As = 0\}$$

where g is the gradient of f at x and where H is the Hessian of f at x. With D defined as in previous sections by $D = \text{diag}(x)$,

$$g = g(x) = c - \mu \cdot D^{-1}\mathbf{1}, \quad H = H(x) = \mu \cdot D^{-2}.$$

By the necessary optimality conditions, an optimal solution s and the Lagrange multipliers u satisfy

$$(c - \mu \cdot D^{-1}\mathbf{1}) + \mu \cdot D^{-2}s = A^T u, \ As = 0.$$

As D is positive definit, the unique solution defines a descent direction for $f(x)$ and can be calculated from

(6.5)
$$AD^2 A^T u := AD(Dc - \mu \cdot \mathbf{1}),$$
$$s := (1/\mu) \cdot D(DA^T u - Dc + \mu \cdot \mathbf{1}).$$

We remark, that the generated search direction s coincides with that generated by Sherali's modification of the scaling method if $\mu = \underline{\mu}$ (cf. section 5, where the search direction is $-Dp$). Formal equivalence to the basic projective method can be achieved when the approach is applied to an LP of the special form considered in section 1 (min-formulation of (1.1)), i.e. to

$$0 = \min\{c^T x | Ax = 0, \mathbf{1}^T x = n, x \geq 0\}.$$

Then, Gill et al. [1985] prove that the search directions of both methods are parallel provided the barrier parameter is $\mu := x^T D(c - A^T w)$ where w is the least squares solution of $DA^T w = Dc$ and where x denotes the current iterate.

The equations defining u in (6.5) are the normal equations fo the least squares problem

$$\min \|Dc - \mu \cdot \mathbf{1} - DA^T u\|.$$

As for the methods in previous sections, the least squares problem is due to severe ill-conditioning when the generated solutions x converge to a degenerate solution. Moreover, maintaining feasiblity with respect to the equality constraints in (6.3) presupposes high accuracy in solving the least squares problem. Computational experience in Gill et al. [1985] shows that the method is comparable in speed to the simplex method on certain problems. Its implementation is discussed in considerable detail (eg. initial feasible solution, solving least squares problems, choice of steplength and of barrier parameters, convergence tests).

The above mentioned relations of (6.2) and (6.4) imply that one may solve (6.2) in order to find a solution to (6.4). Gill et al. [1986] develop the following Newton method. At the current u the gradient of F is $b - Ax'$ with $x'_j := \mu/(c - A^T u)_j$ (cf. (6.3)), and the Hessian of F is $(1/\mu) \cdot AX^2 A^T$ where $X := \text{diag}(x')$. Therefore, the Newton search direction h for the minimization of a quadratic approximation to F can be calculated from

(6.6)
$$AX^2 A^T h = \mu \cdot (Ax' - b).$$

Here, we assume that the current dual solution u strictly satisfies the dual constraints implying $x' > 0$. As $x'(\mu)$ converges to a primal optimal solution, the matrices X

and XA^T remain bounded. (6.6) may be replaced by a least squares problem if we construct some q satisfying

$$AXq := Ax' - b.$$

Then, h solves the least squares problem

(6.7) $$\min \|\mu \cdot q - XA^T h\|.$$

Both dual problems (6.1) and (6.2) contain no equality constraints. Therefore, it may suffice to calculate only an approximation of the direction h by some suitably fast method. Gill et al. propose the use of a truncated conjugate gradient method (cf. e.g. Dembo, Eisenstat, and Steihaug [1982]). For faster convergence they discuss preconditioning using LU factorization of XA^T.

Further related barrier methods for the dual are investigated in Eriksson ([1981], [1985]) and in Osborne [1986]. Osborne modifies the above "log"-barrier function as well as exponential barrier functions. The subproblems are solved similar to the above described approach. Erikson discusses the closely related entropy methods for the primal as well as for the dual. Both report on some computational experience with preliminary implementations which need further development.

7. A Penalty Function Approach

Iri and Imai [1985] develop a penalty method for solving the LP

(7.1) $$\min\{c(x)|a_i(x) \geq 0, 1 \leq i \leq m\}$$

where $c(x) := c^T x - c_0$, $a_i(x) := a_i^T x - b_i$, $1 \leq i \leq m$, under the assumptions:

(1) the set of feasible solutions X has an interior feasible point,
(2) its optimal value is zero.

In the derivation of the algorithm some trivial cases are excluded by assuming that on the set of interior feasible points X_0 the objective $c(x)$ is positive, that the set $\underline{X}$ of optimal solutions is bounded, and that at a basic optimal solution there is at least one inactive constraint. For polytopes the last assumption is satisfied.

In order to solve (7.1), Iri and Imai propose to minimize the positive objective function f defined for interior feasible points by

$$f(x) := (c(x))^{m+1}/\Pi(a(x))$$

where $\Pi(d) := d_1 \cdots \cdots d_m$. If $f(x) \to 0$ for some sequence of interior points, then $x \to \underline{X}$. The converse holds when a sequence converges to an optimal solution in a certain closed polyhedron P with $\underline{X} \subseteq P \subseteq \underline{X} \cup X_0$.

Let $g(x)$ and $F(x)$ denote the gradient and the Hessian of $f(x)$ at $x \in X_0$. Starting from some initial interior point a sequence of interior points is generated by

The iterative step 7.1

1. $x := x_+$.
2. Solve $(1/f(x)) \cdot F(x)s := -(1/f(x)) \cdot g(x)$.
3. $x_+ := x + t_* \cdot s$.

In step 2. the Newton direction is calculated from an unusual system for which simple explicit formulas are available. Let

$$\underline{c}_j := \underline{c}_j(x) := c_j/c(x),$$
$$\underline{a}_{ij} := \underline{a}_{ij}(x) := a_{ij}/a_i(x)$$
$$\underline{\Sigma a}_j := \underline{\Sigma a}_j(x) := (1/m)\Sigma_i \, \underline{a}_{ij}(x),$$

for all $1 \leq i \leq m$, $1 \leq j \leq n$. Then it can be shown that

$$(1/f) \cdot g_j = (m+1) \cdot \underline{c}_j - m \cdot \underline{\Sigma a}_j,$$
$$(1/f) \cdot [F]_{jk} = m(m+1)(\underline{c}_j - \underline{\Sigma a}_j)(\underline{c}_k - \underline{\Sigma a}_k) + \Sigma_i(\underline{a}_{ij} - \underline{\Sigma a}_j) \cdot (\underline{a}_{ik} - \underline{\Sigma a}_k),$$

for all $1 \leq j \leq n$, $1 \leq k \leq n$. The latter formula implies nonnegative definitness of $F(x)$. Due to the last of the technical assumptions (existence of inactive constraint at a basic optimal solution), Iri and Imai can prove that $F(x)$ is positive definit. Thus f is strictly convex.

The line search in step 3 is straightforward. The function $\mathcal{F}(t) := f(x + t \cdot s)$ is strictly convex and, for $t \to t_b := \min\{-a_i(x)/a_i^T s \mid a_i^T s < 0\}$, $\mathcal{F}(t) \to +\infty$. The unique minimum t_* of $\mathcal{F}$ on $(0, t_b$ can be approximated by an appropriately modified Newton method using the formulas

$$\mathcal{F}'(t)/\{(t) = (m+1)\tau(t) - \Sigma_i\alpha_i(t)$$
$$\mathcal{F}''(t)/\mathcal{F}(t) = [\mathcal{F}'(t)/\mathcal{F}(t)]^2 - (m+1)[\tau(t)]^2 + \Sigma_i[\alpha_i(t)]^2$$

where $\tau(t) := c^T s/[c(x) + c^T s \cdot t]$, and where $\alpha_i(t) := a_i^T s/[a_i(x) + a_i^T s \cdot t]$, $1 \leq i \leq m$. Iri and Imai prove that in a suitable neighborhood of some optimal solution x_* the generated sequence converges superlinearly to x_*. Under some technical assumptions they prove $f(x_+) < (3/4)f(x)$, i.e. globally linear convergence.

They report on encouraging results with a preliminary implementation which is tested on several classes of LP (e.g. random LP, assignment problems). In order to satisfy the made assumptions, they consider LP of the form

$$\min\{c^T x | Ax \geq b, x \geq 0\}.$$

By LP-duality, we have equivalence to the feasibility problem

$$Ax \geq b, -A^T y \geq -c, -c^T x + b^T y \geq 0, x \geq 0, y \geq 0,$$

which is of the form $Ax \geq b$, $x \geq 0$, for suitably redefined A, b, x. In order to construct a feasible solution, one solves the auxiliary LP

$$\min\{\alpha \mid Ax + a\alpha - b \geq 0, x \geq 0, \alpha \geq 0\}.$$

where

$$a_i := \begin{cases} 1 - (A\mathbf{1} - b)_i & \text{if } (A\mathbf{1} - b)_i \leq 0 \\ 0 & \text{otherwise.} \end{cases}$$

Again, the number of iterations is small, ranging from $O(n^{1/2})$ to $O(n)$ depending on the number of variables. The theoretical convergence results are experimentically confirmed. However, to become a competitor to existing well developed Simplex methods it needs a more efficient implementation for the generation of the search direction.

References

Introduction

Borgwardt, K. H.: *A probabilistic analysis of the simplex method.* Habilitation thesis, Kaiserslautern, October 1984.

Khachian, L. G.: *A polynomial algorithm in linear programming.* Soviet Mathematics Doklady 20 (1979), 191 – 194.

Khachian, L. G.: *Polynomial algorithms in linear programming.* USSR Computational Mathematics and Mathematical Physics 20 (1980), 53 – 72.

Klee, V. and Minty, G. J.: *How good is the simplex algorithm.* In: Shisha, O. (ed.): Inequalities III (1972), 159 – 175, Academic Press, New York.

The Projective Approach

Anstreicher, K. M.: *Analysis of a modified Karmarkar algorithm for linear programming.* Working paper series B 84 (1985), Yale School of Organization and Management, Box 1A, New Haven, CT 06520.

Benichou, M.; Gauthier, J. M.; Hentges, G. and Ribière, G.: *The efficient solution of large scale linear programming problems - some algorithmic techniques and computational results.* Mathematical Programming 13 (1977), 280 – 322.

Birge, J. R. and Qi, L.: *Solving stochastic linear programs via a variant od Karmarkars algorithms.* Technical report 85-12, University of Michigan, College of Engineering, Ann Arbor, Michigan 48109-2117.

Blair, Ch.: *The iterative step in the linear programming algorithm of N. Karmarkar.* Faculty Working Paper No. 1114 (1985), College of Commerce and Business Administration, University of Illinois at Urbana/Champaign.

Blum, L.: *Towards an asymptotic analysis of Karmarkar's algorithm.* Mills College, Oakland, CA 94613 and the Department of Mathematics, University of California, Berkeley 94720 (1985).

Charnes, A.; Song, T. and Wolfe, M.: *An explicit solution sequence and convergence of Karmarkar's algorithm.* Research report CCS 501 (1984), College of Business Administration 5.202, The University of Texas at Austin, Austin, Texas 78712/1177.

Chiu, S. S. and Ye, Yinyu.: *Recovering the shadow price in projection methods of linear programming.* Engineering-Economics Systems Department, Stanford University, Stanford, California 94305 (1985).

Fletcher, R. and Powell, M.J.D.: *On the modification of LDL^T factorizations.* Math. Comp. 28 (1974), 1067 – 1087.

Gay, D. M.: *A variant of Karmarkar's linear programming algorithms for problems in standard form.* Numerical analysis manuscript 85-10 (1985), AT & T Bell Laboratories, Murray Hill, New Jersey 07974.

Gay, D. M.: *Electronic mail distribution of linear programming test problems.* COAL Newsletter 13 (1985), 10 – 12.

George, J. A. and Heath, M. T.: *Solution of sparse linear least squares problems using Givens rotations.* Linear Algebra and its applications 34 (1980), 69 – 83.

Ghellinck, G. de, and Vial, J. Ph.: *A polynomial Newton method for linear programming.* CORE discussion paper 8614 (1986), Université Catholique de Louvain, B-1348 Louvain-la-Neuve.

Ghellinck, G. de, and Vial, J. Ph.: *An extension of Karmarkar's algorithm for solving a system of linear homogeneous equations on the simplex.* Groupe de Recherches scientifiques en Gestion de l'Université Louis Pasteur de Strasbourg (1985).

Goldfarb, D. and Mehrotra, S.: *A relaxed version of Karmarkar's method.* Report (revised March 1986), Department of Industrial Engineering and Operations Research (1985), Columbia University, New York, NY 10027.

Goldfarb, D. and Mehrotra, S.: *Relaxed variants of Karmarkar's algorithm for linear programs with unkown optimal objective value.* Report , Department of Industrial Engineering and Operations Research (1986), Columbia University, New York, NY 10027.

Golub, G. H. and Van Loan, C. F.: *Matrix computations.* John Hopkins University Press (1983).

Gonzaga, C.: *A conical projection algorithm for linear programming.* Memo No. UCB/ERL M85/61, Electronics Research Laboratory, College of Engineering, University of California, Berkeley, CA 94720.

Grötschel, M.; Lovász, L. and Schrijver, A.: *The ellipsoid method and combinatorial optimization.* Springer, Berlin (1986).

Haverly, C. A.: *Results of a new series of case runs using the Karmarkar algorithm.* Haverly Systems Inc. (1985), Denville, New Jersey 07834.

Haverly, C. A.: *Number of simplex iterations for four model structures.* Haverly Systems Inc. (1985), Denville, New Jersey 07834.

Haverly, C. A.: *Studies on behaviour of the Karmarkar method.* Haverly Systems Inc. (1985), Denville, New Jersey 07834.

Karmarkar, N.: *A new polynomial-time algorithm for linear programming.* Combinatorica 4 (1984), 373 – 395.

Karmarkar, N.: *Some comments on the significance of the new polynomial-time algorithm for linear programming.* AT & T Bell Laboratories (1984),Murray Hill, New Jersey 07974.

Kozlov, A. and Black, L. W.: *Berkely obtains new results with the Karmarkar algorithm.* Progress report in SIAM News 3 (19) 1986, p. 3 and 20.

Lustig, I. J.: *A practical approach to Karmarkar's algorithm.* Technical Report Sol 85-5 (1985), Department of Operations Research, Stanford University, Stanford, CA 94305.

Mehrotra, S.: *A self correcting version of Karmarkar's algorithm.* Report (1986), Department of Industrial Engineering and Operations Research, Columbia University, New York, NY 10027.

Murtagh, B. A. and Saunders, M. A.: *MINOS-5.0 users guide.* Report Sol 83-20 (1983), Department of Operations Research, Stanford University, Stanford, CA 94305.

Nickels, W. ; Rödder, W.; Xu, L. and Zimmermann, H.-J.: *Intelligent gradient search in linear programming.* European Journal of Operational Research 22 (1985),293 – 303.

Padberg, M.: *Solution of a nonlinear programming problem arising in the projective method.* Preprint, New York University, NY 10003 (1985)..

Padberg, M.: *A different convergence proof of the projective method for linear programming .* Operations research letters 4 (1986), 253 – 257.

Paige, C. C. and Saunders, M. A.: *LSQR: An algorithm for sparse linear equations and sparse least-squares.* ACM Transactions on mathematical software 8 (1982), 43 – 71.

Pickel, P. F.: *Approximate projections for the Karmarkar algorithm.* Manuscript (1985), Polytechnique Institute of New York, Farmingdale, NY.

Roos, C.: *On Karmarkar's projective method for linear programming.* Report 85-23 (1985), Department of Mathematics and Informatics, Delft University of Technology, 2600 AJ Delft.

Roos, C.: *A pivoting rule for the simplex method which is related to Karmarkar's potential function.* Department of Mathematics and Informatics, Delft University of Technology, P. O.Box 356, 2600 AL Delft, The Netherlands.

Schreck, H.: *Experiences with an implementation of Karmarkar's LP-algorithm.* Mathematisches Institut der Technischen Universität München, Arcisstrasse 21, München (1985).

Schrijver, A.: *The new linear programming method of Karmarkar.* CWI newsletter 8 (1985), Centre for Mathematics and Computer Science, P. O.Box 4079, 1009 AB Amsterdam, The Netherlands.

Shanno, D. F.: *A reduced gradient variant of Karmarkar's algorithm.* Working paper 85-10 (1985), Graduate School of Administration, University of California, Davis, CA 95616.

Shanno, D. F.: *Computing Karmarkar projections quickly.* Graduate School of Administration (1985), University of California, Davis, CA 95616.

Shanno, D. F. and Marsten, R. E: *On implementing Karmarkar's method.* Working paper 85-1 (1985), Graduate school of administration, University of California, Davis, CA 95616.

Strang, G.: *Karmarkar's algorithm in a nutshell.* SIAM News 18(1985), 13.

Swart, E. R.: *How I implemented the Karmarkar algorithm in one evening.* APL Quote Quad 15.3 (1985).

Swart, E. R.: *A modified version of the Karmarkar algorithm.* Department of Mathematics and Statistics, University of Guelph, Guelph, Ontario, Canada.

Todd, M. J. and Burrell, B. P.: *An extension of Karmarkar's algorithm for linear programming using dual variables.* Technical report 85-648 (1985), School of Operations Research and Industrial Engineering, College of Engineering, Cornell University, Ithaca, New York 14850.

Tomlin, J. A.: *An experimental approach to Karmarkar's projective method for linear programming.* Ketron Inc., Mountain View, CA 94040 (1985).

Ye, Y.: *Barrier projection and sliding current objective method for linear programming.* Presentation at 12th Mathematical Programming Symposium, Boston, 1985a, Stanford, CA 94305: Engineering Economic Systems Department, Stanford University.

Ye, Y.: *Cutting-objective and scaling methods – a polynomial algorithm for linear programming.* Submitted to Math. Programming, August 1985b.

The Scaling Approach

Aronson, J.; Barr, R.; Helgason, R.; Kennington, J.; Loh, A. and Zaki, H.: *The projective transformation algorithm by Karmarkar: A computational experiment with assignment problems*. Technical report 85-OR-3 (1985), Department of Operations Research, Southern Methodist University, and Department of Industrial Engineering, University of Houston, Houston.

Barnes, E. R.: *A variation on Karmarkar's algorithm for solving linear programming problems*. Manuscript, IBM Watson Research Center, Yorktown Heights, NY (1985).

Cavalier, T. M. and Soyster, A. L.: *Some computational experience and a modification of the Karmarkar Algorithm*. Department of Industrial and Management Systems Engineering (1985), 207 Hammond Building, The Pennsylvania State University, University Park, PA 16802.

Chandru, V. and Khochar, B. S.: *Exploiting special structures using a variant of Karmarkar's algorithm*. Research memorandum 86-10 (1985), School of Industrial Engineering, Purdue University, West Lafayette, Indiana 47907.

Chandru, V. and Khochar, B. S.: *A class of algorithms for linear programming*. Research memorandum 85-14 (Revised June 1986), School of Industrial Engineering, Purdue University, West Lafayette, Indiana 47907 (1985).

Chiu, S. S. and Ye, Yinyu: *Simplex method and Karmarkar's algorithm: A Unifying Structure*. Engineering-Economic Systems Department (1985), Stanford University, Stanford, California 94305.

Kennington, J. L. and Helgason, R. V.: *Algorithms for network programming*. Wiley, New York (1980).

Kortanek, K.O. and Shi, M.: *Convergence results and numerical experiments on a linear programming hybrid algorithm*. Department of Mathematics (1985), Carnegie-Mellon University, Pittsburgh.

Megiddo, N.: *A variation of Karmarkar's algorithm*. Preliminary report (1985), IBM Research Laboratory, San Jose, CA 95193.

Mitra, G.; Tamiz, M.; Yadegar, J. and Darby-Dowman, K.: *Experimental investigation of an interior search algorithm for linear programming*. Math. Programming Symposium, Boston, 1985.

Poljak, B. T.: *A general method of solving extremum problems*. Soviet mathematics 8 (1967), 593 – 597.

Sherali, H. D.: *Algorithmic insights and a convergence analysis for a Karmarkar-type of algorithm for linear programming problems.* Department of Industrial Engineering and Operations Research (1985), Virginia Polytechnic Institute and State University, Blacksburg, Virginia 24061.

Shor, N. Z.: *Generalized gradient methods of nondifferentiable optimization employing space dilation operators.* In: Bachem, A.; Grötschel, M.; Korte, B.: "Mathematical Programming: The state of the art" (1983), Bonn.

Vanderbei, R. J.; Meketon, M. S. and Freedman, B. A.: *A modification of Karmarkar's linear programming algorithm.* AT & T Bell Laboratories (1985), Holmdel, New Jersey 07733.

The Barrier Function Approach

Dembo, R. S.; Eisenstat S. C. and Steinhaug, T.: *Inexact Newton methods.* SIAM J. on Numerical Analysis 19 (1982), 400 – 408.

Eriksson, J. R.: *Algorithms for entropy and mathematical programming.* Linköping Studies in Science and Technology, Dissertations No. 63 (1981), Department of Mathematics, Linköping University, S-581 83 Linköping, Sweden.

Eriksson, J. R.: *An iterative primal-dual algorithm for linear programming.* Report LiTH-MAT-R-1985-10 (1985), Institute of Technology, Linköping University, S-581 83 Linköping, Sweden.

Fiacco, A. V. and McCormick, G. P.: *Nonlinear programming: Sequential unconstrained minimization techniques.* Wiley, New York (1968).

Frisch, K. R.: *The logarithmic potential method of convex programming.* Memorandum of May 13, 1955, University Institute of Economics, Oslo (1955).

George, J. A. and Heath M. T.: *Solution of large sparse linear least squares problems using Givens rotations.* Linear Algebra and its applications 34 (1980), 69 – 83.

Gill, Ph. E.; Murray, W.; Saunders, M. A. and Wright, M. H.: *A note on nonlinear approaches to linear programming.* Technical report SOL 86-7 (1986), Department of Operations Research, Stanford University, Stanford, CA 94305.

Gill, Ph. E.; Murray, W.; Saunders, M. A.; Tomlin, J. A. and Wright, M. H.: *On projected Newton barrier methods for linear programming and an equivalence to Karmarkar's projective method.* Technical report SOL 85-11 (1985), Department of Operations Research, Stanford University, Stanford, CA 94305.

Jittorntrum, K.: *Sequential algorithms in nonlinear programming.* Ph. D. Thesis, Australian National University (1978).

Jittorntrum, K. and Osborne, M. R.: *Trajectory analysis and extrapolation in barrier function methods.* Journal of Australian Mathematical Society 21 (1980), 1 – 18.

Mifflin, R.: *Convergence bounds for nonlinear programming algorithms.* Administrative Sciences report 57, Yale University, Connecticut (1972).

Mifflin, R.: *On the convergence of the logarithmic barrier function method.* In: Lootsma, F.: "Numerical Methods for Nonlinear Optimization"(1972), 367 – 369, Academic Press, London.

Osborne, M. R.: *Dual barrier functions with superfast rates of convergence for the linear programming problem.* Report (1986), Department of Statistics, Research School of Social Sciences, Australian National University.

A Penalty Approach

Iri, M. and Imai, H.: *A multiplicative penalty function method for linear programming - another "New and Fast" algorithm.* Department of Mathematical Engineering and Instrumentation Physics, Faculty of Engineering, University of Tokyo, Bunkyo-ku, Tokyo, Japan 113 (1985).